WATER QUALITY CRITERIA FOR FRESHWATER FISH

Water Quality Criteria for Freshwater Fish

Second Edition

J S ALABASTER
Consultant, Pollution and Fisheries
formerly of
Water Research Centre, Stevenage, UK

Assisted by

R LLOYD
Ministry of Agriculture, Fisheries and Food,
Burnham-on-Crouch, UK

Published by arrangement with the
Food and Agriculture Organization of the United Nations
by
BUTTERWORTH SCIENTIFIC
London Boston Sydney Wellington Durban Toronto

First published by Butterworths 1980
Second edition 1982
©FAO 1982

British Library Cataloguing in Publication Data

Water quality criteria for freshwater fish.—2nd ed.
   1. Fishes, Effect of water pollution on—Europe
  —Addresses, essays, lectures
   2. Fishes, Fresh-water—Europe—Addresses,
  essays, lectures 3. Water quality—Europe
  —Addresses, essays, lectures
  I. Alabaster, J. S.   II. Lloyd, R.
  597′.052632   SH174

   ISBN 0-408-10849-5

Typeset in 10/11pt IBM Press Roman by
RDL, 26 Mulgrave Road, Sutton, Surrey
Printed and bound in England by the University Press, Cambridge

EDITORS' NOTE

There has been a considerable demand for the EIFAC reports produced by the Working Party on Water Quality Criteria for European Freshwater Fish (and for the report produced by the Working Party on Toxicity Testing Procedures) and many of them have been out of print for some time. Also, additional information has since been published on the subjects covered by the earlier reports. There was a need, therefore, to update them all where necessary, and to reprint them in a single volume. However, each report had taken a considerable time to produce because the Working Party stressed the need to base them upon comprehensive and critical reviews of the literature, and to update them all to this standard would be a task not only well beyond the resources currently available to us, but one which would also lead to an unacceptable delay in publication. Attention has been given, therefore, mainly to the recent literature that bears most heavily upon the conclusions originally drawn in the reports and reliance has also been placed on other recent reviews of the literature, where appropriate.

In producing their first report, the Working Party attempted to cover the most important information on finely divided solids and inland fisheries throughout the world. However, in updating the data available on this subject, as well as in the reviews covered in other chapters, greater attention has been paid to those species of fish found in Europe, unless data for non-European species illustrated a principle not otherwise documented. Nevertheless, we consider that the revised reports in this volume will be useful not only to the member countries of the European Inland Fisheries Advisory Commission, but to those concerned with the management of inland waters and their fishery resources in other continents.

Each water quality characteristic reviewed in this volume has been considered separately although in each chapter the effects of mixtures with other harmful substances have been described for some of them. However, a more comprehensive review of this subject is now included in a separate chapter in the present edition.

It is recognized that the term 'water quality criteria for fish' is properly defined as the relation between the concentration of the water quality characteristic (e.g. chemical or temperature) and the response of the organism. However, in the early reports the term was used to describe recommended maximum acceptable concentrations (or minima, as in the case of dissolved oxygen and pH value), or temperatures, which could then be used as the basis for setting water quality standards. This terminology was continued into the later reports and has been retained in this volume.

The editors would like to take this opportunity to express their warm appreciation to all those who have participated in this work including those who have commented on, and pointed out errors in, the original reports, and to Mrs R. Flain for collecting information for updating Chapters 1, 5, 6 and 7, Mrs B. C. Alabaster for general editorial assistance and Miss I. M. Lamont for checking the final typescripts of the first edition and of the report which forms the basis of the additional chapter (11) included in this edition. However, the editors accept responsibility for any errors which remain.

November 1981

FOREWORD

This volume is a collection of twelve updated technical papers on water quality criteria for European freshwater fish, together with a report on toxicity testing procedures[1], that have been produced for the European Inland Fisheries Advisory Commission (EIFAC)—an intergovernmental organization with a current membership of 24 countries. The Commission has been active in its efforts to establish water quality criteria for European freshwater fish since its Second Session, Paris, 1962, when it took note of a recommendation of the United Nations Conference on Water Pollution Problems in Europe, 1961, that EIFAC take the initiative in drawing up water quality requirements with respect to fisheries[3].

As was stated in the preface to the reports on water quality criteria, the Commission agreed that

'the proper management of a river system demands that water of suitable quality be provided for each use that is made or intended to be made of it and that the attainment and maintenance of such quality is normally to be sought through the control of pollution. It was necessary, therefore, to know the standards of quality required for each particular use in order to determine the degree of pollution control necessary and to forecast the probable effect of augmented or new discharges of effluents. It was pointed out that water quality standards for drinking water had been well defined by the World Health Organization (WHO) and that standards for certain agricultural and industrial uses are also well defined. However, water quality criteria for fish have not received the attention that they deserve. All too often, water has been considered quite adequate for fish as long as there has been no obvious mortality which can be ascribed to known pollutants. Degradation of the aquatic habitat through pollution and decrease in the annual production and subsequent harvest of fish have often passed unnoted.

With such reasoning in mind, it was agreed that the establishment of water quality criteria for European freshwater fish be undertaken by the Commission. This was to be accomplished by a critical examination of the literature, and very possibly experimentation to clear up contradictions and fill in gaps of knowledge, followed by recommendations as to desirable requirements for various aquatic organisms or groups of aquatic organisms with respect to the various qualities of water. The final criteria were to be published and given wide dissemination.'

To accomplish this task, the Second Session of the Commission appointed a Working Party of experts selected on the basis of their knowledge of physical, chemical and biological requirements of European freshwater fish in relation to the topics to be studied.

This Working Party prepared its first report on finely divided solids and inland fisheries[1] which was submitted to the Commission at its Third Session, Scharfling am Mondsee, 1964, where it was unanimously approved[4].

The Third Session then suggested that the following studies be considered by the Working Party:

Water temperature (including a review of the effect of heated discharges);

Dissolved oxygen and carbon dioxide;

pH;

Toxic substances including heavy metals, phenols, pesticides and herbicides.

Elevated temperature was given first priority, and a draft on this subject was prepared by the Working Party during the following intersessional period. (At the Third Session the work of the Commission was reorganized into three Sub-Commissions, one of which, Sub-Commission III—Fish and Polluted Water—regrouped all the activities of EIFAC in the field of water pollution. The Working Party on Water Quality Criteria for European Freshwater Fish has since functioned under this Sub-Commision.)

The Fourth Session of the Commission, Belgrade, 1966, after having studied this first draft of review of literature on the effects of water temperature on aquatic life, concluded that such a review required more effort than the resources of the Commission permitted at the time. Meanwhile, it suggested that a water quality report for extreme pH values be prepared for the next Session of EIFAC, and that a report on dissolved oxygen be prepared when funds became available for a full-time consultant[5].

The report on extreme pH values and inland fisheries[1] was published in 1968, in time for presentation at the Fifth Session of EIFAC, Rome, 1968, where it was unanimously approved[6].

At its Fifth Session the Commission again reviewed priorities for future studies and decided to undertake critical reviews on the effects of ammonia and phenols on freshwater fishes.

It also recommended that guidance as to its future work in the field of water pollution control, including the development of water quality criteria, be taken from the FAO/EIFAC Symposium on the Nature and Extent of Water Pollution Problems affecting Inland Fisheries in Europe which was later held in Jablonna, Poland, 15–16 May 1970, just before the Sixth Session of EIFAC.

The Fifth Session also approved in draft a report on water temperature and inland fisheries based mainly on Slavonic literature. The report was published in November 1968 as the third in the EIFAC water quality criteria series, and was followed in 1969 by the fourth publication in the series, a list of literature on the effect of water temperature on fish[1].

Following the Jablonna Symposium[7], the Sixth Session of EIFAC, Krakow, 1970, again reviewed the Commission's programme with respect to water quality criteria[8]. Noting that a report on ammonia was almost complete, it approved continuance of work on phenols, and the current work begun by the Working Party on copper, zinc and mercury, and recommended the addition of cyanides, detergents, chlorine and hydrocarbons as items for further reviews. It also recommended eventual resumption of work on water temperature and the preparation of a review based on a critical worldwide report on dissolved oxygen prepared for FAO[9].

After the Sixth Session of EIFAC, the EIFAC Working Party published reports on ammonia and monohydric phenols as the fifth and sixth reviews in this EIFAC series of water quality papers[1]; these were presented to the Seventh Session of EIFAC, Amsterdam, 1972[10], where they were unanimously approved.

After the Seventh Session, the EIFAC Working Party on Water Quality Criteria drafted reviews on dissolved oxygen, chlorine and zinc which were published as the seventh, eighth and ninth reviews of this series[10] and were approved by the Eighth Session of EIFAC (Aviemore, Scotland, 1974)[11]. The Eighth Session gave priority to cadmium as the subject of the next report. In addition it recommended (i) that all completed reports should be updated where necessary and offered to a publisher for printing in a single volume and (ii) that research in the field to provide information essential for the formulation of water quality criteria should be encouraged by EIFAC.

The tenth review, on copper and freshwater fish, was produced for the Ninth Session, Helsinki, 1976, while the review of cadmium[10] together with a report of a field study of the effect on fisheries of zinc and copper pollution (carried out as part of a cooperative project of the United Nations Environment Programme[12]), were presented at the Tenth Session, Hamburg, 1978.

Finally, the review of the combined effects on freshwater fish and other aquatic life of mixtures of toxicants[14] was prepared for the Eleventh Session, Stavanger, 1980.

The EIFAC Working Party on Water Quality Criteria has consisted of the following in order of their appointment:

Dr J. S. Alabaster	(United Kingdom) *Convener*	1962-1980
Dr T. R. Hasselrot	(Sweden)	1962-1975
Mr D. W. M. Herbert	(United Kingdom)	1962-1964
Dr H. Mann	(Federal Republic of Germany)	1962-1964
M. P. Vivier	(France)	1962-1964
Dr T. Backiel	(Poland)	1964-1970
Mr R. Lloyd	(United Kingdom)	1964 to date
Mr A. V. Holden	(United Kingdom)	1964-1968
Dr R. Marchetti	(Italy)	1964-1968
Dr H. Reichenback-Klinke	(Federal Republic of Germany)	1964-1968
Dr V. Mitrović-Tutundzić	(Yugoslavia)	1968-1970
Dr D. Calamari	(Italy)	1970 to date
Mr M. Grande	(Norway)	1970 to date
Dr A. W. Lysak	(Poland)	1970-1978
Dr W. K. Besch	(Federal Republic of Germany)	1973-1978
Dr V. Dethlefsen	(Federal Republic of Germany)	1978 to date
Dr P. Anderson	(Canada)	1979-1980

FAO Secretariat:

M. J. L. L. Chaux	1962-1964
Mr W. A. Dill	1962-1970
M. J.-L. Gaudet	1964-1980
Mr A. Thorslund	1972-1978
Dr R. L. Welcomme	1972-1980
Dr H. Naeve	1973
Mr A. Wemblad	1976

In addition, Mlle M. Nisbet acted as alternate to M. Vivier, and the following have helped the Working Party by commenting constructively on some of the reports at the drafting stages:

Mr V. M. Brown, Dr W. Brungs, Dr A. Coche, Dr P. Doudoroff, Dr J. Gardiner, Dr J. Hall, Dr D. I. Mount, Mr J. F. de L. G. Solbé, Dr W. A. Spoor, Dr J. B. Sprague, Dr R. V. Thurston.

The EIFAC Symposium on the nature and extent of water pollution problems affecting inland fisheries in Europe, which was held in conjunction with the Sixth Session of EIFAC (Jablonna, Poland) in May 1970, recommended that a Working Party be established to investigate the systems in use in toxicity testing with fish, with a view to reaching standardization in this particular field. Although it was not possible to establish the Working Party during the intersessional period, the Commission cooperated with the State Water Authority for Baden-Württemberg of the Federal Republic of Germany in a meeting on toxicity testing with fish at Karlsruhe in October 1971. A summary report was presented to the Seventh Session of EIFAC, held in Amsterdam, in April 1972. The Commission agreed with the conclusion of the meeting that the standardization of fish toxicity procedures should precede standardization of terminology, and recommended that EIFAC should coordinate the international efforts toward standardization of fish toxicity testing procedures and terminology and to that effect set up a Working Party in close collaboration with the Karlsruhe group. The Eleventh Meeting of the EIFAC Working Party on water quality criteria for European freshwater fish (Rome, 1973) also recommended that a Working Party on toxicity testing procedures be created.

This Working Party comprised:

Mr R. Lloyd	(United Kingdom), *Convener*
Dr J. S. Alabaster	(United Kingdom)
Dr K. Besch	(Federal Republic of Germany)
Dr D. Calamari	(Italy)
Mr M. Grande	(Norway)
Dr T. B. Hasselrot	(Sweden)
M. G. Leynaud	(France)
Dr A. Lysak	(Poland)
Dr J. B. Sprague	(Canada)

FAO Secretariat:

M. J.-L. Gaudet
Dr H. Naeve

The Working Party presented its report[1] to the Ninth Session (Helsinki, 1976), where it was approved.

The value and limitations of chemical and toxicological data in the assessment of water quality for fisheries and also the problems of characterizing fish and fisheries for biological monitoring have been considered in a separate technical paper[13].

Jean-Louis Gaudet
Secretary of EIFAC*

*The present secretary of EIFAC is M. D. Charbonnier

References

1 Report on Finely Divided Solids and Inland Fisheries, *EIFAC Tech. Pap.* **1**, 1964

   Report on Extreme pH Values and Inland Fisheries, *EIFAC Tech. Pap.* **4**, 1968

   Report on Water Temperature and Inland Fisheries based mainly on Slavonic Literature, *EIFAC Tech. Pap.* **6**, 1968

   List of Literature on the effect of Water Temperature on Fish, *EIFAC Tech. Pap.* **8**, 1969

   Report on Ammonia and Inland Fisheries, *EIFAC Tech. Pap.* **11**, 1970

   Report on Monohydric Phenols and Inland Fisheries, *EIFAC Tech. Pap.* **15**, 1972

   Report on Dissolved Oxygen and Inland Fisheries, *EIFAC Tech. Pap.* **19**, 1973

   Report on Chlorine and Freshwater Fish, *EIFAC Tech. Pap.* **20**, 1973

   Report on Zinc and Freshwater Fish, *EIFAC Tech. Pap.* **21**, 1973

   Report on Copper and Freshwater Fish, *EIFAC Tech. Pap.* **27**, 1976

   Report on Cadmium and Freshwater Fish, *EIFAC Tech. Pap.* **30**, 1977

   Report on Fish Toxicity Testing Procedures, *EIFAC Tech. Pap.* **24**, 1975

2 EIFAC Report, Second Session, 1962, pp. 21–22

3 UN (1961) Conference on Water Pollution Problems in Europe, held in Geneva from 22 February to 3 March 1961. Document submitted to the Conference. Vols. 1–3, United Nations, Geneva

4 EIFAC Report, Third Session, 1964, p. 11

5 EIFAC Report, Fourth Session, 1966, p. 12

6 EIFAC Report, Fifth Session, 1968, pp. 14–15

7 HOLDEN, A. V. and R. LLOYD (1972). Symposium on the Nature and Extent of Water Pollution Problems affecting Inland Fisheries in Europe. Synthesis of National Reports, *EIFAC Tech. Pap.* **16**

8 EIFAC Report, Sixth Session, 1970, p. 13

9 DOUDOROFF, P. and SHUMWAY, D. L. (1970). Dissolved Oxygen Requirements of Freshwater Fishes, *FAO Tech. Pap.* **86**

10 EIFAC Report, Seventh Session, 1973, p. 18

11 EIFAC Report, Eighth Session, 1975, p. 11

12 Report on the Effect of Zinc and Copper Pollution on the Salmonid Fisheries in a River and Lake System in Central Norway. *EIFAC Tech. Pap.,* **29**, 1977

13 Report on the value and limitations of various approaches to the monitoring of water quality for freshwater fish. *EIFAC Tech. Pap.* **32**, 1978

14 Report on combined effects on freshwater fish and other aquatic life of mixtures of toxicants in water. *EIFAC Tech. Pap.* **37**, 1980

CONTENTS

Foreword
Editors' note

1

FINELY DIVIDED SOLIDS

Foreword

A review of the literature on, and an attempt to define, tentative water quality criteria for finely divided solids and inland fish and fisheries were chosen as the first task of the Working Party on Water Quality Criteria for European Fresh-water Fish and set a pattern for future reports. The preparation of the original report on which this chapter is based was accomplished largely by Mr D. W. M. Herbert, who prepared the basic manuscript for review by other members of the Working Party. It was not possible to study the whole of the world's literature on the subject, but a large proportion of the more important research reports was considered, together with unpublished data provided by fishery biologists in many European countries. Since then much more has been published including several reviews, e.g. by Hollis *et al.* (1964), Shelton and Pollock (1966), Gammon (1970), Ritchie (1972), and Sorensen *et al.* (1977); the data support the conclusions drawn in the original EIFAC report and therefore are not reviewed again here, except in a few cases where European species are concerned. In addition, hitherto unpublished data are included.

1.1 Summary

Water quality criteria for suspended solids are needed by those who have to manage inland fisheries and must sometimes decide, for example, how much solid matter could enter a river or lake without undue risk to a fishery, or whether it is worth attempting to develop a commercial or recreational fishery in water already containing a known concentration of such materials.

There are at least five ways in which an excessive concentration of finely divided solid matter might be harmful to a fishery in a river or a lake. These are:

(a)   By acting directly on the fish swimming in water in which solids are suspended, and either killing them or reducing their growth rate, resistance to disease, etc.

(b)   By preventing the successful development of fish eggs and larvae.
(c)   By modifying natural movements and migrations of fish.
(d)   By reducing the abundance of food available to the fish.
(e)   By affecting the efficiency of methods for catching fish.

Some or all of these factors could operate together to harm a fishery.

There is evidence that not all species of fish are equally susceptible to suspended solids, and that not all kinds of solids are equally harmful. Unfortunately there is very little information on these and many other aspects of the problem, and much of the evidence which does exist is less firmly established than is desirable. It has therefore been concluded that definite water quality criteria which distinguish between the many different kinds of finely divided solids to which different sorts of inland fisheries may be subjected cannot yet be proposed. Nevertheless, when the evidence is considered as a whole, certain general conclusions can be drawn.

There is probably no sharply defined concentration of a solid above which fisheries are damaged and below which they are quite unharmed. It appears that any increase in the normally prevailing concentration of suspended matter above quite a low level may cause some decline in the status and value of a freshwater fishery, and that the risk of damage increases with the concentration. Although there is not enough evidence to allow the relation between solids concentration and risk of damage to be defined at all precisely, the Working Party considers that the degree of risk to fisheries may be divided into four arbitrarily defined categories and that rough estimates may be made of the ranges of concentration to which they would generally correspond. From this approach to the problem the following tentative criteria are presented. With respect to chemically inert solids and to waters which are otherwise satisfactory for the maintenance of freshwater fisheries,

(a)   There is no evidence that concentrations of suspended solids less than 25 mg/ℓ have any harmful effects on fisheries.

(b)   It should usually be possible to maintain good or moderate fisheries in waters which normally contain 25–80 mg/ℓ suspended solids. Other factors being equal, however, the yield of fish from such waters might be somewhat lower than from those in category (a).

(c)   Waters normally containing from 80–400 mg/ℓ suspended solids are unlikely to support good freshwater fisheries, although fisheries may sometimes be found at the lower concentrations within this range.

(d)   At the best, only poor fisheries are likely to be found in waters which normally contain more than 400 mg/ℓ suspended solids.

In addition, although concentrations of several thousand mg/ℓ solids may not kill fish during several hours or days exposure, such temporary high concentrations should be prevented in rivers where good fisheries are to be maintained.

The spawning grounds of salmon and trout require special consideration and should be kept as free as possible from finely divided solids.

1.2 Introduction

Nearly all river and lake waters have some solid matter in suspension and some, at times, contain very high concentrations resulting from soil erosion, from engineering works during which large volumes of earth are disturbed, from forestry operations, and from the discharge of sewage, sewage effluents, mining wastes, pulp and paper mill wastes, and other industrial effluents. Solids of many different kinds are therefore to be found in surface waters. Some of them—basic salts of zinc for example—have toxic properties (Lloyd, 1960; Herbert and Wakeford, 1964), while organic solids are oxidized by micro-organisms which can reduce the concentration of dissolved oxygen to levels at which fish are asphyxiated. Effects of these kinds are not considered in this chapter, nor has particular attention been given to the effects which solids may have by altering physical characteristics of the water such as temperature. Furthermore, some waste waters contain both solids in suspension and potentially harmful substances in solution.

The possibility that suspended solids will modify the resistance of fish to poisons, or to low dissolved oxygen, high temperature and extremes of pH value has not been examined, nor are there included in the chapter the results of laboratory studies or of observation in the field unless it was reasonably certain that any adverse effects were due only to the solids. For example, Rolley and Owens (1967) have shown that dissolved oxygen may be reduced as a result of deposits of organic matter being brought into suspension, consequently we have not used some reports of fish kills during floods when the suspended-solids concentration was high and the dissolved-oxygen concentration was not measured.

Some other research reports have been excluded because we considered that the conclusions reached by their authors were not fully supported by the evidence. In many research papers—especially some of those reporting studies of lakes and rivers—much of the evidence which we have used is less securely established than is desirable because the suspended-solids concentrations were not measured very often.

Although most authors have reported their observations as weight of solids per unit volume of water, others have expressed them as light transmittancies of Secchi disc readings. One of these systems of measurement cannot be converted into another unless the relation between them has been determined for the particular solid under consideration. Because the appropriate relation has seldom been reported, we have not attempted to use one system of measurement throughout the literature survey, but have quoted results in the units employed by the authors.

From our study of the literature it is apparent that there are at least five ways in which an excessive concentration of finely divided solid matter might be harmful to a fishery in a river or a lake. These are:

(a)   By acting directly on the fish swimming in water in which solids are suspended, and either killing them or reducing their growth rate and resistance to disease.
(b)   By preventing the successful development of fish eggs and larvae.
(c)   By modifying natural movements and migrations of fish.
(d)   By reducing the abundance of food available to the fish.
(e)   By affecting the efficiency of methods for catching fish.

In addition, some or all of these factors could operate together to harm a fishery.
    These subjects (except (e)) are considered in the next section of this chapter.

1.3 Literature survey

1.3.1 DIRECT EFFECTS OF SOLIDS IN SUSPENSION

Death or survival of fish

Wallen (1951) kept several species of fish in water containing montmorillonite clay and increased the turbidity to high levels for a short time each day by stirring the sediment. Most individuals of all species—including goldfish (*Carassius auratus*) and common carp (*Cyprinus carpio*)—endured maximum turbidities of 100 000 mg/ℓ occurring during experiments lasting a week or more, and some individuals of these two species survived occasional exposure to 225 000 mg/ℓ for one to three weeks. Herbert (personal communication) found that rainbow trout (*Salmo gairdneri*) survived one day in 80 000 mg/ℓ silt from gravel washing, and the concentration had to be raised to about 160 000 mg/ℓ to kill them within this period. J. S. Alabaster (personal communication) found that harlequin (*Rasbora heteromorpha*), a tropical fish, was killed in a day by about 40 000 mg/ℓ bentonite clay, but survived for a week in 6000 mg/ℓ. Resuspended harbour sediment (containing organic matter, oil and grease, and heavy metals at concentrations of up to 28 000 mg/ℓ) had no observable adverse effects on stickleback (*Gasterosteus aculeatus*) and fry of coho salmon (*Oncorhynchus kisutch*) in 4 days (Le Gore and Des Voigne, 1973). Cole (1935) reported that some fish survived 20 000 mg/ℓ wood fibre, although he said that it undoubtedly hastened the death of unhealthy or moribund individuals, and Griffin (1938) stated that Pacific salmon (*Oncorhynchus*) and trout fingerlings lived for 3-4 weeks in concentrations of 300-750 mg/ℓ silt which were increased to 2300-6500 mg/ℓ for short periods by stirring the sediment each day. Thus it appears that many kinds of fish are unlikely to be killed within a day or so by exposure to suspended matter unless the concentrations are extremely high. To kill within such short times the concentrations of some solids would probably have to exceed 100 000 mg/ℓ. However, Slanina (1962) found that although rainbow trout survived a week in 5000-300 000 mg/ℓ suspended mineral solids, the epithelium of their gills had thickened and proliferated. Similarly-affected gills were observed in rainbow trout which eventually died after exposure to several hundred mg/ℓ solids for longer periods (Herbert and Merkens, 1961). Exposure for relatively short periods to very high concentrations might thus be harmful eventually even though fish are not killed within the period of exposure.

Concentrations of several hundred thousand mg/ℓ are never likely to be present in surface waters for more than a short time, but quite high concentrations can be present for relatively long periods. From 2000 to 6000 mg/ℓ silt, persisting for 15-20 days, have been reported for rivers in flood (Campbell, 1954; Simaika, 1940; and Kemp, 1949); 6000 mg/ℓ and 1000 mg/ℓ appear to have been average levels in two streams continuously polluted with wastes from china-clay mining (Herbert *et al.*, 1961).

In the laboratory, 4250 mg/ℓ gypsum in suspension produced a 50 per cent mortality among rainbow trout in about $3\frac{1}{2}$ weeks (Herbert and Wakeford, 1962). Caged rainbow trout were killed in 20 days in the Powder River, Oregon, when the concentration was 1000 to 2500 mg/ℓ but other conditions were apparently satisfactory (Campbell, 1954). In laboratory studies there were 40-50 per cent kills of trout in 810 and 270 mg/ℓ kaolin and diatomaceous earth after exposure periods of 10 days in some experiments, but only after 85 days in others (Herbert and Merkens, 1961). Spruce fibre at 200 mg/ℓ produced 50 per cent mortality among rainbow trout after 16 weeks exposure, and 70 per cent after 30 weeks (Herbert and Richards, 1963).

On the other hand, M. Grande (personal communication) found that only one rainbow trout out of five was killed during 37 days in 1000 mg/ℓ cellulose fibre, and Vallin (1935) reported that one individual of each of the species *Carassius carassius, Leuciscus rutilis*, and *Thymallus thymallus* was tested and survived 3 weeks in 200 mg/ℓ. Herbert and Wakeford (1962) found that there were no deaths among rainbow trout kept for 4 weeks in a suspension of 553 mg/ℓ gypsum. There was 100 per cent survival of the same species for 9 to 10 months in 200 mg/ℓ of solids from a coal washery (Herbert and Richards, 1963).

Thus there is evidence from properly conducted experiments and reliable observations of rivers that suspended-solids concentrations from 200 to several thousand mg/ℓ have caused deaths among fish exposed for several weeks or months, and other equally reliable evidence that fish have been kept with few or no deaths at concentrations in the range 200–1000 mg/ℓ for similar periods. These differences are probably due in part to the kind of solid: in simultaneous experiments with identical techniques, all the rainbow trout tested in 200 mg/ℓ coal washery solids for 40 weeks survived, whereas nearly 80 per cent died in the same concentration of spruce fibre (Herbert and Richards, 1963). Ellis (1944) states that the larger the particles, and the greater their hardness and angularity, the greater the possibility of injury to gill structures. Another factor is that species of fish are not all equally resistant. Smith, Kramer and McLeod (1965) found that walleye fingerlings (*Stizostedion v. vitreum*) were killed within 72 hours by 100 mg/ℓ of various wood pulps, although 20 000 mg/ℓ did not kill fathead minnow (*Pimephales promelas*) exposed for 96 hours. Whether or not fish in a river or lake will eventually be killed by the continual presence of 200 mg/ℓ suspended solids or more is likely to depend upon the nature of the solids and the species present. Nevertheless, the available evidence suggests that the death rate among fish living in waters which over long periods contain suspended solids in excess of 200 mg/ℓ will often be substantially greater than it would have been in clean water.

There are also a few studies of death rates in concentrations lower than 200 mg/ℓ. Smith, Kramer and McLeod (1965) found that the walleye (which seems to be an extremely sensitive fish) was killed within 3 days by 100 mg/ℓ wood pulp, and a rather special case is provided by ferric hydroxide which when precipitated from acid solutions containing 3 mg/ℓ Fe on to the gills of trout, carp, and tench (*Tinca tinca*) kills them when the pH value rises above 5.5 (H. Mann, personal communication; Krämer, 1924). More recent work by Sykora, Smith and Synak (1972) showed that suspensions of ferric hydroxide of about 96, 48 and 24 mg/ℓ caused juvenile brook trout (*Salvelinus fontinalis*) to reach no more than 16 per cent, 45 per cent and 75 per cent of the weight of control fish and they attributed the effect to reduced feeding caused by impaired visibility of the food.

In the majority of reported cases, however, death rates in 100 mg/ℓ and less have been little or no higher than among control fish in clean water. Herbert and Merkens (1961) found that rainbow trout kept for long periods in 90 mg/ℓ kaolin and diatomaceous earth suffered a slightly higher death rate than did the control fish, but the mortality was low: in five out of six tests lasting for 2–6 months no more than 20 per cent died. There were no deaths of rainbow trout during 8 months exposure to 100 and 50 mg/ℓ spruce fibre or coal washery waste solids (Herbert and Richards, 1963), and no significant increase over control mortality among the same species in 30 mg/ℓ kaolin or diatomaceous earth (Herbert and Merkens, 1961).

Growth

The growth (and survival) of larval lake herring (*Coregonus artedii*) were not affected during exposure for 62 days to a concentration of red-clay of up to 28 mg/ℓ (Swenson and Matson, 1976). Laboratory experiments, in which trout were given equal quantities of food in amounts which were nearly enough to satisfy their appetites, showed that 50 mg/ℓ wood fibre or coal washery waste solids reduced their growth rate, and that they grew more slowly as the suspended-solids concentration was increased (Herbert and Richards, 1963). Nevertheless the fish grew reasonably well in the presence of the abundant food supply; even in 200 mg/ℓ coal washery waste solids, yearling fish more than trebled their weight in 8 months.

Resistance to disease

Herbert and Merkens (1961) found that rainbow trout in 270 mg/ℓ diatomaceous earth suffered more from the disease 'fin-rot' than controls in clean water. Herbert and Richards (1963) report that many of the rainbow trout dying in 200 mg/ℓ wood fibre suffered from fin-rot, and that fish in 100 mg/ℓ showed some symptoms after 8 months, although those in 50 mg/ℓ and the control fish showed no sign of the disease.

1.3.2 SUSPENDED SOLIDS AND REPRODUCTION

If solids settle from suspension and block gravel which contains eggs, high mortalities will result. Shapovalov (1937) showed that silting reduced the survival of rainbow trout eggs (*Salmo gairdnerii*) in gravel, and found the same with silver salmon (*Oncorhynchus kisutch*) eggs in later experiments (Shapovalov and Berrian, 1940). Hobbs (1937) states that the mortality of trout eggs in New Zealand streams was greatest in those redds which contained the greatest proportion of material smaller than 0.03 inch in diameter. According to Ward (1938) who studied the Rogue River, Oregon, where placer mining was extensively practised, '. . . erosion silt in some streams has been found to cover nests and spawning grounds with a blanket such that the bottom fauna was killed and eggs also suffocated in nests.' Campbell (1954) planted eggs in gravel in the Powder River, Oregon, where the turbidity was between 1000 and 2500 ppm as a result of mining operations. All the eggs died in 6 days, although there was only 6 per cent mortality in 20 days at a control site where the water was clean. Other instances of eggs being killed by siltation are given by Heg (1952), Hertzog (1953), Gangmark and Broad (1955 and 1956), and Neave (1947).

Stuart (1953) has shown that Atlantic salmon (*Salmo salar*) and brown trout (*Salmo trutta*) eggs—which are buried in gravel on the stream beds—can develop successfully only if a current of water passes through the gravel, while Gangmark and Bakkala (1960) found that the survival of king salmon (*Oncorhynchus tshawytscha*) eggs increased with the velocity of water through the gravel in which they were laid. Fish eggs require oxygen during development. Alderdice, Wickett and Brett (1958) showed that chum salmon (*Oncorhynchus keta*) eggs needed at least one part oxygen per million in the surrounding water at the early stages and 7 ppm at later stages if they were to hatch successfully, and Alderdice and Wickett (1958) demonstrated that the utilization of oxygen by the eggs was impaired by increasing the carbon dioxide concentration. Wickett (1954) concluded that the amount of oxygen available to eggs depends not only on its concentration in the water, but also upon the rate at which the water flows over the eggs.

The foregoing observations are relevant to the silting up of spawning beds after the eggs have been laid, but there is also evidence that some salmonids will not spawn in gravel which is already blocked. Stuart (1953) found that brown trout do not dig redds in gravel if it is choked with sediment, nor will they do so even if the surface has been cleared of sediment so that it appears indistinguishable from known spawning areas; presumably this is because the fish detects that water is not flowing through the gravel. Rather similar behaviour was observed with cutthroat trout (*Salmo clarkii*); these fish abandon a redd if they encounter silt while they are digging (Snyder, 1959).

Where the harm is done by blocking gravel spawning beds, the concentration of solids suspended in the water is apparently less important than the amount which will settle out of suspension. This will depend upon such factors as the size of the solid particles, the stream velocity and degree of turbulence. Some rivers in British Columbia support large populations of Pacific salmon (*Oncorhynchus*) in spite of carrying heavy loads of glacial silt. Spawning takes place, however, when the rainfall is heavy and silt is flushed out of the spawning beds (Foskett, 1958).

Finely divided solids can be harmful to eggs which are not buried in spawning beds. Stuart (1953) observed that silt in suspension will adhere to the surface of eggs and kill them—probably by preventing sufficient exchange of oxygen and carbon dioxide between the respiring egg and the water. Suspended solids can damage the eggs of species which do not lay them on or in stream beds. The eggs of the yellow perch (*Perca flavescens*), which are laid in gelatinous strings entwined round aquatic plants, etc., were mostly destroyed over an area where silt from the construction of a road increased the turbidity to give an average Secchi disc reading of 0.46 m, but hatching was reasonably successful above the silted area where the average Secchi disc reading was 0.84 m (Muncy, 1962). Pikeperch (*Stizostedion lucioperca*) eggs are also entwined around plants and have been killed in Lake Balaton when the suspended solids content of the water rises during storms (Wynárovich, 1959). On the other hand the survival of eggs of walleye was not affected by wood fibre at a concentration of 250 mg/ℓ, even when the concentration of dissolved oxygen was 33 per cent of the air saturation value (Kramer and Smith, 1966).

1.3.3 SUBLETHAL EFFECTS AND EFFECTS ON BEHAVIOUR

Quite high concentrations of suspended solids in part of a river do not stop salmonid fish from passing through on migration between fresh and sea water.

There are Atlantic salmon in the River Severn in the British Isles and they are netted in the estuary although parts of the estuary naturally contain high concentrations of suspended solids—up to several thousand mg/ℓ at times (Gibson, 1933). Smith and Saunders (1958), when studying the movements of brook trout between fresh and salt water, found that turbidity seemed to have no effect on the fish's movements. Ward (1938) said that the normal concentrations of suspended solids in several Oregon streams were 137-395 mg/ℓ and that salmon run through them. On the other hand, when given a choice, some fish will select clear water. Thus, Sumner and Smith (1939) found that king salmon avoided the muddy water of the Yuba River, California, and entered a clean tributary. These fish also chose a clear streak in a muddy river for spawning rather than more turbid areas nearby. Schools of minnow advancing down a clean tributary to a muddy river have been seen to turn back immediately their heads enter the water of the muddy stream (Moore, 1932).

Bachmann (1958) found that when cutthroat trout in a river in Idaho were subjected for two hours to a turbidity of 35 mg/ℓ they were unharmed, but sought cover and stopped feeding.

Hofbauer (1963), when studying the factors influencing the numbers of migrating fish passing through a fish ladder, considered that the tendency for the barbel (*Barbus barbus*) to migrate decreased with increasing turbidity of the water, even though other conditions such as temperature and water level would favour migration. The opposite tendency appeared to be the case with the European eel (*Anguilla anguilla*): migration occurred when there was notable turbidity, and migration intensity decreased immediately the water became clearer. Ventilation rates of green sunfish (*Lepomis cyanellus*) were affected by concentrations of bentonite clay suspensions greater than about 17 800 mg/ℓ at 5 °C, 13 300 mg/ℓ at 15 °C and 6700 mg/ℓ at 25 °C, but rates of oxygen consumption were not affected by concentrations as high as about 26 700 mg/ℓ (Horkel and Pearson, 1976). However, Heimstra and Damkot (1969) found that turbid conditions reduced the activity and affected normal hierarchical behaviour of this species.

1.3.4 EFFECT ON FOOD SUPPLY

The amount of food for fish in fresh waters depends ultimately upon the growth of green plants (algae and higher aquatic plants). Such plants may be restricted by suspended solids; for example, severe abrasive leaf damage by coal dust to the aquatic moss (*Eurhynchium ripariodus*) was observed at 500 mg/ℓ after one week and at 100 mg/ℓ after three weeks (Lewis, 1973). On the other hand, Hynes (1970) reported that a fairly even discharge, containing silt, can create great stable areas of weed development which can completely alter the substratum (directly and indirectly) and with it the animal population. The considerable literature on this indirect effect on fisheries is not considered in detail in this chapter.

We have found few laboratory studies on the concentrations of suspended solids which can be tolerated by invertebrate animals on which fish feed. Stephan (1953) worked with several Cladocera and Copepoda. The harmful effect of suspended solids on these animals was thought to be partly due to clogging of their filter-feeding apparatus and digestive organs, and the critical concentrations were 300-500 mg/ℓ. Clay was most harmful, while earth and sand caused less damage. Robertson (1957) studied the survival and reproduction rate of *Daphnia magna* in suspensions of several kinds of solids. Apparently harmful levels were:

Kaolinite	392 mg/ℓ
Montmorillonite	102 mg/ℓ
Charcoal	82 mg/ℓ

Pond sediment was not lethal up to 1458 mg/ℓ. After being washed with hydrochloric acid, montomorillonite, pond sediment and charcoal were more toxic. Different kinds of solids thus appear to have different toxicities, and Robertson considers that this may be attributed, at least in part, to differences in absorptive capacity. Much lower concentrations (e.g. 39 mg/ℓ kaolinite, 73 mg/ℓ pond sediment) appeared to increase the reproduction rate of *Daphnia*.

Although they are often important in lakes, small planktonic invertebrates like *Daphnia* are a less important component of the fish-food fauna in rivers than organisms which live on the stream bed or on plants. Benthic animals are at risk not only from the solids in suspension, but from the accumulation of particles which settle on the bottom. Many authors have reported more or less severe reductions in bottom fauna from this cause. Thus, Taft and Shapovalov (1935) studied the abundance of the fauna on the beds of Californian streams into which large quantities of natural silt were washed by mining operations. In samples taken during the summer there were always fewer food organisms per unit area in the places where mining was practised than in clear streams. In the Scott River, silted areas averaged about 300 organisms m^{-2} (36 ft^{-2}), while in clean areas the average was about 2000 m^{-2} (249 ft^{-2}). Smith (1940) quotes earlier work by Surber and Smith which showed that silted areas in the American and Yuba Rivers of California contained only 41–63 per cent as many food organisms on the stream beds as did clear streams. Tebo (1955) found that in North Carolina streams heavy siltation caused by dragging logs over the ground near a small tributary resulted in turbidities of 261–390 mg/ℓ in a trout stream, and during summer and autumn, when the flow of water was low, the stream bed was covered with a layer of sterile sand and micaceous material up to 254 mm (10 inches) deep. In these areas the bottom fauna was only one-quarter as abundant (as volume per unit area) as at clean places above the point where the silt entered. Rainbow trout fed mainly on bottom fauna from January to June, but from June to December this made up only 42 per cent of their food, much of the remainder consisting of terrestrial insects. The bottom fauna (expressed as wet weight per unit area) in clean Cornish streams was found by Herbert *et al.* (1961) to be present at nine times the density occurring in streams containing 1000 and 6000 mg/ℓ suspended solids, although in a stream with an average of 60 mg/ℓ the bottom fauna was about equal in abundance to that in the clean rivers. These authors found during their survey that although a substantial proportion of the food eaten by trout (in May) consisted of bottom fauna, much of the food consisted of terrestial forms. Even a complete destruction of aquatic invertebrates in these streams did not mean that no food was available for those fish, but only that the total quantity was reduced. The effects on the food supplies of other species might be more serious. Gammon (1970) studied a stream where the concentration of suspended solids increased from a range of 13–52 mg/ℓ upstream of a limestone quarry to a range of 21–250 mg/ℓ downstream. Although the numbers of some invertebrate species (of the Trichcorythoides) that preferred a silt or mud substrate increased below the quarry, those of others (the net-spinning species of *Cheumatopsyche*) were reduced during periods of high concentrations. Also the drift rate of macroinvertebrates from an impacted riffle increased with concentration of suspended solids, the increase being 25 per cent with a concentration increase of 40 mg/ℓ above normal and 90 per cent at 80 mg/ℓ above normal.

Several more examples are given in unpublished reports of investigations made in France for administrative purposes and summarized for us by M. P. Vivier. Waste water from a sand-washing plant contained 29 900 mg/ℓ suspended solids, of which 19 750 mg/ℓ was settleable. When discharged to a trout stream in the Côtes du Nord it caused the disappearance of the bottom fauna of Trichoptera (*Hydropsyche, Rhyacophiles*), Ephemeroptera (*Ecdyonurus*), Crustacea (*Gammarus*) and Mollusca (*Ancylus, Limnea*) which were present upstream. Four kilometres downstream, where the suspended-solids concentration had fallen to 29 mg/ℓ, the fauna reappeared except for the Ephemeroptera. Plants and fish-food fauna disappeared from another trout stream after introduction of 250 mg/ℓ suspended solids from a quarry. Another small stream in the Vosges contained 11 300 mg/ℓ solids just below a granite crushing mill and washing plant, and 185 mg/ℓ 7 km downstream at its confluence with the R. Saône. The normal fauna and flora were completely absent from the tributary below the discharge. Coal mines brought the suspended solids in a river in the Gard Department to 570 mg/ℓ 1 km below the pits, and the river was virtually abiotic for 10 km. After this distance the suspended-solid concentration had fallen to about 100 mg/ℓ and a sparse fauna reappeared.

Although the bottom fauna of streams may be drastically reduced by finely divided solids which are chemically inert, deposits of some kinds of organic solids—humus from a sewage-disposal works for example—can support dense populations of some bottom-dwelling invertebrates, such as *Chironomus riparius* and *Asellus aquaticus,* which provide an abundant food supply for fish (Allan, Herbert and Alabaster, 1958).

1.3.5 THE TOTAL EFFECT OF SUSPENDED SOLIDS ON FRESHWATER FISHERIES

The earlier sections of this review have shown that sufficiently high concentrations of suspended solids can kill fish directly, increase their susceptibility to disease, reduce their rate of growth, modify their normal movements within fresh water, reduce the area suitable for spawning, and kill developing eggs. In addition, the quantity of natural food available to fish can be reduced. When a freshwater fishery is harmed by excessive quantities of finely divided solid matter, it is likely that many of these factors will be operating, although the relative importance of each one will probably not be the same in every case. Correlation of the status of fisheries in lakes and rivers with the concentrations of solids found in them should therefore provide data very relevant for the establishment of water quality criteria.

Ellis (1937) made 514 determinations of turbidity at 202 places on rivers in the U.S.A., and classified each site as either having or not having a good mixed fish fauna. His results are summarized in *Figure 1.1*. Precise conclusions cannot be drawn from these data, because few measurements of turbidity were made at most sites and these might not adequately represent the levels occurring in

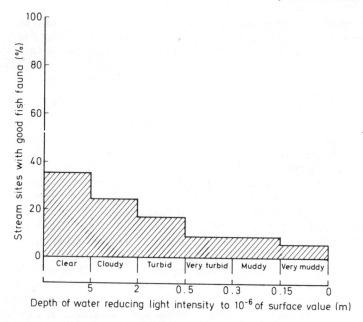

Figure 1.1 Turbidity and freshwater fisheries in the U.S.A. Data from Ellis (1937) (514 determinations of turbidity were made at 202 river stations)

rivers where turbidity can fluctuate considerably. Furthermore, a poor fish population may not have been due to high turbidity in every case but to some other factor such as low dissolved oxygen (see p. 3, para. 2). Nevertheless, the data of Ellis suggest that an increase in turbidity above quite low levels will reduce the chances of maintaining a good fishery, although it should be noticed that good fish populations were found at a few places where the water was very muddy.

It seems that some species of fish are much more tolerant of muddy water than others, and that an increase in suspended solids can lead to an increase in the numbers of the resistant fish as they are freed from competition with less tolerant species. Aitken (1936) said that Iowa streams which once supported trout, smallmouth black bass (*Micropterus dolomeiui*), and other clean-water species were transformed by excessive soil erosion so that they contained rough fish or mud-loving forms. Similar changes in parts of the Ohio river basin are reported by Trautman (1933). Rather more detailed evidence of changes which could eventually alter the species composition of a fishery is provided by an investigation made by the Institute of Freshwater Research, Drottningholm,

Table 1.1

Secchi disc reading (mm)	No. of nets	No. of whitefish caught per net
100–200	11	0.6
400–500	15	1.0
> 1000	10	1.9

which indicated that erosion turbidity in Lake Hotögeln, Sweden, was probably responsible for greatly reduced catches of char (*Salvelinus alpinus*), although the catches of trout and European grayling (*Thymallus thymallus*) were not appreciably affected. *Table 1.1* shows that the catch of whitefish (*Coregonus lavaretus*) in Lake Aisjaur, Sweden, was reduced by turbidity due to mining wastes consisting principally of quartz sand. The catches of perch (*Perca fluviatilis*) and pike (*Esox lucius*) were, however, not affected (Vallin, personal communication). Doan (1942) investigated the fishery statistics for Lake Erie where the turbidities vary between 5 and 230 mg/ℓ. The annual commercial catch of 'yellow pickerel', i.e., the walleye (*Stizostedion v. vitreum*), was inversely correlated to a statistically significant extent with the turbidities during April and May of the same year. On the other hand the catch of sauger (*Stizostedion canadense*) was positively correlated with the turbidities prevailing three years earlier.

Whitefish (*Coregonus* sp.) have suffered severely from suspended solids in several lakes. Many species of whitefish feed mainly on plankton, and typically dwell in lakes where the water is clear and cold. Scheffel, quoted in Stephan (1953), recounts the history of the fishery in the Chiemsee, Upper Bavaria, where suspended solids carried in by streams appear to have been responsible for a decline in the whitefish catch to a few under-nourished fish in 1920, and to zero over the period September 1920 to February 1921. The number of spawning fish was also severely reduced. Previously these fish had fed on zooplankton which was presumably abundant enough for their needs, but the reduced population was feeding on bottom-dwelling animals such as snails and chironomid larvae. Similar observations were made by Einsele (1963) on the Mondsee in Austria. Some large quantities of clay entered this lake during the construction of a road in 1961–62, making the water very turbid. This reduced the development of plankton, particularly *Daphnia*. Einsele estimated that the normal annual production of *Daphnia* in the Mondsee was about 400 000 kg fresh weight, and this fell to 80 000 kg in the turbid conditions. The turbidity also increased the mortality rate of the whitefish, resulting in a very low catch the following year.

Schnedeberger and Jewel (1928) studied ponds in the U.S.A. which naturally contained different concentrations of suspended solids, and found that the production of fish increased as turbidity was reduced down to a value of 100 mg/ℓ. Buck (1956) studied the growth of fish in 39 farm ponds, having a wide range of turbidities, which were cleared of fish and then restocked with largemouth black bass (*Micropterus salmoides*), bluegill (*Lepomis macrochirus*) and red-ear sunfish (*Lepomis microlophus*). After two growing seasons the yields of fish were:

Clear ponds	(< 25 mg/ℓ suspended solids)	161.5 kg/ha
Intermediate	(25–100 mg/ℓ suspended solids)	94.0 kg/ha
Muddy	(> 100 mg/ℓ suspended solids)	29.3 kg/ha

The rate of reproduction was also reduced by turbidity and the critical concentration for all three species appeared to be about 75–100 mg/ℓ. In the same paper, Buck reports that largemouth black bass, crappies (*Pomoxis*) and channel catfish (*Ictalurus punctatus*) grew more slowly in a reservoir where the water had an average turbidity of 130 mg/ℓ than in another reservoir where the water was always very clear.

In rivers, Herbert *et al.* (1961) found that 1000 and 6000 mg/ℓ china-clay wastes had reduced the populations of brown trout to about one-seventh the density found in clean streams, but that a normal trout population was present in a river carrying 60 mg/ℓ. There is much additional evidence in the unpublished reports from France communicated to us by P. Vivier. In a river in the Gard Department of France which supports a cyprinid fish fauna, fish are absent from a stretch which contains up to 570 mg/ℓ solids from coal mines, but a few roach and chub reappear 10 km below the mines where the suspended-solids concentration has fallen to about 100 mg/ℓ. Trout, minnow and bullhead which populate the upper reaches of a stream in the Vosges, disappear completely below the entry of wash waters from a granite-crushing mill which raises the suspended-solids content to 11 300 mg/ℓ immediately below the discharge. The fish do not reappear until the confluence of the stream with the R. Saône: just above the confluence 185 mg/ℓ suspended solids are present. Trout and dace were present in a stream in the Finistère Department of France above the entry of wash water from a tin mine, but the only fish in the polluted zone were eels. When the suspended solids were determined in this stream during a flood, 560 mg/ℓ were present 500 m below the discharge, and 80 mg/ℓ 4 km below. A rich fauna of Ephemeroptera, Trichoptera, Crustacea, Mollusca and worms almost completely disappeared below the discharge. However, in mountain streams fed by melting snow, some 1000 mg/ℓ suspended solids are often present for three to five months of the year and trout are found there, although not in large numbers. In the R. Loirelva (Norway), which is rather muddy with an average concentration of about 50 mg/ℓ suspended solids but with occasional concentrations up to 1331 mg/ℓ, pike, perch, pikeperch and several species of cyprinids are common. A very similar fish fauna is found in another muddy Norwegian stream, the Nitelva, in which the concentration range is 5.9–99.8 with an average of about 25 mg/ℓ, and in the R. Leira where the median and 95 percentile values were 58 and 250 mg/ℓ (M. Grande, personal communication). In the R. Trent catchment (U.K.) the maximum annual 50 and 95 percentile concentrations of suspended solids during the period 1968 to 1972 in areas where fish occurred were 18 and 412 mg/ℓ respectively for trout, and 62 and 965 respectively for coarse fish (J. S. Alabaster and I. C. Hart, personal communication). D. W. M. Herbert (personal communication) installed a suspended-solids recorder for a year in the R. Mimram, Hertfordshire, where there was a good trout fishery, and found that the average suspended-solids concentration was 24 mg/ℓ with maximum values of 80–100 mg/ℓ occurring at times. Liepolt (1961) reports that a trout fishery existed in a stream usually containing 19–23 mg/ℓ solids, and that this was not harmed by dredging operations which raised the concentration to about 160 mg/ℓ for short periods, except that fly-fishing was impeded when the water was turbid. Peters (1957) studied a trout stream containing suspended solids of agricultural origin and found good populations at one station where the median and 95 percentile values were 18 and 35 mg/ℓ, slightly reduced numbers where the percentiles were 70 and 180 mg/ℓ respectively, and a 75 per cent reduction where they were 160 and 300 mg/ℓ respectively. More recently Gammon (1970) found that in a stream in which the concentration of suspended solids increased from a range of 13–52 mg/ℓ upstream of a limestone quarry, to a range of 21–250 mg/ℓ below it, most fish, including common carp, were reduced in numbers downstream.

Herbert and Richards (1963) report the results of a questionnaire sent to River Boards in England, Scotland and Wales. Streams containing suspended solids of industrial origin were classified as either 'Fish present and fish popula-

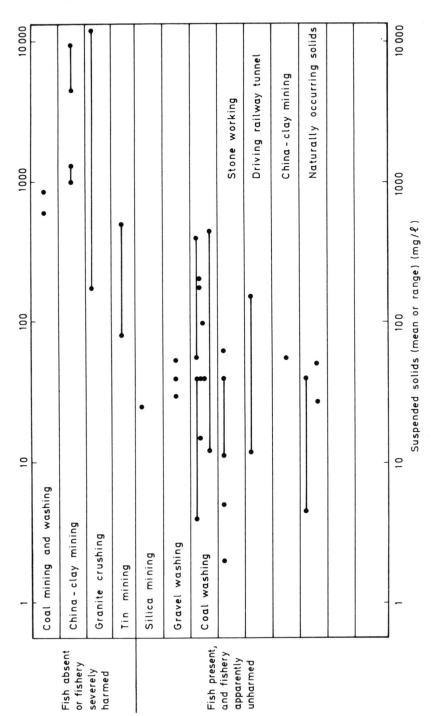

Figure 1.2 Reported status of freshwater fisheries related to the suspended solids content of the water

tion not adversely affected' or 'Fish absent or markedly reduced in abundance'. Care was taken that no data were included if there was reason to suppose that a river was polluted with materials other than inert suspended solids. These data are shown in *Figure 1.2*, together with the information summarized on p. 12, para. 5. Some of the concentrations shown in the figure are means or ranges of a large number of determinations made over a considerable period, whereas some of the others are based on a single observation which may not properly represent the concentrations normally to be found in that stream. However, in spite of this limitation, it may be concluded that nearly all the rivers (or parts of rivers) in which the fisheries were apparently unharmed carried distinctly lower concentrations of suspended solids than those in which the fisheries were either seriously damaged or destroyed. The concentrations in the two categories overlap to some extent and there is not a clearly defined concentration which separates them, but the critical concentration appears to be in the approximate range 100-300 mg/ℓ.

1.4 Tentative water quality criteria for finely divided solid matter

Water quality criteria for suspended solids are needed by those who have to manage inland fisheries and must sometimes decide, for example, how much solid matter could enter a river or lake without undue risk to a fishery, or whether it is worth attempting to develop a commercial or recreational fishery in water already containing a known concentration of such materials. The criteria should therefore be presented in terms of the effect on a fishery which a given concentration of solids is likely to produce.

There is evidence that not all species of fish are equally susceptible to suspended solids, and that not all kinds of solids are equally harmful (p. 5, para. 3). Unfortunately there is very little information on these and many other aspects of the problem, and, as was stated on p. 3, para. 3, much of the evidence which exists is less firmly established than is desirable. The conclusion is that no proposals can be put forward for definite water quality criteria which distinguish between the many different kinds of finely divided solids to which different sorts of inland fisheries may be subjected. Nevertheless, when the evidence is considered as a whole, certain general conclusions can be drawn and some tentative criteria can be based upon them. These are summarized in the following paragraphs, and then are put forward as a basis for discussion and to provide some useful guidance, but it must be emphasized that they are provisional and may well have to be revised when more information becomes available.

The spawning grounds of trout and salmon are very vulnerable to finely divided solids, and quite a small turbidity in the water or deposition of solids on or in the gravel may cause spawning fish to avoid them or prevent successful development of their eggs after they are laid (Section 1.3.2). This may be especially important where a salmon population is restricted by lack of suitable spawning areas.

Except for possible effects on spawning behaviour and egg development and the special case of freshly precipitated iron hydroxide (p. 5, para. 4), there is no evidence that average concentrations less than 25 mg/ℓ have done any harm to fish or fisheries, and there are known to be good fisheries in rivers usually containing about 25 mg/ℓ suspended solids (p. 12, para. 5).

Concentrations above 25 mg/ℓ have reduced the yield of fish from ponds (p. 12, para. 4); 35 mg/ℓ have reduced feeding intensity (p. 8, para. 2); 50 mg/ℓ have reduced the growth rate of trout under laboratory conditions (p. 8, para. 2); 82 mg/ℓ charcoal have killed *Daphnia* (p. 8, para. 5). On the other hand, 85 mg/ℓ is the lowest concentration reported for a stretch of stream containing few or no fish where other factors are satisfactory, and there are many other streams with only slightly lower concentrations where the fishery is not noticeably harmed (p. 12, para. 5 and *Figure 1.2*). In laboratory tests the lowest concentration known to have reduced the expectation of life of fish is 90 mg/ℓ (p. 5, para. 4), and the lowest concentration known to have increased susceptibility to disease is 100 mg/ℓ (p. 6, para. 3).

Some satisfactory fisheries are reported for waters containing 100–400 mg/ℓ suspended solids, but fish are few in number, or absent, in other waters within this range (p. 13, para. 2 and *Figure 1.2*). Similar concentrations of several kinds of solids have also increased susceptibility to disease (p. 6, para. 3), increased mortality rates (p. 4, para. 3), and reduced growth rates (p. 6, para. 2 and p. 12, para. 3). *Daphnia* has been killed by several solids in concentrations within this range (p. 8, para. 5) and, in all the studies considered, the abundance of the invertebrate fauna of stream beds has been drastically reduced (pp. 9, 10).

There is no good evidence that plentiful and varied fish faunas exist in waters normally carrying suspended solids in excess of 400 mg/ℓ although there are streams which carry even 6000 mg/ℓ in which there are very sparse populations of trout (p. 12, para. 5 and *Figure 1.2*). There may be some tolerant species of fish which can provide good fisheries in very muddy waters, but there is no evidence of such fisheries in Europe. An exception is that salmon are netted as they pass through muddy reaches when migrating (p. 7, para. 5).

Many kinds of solids can be present for short periods (possibly up to a few days) in concentrations of at least several thousand mg/ℓ and probably much higher without killing fish, but may damage their gills. This might affect their subsequent survival.

The brief résumé of the evidence on pp. 15, 16 indicates that there is probably no sharply defined concentration of a solid above which fisheries are damaged and below which they are quite unharmed. The impression is rather that any increase in the normally prevailing concentration of suspended matter above quite a low level may cause some decline in the status and value of a freshwater fishery, and that the risk of damage increases with the concentration. However, there is not nearly enough evidence to allow the relation between solids concentration and risk of damage to be defined at all precisely, and the best that can be done at present towards the establishment of water quality criteria for this class of substance is to divide the degree of risk to fisheries into four arbitrarily defined categories and attempt to make rough estimates of the ranges of concentration to which they would generally correspond.

From this approach to the problem the following tentative criteria are presented. With respect to chemically inert solids and to waters which are otherwise satisfactory for the maintenance of freshwater fisheries:

(a)   There is no evidence that concentrations of suspended solids less than 25 mg/ℓ have any harmful effects on fisheries.

(b)   It should usually be possible to maintain good or moderate fisheries in waters which normally contain 25–80 mg/ℓ suspended solids. Other factors being equal, however, the yield of fish from such waters might be somewhat lower than from those in category (a).

(c)   Waters normally containing 80–400 mg/ℓ suspended solids are unlikely to support good freshwater fisheries, although fisheries may sometimes be found at the lower concentrations within this range.

(d)   At the best, only poor fisheries are likely to be found in waters which normally contain more than 400 mg/ℓ suspended solids.

In addition, although several thousand mg/ℓ solids may not kill fish during several hours or days exposure, such temporary high concentrations should be prevented in rivers where good fisheries are to be maintained. The spawning grounds of salmon and trout require special consideration and should be kept as free as possible from finely divided solids.

These tentative criteria apply only to chemically inert solids and to waters which are otherwise satisfactory for the maintenance of freshwater fisheries.

1.5 References

AITKEN, W. W. (1936). The relation of soil erosion to stream improvement and fish life. *J. For., Wash.* **34**, 1059–1061

ALDERDICE, D. F. and WICKETT, W. P. (1958). A note on the response of developing chum salmon eggs to free carbon dioxide in solution. *J. Fish. Res. Bd Can.* **15** (5), 797–799

ALDERDICE, D. F., WICKETT, W. P. and BRETT, J. R. (1958). Some effects of temporary exposure to low dissolved oxygen levels on Pacific salmon eggs. *J. Fish. Res. Bd Can.* **15** (2) 229–250

ALLAN, I. R. H., HERBERT, D. W. M. and ALABASTER, J. S. (1958). A field and laboratory investigation of fish in a sewage effluent. *Fish. Invest., Lond. (1)* **6** (2)

BACHMANN, R. W. (1958). The ecology of four North Idaho trout streams with reference to the influence of forest road construction. Master's thesis. University of Idaho

BUCK, H. D. (1956). Effects of turbidity on fish and fishing. *Trans. N. Am. Wildl. Conf.* **21**, 249–261

CAMPBELL, H. J. (1954). The effect of siltation from gold dredging on the survival of rainbow trout and eyed eggs in Powder River, Oregon. *Bull. Ore. St. Game Commn* (Processed)

COLE, A. E. (1935). Water pollution studies in Wisconsin. Effects of industrial (pulp and papermill) wastes on fish. *Sewage Wks J.* **7**, 280–302

DOAN, K. H. (1942). Some meteorological and limnological conditions as factors in the abundance of certain fishes in Lake Erie. *Ecol. Monogr.* **12**, 293–314

EINSELE, W. (1963). Schwere Schädigung der Fischerei und die biologischen Verhältnisse im Mondsee durch Einbringung von lehmig-tonigem Abraum. *Öst. Fisch.* **16**

ELLIS, M. M. (1937). Detection and measurement of stream pollution. *Bull. U.S. Bur. Fish.* **22**, 365–437

ELLIS, M. M. (1944). Water purity standards for freshwater fishes. *Spec. sci. Rep. U.S. Fish Wildl. Serv.* 2,

FOSKETT, D. R. (1958). The River Inlet sockeye salmon. *J. Fish. Res. Bd Can.* 15 (5), 867–889

GAMMON, J. R. (1970). *The effect of inorganic sediment on stream biota.* Environmental Protection Agency, *Wat. Pollut. Control Res. Ser., Wash.* (18050 DW C12/70)

GANGMARK, H. A. and BAKKALA, R. C. (1960). A comparative study of unstable and stable (artificial channel) spawning streams for incubating king salmon at Mill Creek. *Calif. Fish Game* 46, 151–164

GANGMARK, H. A. and BROAD, R. D. (1955). Experimental hatching of salmon in Mill Creek, a tributary of the Sacramento River. *Calif. Fish Game* 41, 233–242

GANGMARK, H. A. and BROAD, R. D. (1956). Further observations on stream survival of king salmon spawn. *Calif. Fish Game* 42, 37–49

GIBSON, A. M. (1933). *Construction and operation of a tidal model of the Severn Estuary.* London, H.M.S.O.

GRIFFIN, L. E. (1938). Experiments on the tolerance of young trout and salmon for suspended sediment in water. *Bull. Ore. Dep. Geol.* 10 Appendix B, 28–31

HEG, R. T. (1952). Stillaguamish slide study. Summary of data obtained by research division during 1952. *Wash. Dept. Fish*

HEIMSTRA, N. W. and DAMKOT, D. K. (1969). Some effects of silt turbidity on behaviour of juvenile largemouth bass and green sunfish. *Bur. Sport Fish. Wildl. Tech. Pap.* 20

HERBERT, D. W. M., ALABASTER, J. S., DART, M. C. and LLOYD, R. (1961). The effect of china-clay wastes on trout streams. *Int. J. Air Wat. Poll.* 5, 56–74

HERBERT, D. W. M. and MERKENS, J. C. (1961). The effect of suspended mineral solids on the survival of trout. *Int. J. Air Wat. Poll.* 5, 46–55

HERBERT, D. W. M. and RICHARDS, J. M. (1963). The growth and survival of fish in some suspensions of solids of industrial origin. *Int. J. Air Wat. Poll.* 7, 297–302

HERBERT, D. W. M. and WAKEFORD, A. C. (1962). The effect of calcium sulphate on the survival of rainbow trout. *Wat. Waste Treatm. J.* 8, 608–609

HERBERT, D. W. M. and WAKEFORD, A. C. (1964). The susceptibility of salmonid fish to poisons under estuarine conditions. 1. Zinc sulphate. *Int. J. Air Wat. Poll.* 8, 251–256

HERTZOG, D. E. (1953). Stillaguamish slide study. *Wash. Dept. Fish.*

HOBBS, D. F. (1937). Natural reproduction of quinnat salmon, brown and rainbow trout in certain New Zealand waters. *Fish. Bull., Wellington, N.Z.* 6,

HOFBAUER, J. (1963). Der Aufstieg der Fische in den Fishpässen des mehrfach gestauten Mains. *Arch. FischWiss.* 1963, 92–125

HOLLIS, E. J., BOONE, J. G., DE ROSE, C. R. and MURPHY, G. J. (1964). A literature review of the effects of turbidity and siltation on aquatic life. Department of Chesapeake Bay Affairs, Annapolis, Maryland, U.S.A., Staff Report

HORKEL, J. D. and PEARSON, W. D. (1976). Effects of turbidity on oxygen consumption of green sunfish, *Lepomis cyanellus. Trans. Am. Fish. Soc.* 105 (1), 107–113

HYNES, H. B. N. (1970). The ecology of flowing waters in relation to management. *J. Wat. Poll. Control Fed.* 42 (3), 418–424

KEMP, H. A. (1949). Soil pollution in the Potomac River basin. *J. Am. Wat. Wks Ass.* **41**, 792-796

KRAMER, R. H. and SMITH, LLOYD L., Jr. (1966). Survival of walleye eggs in suspended wood fibres. *Prog. Fish Cult.* **28 (2)**, 79-82

KRÄMER, H. J. (1924). Grundlagen für die Beurteilung der Wirkung ausgeflockten Eisenhydroxyds auf Flora und Fauna fliessender Gewässer. 2. *Untersuch. Nahr. u. Genussm.* **47**, 148

LIEPOLT, R. (1961). Biologische Auswirkung der Entschlammung eines Hechgebirgsstausees in einem alpinen Fliessgewässer. *Wass. u. Abwass.* **1961**, 110-113

LEWIS, K. (1973). The effect of suspended coal particles on the life forms of the aquatic moss *Eurhynchium ripariodus* (Hedw.) 1. The gametophyte plant. *Freshwat. Biol.* **3 (73)**, 251-257

LE GORE, R. S. and DES VOIGNE, D. M. (1973). Absence of acute effects on threespine sticklebacks (*Gasterosteus aculeatus*) and coho salmon (*Oncorhynchus kisutch*) exposed to resuspended harbor sediment contaminants. *J. Fish. Res. Bd Can.* **30 (8)**, 1240-1242

LLOYD, R. (1960). The toxicity of zinc sulphate to rainbow trout. *Ann. appl. Biol.* **48**, 84

MOORE, E. (1932). Stream pollution as it affects fish life. *Sewage Wks J.* **4**, 159-165

MUNCY, R. J. (1962). Life history of the yellow perch *Perca flavescens* in estuarine waters of Severn River, a tributary of Chesapeake Bay, Maryland. *Chesapeake Sci.* **3**, 143-159

NEAVE, F. (1947). Natural propagation of chum salmon in a coastal stream. *Prog. Rep. Pacif. Cst. Stns* **PRP. 70**, 20-21

PETERS, J. C. (1957). Effects on a trout stream of sediment from agricultural practices. *J. Wildl. Mgmt* **31 (4)**, 805-812

RITCHIE, J. C. (1972). Sediment, fish and fish habitat. *J. Soil Wat. Conserv.* **27**, 124

ROBERTSON, M. (1957). The effects of suspended materials on the reproductive rate of *Daphnia magna. Publ. Inst. Mar. Sci. Univ. Tex.* **4**, 265-277

ROLLEY, H. L. J. and OWENS, M. (1967). Oxygen consumption rates and some chemical properties of river muds. *Wat. Res.* **1**, 759-766

SCHNEDEBERGER, E., and JEWEL, M. E. (1928). Factors affecting pond fish production. *Bull. Kans. For. Fish Comm.* **9**, 5-14

SHAPOVALOV, L. (1937). Experiments in hatching steelhead eggs in gravel. *Calif. Fish Game* **23**, 208-214

SHAPOVALOV, L. and BERRIAN, W. (1940). An experiment in hatching silver salmon (*Oncorhynchus kisutch*) eggs in gravel. *Trans. Am. Fish. Soc.* **69**, 135-140

SHELTON, J. M. and POLLOCK, R. D. (1966). Siltation and egg survival in incubation channels. *Trans. Am. Fish. Soc.* **95**, 183-187

SIMAIKA, Y. M. (1940). The suspended matter in the Nile. *Phys. Dep. Pap., Cairo* **40**

SLANINA, K. (1962). Beitrag zur Wirkung mineralischer Suspensionen auf Fische. *Wass. u. Abwass.* (in press)

SMITH, LLOYD L., Jr., KRAMER, R. H. and McLEOD, J. C. (1965). Effects of pulpwood fibres on fathead minnows and walleye fingerlings. *J. Wat. Pollut. Control Fed.* **37 (1)**, 130-140

20   *Finely divided solids*

SMITH, M. W. and SAUNDERS, J. W. (1958). Movements of brook trout, *Salvelinus fontinalis* (Mitchill) between and within fresh and salt water. *J. Fish. Res. Bd Can.* 15 (6), 1403-1449

SMITH, O. R. (1940). Placer mining silt and its relation to salmon and trout on the Pacific coast. *Trans. Am. Fish. Soc.* 69, 225-230

SNYDER, G. R. (1959). Evaluation of cutthroat reproduction in Trappers Lake inlet. *Q. Rep. Colo. Fish. Res. Un.* 5, 12-52

SORENSEN, D. L., McCARTHY, M. J., MIDDLEBROOKS, E. J. and PORCELLA, D. B. (1977). *Suspended and dissolved solids effects on freshwater biota: a review.* U.S. Environmental Protection Agency. *Ecol. Res. Ser., Wash.* EPA 600/3-77-042

STEPHAN, H. (1953). Seefischerei und Hochwasser. (Der Einfluss von anorganischen Schwebestoffen auf Cladoceren und Copepoder.) Dissertation, Naturw. Fakultät, Müchen

STUART, T. A. (1953). Spawning migration, reproduction and young stages of loch trout (*Salmo trutta* L.). *Freshw. Salm. Fish. Res.* 5

SUMNER, F. H. and SMITH, O. R. (1939). A biological study of the effect of mining debris, dams and hydraulic mining on fish life in the Yuba and American Rivers in California. Mimeographed report to U.S. District Engineers Office, Sacramento, California. Stanford, California, Stanford University

SWENSON, W. A. and MATSON, M. L. (1976). Influence of turbidity on survival, growth and distribution of larval lake herrings (*Coregonus artedii*). *Trans. Am. Fish. Soc.* 4, 541-545

SYKORA, J. L., SMITH, E. J. and SYNAK, M. (1972). Effect of lime neutralized iron-hydroxide suspensions on juvenile brook trout, *Salvelinus fontinalis,* Mitchell. *Wat. Res.* 6 (8), 935-950

TAFT, A. C. and SHAPOVALOV, L. (1935). A biological survey of streams and lakes in the Klamath and Shasta national forests of California. Washington, D.C., U.S. Bureau of Fish (mimeo)

TEBO, L. B., Jr. (1955). Effects of siltation, resulting from improper logging, on the bottom fauna of a small trout stream in the southern Appalachians. *Progr. Fish Cult.* 17, 64-70

TRAUTMAN, M. B. (1933). The general effects of pollution on Ohio fish life. *Trans. Am. Fish. Soc.* 63, 69-72

VALLIN, S. (1935). Cellulosafabrikerna och fisket. *Medd. UndersöknAnst Sötvattensfisk. Stockh.* 5

WALLEN, I. E. (1951). The direct effect of turbidity on fishes. *Bull. Okla. agric. mech. Coll., (Biol.)* 2, 48

WARD, H. B. (1938). Placer mining in the Rogue River, Oregon, in its relation to the fish and fishing in that stream. *Bull. Ore. Dep. Geol.* 10

WICKETT, W. P. (1954). The oxygen supply to salmon eggs in spawning beds. *J. Fish. Res. Bd Can.* 11, 933-953

WYNÁROVICH, E. (1959) Erbrütung von Fischeiern im Sprühraum. *Arch. Fisch-Wiss.* 13, 179-189

2

EXTREME pH VALUE

Foreword

The preparation of the original report on extreme pH values and inland fisheries was accomplished largely by Mr R. Lloyd who prepared the basic manuscript to be reviewed and supplemented by other members of the Working Party on Water Quality Criteria for European Freshwater Fish as well as a few experts from outside the region, notably Dr P. Doudoroff, Dr W. A. Spoor, and Dr A. Coche.

Subsequently there has been an upsurge of research on the effects of low pH values on fish in connection with three main areas where acid pollution is becoming increasingly recognized as a problem. These areas are:

(a)   Lakes and rivers of Central Europe, Southern Scandinavia, and the U.S.A. (the Adirondacks), where acid rainfall is reducing the pH value of the poorly buffered water draining from granite bedrock.

(b)   The Appalachian mountain region of the U.S.A. where extensive strip mining for coal has led to increased acid run-off from the exposed rock.

(c)   Areas in the vicinity of smelters, particularly in Canada, where again acid rainfall is responsible for reduced pH values in lakes downwind of the chimneys.

Except for the first area, the increasing acidity of the recipient water is accompanied by an increase in the concentration of heavy metals either from leaching or by atmospheric deposition, which may reach concentrations which are themselves harmful to fish populations. Even in Scandinavia, there is evidence that aluminium salts are leached out by acid rainfall. In response to these problems, a considerable number of field and laboratory studies have been carried out using refined techniques.

Much of the recent literature arising from these studies, especially those on acid rainfall, have been reviewed by Schofield (1976), Hendrey et al. (1976) and Leivestad et al. (1976); also Wright (1975) has published an annotated bibliography. In general, the extra data provided by the studies supports the guidelines laid out in the original report. Therefore, no attempt is made to review all the recent literature, and only a selection of papers which contribute new information is included.

2.1 Summary

In establishing water quality criteria for European inland fisheries, the acidity or alkalinity of the water is an important factor to be considered. There is a normal range of pH values for waters which support a good fishery. A critical review has been made, therefore, of published and unpublished data on both the direct and indirect effects of extreme pH values on fish, with an emphasis on European species; from this review it is clear that the existing data are not sufficiently comprehensive to enable definite pH criteria to be established for each important fish species and for different environmental conditions, but it is thought that sufficient is known for the following general conclusions to be reached.

There is no definite pH range within which a fishery is unharmed and outside which it is damaged, but rather there is a gradual deterioration as the pH values are further removed from the normal range. The pH range which is not directly lethal to fish is 5–9; however, the toxicity of several common pollutants is markedly affected by pH changes within this range, and increasing acidity or alkalinity may make these poisons more toxic. Also, an acid discharge may liberate sufficient carbon dioxide from bicarbonate in the water either to be directly toxic, or to cause the pH range 5–6 to become lethal.

Below a pH value of 5.0, fish mortalities may be expected, although some species may be acclimated to values as low as 3.7. However, the productivity of the aquatic ecosystem is considerably reduced below a pH value of 5.0, so that the yield from a fishery would also become less. Some acid waters may contain precipitated ferric hydroxide which may also act as a lethal factor.

Relatively little is known of the effects of alkaline discharges on a fishery and this may reflect the lesser importance of the problem. Laboratory data show that pH values between 9 and 10 may be harmful to a few species of fish, and above 10 lethal to the remainder. However, where high pH values are caused by the vigorous photosynthetic activity of aquatic plants, accompanying high temperatures and supersaturation of dissolved gases (together with other factors) may also contribute to a greater or lesser extent to fish mortality, making it difficult to correlate mortality with laboratory data on pH value alone.

There are insufficient data to enable even general criteria to be made for other aspects of this problem, such as the avoidance by fish of zones of extreme pH value, or on the growth of fish or their resistance to disease. Research needs are indicated in this chapter.

2.2 Introduction

Because the pH values of a river or lake water can be readily measured in the field with some accuracy, a considerable number of such measurements have been made and the results used in the description of the general character of the water. In an American survey of 409 locations, Ellis (1937) found that the pH range of those containing a good fish population was 6.3–9.0, with the majority of water-courses being within the range 6.7–8.6. This range of natural pH values can be extended beyond the lower limit by the direct discharge of acid effluents or, as a secondary effect, following the flushing of peat bogs by heavy rainfall, or from mine drainage. Rivers and lakes may be made more alkaline by either the direct discharge of wastes or as a secondary effect of vigorous photosynthetic activity by aquatic plants.

During the past 30 years, reviews of the effect of acids and alkalis on aquatic life have been made by Doudoroff and Katz (1950), Vivier (1954), Marchetti (1962), Jones (1964), and McKee and Woolf (1963). In establishing the water quality criteria for pH values ORSANCO (1955) pointed out that although fish had been found at pH values of 4-10, the safe range was 5-9 and for maximum productivity the pH value should lie between 6.5 and 8.5. These criteria have become widely quoted and the safe range of 5-9 has been accepted and adopted. However, it is not at all certain whether, in field surveys of acid waters, the absence of fish or the presence of a reduced population were caused by the concentration of hydrogen-ions present or by some associated factor such as a lack of chemical nutrients or presence of heavy metals, which may not have been measured. In the same way, fish kills observed in alkaline waters may have been associated with factors other than the concentration of hydroxyl-ions.

It is becoming increasingly clear that no single water quality criterion can be given for a given pollutant irrespective of other environmental variables or factors. Differences in the chemical constituents of the water, and in the sensitivity of various species of fish, may all modify the potential hazard of any given concentration of poison. The purpose of this review is to examine the existing literature on the effect of extreme pH values on fish to see what criteria can be put forward and where further research is necessary. Only the direct or indirect effects of hydrogen and hydroxyl-ions on fish have been reviewed; reference to the effects of those acids such as acetic, benzoic, chromic, or tannic acids, where the anion may be toxic, or alkalis, such as ammonia, where the undissociated molecule is toxic, have not been included. An exception to this has to be made in the case of waters where the low pH value is associated with the presence of humic acids derived from peat; in general, however, the toxicity of such solutions is not dissimilar to those in which the low pH value has been caused by addition of mineral acids and for the purposes of this review it will be assumed that humic acids have a low anionic toxicity.

Prime consideration has been given to literature dealing with species of fish found in Europe, although references to other species are given if they throw additional light on the particular item under discussion. It is thought that most, if not all, of the important published papers on this subject, where relevant to European waters, have been considered in the preparation of this review. Some references have been excluded where the data were incomplete, such as those referring to field observation of mortalities where the pH value of the water is measured some time after the fish were killed. It may also be noted that methods of pH measurement have progressed significantly within the last three decades.

2.3 Literature survey on effects of acid pH values

2.3.1 LABORATORY DATA ON DIRECT LETHAL ACTION

Variables affecting the lethal levels

Concentration of free carbon dioxide   The discharge of acid wastes into a water containing bicarbonate alkalinity will result in the formation of free carbon dioxide. If the water is hard, sufficient free carbon dioxide may be liberated to be toxic to fish, even though the pH value does not fall to a level normally considered to be lethal (Doudoroff and Katz, 1950). In well aerated waters the toxic levels of free carbon dioxide are usually above 100 mg/ℓ for rainbow trout (*Salmo gairdneri*) (Alabaster, Herbert and Hemens, 1957). However, Lloyd and Jordan (1964) found that much lower levels can considerably reduce the survival times of fish within a range of low pH values which would not otherwise be lethal. In water containing 10 mg/ℓ free carbon dioxide or less, the median lethal pH value for fingerling rainbow trout was 4.5 after 15 days' exposure, but where the water contained more than 20 mg/ℓ free carbon dioxide, the median lethal pH value rose to 5.7; this increased toxicity was apparent only after a day's exposure to the test conditions. It is, therefore, difficult to interpret some published data where the level of free carbon dioxide in the test conditions is either not given or cannot be calculated.

Total hardness, sodium and chloride   It has been shown that although survival times of rainbow trout in rapidly lethal pH values become shorter with a decrease in the calcium content of the water, the median lethal levels after 4 days' exposure are 4.18, 4.22, and 4.25 for water of total hardness of 320, 40, and 12 mg/ℓ as $CaCO_3$ respectively (Lloyd and Jordan, 1964). Recent data have shown that at lower concentrations of calcium the toxicity of acid pH values to fish is increased. Bua and Snekvik (1972) showed that for several species of fish, the hatching success at a given pH value was increased with an increase in calcium concentration; also, for brook trout fry (*Salvelinus fontinalis*) at pH 4.0, the percentage survival after 7 days was 0, 10 and 67 at calcium concentrations of 0.2, 1.0 and 2.0 mg Ca/ℓ respectively (C. L. Schofield, personal communication). Recent data show that the toxic effect of acid pH value is enhanced at low concentrations of sodium and chloride; these results are summarized on p. 30, para. 4 and 6.

Size and age of fish   In tests using bluegill sunfish (*Lepomis macrochirus*) of different size groups, Cairns and Scheier (1958) found that the median lethal pH values for four days exposure were 3.6, 3.6, and 3.5 for fish with mean lengths of 3.9, 6.7, and 14.2 cm respectively. Lloyd and Jordan (1964) found no correlation between sensitivity and the size of rainbow trout of any one age group, but a positive correlation existed between age and sensitivity; 16-month old fish survived more than three times as long as those four months old, although the increase in resistance, in terms of lethal pH value for these two age groups, was only 0.3 of a pH unit.

There is increasing evidence that the young stages of the life cycle are more sensitive than the adult fish. The viability of roach (*Rutilus rutilus*) and perch (*Perca fluviatilis*) eggs kept in natural lake waters with a range of acidities was reduced below pH values of 5.5 and 4.7 respectively (Milbrink and Johansson, 1975) (cf. p. 26, para. 3; p. 27); these authors refer to similar work with pike (*Esox lucius*) which gave a corresponding value of 5.0 (cf. p. 27, para. 3). Kwain (1975) found that no rainbow trout eggs survived at pH values of less than 4.5, but that there was a reasonable survival above pH 5.0; yearling rainbow trout were more resistant to acid pH values than were fingerlings. Menendez (1976) found reduced viability of eggs of brook trout at pH values below 5.1, with alevin mortalities occurring below 6.0; however adult mortalities only occurred below 4.5.

Acclimation pH value   Although in early literature, it was stated that fish could not withstand sudden changes in pH value, both Brown and Jewell (1926) and Wiebe (1931) found that various North American coarse fish species could withstand rapid transfer between waters of widely different pH values within the normal range. Lloyd and Jordan (1964) found no difference between the susceptibility of batches of rainbow trout acclimated to pH values of 8.40, 7.50, and 6.55 when they were exposed to lethal acid solutions. Falk and Dunson (1977) found that short-term (2–24 h) acclimation to low non-lethal pH values in the range 4–6 did not significantly increase the survival times of brook trout in acutely lethal acid solutions, thus confirming earlier work. However, Trojnar (1977) raised brook trout in waters of pH values 4.65, 4.97 and 8.07 in which survival to hatching was 76.4, 84.2 and 91.1 per cent respectively and, when the fry raised for 78 days at pH values of 4.65, 5.64 and 8.07 were exposed to a pH value of 4.0, 76 per cent of those raised in acid waters survived, whereas all those raised in alkaline waters died. This is in agreement with general Swedish experience in stocking acid lakes with non-acclimated yearling salmonids (M. Grande, personal communication). Although acclimation pH values within the normal range may, therefore, be discounted when comparing the results of toxicity tests, it would be incorrect to assume on this evidence that fish might not be able to acclimate or acclimatize slowly to a progressive decrease in the pH value of the water towards that normally considered to be lethal.

There is some evidence that strains of salmonid species may differ in their resistance to low pH values. Gjvedrem (1976) collected 77 different strains of brown trout from acid waters in Norway, bred them, and found a considerable variation between the resistance of the eggs and alevins to pH values of 4.7 and 5.2. Similar studies with inbred strains of brook trout (Robinson *et al.*, 1976) also demonstrated the possibility of inherited acid tolerance even among fish which had not been selected from acid waters. Therefore, some acclimation to low pH values may occur in the juvenile stages of fish, and there may be some selection in acid-polluted waters for strains which have an inherited resistance to these conditions.

Time of year   Sexually mature brook trout were most sensitive to acid pH values in the summer (Dively *et al.*, 1977) although data obtained by Robinson *et al.* (1976) and Falk and Dunson (1977) showed the opposite to be true for immature brook trout.

Other factors   There are no reliable data for the effect of low dissolved oxygen concentration on lethal acid pH values. Kwain (1975) found that rainbow trout embryos were more sensitive to sulphuric acid at 5 °C than at 10 °C, the median lethal pH values being 5.52 and 4.75 respectively.

Summary of toxicity data

Salmonids   Bishai (1960) found that for young Atlantic salmon (*Salmo salar*), and for sea trout and brown trout (*Salmo trutta*), the lethal pH value was 5.8–6.2 in 2-day tests, but since the water was acidified with free carbon dioxide, it is not clear whether dissolved carbon dioxide or hydrogen-ion concentration was the main toxic agent. Dahl (1927), using water acidified with peat, found that 80 per cent of trout in the yolk sac stage died within 20 days at pH values of 4.7-5.4, and 10 per cent died in the range 5.1-5.7. Salmon in the yolk sac stage held in dilutions of peaty waters were found to have a median lethal pH value of 4.5 at 12 days; also, yearling brown trout taken from a soft acid river (pH 5.85) died within 12-14 h at a pH value of 3.3 and survived a pH value of 4.1 for 7 days (M. Grande, personal communication). Lloyd and Jordan (1964), using hydrochloric acid, found that in water of low carbon dioxide content, the median lethal pH for a 15-day exposure was 4.5 for fingerling rainbow trout. This suggests that the brown trout were more resistant than rainbow trout and, even allowing for the larger size, there is a possibility that these fish were acclimated to some extent to the acid environment. Carter (1964), using a continuous-flow apparatus and acidifying 50 per cent sea water with either hydrochloric or sulphuric acid, and without subsequent aeration, found that the median periods of survival of fingerling brown trout at pH values of 4.5 and 4.6 were 61 and 42 h respectively; however, it is possible that more than 20 mg/ℓ free carbon dioxide was present under these test conditions, and, if so, the results would agree with those of Lloyd and Jordan (1964) for rainbow trout.

M. Grande (personal communication) found that the hatching success of salmon eggs in a water acidified with sulphuric acid to give a pH value of 4.59 was 96 per cent compared with only 48 per cent at a pH value of 4.34; moreover, only 50 per cent of eyed-ova of brown trout hatched in a solution acidified with peaty water to give a pH value of 4.77. No mortalities were observed among trout eggs or alevins (species not given) exposed to water acidified with hydrochloric acid in which pH values fluctuated between 4 and 5 (Krishna, 1953) whereas mortalities occurred below a pH value of 4, but neither the duration of the experiment, nor the concentration of free carbon dioxide, are given.

Other species   Using a soft water acidified with nitric acid, Carpenter (1927) found that the survival time of minnow (*Phoxinus phoxinus*) was 28 h at pH 5.0, whereas a pH value of 5.2 had no effect in three days. Under similar conditions, but using hydrochloric acid, stickleback (*Gasterosteus aculeatus*) survived for about $5\frac{1}{2}$ days at pH 4.8 and lived for as long as the control fish (10 days) at pH 5.0 (Jones, 1939). However, the mortality of control fish detracts from these results, and the true lethal limit of pH value may be slightly lower.

Although roach were found to have shorter survival times than rainbow trout in solutions with pH values between 3.0 and 4.1 (Lloyd and Jordan, 1964), the 8-day median lethal pH value was 4.2 for both species. Ellis (1937) found that the 96-hour median lethal pH value for goldfish (*Carassius auratus*) in a hard water acidified with sulphuric acid was 4.0, compared with 4.3 in a soft water and 4.5 for hydrochloric acid in a hard water; it is doubtful whether the differences between these values are of any significance and furthermore the concentration of free carbon dioxide cannot be calculated. A pH value of 4.5, using sulphuric acid, was said to be detrimental to goldfish over a period of two weeks. Lewis and Peters (1956) found that 35-mm common carp (*Cyprinus carpio*) were killed within 4 h at a pH value of 4.9, but the level of dissolved oxygen was low (2.4 mg/ℓ) and the experimental technique almost certainly led to a high level of free carbon dioxide and freshly precipitated ferric hydroxide. Briuchanova (1937) reports a threshold pH value of 5.0 for carp compared with 4.0 for the crucian carp (*Carassius carassius*).

Volodin (1960) showed that the resistance of the various developmental stages of burbot (*Lota lota*) embryos to acid water varied, and successful development could take place only within a narrow pH range. The most sensitive stage was that of embryo segmentation at which a pH value of 6.0 was the critical lower level, but during subsequent development the critical level lowered to 5.0. Dyk and Lucky (1956) found that the period of motility of carp sperm was reduced in water acidified with peat to a pH value of 6.5; Elster and Mann (1950) demonstrated a decreased motility of carp sperm at pH 4.5, and lower pH values were lethal to them.

2.3.2 FIELD OBSERVATIONS

Natural populations   Natural populations of brown trout have been found in waters of pH value as low as 4.5 (Menzies, 1927) and 4.9 (Campbell, 1961). Creaser (1930) reported that the brook trout was found in waters with a pH value of 4.1. Results of a survey of fish populations (mainly brown trout) in 1679 lakes in Norway have been summarized by Leivestad *et al.* (1976); few fishless lakes are found with a pH value above 5.5, although a few lakes within the range 4.5–4.7 contain good fisheries. In acid rivers, salmon are reported to be the first species to disappear, with sea-trout and brown trout showing higher resistance. In lakes, perch and eel (*Anguilla anguilla*) appear to be the most resistant species. Similar phased reductions in fish species have been found by Beamish (1974) in acid-polluted lakes in Ontario, where lake trout (*Salvelinus namaycush*) and small-mouth bass (*Micropterus dolomieui*) are the most sensitive and yellow perch (*Perca flavescens*) the most resistant, although the presence of heavy metals may contribute to these findings. From a survey of acid lakes in Sweden, Almer *et al.* (1974) concluded that the reproduction of roach was affected at pH values below 5.5; the associated calcium and conductivity data are not quoted. Surveys of acid Norwegian lakes have confirmed that where low concentrations of calcium are present, self-sustaining brown trout populations are less likely to be present than in similar acid lakes with higher calcium concentrations (Wright and Snekvik, 1978).

   Vallin (1953) reports that in L. Blamisus (northern Sweden) the water has a pH value of 2.8–3.1 and an iron content of 6–7 mg Fe/ℓ in the surface waters; the flora and fauna are poor and no fish have been reported there. The water from this lake flows into L. Sladen which has a pH value of 3.7–3.8, an iron content of 0.3–1.2 mg Fe/ℓ, and a slightly more abundant flora and fauna including roach, perch and pike together with bream (*Abramis brama*) during the breeding season. However, in the spring, the pH falls to 3.5–3.7 and some local fish kills of roach have been observed. It is evident that these roach can survive at lower pH values than those found to be lethal in laboratory experiments (p. 25, para. 5) and it is possible that some long-term acclimation has taken place. In L. Sysmajarvi (Finland) Ryhanen (1961) reported that, during summer, the pH value ranged from 3.5 at the outlet of an acid stream to 4.6, with a large zone which had a pH value of 4.2–4.4. Bream, perch, roach and pike were present, but only pike were able to breed in the large zone where the pH values were between 4.2 and 4.4. No under-yearlings of bream, perch or roach were present and the older fish presumably migrated from the more alkaline streams feeding the lake. Dyk (1940) states that tench (*Tinca tinca*) can be kept for two weeks in a water of pH 3.6–3.8 without adverse effect, although these values adversely affect carp.

   Although there are several field studies published on the fish population of

American waters polluted by strip-mining activities, the results are difficult to interpret since high hydrogen-ion concentrations are associated with high heavy metal content. A comprehensive survey of six lakes with pH ranges between 2.5-3.2 and 7.4-8.2 has been made by Smith and Frey (1971). The two most acid lakes (pH ranges of surface water of 2.5-3.2 and 3.0-3.4 respectively) were fishless but green sunfish (*Lepomis cyanellus*) only were caught in a lake with a surface pH range of 3.6-6.4; five species of fish were present in a lake with a surface pH range of 4.5-7.6. However, the two most acid lakes contained 2.9 and 0.8 mg Zn/ℓ and 82 and 4.7 mg Fe/ℓ respectively.

A survey of the acid lakes in the vicinity of Sudbury, Ontario, has been made by Beamish (1976); some sensitive species of fish declined in numbers as the pH fell below 6.0, but increasing acidity was accompanied by increased contamination by heavy metals, which may have contributed to the toxicity of the water. Although this was held not to be the case, the data on heavy metal toxicity used for the comparison were for other species of fish and in water of different chemical characteristics.

It is becoming clear that it is not possible to give precise limits of pH value above which a good population of a fish species would be expected. Genetically determined differences between strains of species, selection and acclimation may affect the sensitivity of the fish, and low concentrations of sodium, calcium, and chloride may decrease their ability to osmoregulate (p. 29, para. 6). Data from chronic tests carried out in the laboratory may tend to overestimate the long-term effects of acid pH values on natural fish populations, for example, through not having taken into account the influence of minor components in the water.

Fish kills   Fish kills occur with two main types of acid pollution. Heavy rainfall may flush out peat bogs or strip mining areas and produce a sudden flush of acid water, or acid discharges from industrial sources may temporarily lower the pH value of the water to a lethal level. In both cases, the pH value of the water is usually measured after the fish kill has occurred and, therefore, the figures may bear little relation to the pH values which were actually responsible for the mortality.

The position is further complicated in that these acid run-offs can contain considerable quantities of dissolved ferric sulphate which may become hydrolysed at pH values above 3.0 to form ferric hydroxide (Dahl, J., 1963), a process which might be accelerated by the presence of *Thiobacillus* species (Fjerdingstad, 1958; Dahl, J., 1963). Roach which have been killed in such waters have had brown deposits on their gills (Vallin, 1953). Schiemenz (1937) states that pH values below 5.4 are dangerous to common carp and tench, but a water containing much iron is dangerous at a pH value of 5.4. Haupt (1932) found that one-year-old carp died within five days in a water of pH 4.3-4.4 containing 1.2-10.5 mg Fe/ℓ. Larsen and Olsen (1948) found that fish kills occurred in a trout hatchery when the pH value of the water was 6.2-7.0 and the water contained 1.5-20 mg Fe/ℓ; the cause of death was attributed to the precipitation of ferric hydroxide on the gills, since the pH value of the water was higher than the lethal value. In laboratory experiments, Jones (1939) found that the toxicity of solutions of ferric chloride in soft water could be wholly accounted for by the low pH value, and he concluded that ferric salts had a very low toxicity. However, only 1 mg Fe/ℓ was required to give the threshold pH value of 5.0 with the dilution water used, and it is possible that this concentration was too low to have a toxic action if precipitated. If fish are killed by ferric hydroxide in suspension, the concentrations which appear to be lethal are lower than that found for inert suspended material (Chapter 1), but the presence of the precipitate on the gills of dead fish does not necessarily indicate that this was the primary cause of death. Lewis and Peters (1956), using green sunfish and largemouth bass, found that high concentrations of precipitated ferric hydroxide (up to 27 mg Fe/ℓ) had no effect on these fish in acid waters during a two- or three-day test in which the pH values varied within the range 3.7–4.7.

Recent experiments by Decker and Menendez (1974) showed that the 96-h LC50 for iron to brook trout was 1.75 mg/ℓ at pH 7.0, 0.48 at pH 6.0 and 0.41 at pH 5.5; a constant-flow experimental technique was used which ensured that a continuous supply of freshly-precipitated iron hydroxide was brought into contact with the test fish. However, Sykora *et al.* (1975) found that the maximum level which allowed the normal survival and growth of brook trout was 7.5–12.5 mg/ℓ; in these experiments a 1½-h delay tank was introduced to ensure the oxidation of ferrous hydroxide to the ferric state. It is possible that experimental techniques which can affect the particle size and chemical nature of the suspension may exert a considerable influence on the results. Smith, Sykora and Shapiro (1973) found that fathead minnow were more sensitive, with hatchability and growth being reduced at the lowest concentration tested, 1.5 mg Fe/ℓ.

Surber (1935) found that after rainbow trout were transferred from water with a pH value of 7.1 to a soft hatchery water of pH 5.4, 35 per cent of them died. Lloyd and Jordan (1964) point out that the water was probably high in free carbon dioxide (about 40 mg/ℓ) and the observed mortalities were similar to those which would be predicted for these conditions from their laboratory data, and therefore the mortality was not caused simply by the change in pH value alone.

Vallin (1962) stated that when the R. Morrumsan in southern Sweden (pH value 6.0) was polluted by an increased discharge from a sulphite cellulose factory, the pH value fell to 4.0–4.5 and mortalities of tench, roach and bream were recorded, whereas perch and pike were more resistant. Neutralization of the effluent with lime raised the pH value to above 5.0 and further fish kills were avoided, so that it is very likely that this effect was caused either directly or indirectly by the concentration of hydrogen-ions in the water.

In the cases where the toxicity was not complicated by the presence of ferric salts, the data on fish kills are in reasonable agreement with the results of laboratory experiments.

2.3.3 MODE OF TOXIC ACTION

The toxic action of hydrogen-ions on goldfish has been ascribed by several authors to the precipitation of mucus on the gill epithelium causing death by suffocation, or by precipitation of proteins within the epithelial cells (Ellis, 1937; Westfall, 1945). Kuhn and Koecke (1956), using solutions of hydrochloric and sulphuric acids in distilled water, found that the exposure of goldfish for one hour to a pH value of 4.0 led to complete destruction of the gill epithelium, a rather rapid degeneration since this pH value has been found to be the 4-day median tolerance limit (Ellis, 1937).

Lloyd and Jordan (1964) found no evidence of gill tissue damage or precipitated mucus in rainbow trout taken at death after a 7½-h exposure to a solution of pH value 3.4. Histopathological studies by Daye and Garside (1976) on surficial tissues of brook trout exposed for up to 7 days to a range of pH values above 2.2 showed that the gills were the most sensitive, with hypertrophy of the mucus cells at the base of the filaments at pH 5.2 and accumulation of mucus on the gills of surviving fish. In acutely lethal solutions the gill epithelium became detached from the pilaster cells. The lethal pH limit for this species for a 7-day exposure period was 3.5 (Daye and Garside, 1975). Dively *et al.* (1977) also noted that mucus accumulated on the gills of brook trout in acid solutions when respiratory distress was at a maximum.

Dahl, K. (1927) found that salmon held at a pH value of 4.7–5.4 (which had killed 80 per cent of them in 17 days) recovered on transfer to clean water (pH value 6.4). Lloyd and Jordan (1964) found that rainbow trout which had overturned after 24 h in a solution of pH value 3.8, recovered on transfer to clean water at pH 8.2. It would appear, therefore, that salmonids do not suffer any permanent damage from exposure to acid solutions for periods of time too short to cause death. The pH value of the venous blood of rainbow trout killed by highly acid water (pH value 3.15) was 0.2 units lower than that of control fish in water where little free carbon dioxide was present, and 0.55 units lower in fish dying in water of pH value 4.50 and containing 50 mg/ℓ free carbon dioxide (Lloyd and Jordan, 1964). These authors were of the opinion that, in the rainbow trout, the cause of death is acidaemia.

Dively *et al.* (1977) found an increase in the P_{CO_2} of arterial blood of brook trout, and also increases in gill ventilation rate, haematocrit and activity when the fish were exposed to a pH value of 4.2; little change occurred in the blood pH value. They also found a reduction in serum sodium content, which agrees with the findings of Packer and Dunson (1970, 1972) for this species. Leivestad and Muniz (1976) found that brown trout dying in an acid Norwegian river (pH value approx. 5.2) had low plasma sodium and chloride concentrations (but normal P_{CO_2} and haematocrit) and suggest that inability to osmoregulate is a major cause of mortality. Addition of sodium chloride to snow melt water containing 1.65 mg Na/ℓ to raise the sodium content to 14.4 mg/ℓ increased the survival of brown trout alevins from 30 per cent to 83 per cent at a pH value of 4.9; similar results were obtained with salmon, sea-trout and Arctic char (*Salvelinus alpinus*) (Bua and Snekvik, 1972, quoted in Leivestad *et al.*, 1976). Packer and Dunson (1970) also found that increasing the sodium content of the water prolonged the survival of brook trout exposed to acute lethal pH values; at death the sodium concentration in the blood plasma was normal and it is likely that death was caused by other factors. In other tests at a pH value of 3.0, the blood pH value was reduced by 0.44 units within a 1½-h exposure period.

The influence of acidity on the sodium balance of brown trout has been studied using radio-tracers (P. G. McWilliams and W. T. W. Potts, personal communication). At pH levels greater than 5.0, influx and outflux are approximately equal and body sodium is maintained; below pH 5.0 the influx is increasingly reduced, and the efflux is increased. While the influx is most sensitive to acid pH values, the efflux is more responsive to the calcium concentration of the water; it is thought that lack of calcium increases cell membrane permeability. Brown trout of different strains and different acclimation histories have different sodium exchange rates and so react differently to acid stress. Transfer of these fish to a more acid water produces an initial reduction in sodium uptake followed by an increased level within 1-2 days.

It seems that the prime mode of toxic action is still unresolved; disruption of the gill epithelium, production of mucus on gills, inability to osmoregulate and acidosis of the blood have all been found to be associated with harmful acid pH values.

There are few data on the sublethal effects of hydrogen-ion toxicity; Neess (1949) states that below a pH value of 5.5, carp develop a hypersensitivity to bacteria, and it is commonly believed in fish farming practice that a low pH value increases the susceptibility of fish to disease. It is quite possible that fish weakened by acid pH values may be more susceptible to disease, but there are no controlled laboratory experiments known to us which demonstrate this effect. In the case of field observations, it is difficult to separate pH value from other associated environmental variables, including water hardness, which may also be of importance.

The life cycles of some fish parasites are affected by pH value. *Ichthyophthirus* can reproduce normally within the pH range 7.2-8.7, and can become attached to the host fish only within the range 5.5-10.1; on the other hand, both *Costria necatrix* and *Chilodonella* require an acid environment for reproduction (Bauer, 1959). Frost (1939) found no difference between the incidence of parasites in a natural population of trout living in water at a pH value of 5.6 and those at a pH value of 7.8-8.0.

2.3.4 AVOIDANCE REACTIONS

Several authors have measured the ability of fish to detect and avoid acid pH levels under laboratory conditions. In some of these experiments it is difficult to judge whether the fish were detecting changes in hydrogen-ion concentration or differences in the level of free carbon dioxide.

Jones (1948) found that stickleback definitely avoided acid waters with pH values of up to 5.4, which was slightly above the lethal level of 4.8-5.0, and showed a very vague negative reaction to a pH value of 5.8, when the alternative choice was water with a pH value of 6.8. Ishio (1965) found that carp and goldfish avoided pH values in the range 5.5-7.0, with preference values of 8.4 and 7.2 respectively. Höglund (1961) separated the effects of free carbon dioxide from that of hydrogen-ion concentration and showed that roach tend to avoid pH values below 5.6 and salmon parr pH values below 5.3.

Höglund also found that pH values in the range 5.6-10.5 were non-directive for roach, and that the range 5.3 to at least 7.4 was non-directive for salmon parr. Brown and Jewell (1926), using populations of fish from an acid lake (pH values 6.4-6.6) and from an alkaline lake (pH values 8.4-8.6) found that, in a gradient tank where there was a choice between these two waters, the fish from the acid lake preferred the acid water and those from the alkaline lake the alkaline water. It is not established, however, that the fish were reacting to pH *per se*.

In the discussion to Ishio's paper (1965), Doudoroff questioned the ecological significance of experiments in which fish were exposed to steep concentration gradients of substances, and thought that reactions in the field, where changes in concentration occurred either over a longer distance or during a longer period of time, might well be different since progressive adaptation to the changing conditions might occur.

There are no accurate field data to suggest that fish migrate to an area of optimum hydrogen-ion concentration. The fact that various species of fish have been observed at pH values considerably lower than 5.0 indicates that laboratory tests demonstrate only the ability of fish to detect changes in the pH value of the water, and it does not necessarily follow that changes will be avoided in the field where the fish are also exposed to other, perhaps more powerful, stimuli. Although there are reports of fish moving downstream when an acid flush lowered the pH value of the water (Högbom, 1921; Parsons, 1952), there are no data on the pH value to which these were acclimated, nor on the acidity required to initiate movement.

2.3.5 EFFECT ON GROWTH

It is well known that the growth rate of fish in acid waters is usually less than that under alkaline conditions. Frost (1939) came to the conclusion that some factor other than the amount of food available was responsible for the lower growth rates of trout in the acid head waters of the R. Liffey compared with alkaline reaches further downstream. Campbell (1961) found that there was no correlation between pH value and growth rate of brown trout in nine lakes with pH values ranging from 4.9 to 8.4; however, he suggested that in some acid lakes, where there were ample spawning grounds, the slow growth rates were due to a too high population density for the available food supply. In an acid lake with no natural spawning grounds, the growth rate of trout artificially stocked at a low density was equal to that of fish in alkaline lakes. A similar observation was made by Pentelow (1944). From data supplied by the Department of Agriculture and Fisheries of Eire (E. Twomey, personal communication), the growth rate of brown trout in Irish rivers and lakes was generally higher in alkaline waters, but the best growth rate recorded was in a lake with a pH value of 5.4.

Experiments have now been carried out on the growth rate of fish kept at different pH values and fed the same ration. No difference was found in the growth rate of 18-month-old brown trout kept at pH values 6.26, 5.44 and 5.00 and fed with a daily ration of 2.9 per cent of initial body weight (Jacobsen, 1977). However, Menendez (1976) found that brook trout grew more slowly at pH values of 5.0–6.5 compared with that of the controls, although growth rates after ten weeks exposure appeared to be similar. Muniz and Leivestad (quoted in Leivestad *et al.*, 1976) also found that brook trout grew more slowly in an acid water (pH value 4.2–5.0) over a period of a year, compared with fish kept in the same water supply but neutralized with calcium carbonate to give a pH value of 5.2–6.5. It is not clear whether these apparently contradictory results are due to species difference or to the experimental techniques used. However, Leivestad *et al.* (1976) also quote Scandinavian studies which indicate that acidification of waters can initially increase growth rate of fish because of reduced competition for food.

Briuchanova (1937) found that crucian carp and common carp appeared to feed normally over the tolerated pH range, but that maximum growth was achieved at a pH value of 5.5 for crucian carp and 6.0-6.2 for common carp. In northern Germany the optimum pH range for carp growth was 6.8-7.5; below pH 6.0 the growth rate is reduced, and this is associated with a reduced food supply (H. Mann, personal communication). Parsons (1952) reports 'amazing growth' of bluegill sunfish in a pool at a pH value of 4.5.

The relation between growth rate and hydrogen-ion concentration is unclear, and it is possible that other ions present, such as sodium, calcium, and chloride, may exert a modifying effect.

2.3.6 EFFECT ON FOOD SUPPLY

A major factor in the poor productivity of naturally acid waters is the low concentration of dissolved mineral nutrients entering the ecosystem from surface drainage. It has been estimated that in Belgium, the productivity of ponds is three times greater in the alkaline areas (pH values 7.0-7.5) than in the acid areas (pH values 5.0-5.6) but the difference between the productivity of rivers in these areas is not so great (Huet, 1941).

However, there are several references suggesting that low pH values resulting from pollution affect the recirculation of nutrients in the aquatic ecosystem by reducing the rate of decomposition of organic matter and by inhibiting nitrogen fixation (Neess, 1949; ORSANCO, 1955). Harrison (1956) found that acid pollution from gold mining in South Africa produced typical peat bog conditions, with large accumulations of undecayed plant debris, in a stream with a pH range of 3.7-4.8. It is a common fish culture practice to add calcium carbonate to ponds where the pH value of the water or pond bottom is too low.

Certain species of invertebrates can withstand very high hydrogen-ion concentrations. Lackey (1938) found *Gammarus* species in two streams with pH values of 2.2 and 3.2 respectively, mosquito larvae in a stream at pH 2.3, and caddis larvae (Trichoptera) at pH 2.4. He points out that a wide variety of different species of animals and plants does not occur in waters with pH values below 6.2 but that large numbers of some species may occur in highly acid waters. Harrison (1956) found that species common to alkaline or neutral waters were found at pH values down to 4.0, but a specialized flora and fauna developed below 5.0 to at least as low as 2.9; Robeck (1965) reports six genera of caddis from water of pH value 3.0. Since these lower pH values are well below those lethal to fish, it would seem that absence of invertebrates is unlikely to be a limiting factor for fish in acid waters. Although *Gammarus* is frequently absent from acid streams, this may be correlated with low calcium content, dissolved oxygen distribution or current speed, rather than hydrogen-ion content (Huet, 1941).

There have been no data published since 1969 which indicate that lack of food organisms may be a limiting factor for fish populations in acid waters (except where precipitated iron salts are present) although the number of species present and the productivity of the water may be reduced; recent Scandinavian data have been reviewed by Hendry *et al.* (1976). Also, Tomkiewiez and Dunson (1977) concluded that sufficient fish food organisms were present in a stream at pH 4.5-5.0 to support a limited population of fish.

2.3.7 TOXICITY OF OTHER POISONS

A change in the pH value of the water following the discharge of an acid effluent may modify the toxicity of other poisons already present, particularly those which dissociate into an ionized and an un-ionized fraction of which one is markedly toxic. A classic example is the nickelocyanide complex which is 500 times more toxic at pH 7.0 than at 8.0 (Doudoroff, 1956) because the complex dissociates into cyanide and nickel ions and a proportion of the cyanide forms the highly toxic undissociated HCN. Conversely, ammonia is almost one tenth as toxic at pH 7.0 as at 8.0 (Wuhrmann and Woker, 1948). Other substances whose toxicities are affected by the pH value of the water are cyanide alone (Wuhrmann and Woker, 1948) and sodium sulphide (Longwell and Pentelow, 1935; Bonn and Follis, 1967). Recently, Mount (1966) has shown that the toxicity of zinc to fathead minnows (*Pimephales promelas*) decreases with a fall in pH value from 8.6 to 6.0 (the 4-day median lethal concentration (LC50) being 6.4 and 21.8 mg Zn/ℓ respectively in water of total hardness of 100 mg/ℓ as $CaCO_3$) but there was no further decrease in toxicity when the pH value was reduced further to 5.0. There are other poisons, the toxicities of which are affected by pH changes, but these cannot be considered here.

Poisons which are known to be not affected by changes in pH value of the water within the normal range include ABS (Marchetti, 1966) and gas–liquor phenols (Herbert, 1962).

The discharge of acids to water with a high bicarbonate alkalinity will liberate free carbon dioxide in concentrations high enough to be directly lethal to fish, even though the pH value of the water does not fall to a level considered to be harmful (Doudoroff and Katz, 1950). Sublethal levels of free carbon dioxide may increase the sensitivity of fish to low levels of dissolved oxygen (Alabaster, Herbert and Hemens, 1957) unless given prior acclimation (Doudoroff and Warren, 1965). It is not known whether sudden exposure to high but sublethal levels of free carbon dioxide increases the sensitivity of fish to other dissolved poisons.

Although there is reasonable agreement between laboratory data and field observations of fish kills, there is good evidence that some fish populations can tolerate pH levels lower than those which would be considered lethal from these studies. Moreover, this also indicates that such acid conditions are not necessarily actively avoided. In general, coarse fish appear to be at least as resistant as salmonid species to acid pollution and some species may be more resistant. However, a chronic acid discharge which lowers the pH value of a river or lake to below 5.0 will reduce the primary productivity and therefore the food supply, so that if fish are still present, either their numbers or their growth rate will be reduced. A more detailed summary of the data is given at the end of this review in *Table 2.1*.

There is considerable scope for further research in this field. There is conflicting evidence on the effect of iron salts on fish in acid waters; the presence of soluble iron salts does not appear to harm fish but the precipitated hydroxide may be more toxic than would be expected from studies on other suspended solids. There is little information on the relation between pH value and the resistance of fish to disease, or on their growth rate, or food/body-weight conversion ratios.

2.4 Literature survey on effects on alkaline pH values

2.4.1 LABORATORY DATA ON DIRECT LETHAL ACTION

Variables affecting the lethal levels

Effect of size   Using sodium hydroxide, Cairns and Scheier (1958) found that the 4-day median tolerance limits of pH value for bluegill sunfish were 10.5, 10.5 and 9.9 for fish with mean lengths of 39, 61, and 142 mm respectively, showing that susceptibility increases with size. Bandt (1936), however, states that the median tolerance levels of alkaline pH values are 0.2 units higher for large fish and Mantelman (1967) has shown that the resistance of *Coregonus peled* and common carp increases with age.

Acclimation pH value   Jordan and Lloyd (1964) showed that although the acclimation pH value had no effect on the resistance of rainbow trout to pH values high enough to kill in a few hours, the 1-day median lethal values were 9.86, 9.91 and 10.13 for batches acclimated to pH values of 6.55, 7.50 and 8.40 respectively, and that this difference, although small, was statistically significant.

Dissolved oxygen concentration (DO)   There are no accurate data on the effect of high pH values on fish at different levels of dissolved oxygen, although this might be important since alkaline conditions following from intense photosynthetic activity of aquatic plants are normally accompanied by high levels of dissolved oxygen. Wiebe (1931) found that bluegill sunfish showed distress, and some died, in water of pH value 9.6 and a DO of 5 mg/ℓ, but were unaffected by a pH value of 9.5 and a DO of 10 mg/ℓ. If the toxicity of an alkaline solution is related to the pH value at the gill surface and not to the pH value of the bulk of the solution, then an increase in DO in the water may lead to an increased concentration of excreted free carbon dioxide at the gill surface (Lloyd, 1961) and therefore to a lower pH value there. The extent to which the pH value at the gill surface is changed would also depend in part on the buffering capacity of the water; none of these factors has been the subject of controlled experimentation.

Other factors   There are no data for the effect of temperature, or water hardness, on the toxicity of hydroxyl-ion concentrations.

Summary of toxicity data

Salmonids   In tests using concrete blocks as a source of alkali, Bandt (1936) found that the minimum lethal pH value for trout was 9.2. This is slightly lower than the values found for rainbow trout by Jordan and Lloyd (1964) who found that the median lethal pH value for a 15-day exposure was 9.5, but the difference between these results may be that between the minimum values, which presumably killed no fish, and the median values which killed 50 per cent of a batch. Sprague (1964) reports that only 5 per cent of a batch of 40 yearling Atlantic salmon died within six weeks when kept in a water supply carried through asbestos-cement pipelines and having a pH value of 9.5. Carter (1964) acclimated brown trout to full strength sea water and exposed them to alkaline saline solution; a pH value of 9.6 gave a median lethal period of 20 h, whereas fish at a pH value of 9.5 survived for more than four days. Survival times of these fish in lethal alkaline solutions were considerably less than that for rainbow trout in fresh water at similar pH values (Jordan and Lloyd, 1964). Rosseland (1956) reports that an alkaline effluent was toxic to young salmon and brown trout, a pH value of 9.7 being lethal within a day, whereas none died during $1\frac{1}{2}$ days at pH 9.0. Long-term experiments with young stages of *Coregonus peled* showed that the highest safe pH value was 8.6–9.2 (Mantelman, 1967).

Krishna (1953) found that with eggs and alevins of trout, mortalities occurred above a pH value of 9.0, but the period of exposure is not given.

Other species   Bandt (1936), in experiments similar to that on p. 35, para. 5, found that the minimum lethal value for perch was 9.2, roach 10.4, carp 10.8, pike 10.7, and tench 10.8. Jordan and Lloyd (1964) found that the median lethal pH value for a 10-day exposure was 10.15 for roach, slightly less than that given by Bandt, and Mantelman (1967) gives the highest safe concentration for common carp as 9.2–9.6. Sanborn (1945), using sodium hydroxide, found that goldfish died within 3–20 h at a pH value of 10.9, and lived for more than seven days at a value of 10.4. Experiments using sodium carbonate and calcium hydroxide gave similar results, so that these cations appear to have no effect on the toxicity of the hydroxyl-ions. Rosseland (1956) found that minnow were slightly more sensitive than brown trout to the alkaline effluent described on p. 35, para. 5.

The various developmental stages of burbot eggs showed different sensitivities to alkaline waters, the most sensitive stage being that of embryo segmentation, when a pH value of 8.0 killed half the eggs (Volodin, 1960). Resistance increased after this stage, but even at pH 9.0 hatching was delayed. Sperm of common carp had a lower period of motility when the pH value of the water was raised to 8.2–9.5 (Dyk and Lucky, 1956), and pH values above 9.0 were found to be lethal (Elster and Mann, 1950).

2.4.2 FIELD OBSERVATIONS

Fish kills   In lakes and rivers, where there exists a combination of high plant density (including algae), high temperature, and strong sunlight, vigorous photosynthetic activity can raise the pH value of the water to high levels for short periods. This is usually followed by lower pH values during the night with minimum values just before dawn. Such a diurnal variation was measured in the R. Tweed in 1956 (Jordan and Lloyd, 1964). These authors point out that the harmful effect of these conditions is determined in part by the length of time for which these high pH values are maintained, and in part by the maximum pH value reached. Other factors include temperature and the high level of dissolved oxygen accompanying the high pH value (p. 35, para. 3). Furthermore, other possible lethal factors under these conditions are an increase in the dissolved gas content of the water to values greater than atmospheric pressure, which may give rise to 'gas bubble' disease (Doudoroff, 1957), and also certain algal blooms present may produce toxic by-products.

Since the pH values can show a considerable diurnal fluctuation under these natural conditions, it would be necessary to make frequent analyses of the water in order to correlate pH value with fish kills. Eicher (1946) reports that some rainbow trout in a lake were killed when the pH value rose above 10.2, but that fish in a river tolerated a rise to 9.4. For the reasons given above, this observation cannot be correlated directly with laboratory data but it is not at variance with them. Dahl, J. (1957) records a fish kill in L. Lyngby (Denmark) where the pH value rose to 10.3–10.6. In deep lakes, the high pH values may be limited to surface waters only, and fish may be able to survive in the deeper portions where pH values are lower. Mortalities among pike-perch (*Stizostedion lucioperca*) occurred at Ronninge (south of Stockholm) in 1966 when the pH value of the water rose to 8.4–9.5 (T. Hasselrot, personal communication); it is thought, however, that toxins from the accompanying algal bloom may have contributed to the death of the fish.

Natural populations   Although Neess (1949), referring to carp ponds at Wielenbach, southern Bavaria, states that a high fish production is maintained there even though the pH value of the water reaches 12, this is an unusually high alkalinity if produced by photosynthetic activity and might be regarded as inaccurate. However, pH values of about 10.0 often occur there during the summer (H. Reichenbach-Klinke, personal communication).

An alkaline discharge to the Austrian Millstätter See raised the pH value of the water to 9.3 over an 8-year period (Findenegg, 1962) but primary productivity appeared to be unaffected although some qualitative changes in the composition of the plankton and fish population were observed.

2.4.3 MODE OF TOXIC ACTION

According to several authors (Kuhn and Koeche, 1956; Bandt, 1936; Schäperclaus, 1956) a toxic action of hydroxyl-ions is to destroy the gill and skin epithelium. Daye and Garside (1976) found that the gills of brook trout were the most sensitive of the surficial tissues to high pH values within a 7-day exposure period, with a threshold pH value of injury of 9.0; mucus cells at the base of the gill filaments became hypertrophic and separation of the epithelium from the pilaster cells occurred at high pH values. Eicher (1946) reported that trout found dying at a pH value of 10.2 (p. 37, para. 2) had frayed dorsal and caudal fins and were blind, and a similar condition was reported by Ivasik (1965) for carp in a heavily weeded pond where the pH value rose to above 9.0, but it is not clear whether these symptoms were a direct result of the high pH value. Damage to the eye lens and cornea of brook trout occurred above a pH value of 9.5 (Daye and Garside, 1976); the lethal pH limit for this species within a 7-day exposure period was 9.8.

2.4.4 AVOIDANCE REACTIONS

Jones (1948) showed that stickleback avoided solutions of sodium hydroxide with a pH value above 11.0 but the range 7–11 produced no avoidance response from fish given the choice between tap water at a pH value of 6.8 and the experimental solutions. Ishio's (1965) results suggest that common carp and goldfish avoid lower levels, the median avoidance pH for these species being 9.30 and 8.64 respectively. However, the comments made by Doudoroff to Ishio's paper mentioned on p. 31, para. 7 are pertinent here also.

2.4.5 EFFECT ON GROWTH

There are no data known to us on the effect of high pH values on the growth rate of fish.

2.4.6 EFFECT ON FOOD SUPPLY

There are no data on the effect of high pH values on food supply of fish apart from the observations by Findenegg (1962) on the Millstätter See (p. 37, para. 4).

2.4.7 TOXICITY OF OTHER POISONS

The section on the effect of low pH values on the toxicity of other poisons is applicable here, in respect of those poisons, such as cyanide and ammonia, whose toxicity is affected by the degree of ionization. This is particularly important in the case of ammonia, the toxicity of which increases with an increase in pH value. Although zinc in solution may be precipitated as the basic carbonate at alkaline pH values, the precipitate can be highly toxic to fish if it is kept in suspension (Lloyd, 1960; Herbert and Wakeford, 1964; Mount, 1966). It is not known whether other heavy metals are toxic when precipitated as basic carbonates.

In summary, it appears that chronic exposure to pH values above 10.0 is harmful to all species studied, while salmonid and some other species are harmed at values above 9.0, and that tentative water quality criteria can be based on the existing data. However, it is difficult to correlate laboratory data with field observations on the effect of alkalinity caused by photosynthetic activity because of the possible additional effect of concomitant high dissolved oxygen levels, and the possibility that the water was also supersaturated with dissolved gases or contained toxic algal by-products, or subsequently became deoxygenated during the hours of darkness. If this problem is sufficiently serious to warrant further research, more attention will have to be given to measuring these factors in the field and making the appropriate laboratory experiments.

Table 2.1 SUMMARY OF THE EFFECTS OF pH VALUES ON FISH

Range	Effect
3.0–3.5	Unlikely that any fish can survive for more than a few hours in this range although some plants and invertebrates can be found at pH values lower than this.
3.5–4.0	This range is lethal to salmonids. There is evidence that roach, tench, perch and pike can survive in this range, presumably after a period of acclimation to slightly higher, non-lethal levels, but the lower end of this range may still be lethal for roach.
4.0–4.5	Likely to be harmful to salmonids, tench, bream, roach, goldfish and common carp which have not previously been acclimated to low pH values, although the resistance to this pH range increases with the size and age of the fish. Fish can become acclimated to these levels, but of perch, bream, roach and pike, only the last named may be able to breed.
4.5–5.0	Likely to be harmful to the eggs and fry of salmonids, and to adults particularly in soft water containing low concentrations of calcium, sodium and chloride. Can be harmful to common carp.
5.0–6.0	Unlikely to be harmful to any species unless either the concentration of free carbon dioxide is greater than 20 mg/ℓ, or the water contains iron salts which are freshly precipitated as ferric hydroxide, the precise toxicity of which is not known. The lower end of this range may be harmful to non-acclimated salmonids if the calcium, sodium and chloride concentrations, or the temperature of the water are low, and may be detrimental to roach reproduction.
6.0–6.5	Unlikely to be harmful to fish unless free carbon dioxide is present in excess of 100 mg/ℓ.
6.5–9.0	Harmless to fish, although the toxicity of other poisons may be affected by changes within this range.
9.0–9.5	Likely to be harmful to salmonids and perch if present for a considerable length of time.
9.5–10.0	Lethal to salmonids over a prolonged period of time, but can be withstood for short periods. May be harmful to developmental stages of some species.
10.0–10.5	Can be withstood by roach and salmonids for short periods but lethal over a prolonged period.
10.5–11.0	Rapidly lethal to salmonids. Prolonged exposure to the upper limit of this range is lethal to carp, tench, goldfish and pike.
11.0–11.5	Rapidly lethal to all species of fish.

Reference is made to different species on the basis of information known to us; the absence of a reference indicates only that insufficient data exist.

2.5 Conclusions

2.5.1 TENTATIVE WATER QUALITY CRITERIA

It is becoming increasingly clear that, for many pollutants, no single level or concentration can be put forward as the dividing line between safe and harmful which is universally applicable for all aquatic situations. Effects of the environment on both the toxicity of the pollutant and the susceptibility of the fish, as well as differences between the susceptibility of the various species of fish and the presence of other pollutants, have to be taken into account when attempting to formulate criteria for safe levels.

Although the existing data on the effect of extreme pH values on fish are neither as comprehensive, nor as accurate, as would be ideally required for the formulation of definite criteria, the information presented in this review does, nevertheless, allow general predictions to be made of the effects of acid or alkaline discharges on a fishery. Such effects are summarized in *Table 2.1*; it should be emphasised that these may have to be revised in the light of future experience and research. Data on avoidance reactions have not been taken into account because of the difficulty in correlating laboratory data with field conditions; also, there is no information on a direct effect of pH value on growth. For the alkaline range, the effect of high levels of dissolved oxygen on the susceptibility of fish has not been considered since there are no relevant quantitative data. There is some evidence that the resistance of fish to extreme pH values increases with age.

2.5.2 SCOPE FOR FURTHER RESEARCH

In order to define water quality criteria more fully, further laboratory research is required on the toxicity to fish of acid waters containing iron salts, and on the growth rates of fish in acid waters. Field studies on the productivity of acid polluted streams are also required. There may be a need for laboratory studies on the effect of high dissolved oxygen levels on the resistance of fish to alkaline pH values, together with those other associated factors which may occur in the field.

2.6 References

ALABASTER, J. S., HERBERT, D. W. M. and HEMENS, J. (1957). The survival of rainbow trout (*Salmo gairdneri* Richardson) and perch (*Perca fluviatilis* L.) at various concentrations of dissolved oxygen and carbon dioxide. *Ann. appl. Biol.* **45**, 177-178

ALMER, B., DICKSON, W., EKSTROM, C., HORNSTROM, E. and MILLER, U. (1974). Effects of acidification on Swedish lakes. *Ambio* **3**, 30-36

BANDT, H. J. (1936). Der für Fische 'tödliche pH-Wert' in alkalischem Bereich. *Z. Fisch.* **34**, 359-361

BAUER, O. N. (1959). The ecology of parasites of freshwater fish. *Izv. gozud. nauch. issled. Inst. ozer. rech. ryb. Khoz.* **49 (3)**, 215

BEAMISH, R. J. (1974). Loss of fish populations from unexploited and remote lakes in Ontario, Canada, as a consequence of atmospheric fallout of acid. *Wat. Res.* **8**, 85-95

BEAMISH, R. J. (1976). Acidification of lakes in Canada by acid precipitation and the resulting effects on fishes. *Wat. Air Soil Pollut.* **6**, 501-514

BISHAI, H. M. (1960). The effect of hydrogen-ion concentration on the survival and distribution of larval and young fish. *Z. wiss. Zool.* **164**, 107-118

BONN, E. W. and FOLLIS, B. J. (1967). Effects of hydrogen sulphide on channel catfish (*Ictalurus punctatus*). *Trans. Am. Fish. Soc.* **96**, 31-36

BRIUCHANOVA, A. A. (1937). *Uchen. Zap. mosk. gos. Univ. (Biol.)* **9**, 17-30

BROWN, H. W. and JEWELL, M. E. (1926). Further studies on the fishes of an acid lake. *Trans. Am. microsc. Soc.* **45**, 20-34

BUA, B. and SNEKVIK, E. (1972). Hatching experiments with roe from salmonid fishes, 1966-1971. Effects of acidity and dissolved salt in the water. *Vann.* **7**, 86-93

CAIRNS, J. Jr. and SCHEIER, A. (1958). The relation of bluegill sunfish body size to tolerance for some common chemicals. *Ind. Wastes* **3**, 126

CAMPBELL, R. N. (1961). The growth of brown trout in acid and alkaline waters. *Salm. Trout Mag.* **161**, 47-52

CARPENTER, K. E. (1927). The lethal action of soluble metallic salts on fishes. *Br. J. exp. Biol.* **4**, 378-390

CARTER, L. (1964). Effects of acidic and alkaline effluents on fish in sea water. *Eff. Wat. Treatmt J.* **4**, 484-486

CREASER, C. W. (1930). Relative importance of hydrogen-ion concentration, temperature, dissolved oxygen and carbon dioxide tension, on habitat selection by brook trout. *Ecology* **11**, 246-262

DAHL, J. (1957). Fiskedrabet i Lyngby sø. *FerskvandsfiskBl.* **55**, 216-220

DAHL, J. (1963). Transformation of iron and sulphur compounds in soil and its relation to Danish inland fisheries. *Trans. Am. Fish. Soc.* **92**, 260-264

DAHL, K. (1927). The effects of acid water on trout fry. *Salm. Trout Mag.* **46**, 35-43

DAYE, P. G. and GARSIDE, E. T. (1975). Lethal levels of pH for brook trout *Salvelinus fontinalis* (Mitchell). *Can. J. Zool.* **53**, 639-641

DAYE, P. G. and GARSIDE, E. T. (1976). Histopathologic changes in surficial tissues of brook trout *Salvelinus fontinalis* (Mitchell) exposed to acute and chronic levels of pH. *Can. J. Zool.* **54**, 2140-2155

DECKER, C. and MENENDEZ, R. (1974). Acute toxicity of iron and aluminium to brook trout. *Proc. West. Va Acad. Sci.* **46**, 159-167

DIVELY, J. L., MUDGE, J. E., NEFF, W. H. and ANTHONY, A. (1977). Blood Po_2, Pco_2. and pH changes in brook trout (*Salvelinus fontinalis*) exposed to sublethal levels of acidity. *Comp. Biochem. Physiol.* **57A**, 347-351

DOUDOROFF, P. (1956). Some experiments on the toxicity of complex cyanides to fish. *Sewage ind. Wastes* **28**, 1020-1040

DOUDOROFF, P. (1957). In *The Physiology of Fishes* (Ed. by M. E. Brown), vol. 2, pp. 403-430. New York, New York Academic Press

DOUDOROFF, P. and KATZ, M. (1950). Critical review of literature on the toxicity of industrial wastes and their components to fish. 1. Alkalis, acids and inorganic gases. *Sewage ind. Wastes* **22**, 1432-1458

DOUDOROFF, P. and WARREN, C. E. (1965). Dissolved oxygen requirements of fishes. Biological problems in water pollution, 1962. *Publ. Hlth Serv. Publs, Wash.* **(999-WP-25)**, 145-155

DYK, V. (1940). Ability of fish to resist fluctuations of pH value and to recover from damage by acidified water. *Roč. čsl. Akad. zeměd.* **15**, 378

DYK, V. and LUCKY, L. (1956). Pohyblivost spermii karpa za rozdilných teplot, kyslikatosti pH a tvrdosti vody. *Sb. čsl. Akad. zeměd. Věd. (E)* **29**

EICHER, G. J. (1946). Lethal alkalinity for trout in waters of low salt content. *J. Wildl. Mgmt* **10**, 82-85

ELLIS, H. M. (1937). Detection and measurement of stream pollution. *Bull. U.S. Dep. Commer.* **27**

ELSTER, H. and MANN, H. (1950). Experimentelle Beiträge zur Kenntnis der Physiologie der Befruchtung bei Fischen. *Arch. FischWiss.* **2**, 49-72

FALK, D. L. and DUNSON, W. A. (1977). The effects of season and acute sublethal exposure on survival times of brook trout at low pH. *Wat. Res.* **11**, 13-15

FINDENEGG, I. (1962). Limnologische und fischereibiologische Untersuchungen an einem durch Abwasser alkalisierten Alpensee, dem Millstätter See in Kärnten. *Z. Fisch.* **11**, 115-127

FJERDINGSTAD, E. (1958). Undersøgelse af Timå 1948-1953. Et vandløb forurene ved udløb af draeningsvand fra et brunkulsbrud. *Dansk. IngForen* **12**, 1-52

FROST, W. E. (1939). River Liffey survey. 2. The food consumed by the brown trout (*Salmo trutta* L.) in acid and alkaline waters. *Proc. R. Ir. Acad. (B)* **45 (7)**, 139-206

GJVEDREM, T. (1976). Genetic variation in tolerance of brown trout to acid water. In *Impact of acid precipation on forest and freshwater ecosystems in Norway*. Norges Landbrukshøgskole, Norway, S.N.S.F. project, Norsk institutt for Skogforskning, **FR5/76**

HARRISON, A. D. (1956). The effects of sulphuric acid pollution on the biology of streams in the Transvaal, South Africa. *Verh. int. Verein. theor. angew. Limnol.* **13**, 603-610

HAUPT, H. (1932). Fischsterben durch saures Wasser. *Vom Wass.* **6**, 261-262

HENDREY, G. R., BAALSRUD, K., TRAAEN, T. S., LAAKE, M. and RADDUM, G. (1976) Acid precipitation: some hydrobiological changes. *Ambio* **5**, 224-227

HERBERT, D. W. M. (1962). The toxicity to rainbow trout of spent still liquors from the distillation of coal. *Ann. appl. Biol.* **50**, 755-777

HERBERT, D. W. M. and WAKEFORD, A. C. (1964). The susceptibility of salmonid fish to poisons under estuarine conditions. 1. Zinc sulphate. *Int. J. Air Wat. Pollut.* **8**, 251-256

HÖGBOM, A. G. (1921). Om vitriolbildning i naturen sosom orsak till massdöd av fisk i våra insjöar. *Svensk FiskTidskr.* **30**, 41-51

HÖGLUND, L. B. (1961). The reactions of fish in concentration gradients. *Rep. Inst. Freshwat. Res. Drottningholm* **43**

HUET, M. (1941). Esquisse hydrobiologique des eaux piscicoles de la Haute-Belgique. *Trav. Stn Rech. Groenendaal, (D)* **2**

ISHIO, S. (1965). Behaviour of fish exposed to toxic substances. *Proc. int. Conf. Wat. Pollut. Res.*, pp. 19-40

IVASIK, V. (1965). Saranat zagiva ot prekomerno goljamata alkanost v ezernata voda. *Ribno Stop.* **4**, 13

JACOBSEN, O. J. (1977). Brown trout (*Salmo trutta*) growth at reduced pH. *Aquaculture* **11**, 81-84

JONES, J. R. E. (1939). The relation between the electrolytic solution pressures of the metals and their toxicity to the stickleback (*Gasterosteus aculeatus* L.). *J. exp. Biol.* **16**, 425-437

JONES, J. R. E. (1948). A further study of the reactions of fish to toxic solutions. *J. exp. Biol.* **25**, 22-34

JONES, J. R. E. (1964). *Fish and river pollution*. London, Butterworths

JORDAN, D. H. M. and LLOYD, R. (1964). The resistance of rainbow trout (*Salmo gairdneri*, Richardson) and roach (*Rutilus rutilus* L.) to alkaline solutions. *Int. J. Air Wat. Pollut.* **8**, 405-409

KLARBERG, D. P. and BENSON, A. (1975). Food habits of *Ictalurus nebulosus* in acid polluted waters of North West Virginia. *Trans. Am. Fish. Soc.* **104**, 541-547

KRISHNA, D. (1953). Effect of changing pH on developing trout eggs and larvae. *Nature, Lond.* **171**, 434

KUHN, O. and KOECKE, H. U. (1956). Histologische und cytologische Veränderungen der Fischkieme nach Einwirkung im Wasser enthaltener schädigender Substanzen. *Z. Zellforsch. mikrosk. Anat.* **43**, 611-643

KWAIN, W. (1975). Effects of temperature on development and survival of rainbow trout, *Salmo gairdneri*, in acid waters. *J. Fish. Res. Bd Can.* **32**, 493-497

LACKEY, J. B. (1938). The flora and fauna of surface waters polluted by acid mine drainage. *Publ. Hlth Rep., Wash.* **53**, 1499-1507

LARSON, K. and OLSEN, S. (1948). Okkerkvaelning af fisk i Tim o. *Beret. Minist. Landbr. Fisk. dan. biol. Stn* **50**, 1-25

LEIVESTAD, H., HENDREY, G., MUNIZ, I. P. and SNEKVIK, E. (1976). Effects of acid precipitation on freshwater organisms. In *Impact of acid precipitation on forest and freshwater ecosystems in Norway*. (Ed. by F. J. Braekke). Norges Landbrukshøgskole, Norway, S.N.S.F. project, Norsk institutt for Skogforskning, Research Report **6/76**, 87-111

LEIVESTAD, H. and MUNIZ, I. P. (1976). Fish kill at low pH in a Norwegian river *Nature, Lond.* **259**, 391-392

LEWIS, W. M. and PETERS, C. (1956). Coal mine slag drainage. *Ind. Wastes* **1**, 145-147

LLOYD, R. (1960). The toxicity of zinc sulphate to rainbow trout. *Ann. appl. Biol.* **48**, 84-94

LLOYD, R. (1961). Effect of dissolved oxygen concentrations on the toxicity of several poisons to rainbow trout (*Salmo gairdneri*, Richardson). *J. exp. Biol.* **38**, 447-455

LLOYD, R. and JORDAN, D. H. M. (1964). Some factors affecting the resistance of rainbow trout (*Salmo gairdneri* Richardson) to acid waters. *Int. J. Air Wat. Pollut.* **8**, 393-403

LONGWELL, J. and PENTELOW, F. T. K. (1935). The effect of sewage on brown trout (*Salmo trutta* L.). *J. exp. Biol.* **12**, 1-12

MANTELMAN, I. I. (1967). Predelno dopustimyje znachenija pH dlja molodi nekotorykh vidov ryb. (Maximum permissible values of pH for fry of some fish species.) *Izv. gosud. nauchno-issled. Inst. ozern. rechn. rybn. Khozjaist.* **64**, 79-83. (Russian; English summary)

MARCHETTI, R. (1962). *Biologia e tossicologia delle acque usate.* Milano, ETAS (Editrice Tecnica Artistica Scientifica)

MARCHETTI, R. (1966). Relation entre l'activité de surface, la composition chimique et la toxicité vis-à-vis de la vie aquatique des détergents de synthèse. In *La pollution des eaux*. Paris, Eyrolles

MENENDEZ, R. (1976). Chronic effects of reduced pH on brook trout (*Salvelinus fontinalis*). *J. Fish. Res. Bd Can.* **33**, 118-123

MENZIES, W. J. M. (1927). River pollution and the acidity of natural waters. *Nature, Lond.* **119**, 638-639

MILBRINK, G. and JOHANSSON, N. (1975). Some effects of acidification of roe of roach, *Rutilus rutilus* L., and perch, *Perca fluviatilis* L., with special reference to the Avaa lake system in eastern Sweden. *Rep. Inst. Freshwat. Res., Drottningholm* **54**, 52-62

MOUNT, D. I. (1966). The effect of total hardness and pH on the acute toxicity of zinc to fish. *Int. J. Air Wat. Pollut.* **10**, 49-56

McKEE, J. E. and WOLF, H. W. (1963). Water quality criteria. Sacramento, California Water Quality Control Board, (3-A)

NEESS, J. C. (1949). Development and status of pond fertilization in Central Europe. *Trans. Am. Fish. Soc.* **76**, 335-358

ORSANCO, (1955). Aquatic life water quality criteria. *Sewage ind. Wastes* **27**, 321-313

PACKER, R. K. and DUNSON, W. A. (1970). Effects of low environmental pH on blood pH and sodium balance of brook trout. *J. exp. Zool.* **174**, 65-72

PACKER, R. K. and DUNSON, W. A. (1972). Anoxia and sodium loss associated with the death of brook trout at low pH. *Comp. Biochem. Physiol.* **41A**, 17-26

PARSONS, J. W. (1952). A biological approach to the study and control of acid mine pollution. *J. Tenn. Acad. Sci.* **27**, 304-309

PENTELOW, F. T. K. (1944). Nature of acid in soft water in relation to the growth of brown trout. *Nature, Lond.* **153**, 464

ROBECK, S. S. (1965). Environmental requirements of Trichoptera. In *Biological Problems in Water Pollution, 1962. Publ. Hlth Serv. Publs. Wash.* **(999-WP-25)**, 118-126

ROBINSON, G. D., DUNSON, W. A., WRIGHT, J. E.and MAMALITO, G. E. (1976). Differences in low pH tolerance among strains of brook trout (*Salvelinus fontinalis*). *J. Fish. Biol.* **8**, 5-17

ROSSELAND, L. (1956). Orienterende undersøkelse av vassdragsforurensninger fra halmlutingsanlegg. Norsk Institutt før Vannforskning (NIVA), Rapport 0-9

RYHANEN, R. (1961). Über die Einwirkung von Grubenabfällen auf einen dystrophen See. *Ann. Zool. Soc. Vanamo* **22(8)**

SANBORN, N. H. (1945). The lethal effects of certain chemicals on freshwater fish. *Cann. Trade* **67 (10-12)**, 26

SCHÄPERCLAUS, W. (1956). Ursache und Auswirkungen der Frühjahrs-pH-Werterhöhungen in Karpfenteichen. *Z. Fisch.* **5**, 161-174

SCHIEMENZ, F. (1937). Ein einfacher Säureprüfer für praktische Teichwirte zur Feststellung von Säuregefahr des Wassers. *Allg. FischZtg.* **62**, 71

SCHOFIELD, C. L. (1976). Acid precipitation; effects on fish. *Ambio* **5**, 228-230

SMITH, R. W. and FREY, D. G. (1971). Acid mine pollution effects on lake biology. *Wat. Pollut. Contr. Res. Ser., Wash.* **(EPA 18050)**

SMITH, E. J., SYKORA, J. L. and SHAPIRO, M. A. (1973). Effect of lime-neutralized iron hydroxide suspensions on survival, growth and reproduction of the fathead minnow (*Pimephales promelas*). *J. Fish. Res. Bd Can.* **30**, 1147-1153

SPRAGUE, J. B. (1964). Highly alkaline water caused by asbestos–cement pipeline. *Prog. Fish Cult.* **26**, 111-114

SURBER, E. W. (1935). Effects of carbon dioxide on the development of trout eggs. *Trans. Am. Fish. Soc.* **65**, 194-203

SYKORA, J. L., SMITH, E. J., SYNAK, M. and SHAPIRO, M. A. (1975). Some observations on spawning of brook trout (*Salvelinus fontinalis* (Mitchell)) in lime-neutralized iron hydroxide suspensions. *Wat. Res.* **9**, 451-458

TOMKIEWIEZ, S. M. and DUNSON, W. A. (1977). Aquatic diversity and biomass in a stream marginally polluted by acid strip mine drainage. *Wat. Res.* **11**, 397-402

TROJNAR, J. R. (1977). Egg hatchability and tolerance of brook trout (*Salvelinus fontinalis*) fry at low pH. *J. Fish. Res. Bd Can.* **34**, 574-579

VALLIN, S. (1953). Zwei azidotrophe Seen im Küstengebiet von Nordschweden. *Rep. Inst. Freshwat. Res. Drottningholm* **34**, 71-84

VALLIN, S. (1962). Övre Mörrunmsån. *Vattenhygien* **3**, 71-84

VIVIER, P. (1954). Influence du pH d'une eau résiduaire sur la faune piscicole. *Eau* **41**, 101

VOLODIN, V. M. (1960). Vlijanije temperatury i pH na embrionalnoje razvitije nalima. *Byull. Inst. Biol. Vodokhran* **7**

WESTFALL, B. A. (1945). Coagulation anoxia in fishes. *Ecology* **26**, 283–287

WIEBE, A. H. (1931). Note on the exposure of several species of pond fishes to sudden changes in pH. *Trans. Am. microsc. Soc.* **50**, 380–383

WRIGHT, R. F. (1975). Acid precipitation and its effects on freshwater ecosystems, an annotated bibliography. *Proceedings of the First Symposium on Acid Precipitation and the Forest Ecosystem.* Ohio State University. Norges Landbrukhøgskole, Norway, S.N.S.F. project, Norsk institutt for Skogforskning

WRIGHT, R. F. and SNEKVIK, E. (1978). Chemistry and fish populations in 700 lakes in southernmost Norway. *Verh. int. Verein. theor. angew. Limnol.* **20**

WUHRMANN, K. and WOKER, H. (1948). Experimentelle Untersuchungen über die Ammoniak und Blausäurevergiftung. *Schweiz. Z. Hydrol.* **11**, 210–244

3

WATER TEMPERATURE

Foreword

In examining the literature on water temperature and inland fisheries, it became evident that particular attention should be given to Slavonic material which was not only extensive but, in contrast to that from many other sources, virtually unknown to the rest of the world. In this chapter rather more detail has been included in tabular form than would have been the case with more accessible material and, unless otherwise indicated, all information refers to Eastern Europe. It is recognized that this restriction on sources must unbalance the report, but this is outweighed by the need to disseminate the information.

The preparation of this chapter was accomplished largely by Dr T. Backiel and Dr L. Horoszewicz (Poland) who prepared the basic manuscript for the original report for review by the EIFAC Working Party on Water Quality Criteria for European Freshwater Fish, and also prepared the updated draft utilizing information from 141 additional references.

During its search for relevant information published mainly after 1955, the Working Party noted two lists of literature on this subject, namely:

Kennedy, V. S. and Mihursky, J. A. (1967). Bibliography on the effects of temperature in the aquatic environment. *Contr. nat. Resour. Inst. Univ. Md,* (326)

and

Raney, E. C. and Menzel, B. W. (1967). A bibliography: heated effluents and effects on aquatic life with emphasis on fishes. *Bull. Philad. elect. Co. ichthyol. Associates* (1)

However, a number of publications that do not appear in either of these two bibliographies or in this chapter have been compiled separately in Section 3.11.

3.1 Summary

In establishing water quality criteria for European inland fisheries, temperature plays an important role, since industry uses substantial quantities of water for cooling purposes.

47

There is a normal range of temperatures in the temperate region of 0–30 °C, to which fish are adapted. Fish differ, however, in their tolerance to high temperature, depending on species, stage of development, acclimation temperature, dissolved oxygen, pollution, season and the extent to which the environment is heated. In this chapter, tentative temperature criteria are proposed which take no account of the effect of pollution. It was essential to make a distinction between the temperature conditions permissible at different times of the year and to assess not only maximum permissible temperatures but also maximum permissible increments of temperature.

Winter

An increase in water temperature of 2 °C from about 0 °C in winter at the time of reproduction would severely affect spawning of *Coregonus* sp. and burbot. Raising the temperature 5–6 °C in autumn and winter may adversely affect the embryos and fry of salmonids and also induce premature spawning of cyprinids.

Spring

A rise of 5–6 °C is detrimental to pike embryos. The majority of cyprinids tolerate an increase of temperature of 8–10 °C during the embryonic stage.

Summer

Juvenile and adult fish can usually tolerate a wider range of temperature than embryos. It seems likely that if water temperature gets near the disturbing level most species would continue to feed. For many cyprinids, the permissible increase of temperature is about 6 °C above the natural ambient values, with an upper limit of 30 °C during the warmest season. However, at about 28 °C and higher, the growth of several cyprinids is inhibited.

For salmonids of the genus *Salmo,* 20–21 °C should be accepted as the upper permissible temperature during the warmest season of the year.

Coregonids can withstand a rise of temperature of 5–6 °C but the maximum for the summer months should not exceed 22–23 °C.

Although these criteria would not necessarily ensure the maintenance of existing fisheries, it is reasonable to expect that an increase in temperature of 5 °C to a maximum no greater than 23 °C would destroy salmonid populations except for some species of *Coregonus,* and heating by 8 °C to a maximum no greater than 30 °C would favour a preponderance of certain cyprinids.

3.2 Introduction

The temperature of natural inland waters in the temperate regions generally varies between 0 and 30 °C, the maximum values occurring particularly in shallow waters in summer (Lityński, 1952; Gołek, 1961; Mikulski, 1963) and the minimum exceptionally falling below zero in winter. Freshwater fish indigenous to these regions are adapted to such seasonal changes of temperature, and they (and also introduced species) may also be capable of withstanding changes outside this range, especially those of short-term duration, though at the same time they may succumb to unnatural fluctuations within this range.

Industry, primarily that producing electric power, uses substantial quantities of water for cooling purposes and the discharge of heated effluent can increase the temperature of the receiving waters several degrees above normal and affect aquatic organisms, including fish, both directly and indirectly (for example, by affecting the solubility of gases and the rates of oxidation). It is, therefore, necessary to know to what extent freshwater fish can survive an artificially warmed environment and what upper limits of temperature would be compatible, not merely with the survival of various species, but with the continued existence of flourishing fisheries.

3.3 General considerations

3.3.1 TEMPERATURE AND METABOLISM

The rate of metabolism in poikilothermic animals depends upon temperature; Vinberg (1956), taking the oxygen consumption of fish as an index of their metabolism, found that it was related to temperature according to the so-called 'normal' curve of Krogh. Ivleva (1972) has found substantial evidence that respiratory rates in poikilotherms depend on temperature according to the Arrhenius equation of biochemical processes, provided that respiration is measured after the animals are fully acclimated to the temperature of exposure (p. 50, para. 3 and 4). However, taking into account the variability of respirometric measurements, both the 'normal' curve and the Arrhenius equation predict temperature-dependent changes of oxygen consumption equally well (Backiel, 1977), if resting animals are tested. Nevertheless, according to Stroganov (1956, 1962), the relationship is more complex, there being a plateau, described as the zone of thermal acclimation, in which metabolism increases only slightly in response to increase in temperature. The zone is evident only for fish fully acclimated to temperature, and therefore Stroganov associates it with the normal temperature range to which the species is adapted. This zone of slight response of oxygen consumption to temperature changes was found in larvae and juveniles of Russian species of salmon (*Salmo salar sebago; S. ischan*), and rainbow trout (*S. gairdneri*) but it shifted with change in acclimation temperature (Ryzhkov, 1976).

A similar zone has also been found by Pegel and Remorov (1959) when investigating the level of sugars and nitrogen in blood together with the frequency of respiratory movements and heartbeat. Grodziński (1971) has not found any such plateau in heartbeat in three species but a sudden decrease in the vicinity of 'disturbing' (see p. 55, para. 4) or lethal temperatures. Similarly, in three salmonids studied by Ryzhkov (1976), oxygen consumption fell at 20 or 25 °C, or about 7 °C above the acclimation temperature; this phenomenon was also observed in common carp (*Cyprinus carpio*) at 28 or 32 °C, depending on acclimation temperature (Korovin, 1976).

The metabolic rate of resting fish is, however, easily increased by the excitory effect of extraneous stimuli, and the scope for that and any other excess activity over the basal rate has been studied and found to have an optimal value at temperatures not necessarily the same as those for the maximum for the basic rate itself (Fry, 1957). Rainbow trout in ponds and raceways did not respond to temperature changes between 11 and 18 °C but their oxygen consumption varied substantially with variation in feeding activity (Wieniawski, 1971).

3.3.2 THERMAL ACCLIMATION

From the above remarks it follows that changes in metabolism do not immediately follow changes in environmental temperature, particularly when the change occurs relatively quickly; but, once a new rate of metabolism has been established, the animal is considered acclimated. However, this is possible only over a limited range of temperature—the normal physiological range (Stroganov, 1956)—and its effect on animal tissues and on the whole organism at all ages is reflected in several ways, including an increase in thermal tolerance with increase in acclimation temperature and the converse.

Shkorbatov and Kudriavtseva (1964) found that the time for which isolated muscle remained sensitive to electric stimuli increased from 68 to 140 minutes with increase in acclimation temperature from 3 to 26 °C. This has been confirmed by Kusakina (1962) who also studied the activity of choline-esterase in ten species of fish inhabiting zones of different temperature in L. Baikal. It should, however, be noted that the thermal resistance of tissues and of enzyme systems tested *in vitro* may be higher than that of the intact animal (Shkorbatov, 1964a).

Stroganov (1956) and Shkorbatov (1964a,b) consider that heat death results from a disturbed balance between various metabolic processes, and Prosser, Precht and Jankowsky (1965) suggest that this might be under nervous control.

3.4 Fish embryos

3.4.1 DEVELOPMENT TIME

The consequence of temperature-dependent metabolism is change in the rate of development with temperature, particularly during the early stages; Tatarko (1965, 1966) has shown that at a temperature of 30 °C the time for embryonic development in common carp is approximately half that at 20 °C, and somewhat similar results have been obtained at lower temperatures for Atlantic salmon (*Salmo salar*) (Vernidub, 1963), brown trout (*S. trutta*) (Kowalska, 1959), bream (*Abramis brama*) and pike-perch (*Stizostedion lucioperca*) (Vladimirov, 1955) and pike (*Esox lucius*) (Lecyk, 1960). At the extremes of the range of temperature at which development is possible the development time varies by a factor of 6-7, but within the optimal range it usually varies by a factor of 2 (Kokurewicz, 1979b).

However, growth may not match development, and at high extreme temperature newly hatched larvae may be smaller in size, as for example are Atlantic salmon at 10-12 °C (Vernidub, 1963), trout in excess of about 7.5 °C (Kowalska, 1959) and pike in excess of about 7.6 °C, although development may otherwise be normal (Lecyk, 1960). Furthermore, at high temperature there

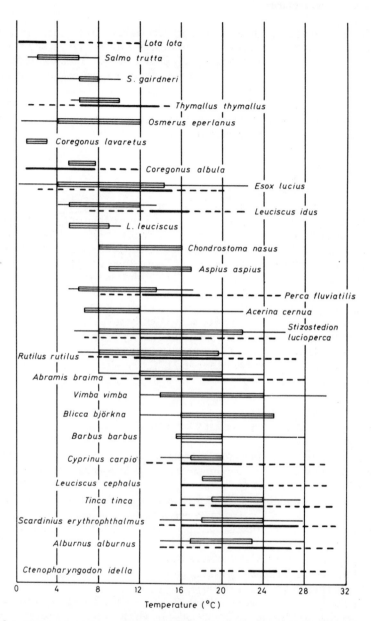

Figure 3.1 Temperatures for spawning and embryonic development of fish observed during spawning of a given species. A continuous thin line indicates extreme values and an open bar indicates the most frequent values (data from Table 3.1) for spawning. Below the bars for a given species, a continuous thick line indicates the optimal range for temperatures of embryonic development, and a broken line indicates the extreme temperatures at which mortalities and abnormalities of development markedly increase. Data are mainly compiled by Kokurewicz (1979b) but are supplemented by data from Aliev (1968), Belyi (1967), Brylinska and Brylinski (1968), Dziekonska (1956), Evropeitseva (1947), Florez (1972), Kokurewicz et al. (1978), Lindroth (1946), Muntian (1967), Penaz (1973; 1974), Resnichenko et al. (1967; 1968), Swift (1965), Tatarko (1965), Wolny (1974), Volodin (1960a), Vovk (1974), and Vladimirov and Zabudskii (1973).

may be an increase in abnormalities and mortalities. With common carp the hatch is less than 60 per cent at 22 °C or higher (Tatarko, 1965), and abnormalities are more than 20 per cent at 27 °C and above (Tatarko, 1965; 1977; Shuliak, 1965); with roach (*Rutilus rutilus*) there is some reduction in hatch at 20 °C and above, and a marked increase in abnormalities above 16 °C (Reznichenko *et al.,* 1962). The prematurely-hatched larvae of tench (*Tinca tinca*) from embryos incubated at temperatures above the optimum (*Figure 3.1*) do not develop the 'sticking glands' (Kokurewicz, 1979b).

3.4.2 ACCLIMATION

Short-term acclimation in the early stage of development has been investigated for various temperature regimes, the criteria most frequently used being the occurrence of abnormalities and mortalities. Persov (1950) and Korovina (1960) found reduced resistance to high fluctuating temperature in embryos of loach (*Misgurnus fossilis*) from females kept at high temperature (16-19 °C) for short periods of time (12 to 25 hours) during ovulation. On the other hand, Vernidub (1951) demonstrated that the higher the temperature at which development of whitefish (*Coregonus lavaretus ludoga*) proceeded within the range 0.5-4 °C, the lower the mortality of embryos subsequently subjected for short periods to 21 °C. Furthermore, non-lethal exposure of embryos to 21 °C for 2 to 3 hours produced increased resistance to a subsequent exposure to 25 °C, compared with embryos which had never been kept at 21 °C, the effect being greatest after an initial exposure of 3 h.

3.4.3 RANGE OF TOLERATED TEMPERATURES

Dziekońska (1958), Orska (1956) and other authors have drawn attention to differences between various developmental stages in resistance to both raised and lowered temperatures lasting for up to 5 h; the gastrula is particularly sensitive in coregonids (Vernidub, 1951) and the sturgeon (*Acipenser stellatus*) (Nikiforov, 1949), but the blastula is the most sensitive stage of pike (Volodin, 1960c). However, pike endured fluctuations between 3 and 24 °C, bream best survived fluctuations in the range 10-18 °C (Volodin, 1960b), common carp best survived a change from 20 to 30 °C and worst a change from 30 to 20 °C (Shuliak, 1965), while fluctuations on roach spawning grounds within the range 9-21 °C caused no mass mortalities (Zuromska, 1967).

Differences in the range and level of temperature tolerated by embryos of some species are related to conditions in which natural propagation occurs (*Table 3.1* and *Figure 3.1*). *Figure 3.1* shows that, for almost all species for which data exist, the range and level of temperature observed at spawning is close to those at which their embryos do not exhibit high mortality and frequent developmental abnormalities. In the 15 species for which data on the embryonic development are available, the well-tolerated range of temperature is 3.5-11.1 °C but if data on rudd (*Scardinius erythrophthalmus*) are excluded the range does not exceed 8 °C. The least tolerant eggs are those of the burbot (*Lota lota*), according to Evropeitseva (1947) the optimal range is from 0-3 °C but Volodin (1960a) gives this range as only 0.5-1.0 °C. Next come salmonids and coregonids,

Table 3.1 TEMPERATURE OF SPAWNING OF DIFFERENT SPECIES (WHEN THREE OR MORE QUANTITIES ARE GIVEN, THOSE IN PARENTHESES ARE THE MOST TYPICAL AND THE OTHERS ARE ONLY RARELY FOUND)

Species	Temperature (°C)	Author
Salmo salar	0 (1–6) 8	Mikhin (1959), Vernidub (1963), Zhukov (1965)
S. trutta trutta	1 (2–6) 8	Vernidub (1963), Kokurewicz (1971)
S. trutta fario	Near 6	Zhukov (1965)
S. gairdnerii	4 (6–8) 10	Privol'nev and Brizinova (1964), Borovik (1969)
Thymallus thymallus	5.3* (6–10)	Peterson (1968), Kupka (1969), Kokurewicz, Kowalewski and Witowski (1978), Kokurewicz (1979a)
Osmerus eperlanus (smelt)	0.5 (4–12)	Kozhevnikov (1955), Gottwald and Nagieć (1967), Altukhov and Erastova (1974)
Coregonus lavaretus ludoga	0–4	Privol'nev and Brizinova (1964)
C. lavaretus	1–3	Lindroth (1957)
C. l. baunti	0–2	Privol'nev and Brizinova (1964)
C. peled	0–3	Privol'nev and Brizinova (1964)
C. albula	4.5–7.7	Bernatowicz (1963)
Esox lucius	0. 2 (4–17) 23	Lindroth (1946), Zakharova (1955), Reznichenko *et al.* (1967), Wilkonska and Zuromska (1967), Statova and Kubrak (1967), Załachowski (1973), Statova (1973), Bergelson (1972, 1977)
Cyprinus carpio	14† (16.8–20)	Kryzhanovskii (1949), Moroz (1968), Leonte (1970), Wolny (1974)
Tinca tinca	16* (18–27.5)	Zakharova (1955), Reznichenko *et al.* (1967), Moroz (1968), Sukhoivan (1970), Kokurewicz (1970)
Barbus barbus	(15.6–20) 27–29	Woźniak (1951), Pliszka (1964), Vladimirov and Bodareu (1975)
Gobio gobio (gudgeon)	Near 12	Kryzhanovskii (1949)
Carassius carassius	16–18 and higher	Kryzhanovskii (1949), Pravdin (1966)
Carassius jacuticus	11.6–12	Kirillov (1972)
Carassius auratus gibelio	(15–19) 22	Statova (1973), Kamilov (1973)
Pelecus cultratus	Near 12–19	Kryzhanovskii (1949), Zhukov (1965)
Abramis brama	8 (12–20) 24	Elizarova (1962), Zakharova (1955), Sych (1955), Vladimirov (1955), Dziekonska (1958), Shaposhnikova (1948), Lukin (1949), Privol'nev and Brizinova (1964), Cieślewicz, Kaj and Włoszczyński (1964), Statova (1973), Bergelson (1974)
A. b. orientalis	16–27	Gosteeva (1957) Shaposhnikova (1948)
A. bolerus	9–12	Poddubnyi (1971)

*Stripping †Induced

Table 3.1 (*cont.*)

Species	Temperature (°C)	Author
Blicca bjoerkna	12 (16–25)	Sych (1955), Zhukov (1965), Pęczalska (1973), Statova (1973), Kutuzov (1974)
Leuciscus leuciscus	(5–9) 10	Kafanova (1953), Zhukov (1965), Mann (1974)
L. cephalus	Near 18.3	Kryzhanovskii (1949)
L. idus	4–15	Pliska (1953b), Vladimirov (1955), Ioganzen *et al.* (1966), Sukhoivan (1970), Cala (1970), Bruenko *et al.* (1974), Bergelson (1977)
Vimba vimba	12 (14–24) 30	Kryzhanovskii (1949), Pliszka (1953a), Vladimirov (1955), Privol'nev and Brizinova (1964), Volskis, Moroz and Sukhanova (1970), Bontemps (1971)
Chondrostoma nasus	8–16.2	Zhukov (1965), Prawocheński (1963), Kostiuchenko (1971), Peňáz (1974)
Aspius aspius	9–15	Atalla Mukheisin (1974), Lange, Dmitrieva and Istamgazieva (1975)
Alburnus alburnus	(14) 17–28	Pravdin (1966), Sukhoivan (1970), Statova (1973), Efimova (1977)
A. bipunctatus	19–24	Kamilov (1973)
Rutilus rutilus	5 (8–19.4) 22	Kryzhanovskii (1949), Zakharova (1955), Pliszka (1953b), Reznichenko *et al.* (1967), Ioganzen, Gundrizer and Krivoshchekov (1966), Zuromska (1967), Pęczalska (1968), Kokurewicz (1970), Sukhoivan (1970), Bergelson (1974, 1977), Efimova (1977), Wilkonska and Zuromska (1977a)
Scardinius erythrophthalmus	(14) 18–28	Kryzhanovskii (1949), Zhukov (1965), Pliszka (1953b), Statova (1973), Popova (1975), Efimova (1977)
Misgurnus fossilis (loach)	13–24	Stroganov (1962)
Nemachilus barbatulus (stone loach)	18–20	Starmach (1966)
Silurus glanis	(18–25) 27	Hochman and Krčal (1957), Koblitskaia (1957), Bugai (1966), Belyi (1966), Horoszewicz (1977)
Ictalurus melas (catfish)	17–20	Zhukov (1965)
Stizostedion lucioperca	5.5 (8–22) 26	Lukin (1949), Kryzhanovskii, Disler and Smirmova (1953), Zhukov (1965), Pliszka (1964),

Table 3.1 (*cont.*)

Species	Temperature (°C)	Author
Stizostedion lucioperca (cont).		Poltavchuk (1965), Muntian (1967), Kokurewicz (1969), Statova (1973), Abdurakhmanov (1960)
Perca fluviatilis	5 (6–15) 17	Zhukov (1965), Kokurewicz (1969), Statova (1973), Kirillov (1972), Boitsov (1974), Bergelson (1974), Efimova (1977)
Acerina cernua (ruffe)	(6.4–12) 22	Kryzhanovskii, Disler and Smirmova (1953), Fedorova and Vetkasov (1974)
Micropterus salmoides (large-mouth bass)	16.4–24	Kryzhanovskii, Disler and Smirmova (1953)
Cottus poecilopus	13.5	Starmach (1962)
Acipenser stellatus *A. guldenstaedti*	15–30 (8) 10.4–23	Privol'nev and Brizinova (1964) Vladimirov (1955), Shilov (1966), Kazanskii (1975)

the most tolerant being those spawning in shallow waters which, even in nature, are exposed to fairly high diurnal fluctuations of temperature.

It should be noted that the temperature ranges that cause no increased mortality of embryos are much narrower than those for the adults, but any criteria based on these ranges should apply only to the appropriate time of year, ie, time of spawning. There is evidence that the range occurs earlier in water bodies affected by heated effluents, gonad development being faster, resulting in depositing of eggs at the temperatures specific for particular fish (see Section 3.5.4).

3.5 Fish fry and adults

3.5.1 LETHAL AND 'DISTURBING' TEMPERATURE

Differences in the experimental methods used by different workers make an unequivocal definition of lethal temperature impossible. Generally, in the Slavonic literature, it is the temperature at which death occurs in 50 per cent of a sample of fish when the temperature is steadily raised 3–10 °C an hour. Increasing the acclimation temperature by 3 °C usually raises the lethal temperature by about 1 °C until a critical value is reached above which further acclimation is not possible. This is called the Critical Thermal Maximum (CTM) (see *Table 3.3*). Consequently, seasonal variation in environmental temperature and differences between the northern and southern extremes of the geographical range of a species can affect lethal temperatures, although other factors may also be important.

Table 3.2 DISTURBING AND LETHAL TEMPERATURES FOR TROUT AND COREGONIDS EXPRESSED AS CRITICAL THERMAL MAXIMA (SEE P. 55, PARA. 1) OR, WHEN MARKED WITH ASTERISKS, AS MEDIAN LETHAL TEMPERATURES

Species (locality)	Month	Acclimation Temp. (°C)	Period	Increase in temp. (°C/h)	Disturb-ing temp. (°C)	Lethal temp. (°C)	Author
Salmo trutta (Laboratory, England)		6		Const.		23.2*	Alabaster and Downing (1966)
		15		Const.		25.0*	
		20		Const.		26.4*	
(Laboratory, England)		6		Const.		24.3*	Bishai (1960)
		15		Const.		25.9*	
		20		Const.		26.7*	
(Laboratory, England)		6		Const.		22.7*	Anon. (1951)
		15		Const.		25.9*	
		25		Const.		27.2*	
Salmò gairdneri		12		Const.		24.9*	Charlon, Barbier and Bonnet (1970)
		16		Const.		25.4*	
		20		Const.		25.8*	
		24		Const.		26.3*	
Salmo trutta lacustris (Poland)	Feb.	9		4	16	25	
	May	18		4	22.5	29	
	May	17		4	22	29	Grudniewski (1961)
	July	21		4	23	30	
	Aug.	18		4	22	30	
	Nov.	6		4	20	26	
Coregonus nasus ponds (Leningrad)	Spring	2–3	14 h	10		22.8	
	Spring	14	14 h	10		26.6	Chernikova (1964)
	Summer	12–14	14 h	10		29.1–29.5	
	Autumn	6–9.5	14 h	10		26.7–27.0	
C. nasus aquaria		12–17	70 days		25	31	Olshanskaia and Krasikova (1960)
C. lavaretus generous (Poland)		14.8 to 10.5	16 h		20	25	Kempińska (1960)
Coregonus l. ludoga (Kharkov)	April	Ambient (Max.30)		6	28	29.5	Shkorbatov (1954)
	July			6	28	30.0–30.3	
C.l. mare-noides (Kharkov)	April			6	28–29	28.6–29.5	
	July	Ambient (Max.30)		6	28	30.0–31.3	Shkorbatov (1954)
	Oct.			6	25–26	29–30	
	Jan.			6	25–26	28.0–29.5	
(Kharkov)	May					28.5	
	July	Ambient (Max.30)				30.3	
	Sept.					29.2	Shkorbatov (1963)
	Oct.					28.0	
(Lake Tawatuj, Sverdlovsk)	Ambient					29.2–30.5	Strel'tsova et al. (1964)

Table 3.2 (*cont.*)

Species (locality)	Month	Acclimation Temp. (°C)	Period	Increase in temp. (°C/h)	Disturb- ing temp. (°C)	Lethal temp. (°C)	Author
C. albula ludoga (Lake Ladoga, Leningrad)		Ambient				23	Strel'tsova *et al.* (1964)
(Lake Tawatuj, Sverdlovsk)		Ambient				30.2	Strel'tsova *et al.* (1964)

*Test period 16 h 40 min

Table 3.3 DISTURBING AND LETHAL TEMPERATURES FOR NON–SALMONID FISH EXPRESSED AS CRITICAL THERMAL MAXIMA (SEE P. 55, PARA. 1) OR, WHEN MARKED WITH ASTERISKS, AS MEDIAN LETHAL TEMPERATURES

Species (locality)	Acclimation Temp. (°C)	Period	Increase in temp. (°C/h)	Disturb- ing temp. (°C)	Lethal temp. (°C)	Author
Cyprinus carpio Pohorelice (CSR)	ambient to 24.5	1½–2 months	6	32.5	40.9	Horoszewicz (1973) (after Opuszynski, 1965)
(heated lake, Poland)	26.3		3	34.8	40.6	
Carassius carassius (heated lake, Poland)	26.5 27.8		6 6	34.6 36.0	38.3 37.7	Horoszewicz (1973)
Tinca tinca (heated lake, Poland	26.1 29–29.3	1–2 months	6 6	32.5–33.2 32.1	37.8 39.3	Horoszewicz (1973)
(Laboratory, England)	15 20 25		Const.		30.2* 32.0* 33.8*	Alabaster and Downing (1966)
Leuciscus cephalus (heated lake)	25.7 30.6–31.0		6 6	33.6 34.0	37.9 38.8	Horoszewicz (1973)

*Test period 16 h 40 min

Table 3.3 (*cont.*)

Species (locality)	Acclimation Temp. (°C)	Period	Increase in temp. (°C/h)	Disturbing temp. (°C)	Lethal temp. (°C)	Author
Leuciscus idus (Laboratory,						
Sweden) 2-day ⎱ 16			Const.		24.1**	
old ⎰ 22					29.1**	
90- ⎱ 6		10			23.7**	Florez (1972)
day ⎰12		days			26.6**	
old ⎰18					27.2**	
(heated lake)	25.0		6		37.9	Horoszewicz (1973)
Scardinius ery- throphthalmus (heated reser- voir, near Moscow)	28.4		5–10		37.2	Filon (1972)
(heated and un- heated lake, Poland)	19.8		6	30.0	35.1	Horoszewicz (1973)
	27.8		6	33.6	38.2	
(Laboratory, England)	20		Const.		31.2*	Alabaster and Downing (1966)
Rutilus rutilus (Karelia)	Ambient				30	Shkorbatov(1964a
(Caucasus reg.)	Ambient				33–34	
(heated and un-	13.6	3–4 mths	1		32.2	
heated part of	19.2	3–4 mths	1		35.8	
reservoir Ivan-	28.4	3–4 mths	1		37.8	Filon (1972)
kovskii near	13.2		5–10		30.6	
Moscow)	19.2		5–10		33.0	
	28.4		5–10		36.0	
(heated and un- heated lakes, Poland)	13.3– 18.6	Period of incuba-	6–9		30.8 ⎫	
	15.0– 18.5	tion	6–9		31.1 ⎪	Horoszewicz
(Laboratory)	12.0– 15.0	Period of incuba-	6–9		29.9 ⎬	(1971a)
	18.0	tion	6–9		34.7 ⎪	
	23.2		6–9		35.5 ⎭	
(heated and un- heated lakes, Poland)	19.8		6	29.2	33.2	Horoszewicz (1973)
	27.4		6	33.0	36.1	
(Laboratory, England)	15.0	1 mth	Const.		28.5*	Cocking (1959)
	20.0		Const.		29.8*	
	25.0		Const.		31.0*	
(Laboratory, England)	15.0		Const.		27.3*	Alabaster and
	20.0		Const.		29.4*	Downing
	25.0		Const.		31.6*	(1966)

*Test period 16 h 40 min
**Test period 48 h

Table 3.3 (*cont.*)

Special (locality)	Acclimation			Increase in temp. (°C/h)	Disturb- ing temp. (°C)	Lethal temp. (°C)	Author
	Temp. (°C)	Period					
Rutilus rutilus (cont.)							
(Laboratory, Montereau, France)	11.4 ⎫ 16.0 ⎪ 19.9 ⎬ 29.6 ⎪ 34.0 ⎭	48 h		Const.		26.9** 27.7** 29.3** 33.0** 35.5**	Barbier and Pascal (1975)
Abramis brama (Caucasus reg.) (Karelia)	Ambient Ambient					33–34 < 30	Shkorbatov (1964a)
(heated and un- heated lakes, Poland)	14.0 25.7			5–6 5–6	27.9 33.0	31.2 35.7	Horoszewicz (1972)
(Laboratory, England)	20			Const.		30.2*	Alabaster and Downing (1966)
Alburnus alburnus (heated lake, Poland)	25.7–26.2			6		37.7	Horoszewicz (1973)
Gobio gobio (heated lake, Poland)	25.5			6	30.8–30.9	36.7	Horoszewicz (1973)
(Laboratory, England)	15 20			Const.		27.2* 28.6*	Alabaster and Downing (1966)
Ctenopharyngo- don idella (pond near Warsaw)	Ambient to 22.5	1–1½ months		6	34	38.5	Opuszyński (1965)
Hypophthalmich- thys molitrix (pond near (Warsaw)	Ambient	1–1½ months		6	34	38.5	Opusszyński (1965)
Stizostedion lucioperca (Dniepr region)	20–22					31.5	Poltavchuk (1965)
(heated lake, Poland)	23.4 24.3 25.6			6 6 6	33.0 33.3 > 31.6	35.4 36.3 37.0	Horoszewicz (1973)
(Laboratory, Holland)	25.0	24 h		0.5–1.0 /day		35.4**	Willemsen (1977)
Perca fluviatilis (Korelia) (Caucassus region)	Ambient					30 33–34	Shkorbatov (1964a)

*Test period 16 h 40 min
**Test period 48 h

Table 3.3 *(cont.)*

Special (locality)	Acclimation Temp. (°C)	Period	Increase in temp. (°C/h)	Disturbing temp. (°C)	Lethal temp. (°C)	Author
Perca fluviatilis (cont.)						
(heated reservoir near Moscow)	0.1 28.4				23.2 36.2	Filon (1972)
(heated lakes, Poland)	20.8 27.8			30.5 32.0	33.0 35.8	Horoszewicz (1973)
(Laboratory, England)	6 15 20 25			Const. Const. Const. Const.		24.0* 28.0* 29.7* 31.4*	Alabaster and Downing (1966)
(Laboratory, Holland)			0.15–0.3 /day	Test period 1 week	33.0*	Willemsen (1977)
Acerina cernua (unheated lake, Poland)	24.1–25.7			29.8	34.5	Horoszewicz (1973)
(Laboratory, England)	15 20		Const. Const.		28.1* 30.4*	Alabaster and Downing (1966)
Esox lucius (Karelia) (Caucassus (region)	Ambient Ambient				30 33–34	Shkorbatov (1964a)
(Laboratory, USA)	17.7	Incubation period (yolk-sac larvae)	Const.	Test period 24 h	28.4**	Hokanson, McCormick and Jones (1973)

* Test period 16 h 40 min   **Test period 24 h

The permissible upper limits of temperature are not necessarily those which individuals can tolerate but are rather those at which whole populations can thrive. One criterion that has been suggested is the 'restlessness' or 'disturbing' temperature, which is the value at which fish first show signs of increased activity or change in behaviour, and presumably also of physiological disturbance, when they are exposed to increasing temperature. If determined while temperatures rise on average 6 °C per hour, it probably corresponds approximately to the upper limit of the zone of thermal tolerance or the upper incipient lethal temperature as defined by Fry (1975), but there are no data available to make a direct comparison.

Lethal and disturbing temperatures are summarized in *Tables 3.2* and *3.3*. It should be noted that, where the experimental method allows the temperatures to continue to rise while the fish are dying, it is liable to underestimate the lethal effect of high temperature, with the result that lethal values, obtained when fish are transferred to constant high temperatures (expressed as median lethal temperatures), are lower than the CTM values given in *Tables 3.2* and *3.3* and are also higher than the disturbing temperatures.

3.5.2 REDUCTION OF FEEDING AND GROWTH

With common carp from Ukrainian ponds, where lethal temperatures ranged from 34 to 36 °C and disturbing temperature did not exceed 31.3 °C (Shkorbatov, 1954), a marked reduction of feeding was recorded at 29 °C (Shpet, 1967). In cages located in thermal plumes below power plants growth was best at temperatures between 23 and 30 °C (Griabanov, Korneev and Korneeva, 1966), but even at 35.2 °C (Maximum recorded by Beliaev, 1969), carp behaviour was normal. Reduction of feeding was recorded in juvenile white bream (*Blicca bjoerkna*) at temperatures above 25 °C (Karzinkin, 1955) and in pike-perch above 26 °C (Poltavchuk, 1965), although they fed intensively at 28 °C in the heated lake Lichenskie (Zamojska, 1971). The maximum temperature at which whitefish (*Coregonus lavaretus marenoides*) were feeding in ponds was about 3 °C below lethal temperatures in July, and close to the disturbing temperature from July to October (Shkorbatov, 1963). Juveniles of *Salmo ischan* showed marked reduction of growth rates above 19 °C (Ryzhkov, 1976). Growth rates of 0+ age group white bream, rudd and roach in L. Lichenskie, heated by cooling-water from a power plant, were almost nil whenever temperatures reached 28 °C or more (Wilkońska and Zuromska, 1977c). Similarly, in the heated bay of Ivankovskoe reservoir, roach and bream juveniles ceased to grow at temperatures above 28 °C (Boitsov, 1971, 1977; Sappo, 1977).

It can be concluded that reduction of feeding or growth rates occurs at temperatures approaching disturbing levels for particular species and particular acclimation conditions, but it is often 3–5 °C below that level.

3.5.3 'PREFERRED' TEMPERATURES

Another indicator of the thermal requirements of a species is the 'preferred' or 'selected' temperature, which is the value at which fish are most frequently found when able to move freely within a thermal gradient that is usually established experimentally. It is partly dependent on the temperature to which the fish are acclimated beforehand; if this has been relatively high, then the selected temperature is lower and vice versa, so that there is one point when the acclimation and selected temperatures are identical—this is the final preferred temperature or final preferendum.

Even a few days of prior acclimation to temperature can alter the preferred value in the direction of the change of acclimation temperature (Mantelman, 1958a, b; Lenkiewicz, 1964; Shkorbatov, 1966), but it has also been shown (Mantelman, 1958a, b) that, with trout fingerlings transferred from 19 °C to 6.5–8 °C, the rapid initial fall in selected temperature is followed by a gradual increase over a period of several months, presumably as a result of further acclimation and of seasonal effects. The latter has been demonstrated by a steady fall in the selected temperature from 15 to 9 °C through July and August with fish kept at 16–18 °C over this period (Mantelman, 1958a). If long-term experiments were to be carried out in a temperature gradient, then some acclimation could take place and selected temperatures would be expected to approach the final preferendum which might change seasonally: such experiments made in Britain with roach suggest a final value for this species between 20 and 25 °C (Alabaster and Downing, 1966).

Generally, Slavonic data give only imprecise indications of final preferenda, because the acclimation temperatures have been relatively low, whereas Canadian experiments have provided more precise final preferenda because they have included much higher acclimation temperatures. Nevertheless, minimum estimates of the final preferred temperatures can be derived from the data in order to compare species and the results of various workers. The value for rainbow trout is between 9 and 17 °C (Mantelman, 1958a, b) compared with a final preferendum of 13.6 °C found by Garside and Tait (1958); for Atlantic salmon the zone is between 9 and 17 °C (Mantelman, 1958a) compared with a final preferendum of 14-15 °C found by Fisher and Elson (1956) for newly hatched fish; for common carp the results extrapolate close to 32 °C (Mantelman, 1958a) as also found by Pitt, Garside and Hepburn (1956). Estimated values for other species are even less reliable: the minimum estimate of the preferred temperatures derived from data of Lenkiewicz (1964) in a vertical temperature gradient is 17 °C for orfe (*Leuciscus idus*), 19 °C for bream and 27 °C for crucian carp (*Carassius carassius*). For whitefish (*Coregonus lavaretus marenoides* and *C.l. ludoga*) the value is estimated at about 15 °C (Shkorbatov, 1965, 1966), lower than this for *C.l. baunti* and *C. automnalis* (Mantelman, 1958a) and higher than 19 °C for the sturgeon (*Acipenser rhutenus*) (Shkorbatov, 1954).

The terms 'preferred' or 'selected' temperature are sometimes considered synonymous with 'optimum' temperature (Ivlev, 1958; Ivlev and Leizerovich, 1960). Mantelman (1958a) has drawn attention to the convergence of the zone of preferred temperatures with the range at which food intake is highest. With Atlantic salmon, Nikiforov (1953a, b) found that feeding and growth were highest at 13-15 °C, though with common carp food intake was highest at 23-27 °C (Shpet, 1952, 1953, quoted by Mantelman, 1958a). On the other hand, with *Coregonus lavaretus marenoides* optimal feeding temperatures in July appear to be much higher than the estimated final preferendum (p. 61, para. 1 and p. 62).

3.5.4 GONAD DEVELOPMENT

As pointed out on p. 52, para. 4 and p. 55 there are relatively narrow temperature ranges within which successful spawning of fish occurs. In a sense these ranges are preferred and selected for spawning by particular species or forms. Thus, e.g. roach, bream, common carp, perch, pike-perch and pike spawn earlier in spring at southern latitudes than in the northern latitude of their natural distribution. This indicates some adjustment of gonad development to the temperature regimes (Kusmin, 1957; Koshelev, 1963; Epler and Bieniarz, 1979; Kokurewicz, 1979b). In waters affected by heated effluents, several species laid eggs 2-8 weeks earlier than in those unaffected in this way (Zawisza and Backiel, 1972; Astrauskas, 1971; Statova, 1973; Wilkońska and Zuromska, 1977a).

In the species that lay eggs in batches, increased temperature caused by heated effluents extended the number of batches from two to four in bleak (*Alburnus alburnus*), from two to three in rudd (Efimova, 1977), and from three to seven in tench in a pond heated by 2-4 °C (Epler and Bieniarz, 1979). In fish with single-batch spawning (roach and perch) unsynchronized development of oocytes was observed at elevated temperatures which brought about partial ovulation and resorption of a considerable portion of maturing oocytes (Zhiteneva and Nikanorova, 1972).

A change in temperature regime affects the whole gonadal cycle, including changes in the duration of consecutive stages of maturity and disruption of oocyte development within the gonad. After vitellogenesis, final maturation requires a certain minimum species-specific temperature which is a prerequisite for ovulation (Detlaf, 1977; Kazanskii, 1975), and is related to that at which spawning occurs naturally (p. 52, para. 4 and *Figure 3.1*).

Although the gonadal cycle of fish exposed to heated effluents is often adjusted to enable spawning at optimum or 'permissible' temperature, some other factors may prevent egg deposition. In the heated bay of Ivankovskoe reservoir, pike, perch and roach are ready to spawn much earlier than in the unheated part, but spawning is retarded due to low water level and, hence, lack of suitable spawning grounds, and occurs only a few days earlier at unduly high temperature (Bergelson, 1974, Nikanorov, 1977). When, in 1969, artificial spawning beds were constructed in the heated bay, perch laid eggs 30 days earlier than in the unheated parts of the reservoir (Nikanorov, 1977).

3.6 Temperature and pollution

Low levels of dissolved oxygen have been shown to reduce the lethal high temperatures for common carp (Shkorbatov, 1963) and also for roach and trout (Alabaster and Downing, 1966). In these cases, reducing the dissolved oxygen to about half the air saturation value has only a small effect on lethal temperature but any further reduction has a much larger one. With *Coregonus lavaretus marenoides*, however, the effect of any reduction below 10 mg/ℓ dissolved oxygen has an immediate effect upon lethal temperatures (Shkorbatov, 1963). The effect of increased temperature on increasing the asphyxial level of the dissolved oxygen has been demonstrated by Privol'nev (1954, 1963), Lozinov (1952) and Kempińska (1960). However, the results may be influenced somewhat by acclimation of the fish to various dissolved-oxygen concentrations and temperatures (Shkorbatov, 1964a, b; Nikiforov, 1953b; Strel'tsova *et al.* 1964), and it may be noted that results of tests using sealed bottles (Lozinov, 1952) are difficult to interpret, because the falling dissolved-oxygen concentration is accompanied by an increase in the carbon dioxide concentration.

In polluted water, the effect of increased temperature depends on the type and concentration of polluting matter (see Chapters 1, 2 and 4 to 10). In general, increase in temperature reduces the period of survival of fish in lethal concentrations of poison, as, for example, Bodrova and Kraiukhin (1956) found in the case of phenol. However, the threshold concentration of a poison may not be reduced at high temperatures; it may be unchanged or even increased, implying a reduction in toxicity with increase in temperature—indeed, in the case of phenol, for example, the 2-day median lethal concentration is increased with temperature (Brown, Jordan and Tiller, 1967).

3.7 Temperature and other aquatic organisms

3.7.1 PHYTOPLANKTON

Studies on L. Lichenskie showed that phytoplankton production decreased when the flow of heated water to it almost doubled, but in moderately affected neighbouring lakes (temperature increase about 4 °C), it increased by about

30 per cent (Hillbricht-Ilkowska *et al.*, 1976). Inhibition of the photosynthetic activity of phytoplankton was observed in the heated bay of Ivankovskoe reservoir at temperatures of 28-30 °C (Tarasenko, 1977).

3.7.2 INVERTEBRATE FOOD ORGANISMS

As with fish, the development of invertebrates is accelerated by increased temperature. Manuilova (1954) found that a temperature rise of about 15 °C reduced the embryonic development time of *Daphnia cucullata* from about 3½ days to 1 day and Cheremisova (1958) has obtained similar results. Data on the effect of temperature on the time of development of the egg and larval stages of various copepoda are given by Malovitskaia (1965), Monakov (1962) and Sushkina (1964) and for cladocerans by Smirnov (1965), Cheremisova (1958), Pechen' (1965) and Hrbácková-Esslová (1966), and the relationship between development time and temperature for crustaceans can be expressed by Krogh's curve (Vinberg, Pechen' and Sushkina, 1965; Hilbricht-Ilkowska and Patalas, 1967). Marked acceleration of development with increase in temperature has also been observed in rotifers (quoted in Patalas, 1966). However, at temperatures above 26 °C in the heated part of Ivankovskoe reservoir there was a decrease in rates of development of zooplankton, their average biomass in the growing season falling by 65 per cent (Gorobii, 1977).

Changes in the temperature regime and flow of water, induced by heated effluents in the L. Konin system, resulted in considerable changes in zooplankton. The biomass of non-predatory plankters (Rotifers, Cladocera, *Eudiaptomus graciloides* and nauplii of *Mesocyclopes* sp.) increased by a factor of six in L. Mikorzynskie after it was utilized as cooling water.

In L. Lichenskie, from 1966, when the discharge was low, to 1973, when the lake became almost a heated river, this group of plankton also increased its biomass by a factor of 2. At the same time the predatory Cyclopidae had creased in biomass (Hillbricht-Ilkowska, *et al.*, 1976).

The rate of development of tendipedid larvae is increased up to three-fold with a temperature rise from 15 to 25 °C, depending upon the species (Konstantinov, 1958). With some (e.g. *Chironomus plumosus*), metabolism increases over the range 4-27 °C but breaks down above an upper limit; with *C. antracinum* maximum growth occurs at 25 °C, there being some reduction at 30 °C; and with *C. dorsalis* lethal temperatures vary between 34 and 37 °C. Kasymov and Khailov (1966) found that *Polypedilium breviantennatum* continued to feed at temperatures up to 35 °C.

Extensive studies of bottom fauna in five lakes near Konin, which provide water for the cooling system of two power stations, revealed a marked decrease in abundance of chironomids in the most heated lake and smaller changes in the less heated ones (Leszczyński, 1976); oligochaetes, however, increased. Another important change was that the size of the chironomids decreased as well as the number of taxa. All these changes were considered by Leszczynski (1976) as diminishing the value of the bottom as a feeding ground for fish, a conclusion supported by the poor condition of the bottom-feeding bream (see p. 65, para. 6).

These data show that within these groups of animals, representing some of the principal sources of fish food, some species have a thermal tolerance equal to that of the most resistant fish. There seems therefore little danger that fish feeding on this group of organisms would suffer from food shortage within a temperature range which they themselves could tolerate.

Mention has already been made (p. 61, para. 2 and p. 62) of optimum temperatures for feeding. These are probably different for each species and probably not the same as the optima for the development of food animals. However, within the narrow limits of summer temperature (17.8-21.4 °C), a close correlation has been found between common carp production in some ponds of Poland and mean temperature for June and July (Backiel and Stegman, 1968) so that, at least in this simple monoculture system, the production of food animals seems to keep pace with the intensity of predation by the fish; over the season, an increase in mean summer temperature of 1 °C increases production by 50 kg/ha. A similar clear relationship between carp production (at 7 weeks of age) and mean temperature between 14.7 and 18.5 °C was found in Belgium by Timmermans (1962). However, in natural fish communities inhabiting artificially heated ecosystems such a relationship is not found (see p. 64, para. 5 and Section 3.8).

3.7.3 PARASITES AND DISEASES

Temperature affects the development of parasites and pathogenic bacteria and may also affect the resistance of fish to disease, for example by affecting antibody production (Lukianenko, 1971). Mass mortality of common carp caused by abdominal dropsy is usually observed in the warmer season of the year. Zmerzlaia (1965) has reported that the time for development of *Bimeria carpelli* in the gut of common carp was reduced from 17 days at 17 °C to 7 days at 19.9 °C. *Bothriocephalus gowkongenis*, a parasite of grass carp (*Ctenopharyngodon idella*), reaches sexual maturity twice as fast at 22-25 °C as at 16-19 °C (Musselius, 1963). The fastest development of *Dactylogyrus vastator* eggs and the most violent invasion of common carp by this parasite has been recorded at 22-24 °C (Bykhovskii and Iziumova, 1963). Bream and roach in the heated bay of Ivankovskoe reservoir exhibited more extensive infestation with *Ichthyophthirius multifilis* than in the unheated part of the reservoir, and some species of *Myxobolus* and *Dactylogyrus* increased while others decreased in fish in heated water (Strizhak, 1972a). It seems that in fish from heated waters some species of protozoa and of monogenoidea are replaced by others.

In winter, the absence of ice cover on heated water attracts water fowl, many of which act as intermediate hosts to some fish parasites. In L. Lichen, a considerable proportion of bream was heavily infested with *Ligula* (Zawisza and Backiel, 1972), but in the heated bay of Ivankovskoe reservoir there was only a slight increase in incidence of this parasite in roach (Strizhak, 1972b).

Parasitological studies of juvenile bleak, white-bream, roach and rudd in heated lakes of the Konin system suggest that metacercaria of *Bucephalus polymorphus* can be responsible for increased mortality (Niewiadomska, 1977).

3.8 Heated effluents and fisheries

Changes in fish communities have been observed in waters affected by heated effluents. An increase in relative abundance of bleak, rudd, and white-bream was found in the heated (by 7-11 °C) bay of Ivankovskoe reservoir (Nikanorov, 1977), although bream, roach and perch continued to dominate the fish community. Similar trends occurred in the Kuchurgan lagoon with only slightly elevated (3.5 °C) temperature (Iaroshenko and Gorbaten'kii, 1973; Vladimirov, 1973). A ten-year sampling programme of juvenile fish in the heated lake system near Konin, Poland, revealed dominance of bleak, white-bream, and especially roach (Wilkonska and Zuromska, 1977b). Some increase in relative abundance of rheophilic species (such as chub (*Leuciscus cephalus*)), especially in the discharge canal, can be attributed to increased water flow as well as to heating (Astrauskas, 1971; Horoszewicz, 1979). Furthermore, a decrease in relative abundance of juvenile rudd in Lichenskie and Goslawskie lakes (of the Konin system), contrary to the findings in the two USSR waters, was also attributed to flow. The warm plume in the Skawinka and upper Vistula rivers attracted many warm-water species, except during the warmest season (Epler and Bieniarz, 1973). However, the behaviour of fish studied by means of tagging revealed that roach, rudd, bream and chub formed separate local populations in the warmest zones (warm plume) of Ivankovskoe reservoir (Nikanorov and Nikanorova, 1974a), in the Litovskoe reservoir (Astrauskas, 1971), and in the middle Vistula near Kozienice power station (Nabialek, after Horoszewicz, 1979).

The effect on fish communities of increased temperature, when accompanied by drastic changes in water flow and in some places the introduction of grass carp, is difficult to elucidate. For example, the decrease in abundance of tench, common carp and goldfish (*Carassius auratus*) in Kuchurgan lagoon (Vladimirov, 1973), and of these and crucian carp (*Carassius carassius*) in L. Lichenskie (Wilkonska and Zuromska, 1977b), was attributed to the destruction of some plant communities by grass carp.

Changes in gonad development, spawning time and growth of juveniles, add to the complexity of effects (Sections 3.5.2 and 3.5.4 and p. 52, para. 4). Change in growth of adults was also observed, e.g. roach and rudd grew as fast in Lichenskie Lake (warmed by at least 8 °C) as in the Aral Sea, but the oldest roach were only 8 years old, whereas such fish were quite common in normal lakes (Zuromska, 1977; Wilkońska, 1977, 1979). Bream grew slightly better than average in the Polish lake but were in poor condition (Marciak, 1977). Pike-perch also showed increased growth rate, but commercial catches decreased in the heated lakes near Konin, Poland (Ciepielewski, 1977). On the other hand, growth rates of several species in the heated bay of Ivankovskoe reservoir and in the Kuchurgan lagoon did not show any change (Boitsov, 1971; Shcherbukha, 1971; Vladimirov and Naberezhnyi, 1973).

In spite of different effects of heated effluents on fish communities found in several studies, it can be concluded that a discharge of effluent producing even relatively minor changes within a small proportion of a water body (e.g. 70 ha of heated bay out of 32 000 ha in the Ivankovskoe reservoir, or a temperature rise of 3.5 °C in the Kuchurgan lagoon) brings about conspicuous changes in fish communities (Nikanorov and Nikanorova, 1974b). Depending on local conditions, the most heat-resistant species begin to dominate while the least resistant disappear.

It has been realized that local fish populations cannot fully utilize the natural production of heated water bodies, and stocking with Chinese carp has been recommended both in the USSR (e.g. Nikanorov, 1977) and in Poland (Zawisza and Backiel, 1972). Stocking of these fish into a small reservoir (420 ha) of

Mironovskoe power station (USSR) resulted in a catch of about 100 kg/ha in 1974 (Nikanorov, 1977). Stocking of the heated Goslawickie lake (Poland) with mainly silver carp (*Hypophthalmichthys molitrix*), and bighead carp (*Aristichthys nobilis*) resulted in a catch of about 70 kg/ha in 1977 (Frieske, 1977). As plankton production increases (p. 64, para. 3) and the food value of the benthic biota for fish is diminished (p. 64, para. 6), the environment in some heated lakes becomes ideal for plankton-feeding fish. In both cases cited above, the catches were several times greater than the usual commercial ones in lakes or reservoirs.

3.9 Tentative temperature criteria

The tolerance of European freshwater fish to high temperatures depends upon many factors, including the species, stage of development, season, the acclimation temperature, and the concentration of dissolved oxygen. In this report, the tentative temperature criteria proposed apply to waters which are not polluted by chemicals.

It is essential to recognize that:

(a)   any change in the natural temperature regime produces changes in the behaviour of fish and in the composition of fish communities,

(b)   different temperature conditions are required at different times of the year to meet the needs of different life stages of the fish, and

(c)   permissible increments of temperature above natural values and maximum permissible levels cannot be envisaged for fish communities as a whole, but may be tentatively assessed for groups of fish having similar thermal requirements at different given times of the year.

3.9.1 AUTUMN AND WINTER

An increase in water temperature of 2 °C above normal in autumn and winter at the time of reproduction of *Coregonus* sp. and burbot (*Lota lota*) would be damaging to the reproduction of these species, although the majority of other species would be almost unaffected.

Raising the temperature by 5-6 °C in autumn and winter may result in higher mortality among the embryos of other salmonids and also reduce the size, weight and vitality of the hatched fry. In pike, percids and cyprinids, such a change in temperature can accelerate maturation of gonads and cause spawning much earlier in the spring (or even in late winter) than would otherwise be the case.

3.9.2 SPRING

For most spring-spawning fish the optimum range of temperatures for spawning and embryonic development is no greater than 8 °C (see *Figure 3.1*).

3.9.3 SUMMER

Juvenile and adult fish can usually tolerate a wider range of temperature than embryos. Also, they can survive short exposure to temperatures which would be ultimately lethal, and can live for somewhat longer periods at temperatures at which initially they become restless and abstain from feeding. However, at a temperature of about 28 °C and higher, the growth rate of bream, white bream, rudd and roach (cyprinids) is reduced. Also, at about this temperature the photosynthetic activity of phytoplankton and the development of zooplankton may also be inhibited and, in heated waters, benthic feeding-grounds may decrease in value for fish.

For members of the genus *Salmo* which inhabit waters in which sustained natural summer temperatures are 20-21 °C, any increase in temperature could be detrimental; 20-21 °C should therefore be accepted as the upper permissible temperature for salmon and trout waters during the warmest season of the year, although natural temperatures may rise above these values.

Coregonids (except at the embryonic stage) can withstand a rise of temperature of 5-6 °C but the sustained maximum for the summer months should not exceed 22-23 °C.

Adoption of these criteria would not necessarily ensure that the composition of existing fish populations is maintained, although the changes which occur may be acceptable. However, it is reasonable to expect that an increase in temperature of 5 °C to a maximum no greater than 23 °C would destroy salmonid populations except for some species of *Coregonus*, and heating by 8 °C to a maximum no greater than 30 °C would favour a preponderance of some cyprinids. In heated lakes and reservoirs, management of the fish population under the changed environmental conditions, including introducing appropriate species such as silver carp and bighead carp, may ensure good fisheries.

3.10 References

ABDURAKHMANOV, I. A. (1960). *Zool. Zh.* **5**, 734

*ALABASTER, J. S. and DOWNING, A. L. (1966). A field and laboratory investigation of the effect of heated effluents on fish. *Fish. Invest., Minist. Agric. Fish., U.K.* **6** (4)

ALIEV, D. S. (1968). In *Novye issledovaniia po ekologii i razvedeniiu rastilelno-iadnych ryb*, pp. 25-35, Moskva, Nauka

ALTUKHOV, K. A. and ERASTOVA, V. M. (1974). Reproduction of the smelt (*Osmerus operlanus*) and the ecology of its early development stages in Kardalaksha Bay, White Sea. *J. Ichthyol.* **14(6)**, 877-886 (Translation of *Vop. Ikhtiol* **14(6)**, 1014-1024

*ANON. (1951). Annual report of the laboratory for experimental limnology. *Res. Rep. Lab. exp. Limnol. Ont.* **23**

ATALLA MUKHEYSIN ALI. (1974). Fecundity and histological description of the gonads of the female asp (*Aspius aspius*). *J. Ichthyol.* **14(6)**, 896-904 (Translation of *Vop. Ikhtiol* **14(6)**, 1036-1045)

ASTRAUSKAS, A. S. (1971). *Biol. Vnutr. Vodoemov, Inform. Biol.* **11**, 55-58

Asterisks (*) mark the few non-Slavonic items of literature quoted in the report.

BACKIEL, T. (1977). An equation for temperature dependent metabolism or for the normal Krogh's curve. *Pol. Archw. Hydrobiol.* **34(2)**, 305-309

BACKIEL, T. and STEGMAN, K. (1968). Temperature and yield in carp ponds. *FAO Fish Rep.* **(44)4**, 334-342

*BARBIER, B. and PASCAL, M.(1975). Resistance du gardon (*Rutilus rutilus* L.) à des variations brusques de temperature. *Bull. franc. Piscic.* **48(258)**, 26-47

BELIAEV, V. V. (1969). *Ryb. Khoz.* **45(7)**, 19-21

BELYI, N. D. (1966). *Ryb. Khoz.* **11**, 22-23

BELYI, N. D. (1967). *Vop. Ikhtiol.* **7(1)**

BERGELSON, B. O. (1972). *Rybokhoz. Izuch. Vnutr. Vodoemov* **8**, 27-30

BERGELSON, B. O. (1974). In *Rybnoe Khoziaistvo Kalininskoi Oblasti* pp. 140-158, Moskva, Nauka

BERGELSON, B. O. (1977). In *Biologicheskii rezhim vodoemov–okhladitelei TETs i vliianie temperatury na gidrobiontov*, pp. 83-93, Moskva, Nauka

BERNATOWICZ, S. (1963). *Mamry. Roczn. Nauk roln.* **(B)82**, 337-352

*BISHAI, H. M.(1960). Upper lethal temperatures for larval Salmonids. *J. Int. Explor. Mer.* **25**, 129-133

BODROVA, N. V. and KRAIUKHIN, B. V. (1965). *Trudȳ Inst. Biol. Vodokhran.* **9(12)**, 39-47

BOITSOV, M. P. (1971). The effect of warm water discharged by the Konakovo Power Station on the distribution and growth of young fishes of Ivan'kovo Reservoir. *J. Ichthyol.* **11(2)**, 257-262 (Translation of *Vop. Ikhtiol* **11**, 325-331)

BOITSOV, M. P. (1974). The morphology of underyearling fishes in the zone affected by warm waters discharged from the Konakovo Power Station into Ivan'kovo Reservoir. *J. Ichthyol.* **14(6)**, 904-910 (Translation of *Vop. Ikhtiol* **14(6)**, 1046-1054

BOITSOV, M. P. (1977). In *Biologicheskii rezhim vodoemov–okhladitelei TETs i vliianie temperatury na gidrobiontov*, pp. 94-107, Moskva, Nauka

BONTEMPS, S. (1971). *Certa.* Warszawa, Państwowe Wydawnictwo Rolnicze i Leśne

BOROVIK, E. A. (1969). *Raduzhnaia forel.* Minsk, Nauka i Tekhnika

*BROWN, V. M., JORDAN, D. H. M. and TILLER, B. A. (1967). The effect of temperature on the acute toxicity of phenol to rainbow trout in hard water. *Wat. Res.* **1**, 587-594

BRUENKO, B. P., MOVCHAN, Yu. V. and SMIRNOV, A. I. (1974). Morphological and ecological characters of the ide (*Leuciscus idus*) from the Kremenchug Reservoir. *Hydrobiol, J.* **10(5)**, 52-60 (Translation of *Gidrobiol. Zh. Kiev* **10**, 70-79)

BRYLIŃSKA, M. and BRYLIŃSKI, E. (1968). *Leszcz.* Warszawa, Państwowe Wydawnictwo Rolnicze i Leśne

BUGAI, K. S. (1966). *Gidrobiol. Zh. Kiev* **2(1)**, 49-54

BYKHOVSKII, B. E. and IZIUMOVA, N. A.(1963). In *Akklimatizatsiia zhivotnykh v SSSR*, pp. 338-339. Alma Ata

*CALA, P.(1970). On the ecology of the ide *Idus idus* (L) in the River Kävlingeon South Sweden. *Rep Inst. Freshw. Drottningholm* **50**, 45-49

*CHARLON, N., BARBIER, B. and BONNET, C.(1970). Resistance de la truite Arc-en-ciel (*Salmo gairdneri*) à des variations brusques de température. *Ann. Hydrobiol.* **1(1)**, 73-89

CHEREMISOVA, K. A. (1958). *Trudȳ belorussk. nauchno-Issled.Inst.ryb.Khoz.* **2**

CHERNIKOVA, V. V.(1964). *Izv.nauchno-Issled.Inst.ozer.rech.ryb.Khoz.* **58**, 117-124

CIEPIELEWSKI, W. (1977). Growth of pike-perch (*Stizostedion lucioperca* L.) in artificially heated Lichenskie Lake. *Roczn. Nauk roln. (H)* **97**, 7-16. Polish; English and Russian summaries)

CIEŚLEWICZ, Z., KAJ, J. and WŁOSZCZYŃSKI, B. (1964). *Roczn. Wyzszej Szkoły Roln. Poznań* **22**, 35-48

*COCKING, A. W. (1959). The effect of high temperature on roach (*Rutilus rutilus* L.)1. The effect of constant high temperatures. *J. exp. Biol.* **36**, 203-216

DETLAF, T. A. (1977) In *Sovremennye problemy oogeneza.*, pp. 99-144. Moskva, Nauka

DZIEKOŃSKA, J. (1956). Studies on embryonic development of fish. 1. Observations on the spawning and the embryonic development of bream in the Vistula lagoon. *Pol. Archw. Hydrobiol.* **3**, 295-305. (Polish; English and Russian summaries)

DZIEKOŃSKA, J. (1958). Studies on early development stages of fish. 2. The influence of some environment conditions on the embryonic development of bream (*Abramis brama*) in the Vistula delta. *Polskie Archwm Hydrobiol.* **4(17)**, 193-206

EFIMOVA, T. A. (1977). In *Biologicheskii rezhim vodoemov-okhladitelei TETs i vliianie temperatury na gidrobiontov.* pp. 63-93. Moskva, Nauka

ELIZAROVA, N. S. (1962). *Trudy seratov. Otd. vses. nauchno-Issled. Inst. ozer. rech. ryb. Khoz.* **7**, 184-192

EPLER, P. and BIENIARZ, K. (1973). Influence of heated discharge waters from the Skawinka Electric Power Station on the ichtiofauna of the rivers Skawinka and Vistula. *Acta Hydrobiol.* **15**, 331-339

EPLER, P. and BIENIARZ, K.(1979). In *Biology of fish as a test for heated effluents* (Ed. by L. Horoszewicz and T. Backiel), Chapter 7. *Pol. Ecol. Stud.* **5(**

EVROPEITSEVA, N. V. (1947). Lichinochnyi period nalima. *Trudy Leningr. Obshchestva Estestvoispyt.* **69**, 4

FEDOROVA, G. V. and VETKASOV, S. A.(1974). The biological characteristics and abundance of the Lake Ilmen ruffe, *Acerina cernua. J. Ichthyol.* **14(6)**, 836-841 (Translation of *Vop. Ikhtiol* **14**, 968-973)

*FISHER, K. C. and ELSON, P.(1950). The selected temperature of Atlantic salmon and speckled trout and the effect of temperature on the response to an electric stimulation. *Physiol. Zool.* **23(1)**, 27-34

FILON, V. V. (1972). Increase in the temperature at which roach, perch, and rudd survive in the warm waters from the Knonakovo Hydroelectric Power Station. *Hydrobiol. J.* **7(4)**, 69-72 (Translation of *Gidrobiol. Zh Kiev* **7(4)**, 81-85)

*FLOREZ, F. (1972). The effect of temperature on incubation time, growth and lethality of embryos, larvae and juveniles of the ide, *Idus idus* (L.), *Rep. Inst. Freshwat. Res. Drottningholm* **52**, 50-64

FRIESKE, Z. (1977). A catch of 25 m. tonnes of silver- and bighead carps. *Gospod. rybna* **29(9)**, 4-7 (in Polish)

*FRY, F. E. J. (1957). The aquatic respiration of fish. In *Physiology of fishes,* (Ed. by M. E. Brown) vol. 1, 1-64. New York, Academic Press

*GARSIDE, E. T. and TAIT, J. S. (1958). Preferred temperature of rainbow trout (*Salmo gairdnerii*) and its unusual relationship to acclimation temperature. *Can. J. Zool.* **36**, 563-567

GOLEK, J.(1961). *Pr. panst. Inst. hydrol. -met.* **62**, 5-79

GOROBII, A. N.(1977). In *Biologicheskii rezhim vodoemov-okhladitelei TETs i vliianie temperatury na gidrobiontov*, pp. 43-62. Moskva, Nauka

GOSTEEVA, M. H. (1957). *Trudy Inst. Morf. Zhivot.* **20**, 121-147

GOTTWALD, S. and NAGIEĆ, C. (1967). Development and course of hatchling of smelt (*Osmerus eperlanus* L.) *Roczn. Nauk roln. (H)* **90**, 59-79

GRIBANOV, L. G., KORNEEV, A. N. and KORNEEVA, L. A. (1966). Use of thermal waters for commercial production of carps in floats in the U.S.S.R. *FAO Fish. Rep.* **(44)5**, 218-226

GRODZIŃSKI, Z.(1971). Thermal tolerance of the larvae of three selected Teleost fishes. *Acta biologica Cracoviensia. ser. Zool.* **14**, 289-298

GRUDNIEWSKI, C. (1961). An attempt to determine the critical temperature and oxygen contents for fry of Wdzydze Lake trout (*Salmo trutta morpha lacustris*). *Roczn. Nauk roln. (D)* **93**, 627-647

HILLBRICHT-ILKOWSKA, A. and PATALAS, K. (1967). *Ekol. pol. (E)* **13(2)**, 50

HILLBRICHT-ILKOWSKA, A., ZDANOWSKI, B., EJSMONT-KARABINOWA, J., KARABIN, A. and WĘGLEŃSKA, T.(1976). Primary and secondary production of plankton in heated lakes. *Roczn. Nauk roln. (H)* **97(3)**, 69-88

HOCHMAN, L. and KRÉAL, J.(1957). Einige Erfahrungen mit der halbkünstlichen Laiche des Welses (*Silurus glanis* L.) in Pohořelice. *Acta Univ. Agricult. Silvicult. Brno* **2**, 239-250 (Czech; Russian and German summaries)

HOCHMAN, L. (1965). Fecundity of *Chondrostoma nasus* L. in the Oslava River. *Zool. listy* **14**, 71-83 (Czech; English summary)

*HOKANSON, K. E. F., McCORMICK, J. H. and JONES, B. R. (1973). Temperature requirements for embryos and larvae of the northern pike, *Esox lucius* (Linnaeus). *Trans. Am. Fish. Soc.* **102(1)**, 89-100

HOROSZEWICZ, L. (1971). Lethal temperatures of roach fry (*Rutilus rutilus* L.) from lakes with normal and artificially elevated temperatures. *Pol. Archiv. Hydrobiol.* **18**, 69-79

HOROSZEWICZ, L. (1972). The influence of parasites, handling of fish and the methods of investigations on the evaluation of their tolerance and thermal resistance. *Roczn. Nauk roln. (H)* **94**, 35-52

HOROSZEWICZ, L. (1973). Lethal and disturbing temperature in some fish species from lakes with normal and artificially elevated temperature. *J. Fish Biol.* **5**, 165-181

HOROSZEWICZ, L. (1977). *Sum. (Shearfish.)* Warszawa, Państwowe Wydawnictwo Rolnicze i Leśne

HOROSZEWICZ, L. (1979). In *Biology of fish as a test for heated effluents*, Chapter 12. *Pol. ecol. Stud.* **5(3)**

HRBÁCKOVA-ESSLOVÁ, M. (1966). Differences in the growth and reproduction in 8 °C and 20 °C of *Daphnia publicaria* Forbes (*Crustacea:Cladocera*) populations inhabiting midland ponds and high Tatra lakes. *Věst.čsl. zemed. Mus.* **30**, 30-38

*HUTCHINSON, V. H. (1961). Critical thermal maxima in Salamanders. *Physiol. Zool.* **34**, 92-125

IAROSHENKO, M. F. and GORBATEN'KII, G. G. (1973). In *Kuchurganskii liman-okhladitel moldavskoi GRES,* pp. 8–18. Kishinev, Shtüntsa

IOGANZEN, B. G., GUNDRIZER, A. N and KRIVOSHCHEKOV, G. M. (1966). *Vop. Ikhtiol.* **6(1)**, 42–50

IVLEV, V. S. (1958). *Trudȳ Soveshch. ikhtiol. Kom.* **8**, 288–296

IVLEV, V. S. and LEIZEROVICH, Kh. A. (1960). *Trudȳ murmansk. biol. Inst.* **5(1)**, 3–27

IVLEVA, I. V. (1972). *Usp. sovrem. Biol.* **73(1)**

KAFANOVA, V. V. (1953). *Trudȳ Tomsk Gosud. Univ.* **125**, 77–99

KAMILOV, G. K. (1973). *Ryby i biologicheskie osnovy rybokhoziaistvennogo osvoeniia vodokhranilishch Uzbekistana.* Tashkent, FAN UzSSR

KARZINKIN, G. D. (1955). *Podstawy biologicznej wydajności zbiorników wodnych.* Warszawa, PWRiL (Polish transliteration)

KASYMOV, A. G. and KHAILOV, A. P. (1966). *Gidrobiol. Zh.* **2(5)**, 24–29

KAZANSKII, B. N. (1975). In *Ekologicheskaia plastichnost' polovykh tsiklov i razmnozheniia ryb,* pp. 3–32. Leningrad, Leningrad Universitet

*KHALANSKI, M. (1976). Relation entre les temperatures léthales et la temperature d'acclimatation des poissons d'eau douce. Construction d'abaques. *Cahiers Lab. Hydrobiol. Montereau* **3**, 35–42

KEMPIŃSKA, H. (1960). *Zesz. nauk. Szk. głów. Gosp. wiejsk. (Zootech.)* **2**, 33–66

KIRILLOV, F. K. (1972). *Ryby Jakutii.* Moskva, Nauka

KOBLITSKAIA, A. F. (1957). *Vop. Ikhtiol.* **9**

KOKUREWICZ, B. (1969). The influence of temperature on the embryonic development of the perches: *Perca fluviatilis* L. and *Lucioperca lucioperca* L. *Zoologica Pol.* **19**, 47–67

KOKUREWICZ, B. (1970). The effect of temperature on embryonic development of *Tinca tinca* (L) and *Rutilus rutilus* (L). *Zoologica Pol.* **20(3)**, 317–337

KOKUREWICZ, B. (1971). *Warunki termiczne a rozród i rozwój niektórych gatunków ryb.* Olsztyn, Instytut Rybactwa Śródlądowego

KOKUREWICZ, B. (1979a). The influence of constant and variable temperatures on the embryonic development of European grayling *Thymallus thymallus* (L). *Zoologica Pol.* **28(1)**

KOKUREWICZ, B. (1979b). In *Biology of fish as a test for heated effluents,* (Ed. by L. Horoszewicz and T. Backiel), Chapter 8. *Pol. Ecol. Stud.* **5(3)**

KOKUREWICZ, B., KOWALEWSKI, M. and WITKOWSKI, A. (1978). *Gospod. rybna* **2**, 6–8

KONSTANTINOV, A. S. (1958). *Trudȳ saratov. Otd. vses. nauchno-Issled. Inst. ozer. rech. ryb. Khoz.* **5**, 359

KOROVIN, V. A. (1976). Metabolic rate of the underyearling of the carp, *Cyprinus carpio,* adapted to different water temperature. *J. Ichthyol.* **16(1)**, 168–172 (Translation of *Vop. Ikhtiol* **16(1)**, 180–184)

KOROVINA, V. M. (1960). *Nauchno-tekh. Biull. gosud. nauchno-Issled. Inst. ozer. rech. ryb. Khos.* **10**

KOSHELEV, B. V. (1963). *Trudȳ Inst. Morf. Zhivot.* **38**, 189–231

KOSTYUECHENKO, L. P. (1971). Distribution of fish plankton in the zone affected by warm water discharge from Novorossiysk Thermal Power

Station. *J. Ichthyol.* **11(6)**, 866–871 (Translation of *Vop. Ikhtiol* **11(6)**, 987–992)

KOWALSKA, A. (1959). *Przegl. zool.* **3(4)**, 253–259

KOZHEVNIKOV, G. P. (1955). *Vop. Ikhtiol.* **3**, 126–129

KRYZHANOVSKII, S. G., DISLER, N. N and SMIRMOVA, E. N. (1953). *Trudȳ Inst. Morf. Zhivot* **10(3)**, 138

KRYZHANOVSKII, S. T. (1949). *Trudȳ Inst. Morf. Zhivot.* **1(5)**, 332

KUPKA, J. (1969). *Bul. VUR Vodnǎny* **5(4)**, 25–29

KUSAKINA, A. A. (1962) *Vop. Ekol. Kiev.* **4**, 45–46

KUSMIN, A. N. (1957). The development of the reproductive system of the carps in the different latitudes. *Izv. vses. nauchno-Issled. Inst. ozer. rech. ryb. Khoz.* **43(1)**, 3–6

KUTUZOV, A. M. (1974). Repeated spawning of the white bream (*Blicca bjoerkna*) in Sviyaga Bay of Kuybyshev Reservoir. *J. Ichthyol.* **14(6)**, 887–890 (Translation of *Vop. Ikhtiol* **14(6)**, 1025–1028)

LANGE, N. O., DMITRIEVA, E. N. and ISLAMGAZIEVA, R. B. (1975). In *Osobennosti razvitiia ryb v raznykh estestrennykh i eksperimentalnykh usloviakh,* pp. 3–33. Moskva, Nauka

LECYK, M. (1960). Effect of temperature on the rate of embrionic development of *Esox lucius* L. *Zoologica Pol.* **15(2)**, 101–110

LENKIEWICZ, Z.(1964). Temperature preferendum of some freshwater fishes. *Folia biol. Krakow* **12(1)**, 95–140

LEONTE, E., BURLACU, G. and MARINESCU, A. G. (1970). Influenta concentratui oxigen asupra metabolismului la *Cyprinus carpio* L. in diferite conditii de temperatura. *Bull cercetari Piscic.* **29(4)**, 5–12

LESZCZYŃSKI, L. (1976). The influence of effluent heated waters on the bottom fauna of lakes in the vicinity of Konin.1. Quantitative relations and qualitative composition of the bottom fauna of Konin Lakes Complex. 2. Changes in time of bottom fauna. 3. An effort to explain the causes and results of changes in the bottom fauna of lakes as influenced by the inflow of heated waters. *Roczn. Nauk roln. (H)* **97(3)**, 7–68. (Polish; Russian and English summaries)

*LINDROTH, A. (1946). Zur Biologie der Befruchtung und Entwicklung beim Hecht. *Meddr. Undersökn. Anst. Sottvattenfisk. Stockh.* **24**, 173

*LINDROTH, A. (1957). A study of the Whitefish (*Coregonus*) of the Sundsvall Bay District. *Rep. Inst. Freshwat. Res. Drottningholm* **38**, 77–108

LITYŃSKI, A. (1952). *Hydrobiologia ogólna.* Warszawa, Państowa Wydawnictwo Naukowa

LOZINOV, A. V. (1952). *Zool. Zh.* **31(5)**, 686–695

LUKIANENKO, V. I. (1971). *Immunobiologia ryb.* Moskva, Pishchevaja Promyshlennost

LUKIN, A. V.(1949). *Izv. kazan. Fil. Akad. Nauk SSSR (Biol. Selkhoz. Nauk)* **1**, 81–86

MALOVITSKAIA, L. M. (1965). *Trudȳ Inst. Biol. vnutr. Vod.* **8(11)**, 58–65

*MANN, R. H. K. (1974). Observations on the age, growth, reproduction and food of the dace, *Leuciscus leuciscus* (L.), in two rivers in southern England. *J. Fish Biol.* **6**, 237–253

MANTELMAN, I. I. (1958a) *Trudy Soveshch. ikhtiol. Kom.* **8**, 297-302

MANTELMAN, I. I. (1958b). *Izv. vses. nauchno-Issled. Inst. ozer. rech. ryb. Khoz.* **47(1)**, 3-61

MANUILOVA, E. F. (1954). *Trudy probl. temat. Sovesch. zool. Inst.* **2**

MARCIAK, Z. (1977). Influence of thermal effluents from an electric power plant on the growth of bream in the Konin Lakes Complex. *Roczn. Nauk roln. (H)* **97**, 17-43. (Polish; Russian and English summaries)

MIKHIN, V. S. (1959). *Vop. Ikhtiol.* **12**, 92-100

MIKULSKI, Z. (1963). *Zarys hydrografii Polski.* Warszawa, Państowa Wydawnictwo Naukowa

MONAKOV, A. V. (1962). *Biull. Inst. Biol. Vodokhran.* **12**, 33-35

MOROZ, V. N. (1968). Biology of the tench *Tinca Tinca* (L.) in the Kiliya Channel, Daunbe Delta. *J. Ichthyol.* **8(1)**, 81-89 (Translation of *Vop. Ikhtiol* **8(1)**, 106-115)

MUNTIAN, S. P. (1967). In *Obmen veschchestv i biokhimiia ryb* (Ed. by G. S. Karzinkin). pp. 135-140. Moskva, Nauka

MUSSELIIUS, V. A. (1963). In *Materialy vses. Soveshch. po rybokhoziaistvennomu osvosniiu rastitelnoiadnykh ryb-belogo amura (Ctenopharyngodon idella) i tolstolobika (Hypophthalmichthys molitrix) v vodoemakh SSSR* pp. 154-160. Ashkhabad, Akad. Nauk Turkm. S.S.R.

NIEWIADOMSKA, K. (1977). Parasites of hatchlings and of fry of some fish species from the Konin Lakes Complex, *Roczn. Nauk roln. (H)* **97**, 45-59 (Polish; English and Russian summaries)

NIKANOROV, I. I. (1977). In *Biologicheskii rezhim vodoemov-okhladitelei TETs i vliianie temperatury na gidrobiontov,* pp. 135-156. Moskva, Nauka

NIKANOROV, I. I. and NIKANOROVA, E. A. (1974a). In *Rybnoe khoziaistvo Kalininskoi oblasti,* pp. 159-195. Kalinin, Moskovskii Rabochii

NIKANOROV, I. I. and NIKANOROVA, E. A. (1974b). In *Rybnoe khoziaistvo Kalininskoi oblasti,* pp. 3-21. Kalinin, Moskorskii Rabochii

NIKIFOROV, N. D. (1949). *Izv. vses. nauchno-Issled. Inst. ozer. rech. ryb. Khoz.* **29**, 156-164

NIKIFOROV, N. D. (1953a). *Ryb. Khoz.* **29(12)**, 35-39

NIKIFOROV, N. D. (1953b). *Dokl. Akad. Nauk SSSR* **88(1)**, 165-167

OLŚHANSKAIA, U. L. and KRASIKOVA, B. A. (1960). *Nauchno-tekh. Biull. gosud. nauchno-Issled. Inst. ozer. rech. ryb. Khoz.* **10**, 49-51

OPUSZYŃSKI, K. (1965). *Gospod. rybna* **17(4-5)**, 6-8, 18-20

ORSKA, J. (1956). The influence of temperature on the development of the skeleton in teleosts. *Zoologica Pol.* **7(3)**, 271-325

PATALAS, K. (1966). *Zesz. probl. Kosmosu* **13**, 57-68

PĘCZALSKA, A. (1968). Development and reproduction of roach (*Rutilus rutilus* L. in the Szczecin Firth. *Pol. Arch. Hydrobiol.* **15(2)**, 103-120

PĘCZALSKA, A. (1973). *Prace Morsk. Inst. Ryb. (A)* **17**, 145-156

PECHEN', G. A. (1965). *Gidrobiol. Zh., Kiev* **1(4)**, 19-26

PEGEL', V. A. and REMOROV, V. A. (1959). *Nauch. Dokl. vyssh. Shk. (biol.)* **(3)**, 86

PEŇÁZ, M. (1973). Embryonic development of the Barb, *Barbus barbus* (Linnaeus, 1758). *Zool. Listy* **22(4)**, 363-374

PEŇÁZ, M. (1974). Influence of water temperature on incubation and hatching in *Chondrostoma nasus* (Linnaeus, 1758). *Zool. Listy* **23(1)**, 53-59

PERSOY, T. M. (1950). *Dokl. Akad. Nauk. SSSR* **73(1)**, 213-216

*PETERSON, H. (1968). The grayling, *Thymallus thymallus* (L.) of the Sundsvaal bay area. *Rep. Inst. Freshwat. Res. Drottningholm* **48**, 36-56

*PITT, T. K., GARSIDE, E. T. and HEPBURN, R. L. (1956). Temperature selection of the carp (*Cyprinus carpio* Linn). *Can. J. Zool.* **34**, 555-557

PLISZKA, F. (1953a). Reproduction and development of *Vimba vimba* L. *Polskie Archwm Hydrobiol.* **1(14)**, 137-163

PLISZKA, F. (1953b). The effect of spawning conditions in lakes on the survival rate of juveniles. *Polskie Archwm Hydrobiol.* **1(14)**, 164-188

PLISZKA, F. (1964). *Biologia ryb.* Warszawa, Państwowe Wydawnictwo Rolnicze i Leśne

PODDUBNYI, A. G. (1971). *Ekologicheskaia topografia populatsii ryb v vodokhranilishchakh.* Leningrad, Nauka

POLTAVCHUK, M. A. (1965). *Biologia i rozvedenie dneprovskogo sudaka v zamknutykh vodoemøy.* Kiev, Naukowa Dumka

POPOVA, K. S. (1975). Osobennosti razvitiia ryb v razlichnykh estest-vennykh i eksperimentalnykh usloviiakh, pp. 33-55. Moskva, Nauka

PRAVDIN, I. F. (1966). *Rukovodstvo po izucheniia ryb.* Moskva, Pishehevaia promyshlennost'

PRAWOCHEŃSKI, R. (1963). Observations in the larval development of the nose carp (*Chondrostoma nasus* L.). *Roczn. Nauk roln. (B)* **82**, 667-678 (Polish; Russian and English summaries)

PRIVOL'NEV, T. I. (1954) *Trudȳ Soveshch. ikhtiol. Kom.* **3**, 40-49

PRIVOL'NEV, T. I. (1963) *Dokl. Akad. Nauk SSSR* **151(2)**, 439-440

PRIVOL'NEV, T. I. and BRIZINOVA, P. N. (1964). *Izv. vses. nauchno-Issled. Inst. ozer. rech. ryb. Khoz.* **58**, 45-57

PROSSER, C. L., PRECHT, H. and JANKOWSKY, H.-D. (1965). Nervous control of metabolism during temperature acclimation of fish. *Naturwissenschaften* **52(7)**, 168-169

REZNICHENKO, P. N., KOTLIAREVSKAIA, N. V. and GULIDOV, M. V. (1967). Vyiavlenie ekologicheskii spetsifiki ikry shchuki k temperaturnomu faktoru metodom inkubatsii pri postoiannykh temperaturakh. In *Obmen veshchestv i biokhimiia ryb* (Ed. by G. S. Karzinkin), pp. 144-148. Moskva, Nauka

REZNICHENKO, P. N., GULIDOV, M. V. and KOTLAREVSKAIA, N. V. (1968). Survival of eggs of the tench *Tinca tinca* (L.) incubated at constant temperatures. *J. Ichthyol.* **8(3)**, 391-397 (Translation of *Vop. Ikhtiol.* **8(3)**, 492-499)

REZNICHENKO, P. N., KOTLAREVSKAIA, N. V. and GULIDOV, M. V. (1962). *Trudȳ Inst. Morf. Zhivot.* **40**, 247-253

RYZHKOV, L. P. (1976). *Morfofiziologicheskie zakonomernosti i transformat-siia veshchestv u energii v rannem ontogeneze presnovodnykh lososevykh ryb.* Petrozavodsk, Kareliia

SAPPO, G. B. (1977). In *Biologicheskii rezhim vodoemov-okhladitelei TETs i vliianie temperatury na gidrobiontov*, pp. 109-119. Moskva, Nauka

SHAPOSHNIKOVA, T. Kh. (1948). *Trudȳ Zool. Inst., Lening.* **8(3)**

SHILOV, V. I. (1966). *Vop. Ikhtiol.* **6(4)**, 663-671

SHKORBATOV, G. L. (1954). *Zool. Zh.* **33(6)**, 1325-1335

SHKORBATOV, G. L. (1963). *Trudȳ vses. gidrobiol. Obshch.* **13**, 242-254

SHKORBATOV, G. L. (1964a). *Zool. Zh.* **43(7)**, 953-564

SHKORBATOV, G. L. (1964b). *Nauch. Dokl. vyssh. Shk. (biol.)* 2, 60-65

SHKORBATOV, G. L. (1965). *Gidrobiol. Zh., Kiev* **1(5)**, 3-8

SHKORBATOV, G. L. (1966). *Zool. Zh.* **14(10)**, 1515-1525

SHKORBATOV, G. L. and KUDRIAVTSEVA, G. S. (1964) *Dokl. Akad. Nauk. SSSR* **156(2)**, 452-454

SHCHERBUKHA, A. Ya. (1971). The growth and condition of fishes of the northern Donets and its tributary, the Aydar, in the area affected by warm water discharged from Lugansk Power Station. *J. Ichthyol.* **11(2)**, 231-240 (Translation of *Vop. Ikhtiol.* **11**, 290-302)

SHPET, G. I. (1967). *Ryb. Khoz. Kiev* **5**, 63-71

SHULIAK, G. S. (1965). *Gidrobiol. Zh., Kiev* **1(4)**, 39-47

SMIRNOV, N. N. (1965). *Trudy Inst. Biol. Vodokhran.* **8(11)**, 54-62

STARMACH, J. (1962). Koppen in den Karpathenflussen. 1. Vermehrung, embryonale und larvale Entwicklung bei *Cottus poecilopus* Heckel. *Acta Hydrobiol.* **4**, 321-343

STARMACH, J. (1966). Über Fortpflanzung und Entwicklung der Bartgrundel (*Nemachilus barbatulus* L.) während der Embryonal- und Larval Periode. *Acta Hydrobiol.* **8(2)**, 111-122

STATOVA, M. P. and KUBRAK, I. F. (1967). *Izv. Akad. Nauk SSSR (Biol. Khem. Nauk)* **1**

STATOVA, M. P., (1973). In *Kuchurganskii liman-okhladitel Moldavskoi GRES*, pp. 148-170. Kishinev, Shiintsa

STREL'TSOVA, S. V. *et al.* (1964). *Izv. vses. nauchno-Issled. Inst. ozer. rech. ryb. Khoz.* **58**, 7-16

STRIZHAK, O. I. (1972a). *Sbornik gosud. nauchno-Issled. Inst. ozer. rech. ryb. Khoz.* **8**, 37-41

STRIZHAK, O. I. (1972b). *Sbornik gosud. nauchno-Issled. Inst. ozer. rechn. ryb. Khoz.* **8**, 42-47

STROGANOV, N. S. (1956). *Fiziologicheskaia prisposoblaemost ryb k temperature sredy.* Moskva, Akad. Nauk SSSR

STROGANOV, N. S. (1962). *Ekologicheskaia fiziologiia ryb.* Moskva, Izd-vo Moskovsk Universitet

SUKHOIVAN, P. G. (1970). In *Voprosy Rybokhoziaistvennogo osvoeniia i sanitarnobiologieheskogo rezhima vodoemov Ukrainy*, Volume 2, pp. 74-75. Kiev, Naukowa Dumka

SUSHKINA, E. A. (1964). Rol'vesłonogikh rakoobraznykh v produktsionnykh protsesakh vovoemov razlichnogo tipa. Autoref. dissert.

*SWIFT, D. R. (1965). Effect of temperature on mortality and rate of development of the eggs of the pike and the perch. *Nature, Lond.*, **206(4983)**, 528

SYCH, H. (1955). Observations on the propagation of fish in the Konfederacka Shoal (Lacha Konfederacka) of Vistula River. *Rocz. Nauk roln. (B)* **69(4)**, 527-546

TARASENKO, L. V. (1977). In *Biologicheskii rezhim vodoemov-okhladitelei TETs i vliianie temperatury na gidrobiontov*, pp. 33-42. Moskva, Nauka

TATARKO, K. I. (1977). In *Biologieheskii rezhim vodoemov-okhladitelei TETs i vliianie temperatury na gidrobiontov*, pp. 157-196. Moskva, Nauka

TATARKO, K. I. (1965). *Gidrobiol. Zh., Kiev* **1(1)**, 62-66

TATARKO, K. I. (1966). *Gidrobiol. Zh., Kiev* **2(3)**, 53-59

*TIMMERMANS, J. A. (1962). Influence de la température sur la production piscicole en étang. *Bull. fr. Piscic.* **35(207)**, 67-71

VERNIDUB, M. F. (1951). *Uchen. Zap. leningr. gosud. Univ. (biol.)* **142(29)**, 3-40

VERNIDUB, M. F. (1963). *Vest. leningr. gosud. Univ.* **3**, 7-22

VINBERG, G. G. (1956). *Intensivnost obmena i pishchevye potrebnosti ryb.* Minsk, Izdat Beloruskogo Universitet

VINBERG, G. G., PECHEN', G. A. and SUSHKINA, E. A. (1965). *Zool. Zh.* **44(5)**, 676-687

VLADIMIROV, M. Z. and ZABUDSKII, J. I. (1973). In *Biologicheskie resursy vodoemov Moldavii*, Volume 11, pp. 72-83. Kishinev, Shtiintsa

VLADIMIROV, M. Z. (1973). In *Kuchurgankii liman-okhladitel moldavskoi GRES*, pp. 119-124. Kishinev, Shtiintsa

VLADIMIROV, M. Z. and NABEREZHNYI, A. I. (1973). In *Kuchutganskii liman-okhladitel moldavskoi GRES*, pp. 125-147. Kishinev, Shtiintsa

VLADIMIROV, M. Z. and BODAREU, J. N. (1975). In *Biologicheskie resursy vodoemov Moldavii* Volume 13, pp. 123-133. Kishinev, Shtiintsa

VLADIMIROV, V. I. (1955). *Usloviia ragmnoozheniia ryb v nizhmen Dnepre i Kakhovskos gidrostroitelstvo.* Kiev, Akademii Nauk Ukrainskago SSR

VOLODIN, V. M. (1960a) *Biull. Inst. Biol. Vodokhran.* **7**, 26-30

VOLODIN, V. M. (1960b). Influence of temperature and dissolved CO_2 on embryonic development of *Abramis brama. Biull. Inst. Biol. Vodokhran.* **7**, 31-34

VOLODIN, V. M. (1960c). *Trudy̆ Inst. Biol. Vodokhran.* **3(6)**, 231-237

VOLSKIS, R., MOROZ, V. N. and SUKHANOVA, E. R. (1970). In *Biologia i promyslovoe znachenie rybtsov (Vimba) Europy. (Biology and fisheries of Vimba in Europe.)* (Ed. by R. Volskis), pp. 105-133. Vilnius, USSR, Mintis

VOVK, P. S. (1974). In *Raznokachestvennost' rannego ontogeneza ryb*, pp. 191-226. Kiev, Naukova Dumka

WIENIAWSKI, J. (1971). Bilans d'oxygen dans les installations à l'élevage de poissons salmonides. *Roczn. Nauk. roln. (H)* **93(3)**, 83-108 (Polish; French summary)

WILKOŃSKA, H. (1977). Growth of roach (*Rutilus rutilus* L.) in heated Licheńskie Lake. *Roczn. Nauk roln. (H)* **97**, 61-75 (Polish; Russian and English summaries)

WILKOŃSKA, H. (1979). In *Biology of fish as a test for heated effluents*, Chapter 10. *Pol. ecol. Stud.* **5(3)**

WILKOŃSKA, H. and ZUROMSKA (1967). Observations of the spawning of pike (*Esox lucius* L.) and roach (*Rutilus rutilus* L.) in Mazury Lake District. *Roczn. Nauk roln. (H)* **90**, 477-502 (Polish; Russian and English summaries)

WILKOŃSKA, H. and SUROMSKA, H. (1977a). Observations on reproduction of fish in the Konin Lakes complex heated by effluent waters from a power plant. *Roczn. Nauk roln. (H)* **97**, 77-89 (Polish; Russian and English summaries)

WILKOŃSKA, H. and ZUROMSKA, H. (1977b). Changes in the species composition of fry in the shallow littoral of heated lakes of the Konin Lakes complex. *Roczn. Nauk roln. (H)* **97**, 113-134 (Polish; Russian and English summaries)

WILKOŃSKA, H. and ZUROMSKA, H. (1977c). Growth of fry in the heated Konin Lakes complex. *Roczn. Nauk roln. (H)* **97**, 91-111 (Polish; Russian and English summaries)

WILLEMSEN, J. (1977). The influence of temperature on feeding, growth and mortality of pikeperch and perch. *Verh. int. Verein. theor. angew. Limnol.* **20**, 2127-2133

WOLNY, P. (1974). *Karp.* Warszawa, Państwowa Wydawnictwo Polnicze i leśne

WOŹNIAK, S. (1951). Sztuczne zapłodnienie ikry brzany oraz przebieg rozwoju embrionalnego i larwalnego. *MS SGGW-AR Warszawa sygn.* 2621R

ZAKHAROVA, L. K. (1955). *Trudȳ biol. stantsii Borok. AN SSR, Leningrad* **2**, 200-265

ZAŁACHOWSKI, W. (1973). *Szczupak.* Warszawa, Państwowa Wydawnictwo Polnicze i leśne

ZAMOJSKA, B. (1971). The food coefficient of young pike-perch from lake Licheń. *Roczn. Nauk. roln. (H)* **93(4)**, 133-140 (Polish; English and Russian summaries)

ZAWISZA, J. and BACKIEL, T. (1972). Some results of fishery biological investigation of heated lakes. *Verh. int. Ver. Theor. Limnol.* **18**, 1190-1197

ZHITENEVA, T. S. and NIKANOROVA, E. A. (1972). *Sb. gosud. nauchno-Issled. Inst. ozer. rech. ryb. Khoz.* **8**, 27-30

ZHUKOV, P. (1965). *Ryby Belorusi.* Minsk, Nauka i Tekhnika

ZMERZLAIA, E. I. (1965). *Zool. Zh.* **45(2)**, 305-307

ZUROMSKA, H. (1967). Some causes of mortality of roach (*Rutilus rutilus* L.) eggs and larvae on lake spawning grounds. *Roczn. Nauk roln. (H)* **3**, 557-579

ZUROMSKA, H. (1977). Growth of rudd (*Scardinius erythrophthalmus* L.) in an artificially heated lake. *Roczn. Nauk roln. (H)* **97**, 135-151 (Polish; Russian and English summaries

3.11 Appendix. Additional references on the effect of water temperature on fish

ALTMAN, P. L. and DITTMER, D. S. (1962). *Growth including reproduction and morphological development.* Washington, Federation of American Societies for Experimental Biology

AUDIGE, M. P. (1921). Sur la croissance des poissons maintenus en milieu de température constants. *C.r.hebd. Séanc. Acad. Sci., Paris* **172**, 287

BACKIEL, T. (1964). *Roczn. Nauk. roln. (B)* **84(2)**, 363-372

BADENHUIZEN, T. R. (1967). Temperatures selected by *Tilapia mossambica* (Peters) in a test tank with a horizontal temperature gradient. *Hydrobiologia* **30**, 541-554

BATTAGLIA, B. and LAZZARETTO, I. (1967). Effect of temperature on the selective value of genotypes of the copepod *Tisbe reticulata. Nature, Lond.* **215, (5104)**, 999-1001

BAUER, O. N. (Translated by L. Kochva). (1962). Parasites of freshwater fish and biological principles of their control. Jerusalem. Program for Scientific Translations, IPST Cat. No. 622

BRETT, J. R. (1967). Swimming performance of sockeye salmon (*Oncorhynchus nerka*) in relation to fatigue time and temperature. *J. Fish. Res. Bd Can.* **24**, 1731–1741

BRIDGES, W. R. (1965). Effects of time and temperature on the toxicity of heptachlor and kepone to redear sunfish. *Publ. Hlth. Serv. Publs.* **(999-WP-25)**, 247–249

BROCK, T. D. (1967). Relationship between standing crop and primary productivity along a hot spring thermal gradient. *Ecology* **48**, 566

BROWN, M. E. (1957). Experimental studies on growth. In *Physiology of fishes* (Ed. by M. E. Brown), pp. 361–400. New York, Academic Press

BUKHOVSKII, B. E., GUSEV, A. B. and DUBININA, M. N. (1964). Parasitological factor in acclimatization of fishes and hydroconstruction. *Parazit. Sb.* **22**, 189–195. (Russian; English summary)

BUSCHKIEL, A. L. (1933). Teichwirtschaftliche Erfahrungen mit Karpfen in den Tropen. *Z. Fisch.* **31**, 619–644

CALDERON, E. G. (1965). L'élevage de la truite fario et de la truite arc-en-ciel dans les eaux à température très élevée. *Stud. Rev. gen. Fish. Coun. Mediterr.* **(30)**

CARLIN, B. (1956). Försök med kläckning och oppfödning av laxungar i varmvatten. (Experimental hatching and rearing of salmon fry and heated waters.) Sundsvall, Sweden, *Medd. Vandringsfiskutr. Laxforskningsinstitutet, No 3*

CHIESA, F., MARCHETTI, R. and NOSEDA, V. (1961). Su di un riflesso cardiaco evocato dalle variazioni di temperatura dell'acqua di perfusione branchiale in *Anguilla anguilla. Rc. Ist. lomb. Sci. Lett.* **95**, 167–175

CORNELIUS, W. O. (1933). Untersuchungen über die Verwertung natürlicher und künstlicher Nahrung durch Regenbogenforellen verschiedenen Alters und unter verschiedenen Bedingungen. *Z. Fisch.* **31**, 535–566

DAVIS, W. S. and SNYDER, G. R. (1967). Aspects of thermal pollution that endanger salmonid fish in the Columbia River. Seattle, Washington, U.S. Bureau of Commercial Fisheries, Staff Report, June (mimeo)

DISLER, N. N., REZNICHENKO, P. N. and SOIN, S. G. (1965). In *Teoreticheskie osnovy rybovodstva* (Ed. by G. W. Nikolskii), pp. 119–128. Moskva, Nauka

DEELDER, C. L. (1952). On the migration of the elver at sea. *J. cons. perm. int. Explor. Mer* **18(2)**, 187–218

DEELDER, C. L. and WILLEMSEN, J. (1964). Synopsis of biological data on pike-perch *Lucioperca lucioperca* (Linnaeus) 1758. *FAO Fish. Synops.* **28**

DENZER, H. W. (1952). Akute Hypoxie und Atemfrequenz bei Regenbogenforellen-Setzlingen. *Fischwirt* **7**, 241–244

DOGEL, V. A., PETRUSHEVSKI, G. K. and POLIANSKI, Y. I. (Eds.) (1958). *Basic problems of the parasitology of fishes.* Leningrad, Izdatelstvo Leningradokogo Universiteta

DOUDOROFF, P. (1957). Water quality requirements of fishes and effects of toxic substances. In *The physiology of fishes* (Ed. by M. E. Brown), Volume 2, pp. 403–430. New York, Academic Press

DOUDOROFF, P. and WARREN, C. E. (1965). Dissolved Oxygen Requirements of Fishes. *Publ. Hlth Serv. Publs.* **(999-WP-25)**, 145–154

FABIAN, G., MOLNAR, G. and TOLG, I. (1963). Comparative data and enzyme kinetic calculations on changes caused by temperature in the duration of gastric digestion of some predatory fishes. *Acta biol. hung.* **2**, 123–129

FABRICIUS, E. and GUSTAFSON, K. J. (1958). Some observations on the spawning behaviour of the pike (*Esox esox*). *Rep. Inst. Freshwat. Res. Drottningholm* **39**, 23-54

FALEEVA, T. I. (1967). In *Obmen veshchestv i biokhimiia ryb* (Ed. by G. S. Karzinkin), pp. 59-65. Moskva, Nauka

FIBICH, S. (1905). Beobachtungen über die Temperatur bei Fischen. *Z. Fisch.* **12**, 29-53

FRENZEL, J. (1895). Temperaturmaxima für Binnenfische. *Z. Fisch.* **3**, 277-287

FRY, F. E. J. (1967). Responses of vertebrate poikilotherma to temperature. In *Thermobiology* (Ed. by A. H. Rose), pp. 375-409. London, Academic Press

GONCHAROV, T. D. (1967). In *Obmen veshchestv i biokhimiia ryb* (Ed. by G. S. Karzinkin), pp. 301-308. Moskva, Nauka

HAMDORF, K. (1961). Die Beeinflussung der Embryonal- und Larvalentwicklung der Regenbogenforellen durch die Umweltfaktoren, O_2-Partialdruck und Temperatur. *Z. vergl. Physiol.* **44(5)**, 523-549

HAMM, A. (1964). Die Hitzeresistenz des Karpfens mit und ohne Anpassung an höhere Temperaturen. *Allg. Fisch. Ztg.* **89(16)**, 488-489

HANEC, W. and BRUST, R. A. (1967). The effect of temperature on the immature stages of *Culiseta Inornata (Diptera: Culicidae)* in the laboratory. *Can. Ent.* **99**, 59

HARTMAN, G. F. (1966). Some effects of temperature on the behaviour of under yearling coho and steelhead. *Mgmt. Publs. Br. Columb. Game Commn.* **51**

HAVINGA, B. (1948). De ontwikkeling van de visstand in het Ijsselmer. *Viss. Nieuws* **1(4)**, 45-47

HAVINGA, B. (1949). De ontwikkeling van de visstand in het Ijsselmer. *Viss. Nieuws* **2(2)**, 22-24

HESSE, R. (1953). Tierbau und Tierleben. 2. Aufl. Jena, Fischer

HÖGLUND, L. B. (1961). Reactions of fish in concentration gradients. *Rep. Inst. Freshwat. Res. Drottningholm* **43**, 147

HUET, M. (1970). Traité de pisciculture. Brussels, Editions de Wyngaert

HUITFELDT-KASS, H. (1927). Studier over aldersforholde og veksttyper hos norske ferskvannfisker. Oslo, Nationaltryckeriet

JANČAŘIK, A. (1957) Physiology of the digestion in the carp, Volume 3. Digestion of the starch by the enzymes from the animal food of the carp. *Sb. čsl. Akad. zeměd. Ved.* **3(30)**, 763-774

JANČAŘIK, A. (1959). Bedeutung der Galle für Eiweiss- und Fettverdauung beim Karpfen. *Sb. čsl. Akad. zeměd. Ved.* **4(32)**, 867-876

JANČAŘIK, A. (1962). Die Bedeutung der tierischen Nahrung für die Verdauung kalorischer Nährstoffe biem Karpfen. *Sb. čsl. Akad. zeměd. Ved. (E)* **7(35)**, 327-342

JAVAID, M. Y. and ANDERSON, J. M. (1967a). Influence of starvation on selected temperature of some salmonids. *J. Fish. Res. Bd Can.* **24(7)**, 1515-1519

JAVAID, M. Y. and ANDERSON, J. M. (1967b). Thermal acclimation and temperature selection in Atlantic salmon, *Salmo salar* and rainbow trout, *S. gairdneri. J. Fish. Res. Bd Can.* **24(7)**, 1507-1513

KARPEVICH, A. F. (1967). In *Obmen veshchestv i biokhimiia ryb* (Ed. by G. S. Karzinkin), pp. 18-23. Moskva, Nauka

KEMPTER, H. (1933). Veränderungen im Blutbild bei Fischen infolge von Temperaturabfall. *Z. Fisch.* **31**, 583-590

KNAUTHE, K. (1895). Maximaltemperaturen, bei denen die Fische am Leben bleiben. *Biol. Zbl.* **15**, 752

KOLACZKOWSKI, S. and JAŚKOWSKI, J. (1966). In *Materialy Sesji Ochr.* Wód PAN i Inst. Gosp. Wodnej, Przy rodnicze skutki zrzutu wód podgrzanych do wód powierzchniowych, Kraków. (Symposium of the Polish Academy of Science on 'Effects of heated effluents on surface waters'.) (Mimeo)

KORNEEV, A., KORNEEVA, L. and TITATEVA, L. (1968). *Rybovod. i Rybolov.* **11**(2), 6-7

KOSHELEV, B. B. (1966). In *Zakonomernosti dinamiki chislennosti ryb belogo moria i ego basseina,* (Ed. by G. V. Nikolskii and Iu. E. Lapin), pp. 79-92. Moskva, Nauka

KRÜGER, F. (1961). Über den Exponenten der Temperaturfunktion biologischer Vorgänge und deren Grössenabhängigkeit. *Biol. Zbl.* **80**, 721-750

LAPORTE, C. (1962). La cholécystographie chez les poissons. *Bull. Soc. Hist. nat. Toulouse* **97**, 38-50

LEDUC, G., GRENIER, F. and PREVOST, G. (1959). Etude du facteur de température sur l'empoissonnement de la truite mouchetée par l'octachloro-camphène (T2). *J. Bord Off. Biol. Univ. Montreal* **2**, 265

LINDROTH, A. (1960). Försök över överlevnad och tilväxt i Bergeforsens laxodling 1959. (Experiments on survival and growth in Bergeforsen rearing plant.) Sundsvall, Sweden, *Medd. Vandringsfiskutr. Laxforsknings-institutet, No 8*

LLOYD, R. (1960). The toxicity of zinc sulphate to rainbow trout. *Ann. appl. Biol.* **48**(1), 84-94

LOOMIS, R. H. and IRWIN, W. H. (1954). Report of a study to determine the depth distribution of fishes in relation to vertical temperature. *Publ. Res. Fdn. Okla. agric. mech. Coll.* **56**

MAJOR, R. L. and MIGHELL, J. L. (1967). Influence of Rocky Reach Dam and the temperature of the Okanogan River on the upstream migration of sockeye salmon. *Fishery Bull. Fish. Wildl. Serv. U.S.* **66**(1), 131-147

MANN, H. (1935). Untersuchungen über die Verdauung und Ausnutzung der Stickstoffsubstanz einiger Nährtiere durch verschiedene Fische. *Z. Fisch.* **33**, 231-274

MANN, H. (1960a). Gewichtsverluste bei überwinternden Karpfen und Schleien. *Fischwirt* **10**(10), 302-304

MANN, H. (1960b). Untersuchungen über die Hälterung von Aalen. *Arch. Fisch. Wiss.* **11**(2), 151-158

MANN, H. (1961). Gewichtsverluste bei der Hälterung von Aalen. *Fischwirt* **11**(8), 233-239

MARCHETTI, R. (1962). *Biologia e tossicologia delle acque usate.* Milano, ETAS (Editrice Tecnica Artistica Scientifica)

McMAHON, J. W. (1965). Some physical factors influencing the feeding behaviour of *Daphnia magna* Straus. *Can. J. Zool.* **43**(4), 603-611

MUNTIAN, S. P. and ROZNICHENKO, P. N. (1967). In *Obmen veshchestv i biokhimiia ryb* (Ed. by G. S. Karzinkin), pp. 140-143. Moskva, Nauka

NÜMANN, W. (1964). Formenkreise der italienischen, jugoslawischen und adriatischen Forellen, zugleich ein Beitrag über den Wert einiger meristischer Merkmale für Art- und Rassenanalysen. *Schweiz. Z. Hydrol.* **26(1)**, 102–146

OLOFSSON, O. (1932). Sikens tillväxt under en varm och en kall sommar. *Svensk Fisk. Tidskr.* **41**, 163–166

OPUSZYŃSKI, K. (1967). Comparison of temperature and oxygen tolerance in grass carp *Ctenopharyngodon idella* Val., silver carp *Hypophthalmichthys molitrix* Val. and mirror carp *Cyprinus carpio* L. *Ecol. Pol.* **(A),(15/17)**, 385–400

PANOV, D. H. (1963). In *Materialy po biologii i gidrobiologii volzhskich vodokhranilishch* (Ed. by B. S. Kuzin), pp. 83–85. Moskva, Izd. A.N. SSSR

PAPERNA, J. (1963). Some observations on the biology and ecology of *Dactylogyrus vastator* in Israel. *Bamidgeh* **15(1)**, 8–28

PATRICK, N. D. and GRAF, P. (1961). The effect of temperature on the artificial culture of aurora trout. *Can. Fish. Cult.* **30**, 49–56

PAVLOV, D. S., SBIKIN, I. N. and USPENSKII, D. S. (1967). In *Povedenie i retseptsii u ryb* (Ed. by G. S. Karzinkin and G. A. Malukina) pp. 86–89. Moskva, Nauka

PEGEL, V. A. and REMOROV, V. A. (1967). In *Obmen veshchestv i biokhimiia ryb* (Ed. by G. S. Karzinkin), pp. 198–205. Moskva, Nauka

PIDGAIKO, M. L., GRIN, V. G., PELIVANNAIA, M. F. and BABKE, M. N. (1967). *Gidrobiol. Zh.* **3(5)**, 81–92

POLTORACKA, J. (1968). Specific composition of phytoplankton in a lake warmed by waste water from a thermoelectric plant and lakes with normal temperature. *Acta Soc. Bot. Pol.* **37(2)**, 297–325. (Polish; English summary)

REICHENBACH-KLINKE, H. H. (1965). Die Temperaturabhängigkeit der Fische. In *Der Fisch in Wissenschaft und Praxis.* Festschr. anl. d. 50 jähr. Bestehens d. Teichwirtschaftl. Abteilung Wielenbach der Bayr. Biol. Versuchsanstalt München. München, Obpacher

REICHENBACH-KLINKE, H. H. (1966). *Krankheiten und Schädigungen der Fische.* Stuttgart, Gustav Fischer Verlag

REZNICHENKO, P. N., KOTLIAREVSKAIA, N. V. and GULIDOV, M. V. (1967). In *Morfo-ekologicheskii analiz rozvitiia ryb* (Ed. by N. N. Disler), pp. 200–213. Moskva, Nauka

ROSENGARTEN, S. (1954). Der Aufstieg der Fische im Moselfischpass, Koblenz. *Z. Fisch.* **3**, 489–532

RUNNSTRÖM, S. (1957). Migration age and growth of the brown trout (*Salmo trutta* L.) in Lake Rensjön. *Rep. Inst. Freshwat. Res. Drottningholm* **38**, 194–246

RUNNSTRÖM, S. (1964). Effects of impoundment on the growth of *Salmo trutta* and *Salvelinus alpinus* in Lake Ransaren (Swedish Lappland). *Verh. int. Verein theor. angew. Limnol.* **15**, 453–461

SCHÄPERCLAUS, W. (1961). *Lehrbuch der Teichwirtschaft.* Berlin, Paul Parey

SCHMIDT, J. (1942). Racial investigations. 11 Ege Vilh. A transplantation experiment with *Zoarces viviparus*. *C.r. Trav. Lab. Carlsberg* **23(17)**

SCHOLZ, C. (1932). Experimentelle Untersuchungen über die Nahrungsverwertung des ein- und zweisömmerigen Hechtes. *Z. Fisch.* **30**, 523–605

SCHULTZE, D. (1965). Beiträge zur Temperaturadaption des Aales (*Anguilla vulgaris* L.) *Z. wiss. Zool. (A)* **172(1/2)**, 104–133

SEGERSTRALE, C. (1932). Über die jährlichen Zuwachszonen der Schuppen und Beziehungen zwischen Sommertemperatur und Zuwachs bei *Abramis brama*. *Acta zool. fenn.* 13, 1–42

SEGERSTRALE, C. (1947). Sommertemperaturens inverkan på braxens årliga tillväxt. In *Fiskodling och fiskevard*, pp. 179–187. Helsingfors

SERFATY, A. and LAFFONT, J. (1965). Influence de la baisse de température sur la valeur de la fréquence respiratoire et du taux lymphocytaire du milieu sanguin chez la carpe commune (*Cyprinus carpio* L.). *Hydrobiologia* 26, 409–419

SMIRNOVA, G. P. (1967). In *Obmen veshchestv i biokhimiia ryb* (Ed. by G. S. Karzinkin), pp. 190–193. Moskva, Nauka

SMITH, M. W. and SAUNDERS, J. W. (1959). Movements of brook trout, *Salvelinus fontinalis* (Mitchill) between and within fresh and salt water. *J. Fish. Res. Bd Can.* 15, 1403–1449

SMITH, S. (1957). Early development and hatching. In *Physiology of fishes*, (Ed. by M. E. Brown), Volume 1, pp. 323–359. New York, Academic Press

SØMME, J. D. (1941). *Ørretboka*. Oslo, J. Dybwads Forlag

SPÄTH, M. (1967). Die Wirkung der Temperatur auf die Mechanoreceptoren des Knochenfisches *Leuciscus rutilus* L. Ein Beitrag zur Thermoreception. *Z. vergl. Physiol.* 56, 431–462

STEFFENS, W. (1964). Die Überwinterung des Karpfens (*Cyprinus carpio*) als physiologisches Problem. *Z. Fisch.* 12(1/2), 97–153

STEGMAN, K. (1960). *Zesz. nauk. Szk. Glow. Gosp. wiejsk. (Zoot.)* 2(1), 67–83

STRELTSOVA, S. V. (1954). *Trudy Soveshch. ikhtiol. Kom.* (3), 50–56

SUKHANOVA, A. I. (1966). O vliianii temperatury na razvitie ikry pestrogo tolstolobika. *Izv. Akad. Nauk. turkmen. SSR (Biol.)* 1, 85–87

SVÄRDSON, G. (1951). The coregonid problem. 3. Whitefish from the Baltic, successfully introduced into fresh water in the north of Sweden. *Rep. Inst. Freshwat. Res. Drottningholm* 32, 79–125

SVÄRDSON, G. (1962). Fiskevardens teori. *Svenskt Fiske* (5), 161–178

SVÄRDSON, G. (1966). Öringen. *Fiske* 66, 8–37

SWIFT, D. R. (1961). The annual growth-rate cycle in brown trout (*Salmo trutta* L.) and its cause. *J. exp. Biol.* 38, 595–604

TATARKO, K. I. (1968). Effect of temperature on the meristic characters of fish. *Vop. Ikhtiol.* 8(3), 425–439

TESCH, F. W. (1962). Witterungsabhängigkeit der Brutentwicklung und Nachwuchs-förderung bei *Lucioperca lucioperca* L. *Kurze Mitt. Inst. Fisch. Biol. Univ. Hambg.* (12), 37–44

TROSHIN, A. S. (1967). *The cell and environmental temperature*. London, Pergamon Press

U.S. BUREAU OF COMMERCIAL FISHERIES. (1967). *Nuclear thermal power plants and salmonid fish*. Seattle, Washington, U.S. Bureau of Commercial Fisheries, Staff Report, May (mimeo)

VOUTE, A. M. (1960). Some investigations about the influence of low tempera-tures on the development of pike-eggs. IJmuiden, Internal Report

WILLEMSEN, J. (1958). Onderzoek ten behoeve van de pootsnoeksproductie. *Jversl. Org. Verbel. Binnenviss.* 1958, 58–65

WOKER, H. (1949). Die Temperaturabhängigkeit der Giftwirkung von Ammoniak auf Fische. *Verh. int. Ver. theor. angew. Limnol.* **10**, 575–579

WÜHRMANN, K. and WOKER, H. (1948). Experimentelle Untersuchungen über die Ammoniak- und Blausäurevergiftung. *Schweiz. Z. Hydrol.* **11**, 210-244

WUNDER, W. (1960). Folgeerscheinungen schlechter Überwinterung des Karpfens. *Allg. Fisch. Ztg.* **85**, 129–131

WUNDER, W. (1966). Das Problem der Überwinterung des Karpfens. *Allg. Fisch. Ztg.* **91**, 115–118

4

AMMONIA

Foreword

The preparation of this chapter was accomplished largely by Mr R. Lloyd who prepared the basic manuscript for the original report and also drafted the amendments for the updating, for review by the EIFAC Working Party on Water Quality Criteria for European Freshwater Fish.

4.1 Summary

In establishing water quality criteria for European inland fisheries, the effect of ammonia is an important factor to be considered. Sewage effluent, effluents from certain industries and from agriculture are common sources of ammonia in water.

The harmful effects of ammonia on fish are related to the pH value and the temperature of the water owing to the fact that only the un-ionized fraction of ammonia is poisonous. The un-ionized fraction increases with rising pH value, and with rising temperature.

Fish differ slightly in their tolerance to ammonia, depending on species. However, the difference in tolerance is more significant for short periods of exposure, and is not great enough to justify different criteria for different species.

The lowest lethal concentration found for salmonids is 0.2 mg NH_3/ℓ (un-ionized), but other adverse effects caused by prolonged exposure are absent only at concentrations lower than 0.025 mg NH_3/ℓ (un-ionized). Concentrations of total ammonia which contain this amount of un-ionized ammonia range from 19.6 mg/ℓ (pH 7.0, 5 °C) to 0.12 mg/ℓ (pH 8.5, 30 °C).

The criterion of 0.025 mg NH_3/ℓ (un-ionized) should not be applied to temperatures below 5 °C or to pH values above 8.0 when other factors have to be taken into consideration.

4.2 Introduction

The purpose of this review is to summarize the state of present knowledge on the effect of ammonia on fish, to see whether firm criteria can be established for this poison, and to indicate areas where further research is necessary. Ammonia is present in most waters as a normal biological degradation product of proteins, although the concentrations may be very small and subsequent conversion to nitrate (nitrification) may take place. Probably the most common source of ammonia in water is sewage or sewage effluent, particularly if nitrification is inhibited at the sewage disposal works, although large quantities of ammonia can be produced by industries such as those producing coal gas, coke and fertilizers, and considerable amounts may be discharged to rivers or estuaries. Another frequent source is from silage and manure and it can also accumulate in fish ponds during winter as an excretory product of the fish. However, ammonia and ammonium salts have been used to fertilize fish-rearing ponds, and also for aquatic weed control. Although ammonia is oxidized to nitrate in well oxygenated natural waters, the reverse process may take place at low concentrations of dissolved oxygen.

As long ago as 1913, it was shown that the toxicity of ammonia to fish was considerably affected by the pH value of the water, but it was not until 1947 that Wuhrmann, Zehender and Woker, in a classic study, demonstrated that it was the un-ionized fraction of ammonia which was poisonous to fish, and that the ionized fraction had little or no toxicity. Subsequent research has shown that other environmental factors could affect the toxic concentration of ammonia to fish and these may account for some of the inconsistencies shown in the early data. As a result, the complexity of the problem appears to have precluded the setting of effective criteria in respect of this poison. Usually the criteria are based on the concentration of total ammonia in the water, and do not allow for the effect of pH value.

Much of the literature issued prior to 1950 has been admirably and critically reviewed by Doudoroff and Katz (1950) and further reviews have been made by Marchetti (1962) and Jones (1964). This review will draw on data mainly from European sources, except where data on non-European species of fish serve to add collaborative evidence, or demonstrate the effect of a variable on which there is no European evidence. Although it is hoped that most of the literature has been surveyed, omissions will be inevitable; in some cases, papers may not

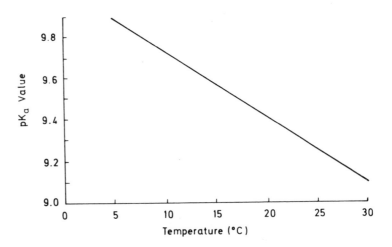

Figure 4.1 Relation between temperature and pK$_a$ values for ammonia

have been quoted where it is felt they do not add a significant contribution to what is already known, or if the data given are incomplete. Too often, field observations on the mortality of fish caused by ammonia are unaccompanied by measurements of oxygen levels, pH values and temperature, without which the data cannot be compared with other field observations or results of laboratory experiments. Also, partial oxidation of ammonia to nitrite, which is also toxic to fish in low concentrations, may have been a contributing factor in some cases.

There is some confusion in the terminology used to describe concentrations of ammonia. In this review, the terms 'ionized ammonia' (NH_4^+) and 'un-ionized ammonia' (NH_3) will be used to describe the two states of ammonia, and 'ammonia' will refer to the combined concentrations of un-ionized and ionized ammonia ($NH_3 + NH_4^+$). Chemical methods of analysis give values for ammonia and the method used for calculating the amounts of un-ionized ammonia present are given below. Concentrations of ammonia will be expressed as mg NH_3/ℓ.

4.3 Literature survey on effects of ammonia

4.3.1. LABORATORY DATA ON DIRECT LETHAL ACTION

Variables affecting the lethal levels

pH value Although there are several reports in the early literature that ammonia is more toxic in alkaline than in acid solutions, the chemical basis for this was first demonstrated by Wuhrmann and Woker (1948) who showed that only the un-ionized molecule was toxic, the ammonium having little or no toxicity. Further studies by Downing and Merkens (1955) confirmed that the toxicity of ammonia could be directly related to the concentration of un-ionized ammonia present.

For practical purposes the formula for calculating the percentage of un-ionized ammonia present in an ammonia solution is as follows:

$$\text{Per cent un-ionized ammonia} = \frac{100}{1 + \text{antilog} \, (pK_a - pH)}$$

where pK_a = the negative logarithm of the ionization constant.

Thus, for example, an increase in pH value of 0.3 units from 7.0 to 7.3 would double the concentration of un-ionized ammonia in an ammonia solution although the effect becomes less above pH 8.5. The value for pK_a depends on temperature, and appropriate values from Emerson *et al.* (1975) are given in *Table 4.1* and depicted graphically in *Figure 4.1*; these values are very close to those of Bates and Pinching (1950). Reference may also be made to the nomogram by Montgomery and Stiff (1971).

It can be calculated that a rise in temperature of 10 °C doubles the concentration of un-ionized ammonia present in an ammonia solution. It can also be shown that the proportion of un-ionized ammonia decreases with increase in ionic strength; the decrease over that in distilled water is about 10 per cent

Table 4.1   VALUES FOR pK_a OF AMMONIA AT TEMPERATURES
BETWEEN 5 AND 30 °C

Temperature (°C)	5	10	15	20	25	30
pka	9.90	9.73	9.56	9.40	9.24	9.09

in a water having a hardness of about 250 mg/ℓ expressed as calcium carbonate
and about 25 per cent in sea water.

Although Tabata (1962) claimed that the ionized fraction of ammonia has a
demonstrable toxicity, it had only one-fiftieth of the toxicity of un-ionized
ammonia for the water flea (*Daphnia pulex*), and even less for some species
of fish. These conclusions are at variance with the data given by Downing
and Merkens (1955).

Free carbon dioxide   Alabaster and Herbert (1954) showed that the toxicity
of a solution of ammonium chloride could be decreased by increasing the level
of free carbon dioxide in the water, which reduced the pH value, until a concentration of free carbon dioxide was reached which was itself toxic to fish. Later
Lloyd and Herbert (1960) proposed a second effect of free carbon dioxide. They
suggested that it was not the pH value of the bulk of the solution which was
important in determining the toxicity of ammonia, but the pH value of the water
at the gill surface; this depends on the effect which the respiratory carbon
dioxide produced by the fish has on the pH value of the water, and its magnitude depends upon the concentration of free carbon dioxide already present in
solution. If the concentration of free carbon dioxide in the water is very low, the
amount excreted by the fish will considerably reduce the pH value at the gill surface, but the extent of this pH change will become less as the level of free carbon
dioxide rises in the bulk of the water. Thus, in experiments in which the ambient
free carbon dioxide levels are very low and the pH value high (following the
addition of ammonium hydroxide, or sodium hydroxide for pH control) the
levels of *un-ionized* ammonia found to be toxic may be about five times greater
than those applicable to polluted waters where the level of free carbon dioxide
is likely to be high and the pH value lower. So far, this effect has been demonstrated only for rainbow trout (*Salmo gairdneri*) and its magnitude may be less
for those species of fish with low respiratory efficiency and which would therefore excrete only relatively small amounts of carbon dioxide into the respiratory
water flow.

Dissolved oxygen   A reduction in the level of dissolved oxygen in the water
increases the toxicity of several poisons to fish, and this has been found for ammonia by Wuhrmann (1952) and Downing and Merkens (1955), the latter showing that a reduction in the oxygen content of the water to 50 per cent of the air
saturation value reduced the survival times of several species of fish in lethal
solutions to one-third of the time in aerated water. Lloyd (1961a) showed that
the effect of low oxygen concentrations on the threshold LC50 for ammonia
(the value where the curve relating median period of survival to concentrations
becomes parallel to the survival time axis) was greater than its effect on other

poisons, and put forward a hypothesis to explain this difference and for varia-tions caused by free carbon dioxide in the water. Using this hypothesis, it can be calculated that the effect of low oxygen levels on the toxicity of ammonia will become less as the level of free carbon dioxide in the water rises. In field situa-tions where a lowering of the dissolved-oxygen levels is likely to be accompanied by an increase in the level of free carbon dioxide and a concomitant reduction in pH value, this latter factor is likely to reduce the toxicity of ammonia to a greater extent than the increased toxicity caused by low oxygen levels. In the experi-ments which have been reported here, fish have been transferred direct from clean aerated water to ammonia solutions of lower oxygen content; no reference has been found to similar experiments with fish already acclimated to the low dissolved oxygen level of the water, but Alabaster, Shurben and Knowles (1979) have found similar results in such tests with Atlantic salmon (*Salmo salar*).

Water hardness   Both Wuhrmann and Woker (1953) using minnows (*Phoxinus phoxinus*), and Herbert (unpublished data referred to in Herbert, 1961) using rainbow trout, showed that variations in the hardness of the water had no effect on the toxicity of ammonia to these fish.

Alkalinity   So far as is known, alkalinity (bicarbonate concentration) only affects the toxicity of ammonia by its part in determining the pH value of the water in conjunction with the level of free carbon dioxide present. This effect has been described graphically by Lloyd (1961b).

Temperature   It has already been stated that an increase in temperature will increase the proportion of un-ionized ammonia present in an ammonia solution (p. 87, para. 4). It has been shown by Woker (1949) that although survival times of chub (*Squalius cephalus*) at constant levels of un-ionized ammonia decreased with a rise in temperature, the threshold LC50 remained the same. Similar results for rainbow trout were found by Herbert (1962).

However, it is possible that these findings apply only to temperatures above 10 °C. Burrows (1964) showed that at lower temperatures, un-ionized ammonia became markedly more toxic to chinook salmon (*Oncorhynchus tshawytscha*) and recent work by Brown (1968) suggests that at 3 °C the threshold LC50 of un-ionized ammonia for rainbow trout is about half that at 10 °C, which would cancel the effect of temperature on the dissociation of ammonia. This is of some importance if ammonia concentrations rise in rivers or carp ponds during the winter.

Salinity   The toxicity of ammonia to rainbow trout decreases with a rise in salinity up to 30 per cent seawater (a concentration approximately isotonic with the blood) but increases again up to 100 per cent seawater (Herbert and Shurben, 1965) under laboratory conditions of constant pH value. Examination of the data shows that the curve relating threshold LC50 of ammonia to log concentration of seawater is symmetrical about the concentration isotonic with fish blood, the threshold in isotonic solutions being just over twice that found in freshwater. The dissociation constants for ammonia used in this study were those for freshwater. Similar results have been obtained with salmon smolts (Alabaster, Shurben and Knowles, 1979).

Acclimation to low ammonia concentrations   It is well established that exposure of fish to sublethal levels of ammonia increases their subsequent resistance to lethal concentrations (Vamos, 1963; Malacea, 1968; Lloyd and Orr, 1969). The resistance obtained by rainbow trout is held for at least one day, but is lost after three days (Lloyd and Orr, 1969). None of the data available allow an estimate to be made of the maximum concentration to which fish can be acclimated.

Other factors   It has been shown by Herbert and Shurben (1963) that the resistance of rainbow trout to ammonia poisoning was unchanged at swimming speeds up to 2 body lengths/s but decreased thereafter, and at 3 body lengths/s the threshold LC50 was 70 per cent of that in still water.

Hemens (1966) found that female mosquito fish (*Gambusia affinis*) were slightly more resistant than males to ammonia poisoning, but that size differences had no effect on their susceptibility.

There is some circumstantial evidence (Lloyd and Orr, 1969) that the physical handling of fish immediately before exposing them to ammonia increases their resistance to this poison (p. 90, para. 6).

Summary of toxicity data

Salmonids   Data have been presented by Penaz (1965) which show that the ova of brown trout (*Salmo trutta v. fario*) are very resistant to short exposures (120 min) to concentrations as high as 50 mg NH_3/ℓ of un-ionized ammonia at 10 °C, although there was some indication that hatching success was reduced if the eggs were exposed to this high concentration during the later stages of development. Wuhrmann and Woker (1948) found that the threshold for trout spawn was 0.3–0.4 mg NH_3/ℓ un-ionized ammonia. However, Rice and Stokes (1975) found that the 1-day LC50 values for trout eggs were greater than 3.58 mg NH_3/ℓ un-ionized ammonia and that the alevins became increasingly sensitive to ammonia just before the absorption of the yolk sac. Similar data have been obtained by D. Calamari (personal communication) who found that the 4-day LC50 for developing rainbow trout eggs was greater than 0.49 NH_3/ℓ, although the 12-day LC50 was 0.35 mg NH_3/ℓ, in agreement with the data of Wuhrmann and Woker (1948).

Further experiments by Penaz (1965) on the fry of brown trout gave a 10-h LC50 of 3.60 mg NH_3/ℓ although the data presented show that there was a 60 per cent mortality in 0.4 mg NH_3/ℓ at the end of this period, and this concentration was suggested as the threshold level. D. Calamari (personal communication) found that developing rainbow trout alevins became increasingly sensitive to short-term exposure to un-ionized ammonia, the 96-h LC50 falling from 0.37 at the stage when the yolk sac was absorbed, to 0.16 mg NH_3/ℓ 32 days later (temperature 14.5 °C), before rising to 0.44 at the fingerling stage. The mortality among controls was high (at 30 per cent) but since it is probably lower than what would occur in nature it is considered acceptable in this kind of experiment. Threshold LC or EC50 values of 0.2 mg NH_3/ℓ reported for rainbow trout fry (Liebmann, 1960) and for rainbow trout fingerlings (Danecker, 1964) also reflect the greater sensitivity of salmonids at this stage of the life cycle, although Danecker used diluted liquid manure to produce the required ammonia concentration. Data from Rice and Stokes (1975) indicate an even greater sensitivity of developing rainbow trout fry with a 1-day LC50 of 0.07 mg NH_3/ℓ, but the corresponding value for adult rainbow trout in similar experiments was 0.1 mg NH_3/ℓ; the pH value of the water in these experiments was controlled by the addition of tris buffer, and this procedure may have affected the toxicity of ammonia. Lloyd and Herbert (1960) showed that the threshold LC50 at the gill surface of rainbow trout was 0.49 mg NH_3/ℓ, although higher concentrations were required in the bulk of the solution to produce these levels. This accounted for the high threshold LC50 values (1.8 mg NH_3/ℓ) found by Merkens and Downing (1957) who used water of very low free carbon dioxide content. In order to take into account the many different variables which affect the toxicity of ammonia solutions, Lloyd (1961b) published a series of graphs from which the threshold LC50 of this poison for rainbow trout could be calculated. From the data then available, there was a close correlation between predicted and observed threshold LC50 values. However, recent experiments by Ball (1967) gave a 1-day LC50 value for rainbow trout of 0.50 mg NH_3/ℓ, similar to that found by Herbert and Shurben (1963) of 0.50 mg NH_3/ℓ and by Herbert and Shurben (1965) of 0.49 mg NH_3/ℓ, although a second test gave a 1-day LC50 of 0.70 mg NH_3/ℓ. Lloyd and Orr (1969) found a 1-day LC50 of 0.47 mg NH_3/ℓ for rainbow trout fitted with a urinary catheter and kept in aerated water. These values are lower than those predicted from the graphs of Lloyd (1961b) for the experimental conditions and it has been suggested (Lloyd and Orr, 1969) that differences in the experimental techniques used, such as the handling of the fish immediately before the start of the experiment, may cause variations in the results.

Most of the data on the toxicity of ammonia to fish referred to on p. 90, para. 6 have been obtained from tests which continued for a few days only. However, tests over a three-month period with batches of 200 rainbow trout have shown that a small proportion of the fish population is killed by concentrations lower than the 2-day LC50; at 0.22 mg NH_3/ℓ, fifteen per cent died, and at 0.11 and 0.06 mg NH_3/ℓ, five per cent died (Ministry of Technology, 1968). On the other hand, there was no mortality of chinook salmon fingerlings exposed to 0.018 mg NH_3/ℓ or less for a six-week period (Burrows, 1964), though some hyperplasia of the gill lamella epithelium was observed (p. 95, para. 4). Calamari, Marchetti and Vailati (1977) exposed rainbow trout to ammonia from the egg stage through to alevins; the 72-day LC50 (temperature 14.5 °C) was 0.056 mg NH_3/ℓ as un-ionized ammonia; this lower result is probably attributable to the extra sensitivity of developing alevins.

Atlantic salmon smolts (*Salmo salar*) in fresh water are more sensitive to ammonia poisoning than rainbow trout of the same size, having a 1-day LC50 of 0.28 mg NH_3/ℓ for handled fish (Herbert and Shurben, 1965) and 0.15 mg NH_3/ℓ for fish not handled (J. S. Alabaster, personal communication).

Since the pH value of natural waters may not remain constant, but show a diurnal fluctuation, the level of un-ionized ammonia present will certainly vary. Results of experiments by Brown, Jordan and Tiller (1969) on the toxicity of fluctuating ammonia levels, are difficult to evaluate, in that fluctuating concentrations between 1½ and ½ times the 2-day LC50 on a two-hour cycle caused a greater mortality of rainbow trout that would have been expected from the 2-day LC50 alone (the average concentration) with the survival time being about twice as long as that found for 1½ times the 2-day LC50. On this evidence therefore, one could assume that successive exposures to lethal concentrations of ammonia were cumulative. However, fluctuations of a similar magnitude on a one-hour cycle produced mortalities similar to that at a constant 2-day LC50, and in this case the fish could be assumed to be reacting to the average value of the ammonia concentrations to which they were exposed. One explanation for these different results might be that it takes one to two hours for ammonia to have a physiological effect on the fish (Lloyd and Orr, 1969) and that this might affect the reactions of fish to exposure to ammonia under these test conditions. Further experiments are needed to determine the effect of diurnal variations of un-ionized ammonia on the survival of fish, with associated changes in pH value and temperature, which can occur in both natural and polluted waters.

Other species   A recent study by Ball (1967) on the toxicity of ammonia to roach (*Rutilus rutilus*), rudd (*Scardinius erythrophthalmus*), bream (*Abramis brama*), and perch (*Perca fluviatilis*), showed that the threshold LC50 values for these species at British summer temperatures were 0.42, 0.44, 0.50, and 0.35 mg NH_3/ℓ (un-ionized ammonia) respectively, and that the experiments had to be continued for between 2½ and 4 days before an estimate of the threshold LC50 could be made. These values were comparable with those obtained within 24 hours for rainbow trout under the same test conditions. Therefore, although these species have a greater resistance than trout to ammonia during tests lasting two days, their survival time in 0.73 mg NH_3/ℓ being eight times longer, the threshold LC50 for all five species were similar. These results make a comparison between data from other experiments difficult where tests were short-term only, since survival times in lethal solutions can be affected by many factors. The 95-day LC50 for rudd was found to be 0.24 mg NH_3/ℓ un-ionized ammonia (Department of the Environment, 1971), which was 0.5 of the 7-day LC50 under these test conditions; no fish died at 0.2 of the 7-day LC50.

Flis (1968a) working with common carp (*Cyprinus carpio*) in a water temperature of 11 °C, found that there was 16 per cent mortality in un-ionized ammonia concentrations of 1.3 mg NH_3/ℓ in one test, and 18 per cent mortality in 0.9 mg NH_3/ℓ in another, during a 10-day test period. In these experiments, ammonia was added as ammonium hydroxide, and the high pH values of 8.3 to 8.7 would indicate a low concentration of free carbon dioxide, so that the toxic concentrations may be slightly higher than normal. In further tests at an average pH value of 8.05, Flis (1968b) found an 8 per cent mortality of common carp in 35 days at 0.11 mg NH_3/ℓ, although in a second series at this concentration there were no mortalities. Although Danecker (1964) estimated an un-ionized ammonia concentration of 1.5 mg NH_3/ℓ to be the lethal level of common carp at about 16 °C, the tests were of less than two days duration, and a replotting of the data indicates that a threshold concentration might not have been reached within this period. Vamos (1963) found that the concentration of un-ionized ammonia required to overturn common carp was 0.5 mg NH_3/ℓ in tests of only a few hours duration.

Since Ball (1967) showed that tests of several days duration were required to obtain a measure of threshold LC50 of ammonia for coarse fish, tests of shorter duration are unlikely to give threshold values, and therefore it is difficult to make a comparison between the results obtained for other species. In general, however, the toxic levels of un-ionized ammonia for short-term tests for several species of fish lie between 0.6 mg NH_3/ℓ for perch and 2.0 mg NH_3/ℓ for carp and tench (*Tinca tinca*), with chub and minnow being intermediate in sensitivity (Woker and Wuhrmann, 1950; Liebmann, 1960; Nehring, 1962; Danecker, 1964; Malacea, 1966).

Therefore, it is likely that the various species of coarse fish have similar sensitivities to ammonia poisoning after prolonged exposure, but over a short period some are more resistant, especially carp and tench. This may be important in situations where the level of un-ionized ammonia fluctuates, either by variations in concentration of total ammonia or by changes in the pH value or temperature of the water, and some species may be able to survive for short periods in high concentrations which would be lethal to more sensitive fish.

Toxicity of ammonia in the presence of other poisons   Several tests have been made with rainbow trout on the toxicity of mixtures of ammonia with other poisons. Experiments with solutions containing both ammonia and cyanide showed that the combination was more toxic that either substance alone (Wuhrmann and Woker, 1948). Herbert (1962) showed that the threshold LC50 of a mixture of ammonia and phenol was obtained when the sum of the individual concentrations, expressed as the proportion of their separate threshold LC50 values, equalled unity. Further tests with zinc and ammonia (Herbert and Shurben, 1964), and copper and ammonia (Herbert and Van Dyke, 1964) gave similar results, in that the toxicity of the individual poisons could be added together in this manner. However, Brown, Jordan, and Tiller (1969) showed that mixtures of zinc, phenol, and ammonia, in which the proportion of the total toxicity contributed by phenol and ammonia was small, were less toxic than the predicted values and it is possible that this method of summing toxicities is not valid for low concentrations of poisons (p. 95, para. 3). Vamos and Tasnadi (1967) used copper sulphate to reduce the toxicity of ammonia in carp ponds, and suggested that the cupro-ammonium compounds formed are not toxic, a finding opposite to that of Herbert and Van Dyke (1964) in laboratory experiments.

4.3.2 FIELD OBSERVATIONS

Although there are many recorded cases of fish kills following the discharge of ammonia to streams or rivers and from the accumulation of ammonia in carp ponds, the chemical data available are insufficient to enable a correlation to be made with the laboratory evidence. Furthermore, it is uncommon for ammonia to be the only poison present and it is difficult to make an estimate of the part played by other toxic substances.

However, Vamos and Tasnadi (1967) have made some interesting observations on the mortality of carp in fish ponds. Mortality occurred when the concentration of un-ionized ammonia reached 0.5 mg NH_3/ℓ with a level of dissolved oxygen of 6 mg/ℓ, but when the oxygen concentration was 2 mg/ℓ, the lethal level of un-ionized ammonia was 0.2 mg NH_3/ℓ. These observations also support the laboratory data on the effect of low oxygen levels on the toxicity of ammonia to fish. There are several other instances recorded of common carp mortality in ponds where a combination of high temperatures, high pH value and high ammonia concentration were present in varying degrees. Usually the lethal conditions persist for a few hours only, and insufficient measurements are made of the water quality before and during this period to make a correlation with laboratory data possible. Kempinska (1968) recommends that ammonia should not be used as a fertilizer for fish ponds if the pH value of the water exceeds 8.5. Calamari and Marchetti (1975) exposed caged rainbow trout for 48 h to high concentrations of ammonia in the surface water of L. Orta, Italy; mortalities occurred when the concentration of un-ionized ammonia exceeded 0.4 NH_3/ℓ.

Examination of data on water quality in the R. Trent system in England (J. H. N. Garland and I. C. Hart, personal communication) shows that species of coarse fish are present where the median concentration of un-ionized ammonia over a period of a year is between 0.01 and 0.04 mg NH_3/ℓ (with median dissolved-oxygen concentrations between 6.8 and 8.5 mg/ℓ. The upper value is about 10 per cent of the threshold LC50 found for coarse fish found by Ball (1967). Recently data have been made available by R. J. S. Linfield (personal communication) for the Anglian Water Authority area, U.K. These show that the median concentrations of un-ionized ammonia where there were good mixed coarse fisheries were as follows: in the Willow Brook, 0.02, R. Ise, 0.02, R. Yar, 0.03 and R. Nene, 0.12 mg/ℓ and where there were only fair, mixed coarse fisheries, the values were: in the R. Welland, 0.06 and R. Nene, 0.18 mg/ℓ. However, no data are available on daily variations in pH value or on the concentrations of carbon dioxide present.

4.3.3. MODE OF TOXIC ACTION

Several authors have demonstrated that exposure of fish to lethal or sub-lethal ammonia solutions results in damage to the gill epithelium (Kuhn and Koecke, 1956; Burrows, 1964; Reichenbach-Klinke, 1967; Flis, 1968a, Smart, 1976), and Marchetti (1960) found that prolonged exposure to sublethal levels of ammonia caused severe caudal damage to Crucian carp (*Carassius carassius*). Reichenbach-Klinke (1967) also described some effects on the blood of rainbow trout in which the number of erythrocytes falls as the ammonia level reaches a toxic concentration, and he considers that trout fry are seriously affected by a concentration of 0.27 mg NH_3/ℓ. In a more extensive study on the effects of lethal and sublethal concentrations of ammonia on various organs of common carp, Flis (1968b) demonstrated severe tissue damage after 35 days exposure to an un-ionized ammonia concentration of 0.11 mg NH_3/ℓ which, although not lethal in one test, killed 8 per cent in a second experiment. Damage to the liver and kidneys appeared to be associated with disruption of the blood vessels. Danecker (1964) reports both gill damage and haemolysis occurring in carp. Rudd exposed for 95 days to a sublethal un-ionized ammonia concentration of 0.10 mg NH_3/ℓ showed histopathological changes only in the epidermis (Department of the Environment, 1971); similar results were obtained by D. Calamari (personal communication) who found that rainbow trout exposed to ammonia from the egg to the alevin stage showed epidermal changes at concentrations greater than 0.025 mg NH_3/ℓ. The significance of these changes in terms of survival is not clear.

Sousa and Meade (1977) exposed coho salmon (*Oncorhynchus kisutch*) for 13 days to un-ionized ammonia concentrations which fluctuated within the range 0.04-0.18 mg NH_3/ℓ, and measured a progressive acidaemia which led to a reduction in blood oxygen-carrying capacity. The fish showed signs of hyper-excitability and hyperventilation, which were also noted by G. Smart (personal communication) when rainbow trout were exposed to acutely lethal concentrations of un-ionized ammonia (0.6 mg NH_3/ℓ); however, in these latter experiments no change in blood pH was recorded and further experiments led Smart to conclude that the primary cause of ammonia intoxication may be a reduction in the energy reserves of the brain.

Lloyd and Orr (1969) demonstrated that exposure to ammonia concentrations greater than 12 per cent of the threshold LC50 increased the absorption of water by rainbow trout. By measuring changes in the rate of urine production, they showed that the threshold LC50 was associated with a urine flow rate of 12 mℓ/kg/h, compared with a normal rate of 2 mℓ/kg/h at 10.5 °C, showing a six-fold increase in absorption. These findings may account for the greater resistance of rainbow trout to un-ionized ammonia in isotonic saline solutions (p. 89, para. 4); also, the stress imposed by this water intake on the kidneys, and the water balance of the fish generally, may account for the effects found by other authors on the blood system and tissues. Lloyd and Orr (1969) further suggest that any factor which affects the water balance in fish will also influence their susceptibility to ammonia poisoning, and this may account for the increased susceptibility of ulcerated fish (Vamos, 1963) and of salmon smolts (Herbert and Shurben, 1965).

The reasons for the increase in the permeability of fish to water is not known. Fromm and Gillette (1968) found evidence of some accumulation of ammonia in the blood of rainbow trout exposed to ammonia solutions, although the amount was small and is considered to have been derived endogenously. It is possible that the increase in permeability occurs only when the normal excretory mechanism becomes overloaded and Fromm and Gillette (1968) showed that the proportion of ammonia to total nitrogen excreted decreased with increasing ambient ammonia levels. In those solutions where the amount of ammonia entering the fish can be readily excreted, or detoxified, there would be no harmful effect, and this may occur in ammonia concentrations below 12 per cent of the lethal level. If fish change from ammonia to urea excretion at temperatures below 11 °C, as shown for the chinook salmon by Burrows (1964) their resistance to ammonia might be expected to decrease as shown by Brown (1968).

There is conflicting evidence on the permanence of damage caused by short-term exposure to ammonia; Grindley (1946) reported that few overturned rainbow trout survived on transfer to clean water, whereas Vamos (1963) found the reverse with carp, and that overturned fish had a greater resistance to subsequent exposure to ammonia solutions. Burrows (1964) exposed chinook salmon to low concentrations of ammonia for six weeks, and found progressive hyperplasia of the gill epithelium during the first four weeks of exposure; subsequent exposure to clean water led to recovery of the gill epithelium where the water temperature was 14 °C, but not at 6 °C.

4.3.4 AVOIDANCE REACTIONS

Both Jones (1948), using stickleback (*Gasterosteus aculeatus*) and Summerfelt and Lewis (1967), using green sunfish (*Lepomis cyanellus*), found that these fish were repelled by lethal solutions of ammonia in a gradient tank. Green sunfish were not repelled by concentrations in which the fish showed obvious signs of distress, and stickleback were attracted to sublethal levels. Hepher (1959) observed that common carp avoided local high concentrations of ammonia after it had been applied as a fertilizer in pond culture. There is no evidence to suggest that fish avoid sublethal levels of this poison.

4.3.5 EFFECT ON GROWTH

Recent developments in high-density fish culture, involving the recirculation of water, have given rise to renewed interest in the toxicity to fish of metabolic by-products, including ammonia. Burrows (1964) stated that chinook salmon were adversely affected when the un-ionized ammonia concentration became greater than 0.005 mg NH_3/ℓ; a similar upper limit has been quoted by Liao and Mayo (1972) for salmonids reared in intensive culture systems with recirculated water, but with no supporting experimental evidence. More recently, Robinson-Wilson and Seim (1975) studied the growth rates of chinook salmon in ammonia solutions at 15 °C and found that growth was affected only at concentrations of un-ionized ammonia greater than 0.026 mg NH_3/ℓ; below this value the salmon grew faster than those in clean water. Larmoyeux and Piper (1973) found that 0.015 mg NH_3/ℓ as un-ionized ammonia was harmful to rainbow trout in water re-use systems when the dissolved-oxygen concentration fell below 5.0 mg/ℓ; nitrite levels were not measured in this experiment. Rainbow trout were also found to grow satisfactorily in a recirculation unit where the total ammonia ranged from 4 to 23 mg NH_3/ℓ at a pH range of 6.5-7.5 at 10 °C (Scott and Gillespie, 1972); assuming an average pH value of 7.0, the un-ionized ammonia concentration ranged from 0.008 to 0.044 mg NH_3/ℓ. Schulze-Wiehenbrauck (1976) found that exposure to un-ionized ammonia concentrations of 0.05-0.13 mg NH_3/ℓ initially limited the growth of rainbow trout, but after 2 weeks the subsequent growth rate was good; concentrations greater than 0.13 mg NH_3/ℓ inhibited growth rate. In these experiments the temperatures ranged from 8.3 to 10.9 °C and there was some evidence of acclimation to ammonia toxicity.

The growth of rudd was reduced at un-ionized ammonia concentrations above 0.19 mg NH_3/ℓ but was increased at and below 0.1 mg NH_3/ℓ (Department of the Environment, 1971). Similar data have been obtained for channel catfish (*Ictalurus punctatus*) by Robinette (1976).

4.3.6 EFFECT ON AQUATIC FOOD ORGANISMS

In an extensive study of invertebrate organisms typical of different zones of pollution, Stammer (1953) found the threshold acute lethal concentration of total ammonia (pH 8.5, temperature 12-18 °C) was, for *Eristalis arbustorum* 200 mg/ℓ, for *Perlodes microcephala* 9 mg/ℓ, for *Chironomus thummi* 4.3 mg/ℓ and for *Ecdyonurus venosus* 3 mg/ℓ. In general all the organisms tested were more resistant than trout. Malacea (1966) gives the 2-day LC50 for *Daphnia magna* as 0.66 mg NH_3/ℓ which is close to values obtained for trout.

It is unlikely, therefore, that the presence of ammonia in a river at concentrations lower than those toxic to fish would affect adversely the food supply of fish; indeed, it may have a significant beneficial effect on productivity, and therefore the total biomass present, as can also occur when carp ponds are fertilized with ammonia.

4.4 Conclusions

It is clear that the major factor controlling the toxicity of ammonia is the pH value of the water which, together with temperature, governs the concentration of un-ionized ammonia present in ammonia solutions. Many laboratory experiments of relatively short duration have demonstrated that the acute lethal concentrations of ammonia for a variety of fish species lie in the range 0.2–2.0 mg NH_3/ℓ, with trout being the most sensitive and common carp being the most resistant. Discrepancies between results for any one species may reflect differences in other environmental variables (such as the level of free carbon dioxide in the water) which has a small, but significant, effect on the toxicity of ammonia, and the greater sensitivity of juvenile fish compared with adults, or they may be caused by differences in experimental technique, such as in the handling of the fish. Although it is clear that the more sluggish of coarse fish species survive much longer in toxic solutions than do salmonids, the difference in sensitivity between various fish species to prolonged exposure is probably less than the tenfold range given above. Therefore, it seems that a water quality criterion for ammonia based on a trout standard would not be too harsh for waters containing only resistant species of coarse fish.

From the laboratory evidence which is available, the lowest toxic concentration found for salmonids is 0.05 mg NH_3/ℓ for long-term exposure of rainbow trout fry (D. Calamari, personal communication); minimum short-term toxic concentrations found for salmonids have been 0.16 mg NH_3/ℓ for rainbow trout fry (D. Calamari, personal communication) with slightly higher values being found for Atlantic salmon smolts (Herbert and Shurben, 1964) and for rainbow trout (Liebmann, 1960) and for the same species at 3 °C (Brown, 1968).

Although short-term exposure to concentrations of un-ionized ammonia below 0.15 mg NH_3/ℓ may not kill a significant proportion of a fish population, it may still exert an adverse physiological or histopathological effect (Flis, 1968b; Lloyd and Orr, 1969). The only evidence from laboratory tests on which a level of no adverse effect can be based is that of Lloyd and Orr (1969) who showed that concentrations lower than 12 per cent of a lethal threshold concentration did not increase the permeability of rainbow trout to water. This evidence relates to sudden exposure of the fish to ammonia solutions, and there is some evidence that acclimation to sublethal concentrations can take place. It is possible, therefore, that a criterion based on 12 per cent of a threshold LC50 would be unduly low. However, acclimation to sublethal levels has only been shown to give an increased resistance to toxic concentrations and a reduced physiological response, and it is still possible that the fish might undergo deleterious histopathological changes during a prolonged exposure (p. 91, para. 2; p. 94). It is very unlikely that a constant concentration of un-ionized ammonia could be maintained in any natural water system and fish which have been adversely affected might recover when the level of un-ionized ammonia fell, but such recovery may not occur in cold water (p. 95, para. 4). There are some field data (p. 94, para. 2) to suggest that coarse fisheries can be maintained in the presence of a median concentration of ammonia which is about 10 per cent of the threshold LC50 with higher levels being present at times. On balance, therefore, healthy salmonid populations would be expected to occur where the 95 percentile concentration was below 0.025 mg NH_3/ℓ, and it is possible that higher concentrations occurring for short periods would be harmless if the fish became acclimatized to them.

For coarse fish species, laboratory data have shown them to be similar in sensitivity to salmonids, but field data have shown that some species can live in good conditions where the 50 percentile is 0.025 mg NH_3/ℓ. There is evidence that good coarse fish populations can live in waters where the concentrations of un-ionized ammonia are higher, but whether this is the result of acclimatization, or very low levels of free carbon dioxide in the water at the time of sampling, is not known.

It should be borne in mind that, during the summer months, active photosynthesis by aquatic plants can cause the pH value of the water to rise well above 8.0 and sometimes to exceed 9.0; this is accompanied by a reduction in the free carbon dioxide concentration of the water and under these conditions, un-ionized ammonia becomes apparently less toxic. It can be shown (R. Lloyd, personal communication) that under these conditions, the average pH value of the water at the gill surface is unlikely to exceed 8.0, and that effective concentrations of un-ionized ammonia for pH values above 8.0 should be calculated by substituting 8.0 for the measured pH of the water.

Total ammonia concentrations which correspond to an un-ionized concentration of 0.025 mg NH_3/ℓ are shown in *Table 4.2* and expressed graphically in *Figure 4.2*.

The values given in *Table 4.2* are related to the pH value and temperature of the water; for example, where the pH value of the water is 8.0, and the temperature 20 °C, the total ammonia concentration should not exceed 0.66 mg NH_3/ℓ. It must be stressed, however, that these concentrations may add to the toxicity of other poisons present in the water, although more research is required to demonstrate whether this actually occurs.

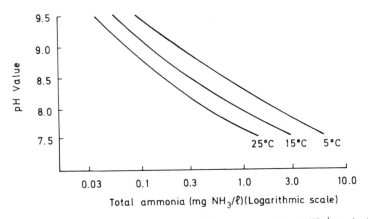

Figure 4.2 Concentrations of total ammonia which contain 0.025 mg NH_3/ℓ un-ionized ammonia for waters of different pH and temperature

Table 4.2   CONCENTRATIONS OF AMMONIA ($NH_3 + NH_4^+$) WHICH CONTAIN AN UN-IONIZED AMMONIA CONCENTRATION OF 0.025 mg NH_3/ℓ

Temperature (°C)	pH value					
	6.5	7.0	7.5	8.0*	8.5*	9.0*
5	63.3	20.0	6.3	2.0	0.66	0.23
10	42.4	13.4	4.3	1.4	0.45	0.16
15	28.9	9.2	2.9	0.94	0.31	0.12
20	20.0	6.3	2.0	0.66	0.22	0.088
25	13.9	4.4	1.4	0.46	0.16	0.069
30	9.8	3.1	1.0	0.34	0.12	0.056

*Concentrations of ammonia derived for pH values above 8.0 may be too stringent if the concentration of free carbon dioxide in the water is very low.

4.5 References

ALABASTER, J. S. and HERBERT, D. W. M. (1954). Influence of carbon dioxide on the toxicity of ammonia. *Nature, Lond.* **174**, 404-405

ALABASTER, J. S., SHURBEN, D. G. and KNOWLES, G. (1979). The effect of dissolved oxygen and salinity on the toxicity of ammonia to smolts of salmon, *Salmo salar* L. *J. Fish. Biol.* **15**, 705-712

BALL, I. R. (1967). The relative susceptibilities of some species of freshwater fish to poisons—I. Ammonia. *Wat. Res.* **1**, 767-775

BATES, R. G. and PINCHING, G. D. (1950). Dissociation constant of aqueous ammonia at 0-50 °C from e.m.f. studies of the ammonium salt of a weak acid. *J. Am. chem. Soc.* **72**, 1993-1996

BROWN, V. M. (1968). The calculation of the acute toxicity of mixtures of poisons to rainbow trout. *Wat. Res.* **2**, 723-733

BROWN, V. M., JORDAN, D. H. M. and TILLER, B. A. (1969). The acute toxicity to rainbow trout of fluctuating concentration and mixtures of ammonia, phenol and zinc. *J. Fish. Biol.* **1**, 1-9

BURROWS, R. E. (1964). Effects of accumulated excretory products on hatchery-reared salmonids. *Res. Rep. U.S. Fish. Wildl. Serv.* **66**, 1-12

CALAMARI, D. and MARCHETTI, R. (1975). Predicted and observed acute toxicity of copper and ammonia to rainbow trout (*Salmo gairdneri* Rich.). *Prog. Wat. Technol.* **7**, 569-577

CALAMARI, D., MARCHETTI, R. and VAILATI, G. (1977). Effetti di trattamenti prolungati con ammoniaca su stadi di sviluppo del *Salmo gairdneri*. *Nuovi Annali Ig. Microbiol.* **28 (5)**, 333-345

DANECKER, E. (1964). Die Jauchevergiftung von Fischen—eine Ammoniakvergiftung. *Österreichs Fischerei* 3/4, 55-68

DEPARTMENT OF THE ENVIRONMENT, U.K. (1972). *Water Pollution Research 1971*. London, H.M.S.O.

DOUDOROFF, P. and KATZ, M. (1950). Critical review of literature on the toxicity of industrial wastes and their components to fish. 1. Alkalis, acids and inorganic gases. *Sew. ind. Wastes* **22**, 1432-1458

DOWNING, K. M. and MERKENS, J. C. (1955). The influence of dissolved-oxygen concentration on the toxicity of un-ionized ammonia to rainbow trout (*Salmo gairdnerii* Richardson). *Ann. appl. Biol.* **43**, 243-246

EIFAC (1964). Water quality criteria for European freshwater fish. Report on finely divided solids and inland fisheries. *EIFAC tech. Pap.* 1

EIFAC (1968). Water quality criteria for European freshwater fish. Report on extreme pH values and inland fisheries. *EIFAC tech. Pap.* 4

EMMERSON, K., RUSSO, R. C., LUND, R. E. and THURSTON, R. V. (1975). Aqueous ammonia equilibrium calculations: effect of pH and temperature. *J. Fish. Res. Bd Can.* 32 (12), 2379-2383

FLIS, J. (1968a). Anatomicohistopathological changes induced in carp (*Cyprinus carpio* L.) by ammonia water. Part 1. Effects of toxic concentrations. *Acta Hydrobiol.* 10, 205-224

FLIS, J. (1968b). Anatomicohistopathological changes induced in carp (*Cyprinus carpio* L.) by ammonia water. Part 2. Effects of subtoxic concentrations. *Acta Hydrobiol.* 10, 225-238

FROMM, P. O. and GILLETTE, J. R. (1968). Effect of ambient ammonia on blood ammonia and nitrogen excretion of rainbow trout (*Salmo gairdnerii*). *Comp. Biochem. Physiol.* 26, 887-896

GRINDLEY, J. (1946). Toxicity to rainbow trout and minnows of some substances known to be present in waste waters discharged to rivers. *Ann. appl. Biol.* 33, 103-112

HEMENS, J. (1966). The toxicity of ammonia solutions to the mosquito fish (*Gambusia affinis* Baird on Girard). *J. Proc. Inst. Sew. Purif.* 1966, 265-271

HEPHER, B. (1959). Use of aqueous ammonia in fertilizing fish ponds. *Bamidgeh* 11, 71-80

HERBERT, D. W. M. (1961). The toxicity to rainbow trout of spent still liquors from the distillation of coal. *Ann. appl. Biol.* 50, 755-777

HERBERT, D. W. M. and SHURBEN, D. G. (1963). A preliminary study of the effect of physical activity on the resistance of rainbow trout (*Salmo gairdnerii* Richardson) to two poisons. *Ann. appl. Biol.* 52, 321-326

HERBERT, D. W. M. and SHURBEN, D. G. (1964). The toxicity to fish of mixtures of poisons. 1. Salts of ammonia and zinc. *Ann. appl. Biol.* 53, 33-41

HERBERT, D. W. M. and SHURBEN, D. G. (1965). The susceptibility of salmonid fish to poisons under estuarine conditions. II. Ammonium chloride. *Int. J. Air Wat. Pollut.* 9, 89-91

HERBERT, D. W. M. and VAN DYKE, J. M. (1964). The toxicity to fish of mixtures of poisons. 2. Copper-ammonia and zinc-phenol mixtures. *Ann. appl. Biol.* 53, 415-421

JONES, J. R. E. (1948). A further study of the reactions of fish to toxic solutions. *J. exp. Biol.* 25, 22-34

JONES, J. R. E. (1964). *Fish and River Pollution.* London, Butterworths

KEMPINSKA, H. (1968). Influence of ammonia fertilizers on fish. *Gospod. Rybna.* 20, 3-5

KUHN, O. and KOECKE, H. U. (1956). Histologische und cytologische Veränderungen der Fischkeime nach Einwirkung im Wasser enthaltener schädigender Substanzen. *Z. Zellforsch.* 43, 611-643

LARMOYEUX, J. D. and PIPER, R. G. (1973). Effects of water re-use on rainbow trout in hatcheries. *Prog. Fish Cult.* 35, 2-8

LIAO, P. B. and MAYO, R. D. (1972). Salmonid hatchery water re-use systems. *Aquaculture,* 1, 317-335

LIEBMANN, H. (1960). *Handbuch der Frischwasser- und Abwasserbiologie,* Band 2. München, Oldenbourg

LLOYD, R. (1961a). Effect of dissolved-oxygen concentrations on the toxicity of several poisons to rainbow trout (*Salmo gairdnerii* Richardson). *J. exp. Biol.* **38**, 447-455

LLOYD, R. (1961b). The toxicity of ammonia to rainbow trout (*Salmo gairdnerii* Richardson). *Wat. Waste Treat. J.* **8**, 278-279

LLOYD, R. and HERBERT, D. W. M. (1960). The influence of carbon dioxide on the toxicity of un-ionized ammonia to rainbow trout (*Salmo gairdnerii* Richardson) *Ann. appl. Biol.* **45**, 521-527

LLOYD, R. and ORR, L. D. (1969). The diuretic response by rainbow trout to sub-lethal concentrations of ammonia. *Wat. Res.* **3**, 335-344

MALACEA, I. (1966). Contributii la cuncasterea actiunii toxice a cianurilor, amon-iacului, mercurului si arsenului asupra unor specii de pesti si a dafniei. *Studii de protectia si epurarea apelor* VII, **2**, 751-790

MALACEA, I. (1968). Untersuchungen über die Gewohnung der Fische an hohe Konzentrationen toxischer Substanzen. *Arch. Hydrobiol.* **65**, 74-95

MARCHETTI, R. (1960). Nouvelles études sur la toxicologie des poissons au point de vue du controls des eaux usées. *Ann. Stat. Centr. Hydrobiol. Appl.* **8**, 107

MARCHETTI, R. (1962). *Biologia e tossicologia delle acque usate.* Milan, ETAS (Editrice Tecnica Artistica Scientifica)

MERKENS, J. C. and DOWNING, K. M. (1957). The effect of tension of dissolved oxygen on the toxicity of un-ionized ammonia to several species of fish. *Ann. appl. Biol.* **45**, 521-527

MONTGOMERY, H. A. C. and STIFF, M. J. (1971). Differentiation of chemical states of toxic species especially of cyanide and copper in water. Paper presented to the International Symposium on Identification and Measure-ment of Environmental Pollutants, 14-17 June 1971. Ottawa, Ontario, Canada, National Research Council of Canada

NEHRING, D. (1962). Die Giftwirkung ureashaltiger Harnstofflösungen auf verschiedene Fischarten. *Z. Fisch.* **9**, 539-547

PENAZ, M. (1965). Vliv amoniaku na jikry a pludek pstruha obecheho *Salmo trutta m. fario. Zool. listy* **14**, 47-54

REICHENBACH-KLINKE, H. H. (1967). Untersuchungen über die Einwirkung des Ammoniakgehalts auf den Fischorganismus. *Arch. Fisch. Wiss.* **17**, 122-132

RICE, S. D. and STOKES, R. M. (1975). Acute toxicity of ammonia to several developmental stages of rainbow trout (*Salmo gairdneri*). *Fish. Bull.* **73**, 207-211

ROBINETTE, H. R. (1976). Effect of selected sublethal levels of ammonia on the growth of channel catfish (*Ictalurus punctatus*). *Prog. Fish Cult.* **38** (1), 26-29

ROBINSON-WILSON, E. F. and SEIM, W. K. (1975). The lethal and sub-lethal effects of a zirconium process effluent on juvenile salmonids. *Wat. Res. Bull.* **11**, 975-986

SCHULZE-WIEHENBRAUCK, H. (1976). Effects of sublethal ammonia concentra-tions on metabolism in juvenile trout (*Salmo gairdneri* Richardson). *Ber. dt. wiss. Kommn. Meeresforsch* **24**, 234-250

SCOTT, K. R. and GILLESPIE, D. C. (1972). A compact recirculation unit for the rearing and maintenance of fish. *J. Fish. Res. Bd Can.* **29**, 1071-1074

SMART, G. (1976). The effect of ammonia exposure on gill structure of the rainbow trout (*Salmo gairdneri*). *J. Fish. Biol.* **8**, 471-475

SOUSA, R. J. and MEADE, T. L. (1977). The influence of ammonia on the oxygen delivery system of coho salmon hemoglobin. *Comp. Biochem. Physiol.* **58A**, 23–28

STAMMERS, H. A. (1953). Der Einfluss von Schwefelwasserstoff und Ammoniak auf tierische Leitformen des Saprobiensystems. *Vom Wasser* **20**, 34–71

SUMMERFELT, R. C. and LEWIS, W. M. (1967). Repulsion of green sunfish by certain chemicals. *J. Wat. Pollut. Control Fed.* **39**, 2030–2038

TABATA, K. (1962). Toxicity of ammonia to aquatic animals with reference to the effect of pH and carbon dioxide. *Bull. Tokai. reg. Fish. Res. Lab.* **34**, 67–74

U.S. FEDERAL WATER POLLUTION CONTROL ADMINISTRATION (1968). Water Quality Criteria: Report of the National Technical Advisory Committee. Washington, D.C., U.S. Department of the Interior

VAMOS, R. (1963). Ammonia poisoning in carp. *Acta biol. Szeged* **9**, 291–297

VAMOS, R. and TASNADI, R. (1967). Ammonia poisoning in carp. 3. The oxygen content as a factor in influencing the toxic limit of ammonia. *Acta biol. Szeged* **13**, 99–105

WOKER, H. (1949). Die Temperaturabhängigkeit der Giftwirkung von Ammoniak auf Fische. *Ver. Int. Limnol.* **10**, 575–579

WOKER, H. and WUHRMANN, K. (1950). Die Empfindlichkeit verschiedener Fischarten gegenüber Ammoniak, Blausäure und Phenol. *Rev. Suisse de Zool.* **57**, 548–553

WUHRMANN, K. (1952). Sur quelques principes de la toxicologie du poisson. *Bull. Cent. Belge Étud. Docum. Eaux* **15**, 49

WUHRMANN, K. and WOKER, H. (1948). Experimentelle Untersuchungen über die Ammoniak- und Blausäurevergiftung. *Schweiz Z. Hydrol.* **11**, 210–244

WUHRMANN, K. and WOKER, H. (1953). Über die Giftwirkungen von Ammoniak- und Zyanidlösungen mit verschiedener Sauerstoffspannung und Temperatur auf Fische. *Schweiz Z. Hydrol.* **15**, 235–260

WUHRMANN, K., ZEHENDER, F. and WOKER, H. (1947). Über die fischereibiologische Bedeutung des Ammonium- und Ammoniakgehaltes fliessender Gewässer. *Z. natur. Ges. Zurich* **92**, 198–204

5

MONOHYDRIC PHENOLS

Foreword

The preparation of the original report on monohydric phenols and inland fisheries on which this chapter is based was accomplished largely by Dr V. Mitrovic-Tutundzic who prepared the basic manuscript to be reviewed by other members of the Working Party on Water Quality Criteria for European Freshwater Fish, and who also provided the Working Party with up-to-date references to relevant Slavonic publications.

5.1 Summary

Phenolic wastes can contain monohydric phenols, including phenol, the three cresol isomers, and the six xylenol isomers, together with other substances. They may adversely affect freshwater fisheries by their direct toxicity to fish and fish-food organisms, by their high oxygen demand resulting in oxygen depletion of the receiving water, and by the production of undesirable flavours in the edible flesh of fish.

Laboratory tests show that the toxicity of phenol is increased by decrease in dissolved-oxygen concentration, increase in salinity, and decrease in temperature. Salmonids and newly hatched fish are more sensitive than coarse fish and adults respectively. Cresols, xylenols, and phenols are of similar toxicity, and the toxicity of mixtures of phenols is apparently additive, although the toxicity of phenolic wastes may be greater than expected from chemical analyses, since these may not be equally sensitive to all phenols and may neglect the contribution from other poisons.

Because of difficulties caused by inadequate chemical analysis, there are few field observations which can be used to reinforce laboratory findings. For this reason, and also because of gaps in our knowledge of the effect of temperature on toxicity, only tentative criteria can be established, which may have to be modified in the light of further experience.

These criteria are expressed as maximum concentrations which should not be exceeded but it should be appreciated that, because of the natural fluctuation in the water quality found in rivers over a period of time, the average concentration will be lower to an extent depending on local circumstances.

Salmonid fish   To ensure long-term survival of salmonids in the presence of phenolic wastes, the concentration of phenol, cresols or xylenols should not exceed 1.0 mg/ℓ, either singly or collectively. Where 2,5-xylenol is the main constituent, the concentration should not exceed 0.5 mg/ℓ. Where the temperature is lower than 5 °C, concentrations may have to be halved to ensure the survival of fish.

Coarse fish   Since laboratory data show that coarse fish are more resistant than salmonids to phenols, the concentration of phenol, cresol or xylenol should not exceed 2.0 mg/ℓ, either singly or collectively, provided that oxidation of this concentration does not produce an adverse reduction in the dissolved-oxygen concentration of the water. In the absence of data on the effect of temperature on the toxicity of phenols to coarse fish it is proposed that the reduction in concentration of 50 per cent adopted for salmonids at temperatures below 5 °C, should also apply to these species.

Where other poisons are present in addition to phenols, due allowance must be made for their contribution to the toxicity, particularly in the case of free chlorine.

Commercial fisheries   There is no laboratory evidence to indicate that levels of phenol and cresols that are safe for fish cause their flesh to become tainted, but xylenols should not exceed 0.5 mg/ℓ. Other phenolic substances, particularly the chlorophenols, are known to cause taint at very low concentrations; strictly these are outside the scope of this chapter, but the information that has been considered suggests that they should be excluded from waters supporting commercial fisheries.

5.2 Introduction

Phenolic wastes arise from the distillation of coal and wood, from oil refineries, chemical plants, livestock dips, and human and animal wastes. They are still one of the main causes of river pollution in several European countries, though in others, for example Czechoslovakia and the United Kingdom, the quantity discharged to flowing waters has been considerably reduced in recent years. Phenols are normally present in purely domestic sewage at low concentrations (0.07–0.1 mg/ℓ) and can also be released into water by aquatic plants and decaying vegetation (Hoak, 1956).

Phenolic wastes can consist of mono-, di-, and polyhydric phenols, together with aldehydes, ketones, alcohols, organic acids, gases (CO_2, NH_3) and often cyanide, the proportions of which vary. The monohydric phenol fraction of gas liquors (Blackburn, Barker and Catchpole, 1954) and coke-oven effluent (Herbert, 1962) consists largely of pure phenol (C_6H_5OH) but includes cresols and xylenols, *m*-cresol usually being present in greater quantities than the *o*- and *p*-isomers and the xylenols.

These wastes affect fisheries by their direct toxicity to aquatic life and by tainting the flesh of fish, especially when chlorinated. Being mainly oxidizable they can also contribute to the depletion of the dissolved-oxygen concentration of polluted waters, so making it difficult to assess the direct importance of phenols as poisons simply from an examination of analytical data.

Extensive literature reviews of the effect of phenol on fish include that of Bandt (1958), and more recently that of Lukanenko (1967), which covers

Russian literature. This chapter will deal principally with the effect of monohydric phenols, namely phenol (C_6H_5OH), *o*-, *m*-, and *p*-cresol ($CH_3C_6H_4OH$), and the six xylenols, 2,3-xylenol, 2,4-xylenol, 2,5-xylenol, 2,6-xylenol, 3,4-xylenol, and 3,5-xylenol ((CH_3)$_2C_6H_3OH$), but some reference will be made to gas liquors and coke-oven wastes and their components.

Because of the failure in much of the early literature to distinguish between the different isomers, and differences in the nomenclature adopted, particularly for the xylenols, together with the use of analytical methods that measure different proportions of the isomers, polyhydric phenols, and other substances (see *Table 5.1*), the value of much of the published information has been reduced. To clarify the nomenclature we have chosen to use the term 'phenols' only when it is not possible to refer to monohydric phenols, dihydric phenols, polyhydric phenols or to a specific isomer for which data are available, in which case we have used, whenever possible, the system given by the International Union of Pure and Applied Chemistry (1965).

5.3 Direct lethal action on fish

5.3.1 SYMPTOMS OF POISONING AND MODE OF ACTION

Fish exposed to concentrations of phenol and cresols that are lethal within a few days soon become excited, swimming rapidly and becoming more sensitive to outside stimuli and showing increased respiration (e.g., Veselov, 1957). In

Table 5.1 RELATIVE COLOUR INTENSITY PRODUCED BY DIFFERENT PHENOLS AND ANILINE

Phenols	Analytical method		
	Aminoantipyrene (Ochynski, 1960)	Folin and Denis (1915)	p-nitroaniline (Nolte, 1933)
Monohydric			
phenol	100	100	100
o-cresol	72	78	147
m-cresol	62	85	120
p-cresol	6	68	21
2,3-xylenol	44		16
2,4-xylenol	22		52
2,5-xylenol	42		92
2,6-xylenol	42		52
3,4-xylenol	4		16
3,5-xylenol	33		52
Dihydric			
pyrocatechol (catechol)	0		
3-methyl catechol	0	148	29
4-methyl catechol	0		
resorcinol	62	117	
2-methyl resorcinol	22		
4-methyl resorcinol	10		
5-methyl resorcinol	28		
hydroquinone (quinol)	0		
guaiacol			165
naphthol			23
aniline		59	

addition there may be colour changes (Wuhrmann and Woker, 1950) and increased secretion of mucus (e.g., Greven, 1953). Death may occur quickly or follow after a stage of depressed activity and loss of equilibrium interrupted by occasional convulsions (Lukanenko, 1967). With xylenols, however, Lukanenko did not find increased sensitivity to stimuli in Crucian carp (*Carassius carassius*), whereas Albersmeyer and Erichsen (1959) found the contrary. Acute poisoning by phenol is generally attributed to nervous paralysis, and Lukanenko (1967) has shown that the brain is involved in the specific reaction of poisoned fish. Halsband and Halsband (1954) found that the threshold concentration for disturbance of trout was 1.3 mg/ℓ phenol.

Fish surviving long-term exposure to low concentrations of phenol show general inflammation and necrosis of the tissues, including the erythrocytes (Waluga, 1966a, b) possibly because of irreversible changes induced in the proteins (see also p. 145, para. 5). In a detailed study with bream held for seven days in 9 mg/ℓ of phenol, she found haemorrhage and necrotic and degenerative changes in several tissues, including skin, muscle, gills, liver, spleen and kidney. There was also a sharp decrease in the number of erythrocytes in the peripheral blood and leucopenia; the high count of abnormal and juvenile cells was thought to be evidence of damage to the blood-producing tissues. At high concentrations of phenol (> 6 mg/ℓ) the blood cells are destroyed (Andres and Kurazhovskaia, 1969). Halsband and Halsband (1963), using trout exposed to 1.5 mg/ℓ for 24 h, found a reduction in number and an increase in surface area of erythrocytes. V. M. Brown and D. G. Shurben (personal communication) studied the effect on rainbow trout (*Salmo gairdneri*) of concentrations of 1, 2, 3, 4 and 5 mg/ℓ of phenol over a period of 18 weeks and found pronounced histopathological changes in the liver, heart, skin, and spleen, while the intestinal tract, spinal cord, and excretory part of the kidney were similar to those of the control fish.

Mikriakov (1969) found that serum proteins decreased and immunoglobulin formation was inhibited in common carp (*Cyprinus carpio*) held for two months at 12.5 mg/ℓ of phenol. Reduction in serum proteins of common carp was also observed by Lebedinski and Pomarzanskia (1968) in fish exposed for 30 days to phenol at concentrations of 25 and 10 mg/ℓ, and a very slight reduction at 1 mg/ℓ; changes were also reported in concentrations of metals in various organs, including blood, muscle, and bones, the significance of which is unknown.

Specific sublethal actions are dealt with in Section 5.4.

5.3.2 FACTORS AFFECTING LETHAL LEVELS

Temperature

Several authors (e.g. Bucksteeg, Thiele and Stöltzel, 1955) have shown that increase in temperature shortens the time of reaction and period of survival of fish in solutions containing high concentrations of phenols. However, Brown, Jordan and Tiller (1967), using fish which had been previously acclimated for three days to the test temperatures, found that the resistance of rainbow trout to low concentrations of phenol increased with increase in temperature, the concentration lethal to 50 per cent of the fish in two days (the 2-day LC50) at 6, 12 and 18 °C being approximately 5, 8 and 9.8 mg/ℓ respectively, and a somewhat similar relationship was found with a simulated gas liquor. More recent tests (U.K., Ministry of Technology, 1968) carried out with juvenile rainbow trout 30-50 mm long at 3-4 °C and 12-13 °C, after prior acclimation to the test temperature for 3-4 days, showed that the 2-day LC50 values were about 3 and 5 mg/ℓ respectively.

Dissolved oxygen

Low dissolved-oxygen concentration shortens the time of response of fish to monohydric phenols and reduces the concentrations that are lethal (as for example, in tests with *p*-cresol by Southgate, Pentelow and Bassindale, 1933). Tests with rainbow trout in a mixture of phenols (Herbert, 1962) have also demonstrated that a reduction in dissolved oxygen from 100 per cent to 50 per cent of the air-saturation value reduces the estimated 'threshold'* LC50 by about 20 per cent, a reduction similar to that found for zinc, copper and lead (Lloyd, 1961).

pH value

Within the range of pH values from 6.5 to 8.5 there was little or no difference in toxicity of monohydric phenols to rainbow trout (Herbert, 1962) and similar results have been reported with Crucian carp within the range of pH 4-11 (Lukanenko, 1967).

Water hardness

At a total water hardness of 50 mg/ℓ as calcium carbonate, the threshold LC50 of monohydric phenols was no lower than at 310 mg/ℓ (Herbert, 1962) but at lower hardnesses toxicity increased slightly; the 2-day LC50 values of phenol for rainbow trout in water having a hardness of 320 and 10 mg/ℓ as calcium carbonate were 6.8 and 5.2 mg/ℓ respectively (U.K., Ministry of Technology, 1968). This accords with the results of Pickering and Henderson (1966) for fathead minnow (*Pimephales promelas*), of Lukanenko (1967) for Crucian carp, and of Leclerc and Devlaminck (1950) for mosquito fish (*Gambusia affinis*), for which the minimum lethal concentrations of phenol in a hard and in a distilled water were 24-28 and 18-20 mg/ℓ respectively.

Salinity

Holland *et al.* (1960) found that young coho salmon (*Oncorhynchus kisutch*) tested in a crude mixture of cresols (cresylic acids) were about twice as sensitive in sea water as in fresh water, concentrations tolerated for four days being

---

*The concentration lethal after long-term exposure of the fish (see Chapter 11). Also defined in Chapter 4, p. 88, para. 4.

1.6–3.1 and 3–5.5 mg cresol/ℓ respectively. A similar effect was reported by Brown, Shurben, and Fawell (1967) for rainbow trout tested in phenol, sensitivity increasing linearly with increase in salinity; at 15 °C the 2-day LC50 was 9.3 mg/ℓ in fresh water and 5.2 mg/ℓ in 60 per cent sea water, and there was also a decrease in the time of response of fish in sea water. Lukanenko (1967) found that *Acipenser stellatus* and *A. güldenstaedti,* both migratory species of sturgeon, were more resistant than the freshwater species, *A. rhutenus,* when tested in fresh water.

Age of fish

Concentrations of phenol that were lethal to adult Crucian carp, tench (*Tinca tinca*), and stickleback (*Gasterosteus aculeatus*) were not apparently harmful to their eggs and sperm (Albersmeyer and Erichsen, 1959), the first symptoms of damage to these stages being observed at concentrations greater than 50 mg/ℓ, as judged only from the appearance of the eggs and the mobility of the sperm. No observations were made, however, of the fertilization, development, and hatching of the eggs.

Volodin, Lukanenko and Flerov (1965, 1966) found that resistance to poisoning changes during development, embryos of bream (*Abramis brama*) and a similar species, *A. ballerus,* being most sensitive to phenol from the beginning of cleavage to gastrulation and again towards the end of the larval period, although the larvae survived 4–11 times longer than the fry at concentrations of 25–150 mg/ℓ of phenol. Nevertheless, embryos of *A. brama* died at a concentration of 50 mg/ℓ phenol and hatching was delayed at 25 mg/ℓ. Eggs and fry of perch (*Perca fluviatilis*) were more resistant to phenol than 1-year-old fish (Mosevich *et al.,* 1952).

V. M. Brown (personal communication) using brown trout (*Salmo trutta*) and rainbow trout, found that the 5-day LC50 of phenol was greater than 16 mg/ℓ for pre-eyed eggs (17 days post-fertilization), greater than 40 mg/ℓ for eyed eggs (25 days post-fertilization), and 1-day-old rainbow trout alevins, and greater than 60 mg/ℓ for 3-day-old brown trout alevins, whereas it was less than 10 mg/ℓ for 15-day-old brown trout fry. On the other hand, Albersmeyer and Erichsen (1959) reported that 'trout' embryos were more sensitive than adult fish to monohydric phenols, but gave no data on developmental state. Lukanenko and Flerov (1966a, b) found that the 1-day LC50 was 11 mg/ℓ for 1-year-old rainbow trout and 7.5 mg/ℓ for 2- to 3-year-old fish.

Size of fish

Bluegill sunfish (*Lepomis macrochirus*) 140 mm long were less tolerant of phenol than fish 70 mm long, the 4-day LC50 being 11.5 mg/ℓ and 20 mg/ℓ respectively (Cairns, 1956). Similar results were obtained by Holland *et al.* (1960) using coho salmon, and by Lukanenko and Flerov (1966a, b) using rainbow trout, who also found that resistance decreased with increase in body weight.

Acclimation to phenol

Some authors report that fish that have overturned in the presence of phenol tend not to recover when transferred to clean water, whereas with cresols and xylenols they do (Embody *et al.*, 1940; Jones, 1951; Albersmeyer and Erichsen, 1959; and Holland *et al.*, 1960). Other workers, however, (V. M. Brown and J. F. de L. G. Solbé, personal communication) have found that all rainbow trout overturned on exposure to 20 mg/ℓ phenol apparently recovered when placed in clean water.

Perch kept for 7 days in 6 mg/ℓ of phenol (Bucksteeg, Thiele and Stöltzel, 1955), and bitterling (*Rhodeus sericeus amarus*) kept for 4 days in 4 mg/ℓ (Malacea, 1968) took at least twice as long to react to higher concentrations as did unacclimated fish. Similar results were obtained by Volodin, Lukanenko and Flerov (1965 and 1966) with embryos of bream kept in 5 mg/ℓ, and by Lukanenko (1967) with Crucian carp held in 1-5 mg/ℓ for 25–40 days; this could perhaps be explained by diminished excitability of the fish. On the other hand, Crucian carp kept for 60 days at 1-5 mg/ℓ were more sensitive than controls. However, none of these experiments indicated that any alterations in the threshold concentrations had occurred.

Water velocity

Goldfish (*Carassius auratus*) 120–150 mm in length survived exposure to 20 mg/ℓ phenol for 25 h when subject to water currents of 90 or 160 mm/s for 5 minutes every 10 minutes, but suffered up to 100 per cent mortality when subject to the current for 10-min periods with 5 min rest in between (Besch *et al.*, 1977).

Other factors

The 2-day LC50 of phenol for a 'stock' of hatchery rainbow trout was measured in hard water (320 mg/ℓ as $CaCO_3$) at ambient temperatures (between 9.5 and 13.2 °C), at monthly intervals from October to May; considerable variation was found and the maximum range for the 95 per cent confidence limits of the estimates of the 2-day LC50 was from 1.8 to 8.5 mg/ℓ (V. M. Brown, personal communication).

5.3.3 SUMMARY OF TOXICITY DATA

Phenol

A wide range of phenol concentrations (0.08–1900 mg/ℓ) has been reported as harmful to fish, thus reflecting differences in the sensitivity of the different species used, in the ways of expressing toxicity, in the conditions of exposure, and in the duration of the tests. The lowest values, however, are often misquoted. Those of Symons and Simpson (1938), for example, relate to North American species of 'minnow' killed in 30 min in samples of river water containing not only 0.08 mg/ℓ of phenol but a variety of other wastes in addition; these authors also found that 10 mg/ℓ of phenol did not kill common carp within 6 h. Furthermore, data from older references (e.g., Weigelt, Saare and Schwab, 1885) have occasionally been quoted ten times lower than the original. It is also noteworthy that the response of individual fish to phenol not only varies widely but also involves the elapse of a long time interval between overturning and death; for example, the survival time of Crucian carp was 21-171 h in 25 mg/ℓ of phenol, and 3-148 h in 50 mg/ℓ (Lukanenko, 1967), and similar results have been found by other authors (e.g., Mitrović *et al.*, 1968). Taking reliable figures for median lethal concentrations for periods of 6-96 hours, the range is 4-56 mg/ℓ, the most frequent values for adult fish in well-aerated fresh water being 9-25 mg/ℓ.

Coarse fish   One of the most resistant coarse fish appears to be goldfish, the 2-day LC50 at 25 °C being 44.5 mg/ℓ according to Pickering and Henderson (1966), and Bach (1929) (in Southgate, Pentelow and Bassindale, 1933) reported that 'this species survived 3 months in 4.2 mg/ℓ at 16.5-23 °C and 7-12 mg/ℓ dissolved oxygen. For Crucian carp the 129-h LC50 at 12-14 °C has been reported as 25 mg/ℓ (Lukanenko and Flerov, 1963), and the same concentration has been given as the 1-day LC50 at 18 °C (Albersmeyer and Erichsen, 1959). The 2-day LC50 for gudgeon (*Gobio gobio*) at 10 °C is approximately 25 mg/ℓ (unpublished work at the Water Research Centre, U.K.), while that of orfe (*Idus idus*) is between 14 and 25 mg/ℓ (D. Lüdeman and I. Juhnke, personal communication). The minimum lethal concentration for the bitterling is given as 20 mg/ℓ by Malacea, Cure and Weiner (1967). For roach (*Rutilus rutilus*) the 1-day LC50 at 18 °C is 14.5 mg/ℓ and for tench 17 mg/ℓ (Albersmeyer and Erichsen, 1959). Some work (U.K., Ministry of Technology, 1969) indicates that although the 1-day LC50 values for roach and perch at 18 °C are approximately 25 and 15 mg/ℓ respectively, the median threshold concentration for both is close to 12 mg/ℓ; and more recent tests (U.K., Ministry of Technology, 1971) have shown that while perch, pike (*Esox lucius*), and rainbow trout all responded more quickly than common carp, rudd (*Scardinius erythrophthalmus*) and eel (*Anguilla anguilla*) at any given concentration, the 7-day LC50 was similar (8-11 mg/ℓ) for all these species except in the case of carp (15 mg/ℓ). McKim *et al.* (1974) give the 3-day LC50 for pike as 8.9 mg/ℓ at 10 °C, while Kristoffersson, Broberg and Oikari (1973) found that 5 mg/ℓ was the highest concentration of phenol this species was able to survive for one week at the same temperature.

Salmonids   The concentrations of phenol reported as lethal to rainbow trout are generally lower than the corresponding values for coarse fish; the 1-day LC50 varies from 5 mg/ℓ at 18 °C (Albersmeyer and Erichsen, 1959) for embryos to 11 and 7.5 mg/ℓ for 1- and 3-year-old fish at 12-14 °C (Lukanenko and Flerov, 1966a); the 2-day LC50 was 9.8 mg/ℓ at 17 °C (Herbert and Vandyke, 1967) and 9.3 mg/ℓ at 15 °C (Brown, Shurben and Fawell, 1967). Coho salmon are possibly slightly more sensitive, the 3-day LC50 being 3.2 to 5.6 mg/ℓ at 6-11 °C (Holland *et al.*, 1960). M. Grande (personal communication) has found that the 5-day LC50 for Atlantic salmon fry (*Salmo salar*) at 10 °C was about 5 mg/ℓ. The 1-day LC50 for brook trout (*Salvelinus fontinalis*) is 11.7 mg/ℓ according to Miller and Ogilvie (1975) who found that 10 mg/ℓ caused only 30 per cent mortality and that no deaths occurred within one day at 7.5 mg/ℓ.

V. M. Brown and D. G. Shurben (personal communication) kept batches of 25 rainbow trout at concentrations of 1, 2, 3, 4 and 5 mg/ℓ at 14–18 °C over a period of 18 weeks. There was a 75 per cent mortality at the highest concentration and 28 per cent at 3 mg/ℓ and the 18-week LC50 was estimated as approximately 4.0 mg/ℓ.

Cresols

Cresols have been studied to a lesser extent than phenol. Of the three isomers the least toxic is *m*-cresol, while reports for the relative toxicity of *o*- and *p*-cresol are inconsistent.

Lethal concentrations of cresols and phenol are usually within a two-fold range, but differences are not consistent between species. Comparable data on the acute toxicity of phenol and the three isomers of cresol are given by Albersmeyer and Erichsen (1959) for several species over a range of temperatures of 13–19 °C (see *Table 5.2*). Bucksteeg, Thiele and Stöltzel (1955) found that the threshold concentrations for loss of coordinated movement in perch were 6 mg/ℓ for phenol and 10 mg/ℓ for the cresols. Pickering and Henderson (1966) give the 4-day LC50 of *o*-cresol for goldfish as 17–31 mg/ℓ at 25 °C while D. Lüdeman and I. Juhnke (personal communication) give the 2-day LC50 for orfe as 17–19 mg/ℓ cresols.

Table 5.2 APPROXIMATE 1-DAY LC50 OF PHENOLS TO FISH (mg/ℓ) (FROM ALBERSMEYER AND ERICHSEN, 1959)

Phenols	Crucian carp	Roach	Tench	'Trout' embryos
Phenol	25	15	17	5
o-cresol	30	16	15	2
m-cresol	25	23	21	7
p-cresol	21	17	16	4
2,4-xylenol	30	–	13	28
2,5-xylenol	10	10	9	2
3,4-xylenol	21	16	18	7
3,5-xylenol	53	–	51	50

Xylenols

Of the monohydric phenols, xylenols are the least studied and no work has been carried out specifically on 2,3-xylenol or 2,6-xylenol. A mixture of xylenols used by Pickering and Henderson (1966) was intermediate between phenol and *o*-cresol in its toxicity to goldfish, fathead minnow, and the guppy (*Lebistes reticulatus*). Based on 24-h LC50 values for Crucian carp and tench, 2,5-xylenol is roughly twice as toxic, and 3,5-xylenol about half as toxic, as 2,4-xylenol and 3,4-xylenol (Albersmeyer and Erichsen, 1959) and phenol (*Table 5.2*). The comparatively low toxicity of 3,5-xylenol to coarse fish is confirmed by the concentrations reported as 'having no toxic effect' in 3–5 days (Bandt, 1958), being 15, 18 and 20 mg/ℓ for perch, roach, and bream respectively, while the corresponding values for 2,4-xylenol were 8, 8 and 10 mg/ℓ respectively. Rainbow trout embryos appear to be as resistant as adult carp to 2,4-xylenol and 3,5-xylenol (Albersmeyer and Erichsen, 1959).

Other components of phenolic wastes

Some polyhydric phenols, including hydroquinone, 8-oxyquinolin, and naphthols were reported more toxic than phenol (0.1–4.0 mg/ℓ) by Sollman (1949) and Bandt (1958) but these are usually present in only small quantities in phenolic wastes.

Mixtures of phenols and other substances

Where the toxicities of phenol or individual cresols and xylenols have been investigated, the concentrations are given in terms of weight of substance used. With mixtures of unknown composition, however, the concentration may be determined by colorimetric analysis and the colour produced compared with that given by pure phenol. For example, in Herbert's (1962) experiments with a simulated gas liquor, one part by weight of gas liquor phenols was colorimetrically equivalent to 0.72 parts phenol by analysis. For rainbow trout at 9 °C, the median threshold concentration of this prepared mixture was 6.1 mg/ℓ by weight and 4.4 mg/ℓ by analysis. The close agreement with the data obtained for phenol alone at this temperature indicates that the cresols, which comprised 38 per cent of the mixture by weight, did not markedly affect the toxicity of the phenol present (54 per cent by weight).

Liepolt (1954) found that a gas liquor killed rainbow trout in 12 hours at a concentration equivalent to 4.3 mg/ℓ of phenol, and other authors have reported toxic concentrations of phenol in the range 3–5 mg/ℓ in water polluted by phenolic wastes (Ebeling, 1940; Mann, 1951; Bandt, 1958).

When tar is removed from coal-processing wastes, the main components remaining are monohydric phenols, ammonia, cyanide, sulphide, thiosulphate, and thiocyanate, of which the first three contribute most to short-term toxicity (Herbert, 1962). Studies with mixtures of ammonia and phenol (Herbert, 1962), phenol and zinc (Herbert and Vandyke, 1967), ammonia, phenol and zinc (Brown, Jordan, and Tiller, 1969), and copper and phenol, and also copper, zinc and phenol (Brown and Dalton, 1970) have shown that the toxicity of the mixture is approximately additive in terms of the fractions of the median lethal concentrations of the individual poisons at 2 or 3 days (which are often close to the median threshold concentrations of these poisons); the mixture kills 50 per cent of the fish at 2 or 3 days when the sum of the fractions equals unity. Using this procedure, the predicted toxicities of samples of effluents and polluted river waters (Lloyd and Jordan, 1963, 1964; Herbert, Jordan and Lloyd, 1965; and Brown, Shurben and Shaw, 1970) which contained monohydric phenols, ammonia, cyanide, zinc, and copper, were close to the observed values, although some samples were more toxic than predicted, perhaps because of the presence of other poisons. Again, it must be emphasized that at ambient water temperature phenol reacts with chlorine to form chlorinated phenols which are more toxic than phenol; for example, the 4-day LC50 of pentachlorophenol is 0.21 mg/ℓ for goldfish and fathead minnow (Adelman and Smith, 1976) and for mosquitofish the 6-day LC50 is reduced to about a third of that for phenol (Katz and Cohen, 1976). (See also Chapter 7.)

Field observations of fish kills

There are very few cases where fish kills or adverse effects on natural fish populations can be clearly attributed solely to phenols. Again, one of the main problems is that of analysis, since the identities and proportions of the various monohydric phenols in the water are rarely, if ever, determined, and the analytical results can include other phenols. It is very difficult, therefore, to correlate field data with results from laboratory tests with individual phenols.

Müller and Anwand (1967) could attribute only 3 out of 19 recorded fish kills to phenol, which is perhaps to be expected since phenol pollution is almost always accompanied by reduced dissolved oxygen and the presence of other poisons. Liepolt (1954) ascribed a kill of trout and grayling (*Thymallus thymallus*) in the R. Mürtz to a discharge of concentrated gas liquor. Lüdemann (1954), who studied Berlin waters, was of the opinion that fish would be killed when the phenol concentration was more than 3–5 mg/ℓ. Kalabina (1935) did not find fish in parts of a river containing 0.3 mg/ℓ phenol, and found an abundant and diversified fish fauna where it was 0.02 mg/ℓ. Perhaps the most interesting data have been given by Krombach and Barthel (1964) for a small stream in Luxembourg which was chronically polluted by phenolic wastes and had a concentration of phenols of about 1 mg/ℓ and yet supported fish, including salmonids. After a sudden increased discharge in August all animal life was destroyed within a 9-km stretch where the phenol concentration exceeded 10 mg/ℓ and the dissolved oxygen was 0–10 per cent of the air-saturation value. Further downstream, where the phenol concentration was 3–10 mg/ℓ and the dissolved-oxygen concentration 10–50 per cent of the air-saturation value, salmonids were killed, while in a length where the phenol was less than 3 mg/ℓ there were no fish kills.

Observations on the R. Péstan in Yugoslavia, also chronically polluted by phenolic wastes (V. Mitrović and J. S. Alabaster, personal communication), showed that good populations of chub (*Leuciscus cephalus*) and gudgeon, together with smaller numbers of barbel (*Barbus* spp) occurred where the concentration of phenols ranged from 0 to 4.4 mg/ℓ, but that fish were absent where it was between 3.2 and 130 mg/ℓ.

These data corroborate those from laboratory tests insofar as there are no recorded instances of fish living at concentrations of phenols higher than those found toxic under experimental conditions.

5.4 Sublethal action on fish

5.4.1 GROWTH

Mikriakov (1969) observed a loss in weight of common carp exposed for 2 months to 12.5 mg/ℓ phenol. Stepanov and Flerov (1969) reported that guppies kept for a year in 12.5 mg/ℓ phenol first spawned at the age of 5 months, compared with 10 months for the controls, but there was no reduction in growth. There was, however, decreased sexual activity in this species (Flerov, 1969) as well as alteration of reflexes at this concentration and at 6.3 mg/ℓ, but not at 3.1 mg/ℓ (Matay, 1969).

V. M. Brown and D. G. Shurben (personal communication) studied the effect on rainbow trout of concentrations of 1, 2, 3, 4 and 5 mg/ℓ of phenol over a period of 18 weeks and found that there was a 20 per cent reduction in growth at 1 mg/ℓ and greater reductions at higher concentrations.

5.4.2 RESISTANCE TO DISEASE

Some reports suggest that fish that are exposed to relatively high concentrations of phenols are subsequently more susceptible to attack by *Saprolegnia* or *Ichthyophthirius* (Lukanenko, 1967; Lammering and Burbank, 1960), but to what extent this may be important in harming fish in polluted waters is not known. It has also been shown that the formation of immunoglobulins decreases in common carp exposed to 12.5 mg/ℓ of phenol (Goncharov and Mikryakov, 1970) which could increase their susceptibility to disease.

5.4.3 AVOIDANCE REACTIONS

Hasler and Wisby (1949) showed that the bluntnose minnow (*Pimephales notatus*) could be trained to detect phenol at concentrations below 0.01 mg/ℓ (some individuals being capable of detecting as little as 0.5 μg/ℓ) and to distinguish between phenol and *o*-chlorophenol. Yet, when given the choice of clean water or water containing phenol in a small horizontal tube, minnow (*Phoxinus phoxinus*) did not choose clean water in preference to either 400 mg/ℓ or 4 mg/ℓ of phenol (Jones, 1951), and rainbow trout did not avoid the lower concentrations (0.001–10 mg/ℓ) that were used by Sprague and Drury (1969). Minnow avoided 400 mg/ℓ of *p*-cresol and *o*-cresol but not lower concentrations (Jones, 1951), a behaviour pattern that is paralleled by that of *Lepomis cyanellus,* the green sunfish (Sommerfelt and Lewis, 1967). On the other hand Ishio (1965), using a different kind of apparatus, presented a very brief summary of pooled data for several species, including carp and goldfish, showing that the median position occupied by the fish in his gradient channel coincided with concentrations of phenol (15 mg/ℓ) and cresol (47 mg/ℓ) that were only slightly lower than the 'lowest lethal levels'.

Evidence of avoidance of phenolic wastes under field conditions is also conflicting. Kalabina (1935) reported that fish would leave parts of a river containing 0.2–10 mg/ℓ of phenol, whereas Shelford (1917) said that they would tend to enter and remain in portions of a stream polluted with gas liquor.

Definite conclusions cannot be drawn about avoidance reactions of fish in phenol from this conflicting and sparse evidence, together with that given on p. 113, para. 4 on the distribution of fish in the R. Péstan, but it seems that if there is avoidance of polluted waters containing low concentrations of phenol, it is unlikely to be caused by the phenol alone.

5.4.4 BEHAVIOUR

Temperatures selected by brook trout exposed for 24 hours to 7 mg phenol/ℓ and more were higher than those of controls (Miller and Orgilvie, 1975).

5.4.5 UPTAKE AND LOSS OF PHENOL

Phenols in both free and conjugated forms are normally found in mammalian tissues, but few observations have been made on fish; Reichenbach-Klinke (1965) usually found less than 0.3 mg phenol/kg in *Alburnus punctatus* and roach from the unpolluted R. Isar, whereas there was up to 3.2 mg/kg in bream and barbel (*Barbus barbus*) from polluted parts of the Elbe and Rhine that contained 0.2–0.7 mg/ℓ phenol, values almost as high as in roach kept in 6 mg/ℓ phenol for 14 days. In the American brown bullhead (*Ictalurus nebulosus*) kept for 4 days in 5 mg/ℓ phenol, Mann (1953) found 10 mg/kg in viscera and 6 mg/kg in muscle; he also showed that accumulation in common carp held for 5 days in 10 mg/ℓ phenol was increased by the addition of 2 mg/ℓ of dodecyl-benzol sulphonate (Mann, 1962). Common carp held for 3 days in 10 mg/ℓ phenol (Schultze, 1961) had the highest concentration in liver (19 mg/kg) and progressively lower concentrations in gill, kidney, testis, muscle, and intestine (7 mg/kg). Waluga (1966a, b) obtained similar results with bream held for seven days in 9 mg/ℓ phenol, concentrations being high in the blood and body cavity fluid and low in the cerebral fluid and brain. Concentrations in rainbow trout killed by 10 mg/ℓ phenol were also highest in skin as well as spleen, liver, kidney, and gill (11–25 mg/kg), and lowest in muscle (3.2 mg/kg) (Kariya, Eto and Ogasawara, 1968). In fish killed and then held for 5 h in 10 mg/ℓ phenol, phenols were detected only in skin, muscle, and gill at 5.7, 2.8, and 6.5 mg/kg respectively.

Although Mackiel, Joudorf and Brodie (1958) (in Brodie, Gillett and LaDu, 1958) reported that goldfish and perch were not able to detoxify phenol by the otherwise ubiquitous formation of conjugation products with glucuronides and sulphates, Hickmann and Trump (1969) have stated that these processes do occur in fish.

Kariya, Eto and Ogasawara (1968) found a lower concentration of phenol (2.0 mg/kg) in goldfish which survived exposure to the 2-day LC50 and were then kept for 1 day in tap water, than in fish killed by the same concentration and washed afterwards in tap water for 1 day (9.4 mg/kg). R. Lloyd (personal communication) has found a normal urinary excretion rate in rainbow trout of 0.7 mg monohydric phenols per kg per day, and about 8 mg total phenols per kg per day, and that these rates are increased as a graded response in fish exposed to phenol in the range 1.5–6 mg/ℓ; the data indicate that phenol concentrations less than 1.0 mg/ℓ are unlikely to lead to an increased phenol excretion rate.

5.4.6 TASTE AND ODOUR

Short-term exposure of fish to 25 mg/ℓ phenol (Ebeling, 1940) or for up to four days at 2.5 mg/ℓ (Krishnaswami and Kupchanko, 1969) did not impair the flavour of the flesh, while 10 mg/ℓ cresol induced only a slight taint

(Albersmeyer and Erichsen, 1959). On the other hand, xylenols and some other constituents of phenolic wastes, including naphthols and quinols, tainted bream and common carp at concentrations between 0.5 and 5.0 mg/ℓ (Bandt, 1955, 1958), while *p*-chlorophenol and *o*-chlorophenol produced an undesirable taint in common carp at concentrations of 0.06 and 0.015 mg/ℓ respectively (Schulze, 1961); the latter substance at a concentration of 0.001 mg/ℓ also tainted the flesh of eels (Boetius, 1954). Thus it is possible that substances such as these were responsible for the taste reported in fish caught in the Rhine when 0.02–0.03 mg/ℓ phenols were present (Ebeling, 1940) and in the Elbe containing 0.02 mg/ℓ (Bandt, 1958).

Phenolic flavour may be acquired by fish flesh not only directly from the water but also by the fish eating contaminated food, for example tubifex worms that have been kept in water containing phenol (Mann, 1951). This author and Müller (1962) have both also shown that flavour can be acquired by other animals fed upon tainted fish.

Some phenolic taints may persist in fish flesh for several weeks when fish are kept in clean water (Mann, 1960a, b; Boetius, 1962), unlike some taints, for example those produced by sublethal exposure of fish to the herbicide 2,4-dichlorophenoxyacetic acid (2,4-D) (J. S. Alabaster, personal communication) or by actinomyces (Thaysen and Pentelow, 1936), which may be lost within 1 day under these conditions.

Large amounts of phenol can be taken up from water by aquatic plants, e.g. *Eichornia crassipes* (Wolverton and McKown, 1976).

5.5 Summary of data on invertebrates and algae

5.5.1 PHENOLS

Generally it has been found that bacteria, algae, protozoa, crustacea and mollusca are 10–100 times more resistant than fish to phenols (e.g., Anderson *et al.*, 1948; Beer, 1954; Greven, 1956; Bandt, 1958; and Albersmeyer and Erichsen, 1959). However, the cladoceran, *Daphnia* sp. appears to be somewhat more sensitive than most other invertebrates (Anderson *et al.*, 1948; Bruun, 1948; Ellis, 1937; Bringmann and Kühn, 1959a and 1959b; Patrick, Cairns, and Scheier, 1968; Alekseev and Antipin, 1976); the threshold concentration for *D. magna* is 7 mg/ℓ (Anderson *et al.*, 1948), but with the young (Dowden and Bennett, 1965) and also breeding adults (Mosevich *et al.*, 1952) being most sensitive. There are, however, few laboratory data for other groups, although it has been reported (U.K., Ministry of Transport and Ministry of Agriculture, 1930) that freshwater shrimps, snails, and larvae of caddis flies (Trichoptera) and mayflies (Ephemeroptera) were unaffected at 10 mg/ℓ of either phenol or *o*-cresol in 26 h. Also Kovachev and Uzunov (1975) report that 10–20 mg/ℓ are toxic to Plecoptera and Ephemeroptera and 400–500 mg/ℓ are toxic to Oligochaetes. The leech (*Hirudo medicinalis*) is reported to avoid a concentration of 50 mg/ℓ (Ferov and Lapkina, 1976).

Alymova (1975) found during the course of 30 parthenogenic generations of *Daphnia* that the survival, embryonic development and moulting were not affected by 2 mg/ℓ but that with *D. magna* rate of reproduction was increased at 1 and 2 mg/ℓ and decreased at 0.1 and 0.5 mg/ℓ, while with *D. pulex* the rate of growth of the young was decreased at 0.5 and 2 mg/ℓ.

A concentration of 2 mg/ℓ phenol significantly reduced the oxygen consumption of the Planorbid snail *Helisoma trivolvis* (Sheanon and Trama, 1972), and a concentration of 2.8 mg/ℓ increased that of larval *Chironomus attenuatus* and decreased the weight gain, although behaviour was not altered even at 22.4 mg/ℓ (Cole and Wilhm, 1973).

The interpretation of field observations is complicated by low dissolved-oxygen concentrations being associated with high concentrations of phenol, but it has been observed (Beer, 1954) that algae reappeared in the R. Plaisse where the oxygen concentration had increased to 5.3 mg/ℓ and the phenol concentration had decreased to 4.3 mg/ℓ. In the R. Péstan, Mitrović (1963) found tubificids where the dissolved-oxygen concentration was 0.1–3.1 mg/ℓ and the phenol concentration 17 mg/ℓ; shrimp, larvae of some chironomids, caddis flies, and mayflies where the water was well aerated and phenol concentrations 1–2.5 mg/ℓ; and a diversified and abundant invertebrate community where the maximum concentration of phenol was 1–1.5 mg/ℓ.

5.5.2 CRESOLS

Comparative studies of all three isomers and phenol with *Microregma heterostoma* (a ciliate) and *Daphnia magna* (Bringmann and Kühn, 1959b) and of *m*-cresol and phenol with the larvae of the mosquito *Culex pipiens* and the phantom midge *Chaoborus cristalinus*, as well as with the copepod *Cyclops strenuus*, the ostracod *Pionocyprus vidua* and *Daphnia pulex* (Albersmeyer and Erichsen, 1959) show that these invertebrates, like fish, are somewhat less resistant to cresols than to phenol, and that *m*-cresol is the least toxic and *p*-cresol the most toxic isomer. However, the ciliate *Paramecium caudatum* seems to be much more resistant to a mixture of cresols than to phenol (Halsband and Halsband, 1954) and there is an isolated report (Ellis, 1937) suggesting, contrary to the results of Adams (1927), that the lethal concentration of a mixture of cresols to *Daphnia magna* is much lower (0.01 mg/ℓ) than it is for phenol (8 mg/ℓ) or as Bringman and Kuhn (1959a) found for cresol (2-day LC50, 16 mg/ℓ). Canton and Adema (1978) have reported the results of replicate 2-day static tests carried out with *Daphnia* sp. using *o*-cresol; mean values found for *D. magna*, *D. pulex* and *D. cuculla* were 15.7, 9.6 and 16.4 mg/ℓ respectively.

With a mixture of cresols, as with phenol, there is some evidence that immature organisms are more sensitive than adults; the 2-day LC50 values for immature *Asellus militaris* (an isopod) and *Gammarus fasciatus* (an amphipod) were 33 and 8.6 mg/ℓ respectively and the corresponding values for the adults were 2–3 times higher (Emery, 1970).

5.5.3 XYLENOLS

There are few data on the toxicity of xylenols to invertebrates. Meissner (in Bandt, 1958) apparently found that the 2,4-isomer was more toxic than either phenol or *o*-cresol to protozoa, rotatoria, crustacea and mollusca, with little difference between groups, although the type of response measured is not known. Bringmann and Kühn (1959a, b) using young *Daphnia* found that, as with fish, 2,5-xylenol was more toxic than the '*m*-isomer' (which could include 2,4-, 2,6-, and 3,5-xylenol), the 1-day LC50 being 10 and 24 mg/ℓ respectively. With the ciliate *Microregma* the same authors found that food intake was inhibited by various isomers at 10-50 mg/ℓ, while the effective concentration for phenol was 30 mg/ℓ. Albersmeyer and Erichsen (1959) found that, although 2,5-xylenol was more toxic than phenol to various invertebrates, it was not as toxic to these organisms as it was to fish.

5.6 Conclusions

Phenolic wastes can contain monohydric phenols, including phenol, the three cresol isomers, and the six xylenol isomers, together with other substances. They may adversely affect freshwater fisheries by their direct toxicity to fish and fish-food organisms, by their high oxygen demand resulting in oxygen depletion of the receiving water and by the production of undesirable flavours in the edible flesh of fish.

Of the various phenolic substances, phenol has been the most studied under laboratory conditions. Measurements of the effects of various environmental factors have shown that the toxicity of phenol (2-day LC50) to rainbow trout is increased by a decrease in dissolved-oxygen content (p. 107, para. 2), an increase in water salinity (p. 107, para. 5), and a decrease in temperature (p. 106, para. 5), but is not markedly affected by variations in pH value (p. 107, para. 3) or water hardness (p. 107, para. 4), similar effects of salinity, pH value, and hardness have been observed with coarse fish species, but there are no data available on the effects of dissolved oxygen and temperature.

Salmonids are more sensitive to phenol poisoning than coarse fish such as carp (p. 110, para. 2 and 3), and newly hatched fish are generally more sensitive than adults (p. 108, para. 3-5). The concentrations which have been found lethal within a few days lie within the range 4-25 mg/ℓ.

Concentrations of phenol of 1-2 mg/ℓ maintained for several months are likely to cause slight mortality of part of a trout population as well as reduced growth of the remainder (p. 111, para. 2 and p. 114, para. 2) and there is some physiological evidence (p. 106, para. 2 and 3) and histopathological evidence (p. 106, para. 2) to suggest that stress occurs at concentrations greater than 1.0 mg/ℓ. These results were obtained at temperatures greater than 12 °C and it is not known whether at lower temperatures these effects would be produced by lower concentrations.

From the few data which exist on cresols and xylenols, it appears that their acute toxicity to fish is of the same order of magnitude as that of phenol (p. 111, para. 3-5), but there is no information on long-term effects.

In natural waters, the reported phenol concentration usually represents most of the monohydric phenols of phenolic wastes, but may exclude part of the cresols, especially the *p*-isomer and the xylenols, and include some other phenolic compounds (p. 105, para. 2). Salmonids have been recorded in natural waters where the phenols level is about 1 mg/ℓ, although killed (in the same stream) at 3 mg/ℓ (p. 113, para. 3). Chub, gudgeon and barbel have been recorded where the phenol concentration has reached 4.4 mg/ℓ (p. 113, para. 4) but there have also been frequent kills of fish associated with a phenol concentration of 3-5 mg/ℓ or more. Unfortunately, it is not possible to say what any of these concentrations represent in terms of phenols, cresols, xylenols and other substances, and therefore the field observations cannot be used to substantiate the results of the laboratory experiments described here.

There is no strong evidence that fish avoid low concentrations of phenol in laboratory tests (p. 114, para. 4–6); avoidance reactions reported in the field could result from the reaction of fish either to components of phenolic wastes or to low dissolved oxygen, or to both.

Some phenols impair the taste of fish only at relatively high concentrations, but other constituents of phenolic wastes, and chlorinated phenols, which taint the fish flesh at extremely low concentrations, may account for the presence of taints in fish from rivers containing such wastes and where the concentrations of total phenols by analysis were in excess of 0.02 mg/ℓ (p. 115, para. 5).

Those aquatic invertebrates which have been studied in the laboratory are more resistant than fish to phenol poisoning (p. 116, para. 5 and 6), but there is a dearth of information on the resistance of organisms characteristic of trout streams. However, some field observations have shown that abundant and diversified invertebrate communities exist where the phenol concentration has not exceeded 1.5 mg/ℓ (p. 116, para. 5).

5.7 Tentative water quality criteria

Although there are extensive data on the toxicity of the monohydric phenols to fish under laboratory conditions, there are few field observations which can be used to reinforce these. One of the main difficulties is that of analytical techniques, in that the levels of cresols and xylenols in rivers may be underestimated. For this reason, only tentative criteria can be established which may have to be modified in the light of further experience, especially when more data on the effect of temperature become available. These criteria are expressed as maximum concentrations which should not be exceeded; it should be appreciated that because of the natural fluctuation in the water quality found in rivers over a period of time, the average concentration will be lower to an extent depending on local circumstances.

Salmonid fish To ensure long-term survival of salmonids in the presence of phenolic wastes, the concentration of phenol, cresols or xylenols should not exceed 1.0 mg/ℓ, either singly or collectively. Where 2,5-xylenol is the main constituent, the concentration should not exceed 0.5 mg/ℓ. Where the temperature is lower than 5 °C, concentrations may have to be halved to ensure the survival of fish. Where other poisons are present due allowance must be made for their contribution to the toxicity, particularly in the case of free chlorine.

Coarse fish Since laboratory data show that coarse fish are more resistant than salmonids to phenols, the concentration of phenol, cresol or xylenol should not exceed 2.0 mg/ℓ, either singly or collectively, provided that oxidation of this concentration does not produce an adverse reduction in the dissolved-oxygen concentration of the water. In the absence of data on the effect of temperature on the toxicity of phenols to coarse fish it is proposed that the reduction in concentration of 50 per cent adopted for salmonids at temperatures below 5 °C, should also apply to these species. Where other poisons are present due allowance must be made for their contribution to the toxicity, particularly in the case of free chlorine.

Commercial fisheries There is no laboratory evidence to indicate that levels of phenol and cresols that are safe for fish cause their flesh to become tainted, but xylenols should not exceed 0.5 mg/ℓ (p. 115, para. 5). Other phenolic substances, particularly the chlorophenols, are known to cause taint at very low concentrations; strictly these are outside the scope of this chapter, but the information that has been considered suggests that they should be excluded from waters supporting commercial fisheries.

5.8 References

ADAMS, B. A. (1927). The lethal effect of various chemicals on *Cyclops* and *Daphnia*. *Wat. & Wat. Engng* **29**, 361-364

ADELMAN, I. R. and SMITH, L. L. Jr. (1976). Fathead minnows (*Pimephales promelas*) and goldfish (*Carassius auratus*) as standard fish in bioassays and their reaction to potential reference toxicants. *J. Fish. Res. Bd Can.* **33**, 209-214

ALBERSMEYER, W. and VON ERICHSEN, L. (1959). Untersuchungen zur Wirung von Teerbestandteilen in Abwässern. Mitteilungen 1-7. *Z. Fisch.* **8(1/3)**, 29-66

ALEKSEEV, V. A. and ANTIPIN, V. Kh.(1976). Toksikologicheskaya Kharakteristika i simptomokompleks' ostroi fenol'noi intoksikatsii nekotorykh presnovodnykh rakoobraznykh i mollyuskov. (Toxicological characteristics and symptoms of acute phenol poisoning in some freshwater crustaceans and molluscs). *Gibrobiologicheskii Zhurnal* **12(2)**, 37-44

ALYMOVA, T. P. (1975). Vliyanie khronicheskogo fenol'nogo otravleniya na biologiyu dafnii (The effect of chronic phenolic poisoning on the biology of *Daphnia*). In *Formir. e Kontrol' kachestva poverkhnost. Vod.* First Issue, pp. 34-39. Kiev, Nauka Dumka

ANDERSON, B. G., CHANDLER, D. C., ANDREWS, T. F. and JAHODA, W. J. (1948). The evaluation of aquatic invertebrates as assay organisms for the determination of the toxicity of industrial wastes. *Am. Petroleum Inst. Final Rep. Inst. Proj.* **51**

ANDRES, A. G. and KURAZHOVSKAIA, T. H. (1969). Gistspatologicheskie izmeneniia u leshcha (*Abramis brama*) pri ostrom otravlenii fenolom v eksperimentie. *Tr. Biol. Inst. Vodokhran. SSSR* **19(20)**, 73-86

BACH, H. (1929). Phenolschwund im Wasser. *Gesundheitsingenieur* **52**, 796

BANDT, H. J. (1955). Fischereischaden durch Phenolabwässer. *Wasserwirtsch. Wassertech.* **5**, 290-294

BANDT, H. J. (1958). Phenolabwässer und Abwasserphenole, ihre Entstehung, Schadwirkung und abwassertechnische Behandlung. Eine monographische Studie. Berlin, Academia-Berlag

BEER, W. D. (1954). Über den Einfluss des Phenolgehaltss des Pleissewassers auf die Mikrolebewelt. *Wasserwirtsch. Wassertech.* **4**, 125-131

BESCH, W. K., KEMBALL, A., MEYER-WAARDEN, K. and SCHARF, B. (1977). A biological monitoring system employing rheotaxis of fish. In *Biological Monitoring of Water and Effluent Quality* (ASTM STP 607) (Ed. by John Cairns, Jr., K. L. Dickson and G. F. Westlake). *Am. Soc. Test. Materials*, 56-74

BLACKBURN, W. H., BARKER, L. and CATCHPOLE, J. R. (1954). An investigation into the composition of ammoniacal liquor. 1. Continuous vertical retort liquor. *Gas Counc. Res. Commun., Lond.* **(G C 17)**

BOETIUS, J. (1954). Foul taste of fish and oysters caused by chlorophenol. *Medd. Dan. Fisk. Havunders.* **1(4)**, 1-8

BOETIUS, J. (1962). Fiskeforgiftnungen forasaget of kemiske stoffer fra industri og landbrug. Fiskeriundersøgelser 1961. *Skr. Dan. Fisk.-og Havunders.* **22**, 71-78

BRINGMANN, G. and KÜHN, R.(1959a). Wasser-toxikologische Untersuchungen an Bakterien, Algen, und Kleinkrebsen. *Gesundheitsingenieur* **80**, 115-120

BRINGMANN, G. and KÜHN, R. (1959b). Wasser-toxikologische Untersuchungen mit Protozoen als Test Organismen. *Gesundheitsingenieur* **80**, 239-242

BRODIE, B., GILLETT, J. and LADU, B.(1958). Enzymatic metabolism of drugs and other foreign compounds. *Ann. Rev. Biochem.* **27**, 427-454

BROWN, V. M. and DALTON, R. A. (1970). The acute lethal toxicity to rainbow trout of mixtures of copper, phenol, zinc, and nickel. *J. Fish. Biol.* **2**, 211-216

BROWN, V. M., JORDAN, D. H. M. and TILLER, B. A. (1967). The effect of temperature on the acute toxicity of phenol to rainbow trout in hard water. *Wat. Res.* **1**, 587-594

BROWN, V. M., JORDAN, D. H. M. and TILLER, B. A.(1969). The acute toxicity to rainbow trout of fluctuating concentrations and mixtures of ammonia, phenol, and zinc. *J. Fish. Biol.* **1**, 1-9

BROWN, V. M., SHURBEN, D. G. and FAWELL, J. K. (1967). The acute toxicity of phenol to rainbow trout in saline waters. *Wat. Res.* **1**, 683-685

BROWN, V. M., SHURBEN, D. G. and SHAW, D. (1970). Studies on water quality and the absence of fish from some polluted English rivers. *Wat. Res.* **4**, 363-382

BRUUN, A. F.(1948). Afsluttende Beretning vedrorende undersogelse af og Afvaargelse af ulemperne fra Sugensasanlaeg. *Acad. tekn. Vid. Beretning*, **9**, 6-12

BUCKSTEEG, W., THIELE, H. and STÖLTZEL, K. (1955). Die Beeinflussung von Fischen durch Giftsstoffe aus Abwässern. *Vom Wasser* **22**, 194-211

CAIRNS, J. (1956). The relationship of body size of the bluegill sunfish to the acute toxicity of some common chemicals. Philadelphia, Philadelphia Academy of Science

CANTON, J. H. and ADEMA, D. M. M. (1978). Reproducibility of short-term and reproductive experiments with *Daphnia magna* and comparisons of the sensitivity of *D. magna* with *D. pulex* and *D. cuculla* in short-term experiments. *Hydrobiologia* **59(2)**, 135-140

COLE, S. L. and WILHM, J. (1973). Effect of phenol on oxygen uptake rate of a laboratory population of *Chironomus attenuatus* (Walk). *Wat. Res.* **7**, 1691-1700

DOWDEN, B. F. and BENNETT, H. J.(1965). Toxicity of selected chemicals to certain animals. *J. Wat. Pollut. Control Fed.* **37**, 1308-1316

EBELING, C. (1940). Versuche über die Wirkung phenolhaltiger Abwässer in Zusammenhang mit Rheinuntersuchungen auf der Strecke von Mainz bis Emmerich in den Jahren 1935-1937. *Vom Wasser* **14**, 81-91

ELLIS, M. M. (1937). Detection and measurement of stream pollution. *Bull. U.S. Bur. Fish.* **48(22)**, 365-437

EMBODY, D. R., SCHUCK, H. A., CRUMP, S. L., FREESE, J. W. and ROSS, L. (1940). The effect of cresol on brook trout *Salvelinus fontinalis*. *Trans. Am. Fish. Soc.* **70**, 304

EMERY, R. M.(1970). The comparative acute toxicity of cresol to two benthic crustaceans. *Wat. Res.* **4**, 485-491

FLEROV, B. A. (1969). *Trudy Inst. Biol., Vodokhran.* **19(22)**, 66-69

FLEROV, B. A. and LAPKINA, L. N. (1976). Izbeganie rastvorov nekotorykh toksicheskikh veschchestv medintsinskoi piyavkoi. (Avoidance of the solutions of certain toxic substances by medicinal leeches). *Biol. Vnutr. Vod., Inform. Byul.* **30**, 48-52

FOLIN, O. and DENIS, W. J. (1915). A colorimetric method for the determination of phenols (and phenol derivatives) in urine. *J. Biol. Chem.* **22**, 305-308

GONCHAROV, G. D. and MIKRYAKOV, V. R. (1970). Vliyanie Malykh Kontsentrastsii Ferola na Antiteloobrazovanie u Karpov *Cyprinus carpio* L. (The effect of low concentrations of phenol on antibody formation in carp.) In *Voprosy Vodnoi Toksikologii* (Problems of Aquatic Toxicology), pp. 171-175, Moscow. (Translation by R. M. Howland, Bureau of Commercial Fisheries)

GREVEN, U. (1953). Untersuchungenmethoden zur Feststellung der Einwirkung von Abwässern auf Tiere und Pflanzen. *Gewäss., u. Abwäss.*, **3**, 46-60

GREVEN, U. (1956). Die Wirkung von Karbolsäure auf den Schlammröhrenwurm (*Tubifex tubifex*). *Arch. Hydrobiol.* **52**, 278-286

HALSBAND, E. and HALSBAND, I. (1954). Untersuchungen über die Storunggesschwellen im Stöffwechsel der Fische und Fischnährtiere nach einwirkung verschiedener Abwassergifte. *Arch. Fischereiwiss.* **5(3/4)**, 120-132

HALSBAND, E. and HALSBAND, I. (1963). Veränderungen des Blutbildes von Fische infolge toxischer Schaden. *Arch. Fischereiwiss.* **14(1-2)**, 68-84

HASLER, A. and WISBY, W. (1949). Use of fish for the olfactory assay of pollutants (phenols) in water. *Trans. Am. Fish. Soc.* **79**, 64-70

HERBERT, D. W. M. (1962). The toxicity to rainbow trout of spent still liquors from the distillation of coal. *Ann. appl. Biol.* **50**, 755-777

HERBERT, D. W. M. and VANDYKE, J. M. (1967). The toxicity to fish of mixtures of poisons. 2. Copper-ammonia and zinc-phenol mixtures. *Ann. appl. Biol.* **53**, 415-421

HERBERT, D. W. M., JORDAN, D. H. M. and LLOYD, R. (1965). A study of some fishless rivers in the industrial Midlands. *J. Proc. Inst. Sewage Purif.* **1965**, 569-582

HICKMAN, C. P. and TRUMP, B. J. (1969). The Kidney. In *Fish Physiology* (Ed. by W. S. Hoar and D. J. Randall), vol. 1, p. 201. London, Academic Press

HOAK, R. D. (1956). The causes of taste and odours in drinking water. *Proc. Ind. Waste Conf. Purdue Univ. (Eng. Ext. Ser.)* **11(91)**, 229-241

HOLLAND, G. A., LASATER, H. A., NEWMANN, E. D. and ELDRIDGE, W. R. (1960). Toxic effects of organic and inorganic pollutants on young salmon and trout. *Res. Bull. Wash. Dep. Fish.* **5**

INTERNATIONAL UNION OF PURE AND APPLIED CHEMISTRY. (1965). *Nomenclature of organic chemistry, Section C.* London, Butterworths

ISHIO, S. (1965). Behaviour of fish exposed to toxic substances. *Adv. Wat. Pollut. Res.* **2(1)**, 19-40

JONES, J. R. E. (1951). The reactions of the minnow *Phoxinus phoxinus* (L.), to solutions of phenol, ortho-cresol and para-cresol. *J. exp. Biol.* **28**, 261-270

KALABINA, M. M. (1935). Der Phenolzerfall in Fliess- und Staugewässern. *Z. Fisch.* **33**, 295-317

KATZ, B. M. and COHEN, G. M. (1976). Toxicities of 'excessively' chlorinated organic compounds. *Bull. Envir. Contam. Toxic.* **15(6)**, 611-617

KARIYA, T., ETO, S. and OGASAWARA, S. (1968). Studies on the post-mortem identification of the pollutant in fish killed by water pollution. 8. On acute poisoning with phenol. *Bull. Jap. Soc. Sci. Fish.* **34**, 764-769

KLINKE, H. R. (1965) Der Phenolgehalt des Wassers in seiner Auswirkung auf den Fischorganismus. *Arch. Fischerewiss.* **16**, 1-16

KOVACHEV, S. and UZUNOV, I. (1975). Toksichno deistve na fenol v'rkhu nyakoi bezgrbnachni khidrobionti. (The toxic effects of phenol on certain aquatic invertebrates.) *Khidrobiologia* **1**, 65-74 (in Bulgarian)

KRISHNASWAMI, S. K. and KUPCHANKO, E. E. (1969). Relationship between odour of petroleum refinery waste water and occurrence of 'oily' taste-flavour in rainbow trout (*Salmo gairdneri*). *J. Wat. Pollut. Control Fed.* **41**, 189-196

KRISTOFFERSSON, R., BROBERG, S. and OIKARI, A. (1973). Physiological effects of a sublethal concentration of phenol in the pike (*Esox lucius* L.) in pure brackish water. *Annali Zool. Fennici* **10**, 392-397

KROMBACH, H. and BARTHEL, J. (1964). Investigation of a small watercourse accidentally polluted by phenol compounds. *Adv. Wat. Pollut. Res.* **1**, 181-203

LAMMERING, M. W. and BURBANK, N. C. (1960). The toxicity of phenol, *o*-chlorophenol, and *o*-nitrophenol to bluegill sunfish. *Proc. Ind. Waste Conf. Purdue Univ. (Eng. Ext. Ser.)* **15(106)**, 541-555

LEBEDINSKI, N. V. and POMARZANSKIA, V. L. (1968). In *Materialy XIV konferencii po izucheniu vnutrennyh vodoemov Pribaltikii*, Volume 2, 81-85. Latviiskol SSR, Instututa Biologicheakoi, A.N.

LECLERC, E. and DEVLAMINCK, F. (1950). Étude toxicologique de quelques substances généralement presents dans les effluents d'usines à gaz. *Bull. Cent. Belge Doc. Eaux* **8**, 483-485

LIEPOLT, R. (1953). Abwässer vergiften Fische in der Mürz. *Oesterr. Wasserwirtsch.* **5(3)**, 56

LLOYD, R. (1961). Effect of dissolved-oxygen concentrations on the toxicity of several poisons to rainbow trout (*Salmo gairdnerii* Richardson). *J. exp. Biol.* **38**, 447-455

LLOYD, R. and JORDAN, D. H. M. (1963). Predicted and observed toxicities of several sewage effluents to rainbow trout. *J. Proc. Inst. Sewage Purif.* **1963(2)**, 167-173

LLOYD, R. and JORDAN, D. H. M. (1964). Predicted and observed toxicities of several sewage effluents to rainbow trout: a further study. *J. Proc. Inst. Sewage Purif.* **1964**, 183-186

LÜDEMANN, D. (1954). Die Verunreinigung der Berliner Gewässer und ihre Auswirkung. *Gesundheitsingenieur* **75(15/16)**, 260-262

LUKANENKO, V. I. (1967). *Fish Toxicology*. Moskva, Izd. Pishchevaia Promishlennost

LUKANENKO, V. I. and FLEROV, B. A. (1963). In *Materialy po gidrobiologii i biologii volzshih vodohranilishch*. Moskva, Izd-vo Akademii Nauk

LUKANENKO, V. I. and FLEROV, B. A. (1966a). *Trudy Inst. Biol., Vodokhran.* **10(13)**, 235-299

LUKANENKO, V. I. and FLEROV, B. A. (1966b). *Vop. Ikhtiol.* **6(2)**, 275-281

MALACEA, I. (1968). Untersuchungen über die Gewöhnung der Fische an hohe Konzentrationen toxischer Substanzen. *Arch.Hydrobiol.* **65**, 74-95

MALACEA, I., CURE, V. and WEINER, L. (1967). Actiunea toxică a titreiului si fenolului asupra unor organisme acvatice. *Stud. Protect. Epurapea Apelor* **5**, 351-397

MANN, H. (1951). Zur Frage der Geschmackbeeinflussung bei Fischen. *Fischwirt* **1**, 164-165

MANN, H. (1953). Uber Geschmackbeeinflussung bei Fischen. *Fischwirt* **3**, 330-334

MANN, H. (1960a). Die Uberstragung des Phenolgeschmacks bei Verfütterung von Weissfischen an Forellen und Geflügel. *Fischwirt* **10**, 259-262

MANN, H. (1960b). Untersuchungen über die Halterung von Aalen. *Arch. Fischereiwiss.* **11**, 145-151

MANN, H. (1962). Die Förderung der Geschmacksbeeinflussung bei Fischen durch Detergentien. *Fischwirt* **12**, 237-240

MATAY, V. E. (1969). *Trudȳ Inst. Biol., Vodokhran.* **19(22)**, 62-65

McKIM, J. M., BENOIT, D. A., BRESINGER, K. E., BRUNGS, W. A. and SIEFERT, R. E. (1974). Effects of pollution on freshwater fish. *J. Wat. Pollut. Control Fed.* **47(6)**, 1711-1768

MILLER, D. L. and ORGILVIE, D. M. (1975). Temperature selection in brook trout (*Salvelinus fontinalis*) following exposure to DDT, PCB or phenol. *Bull. Envir. Contam. Toxicol.* **14**, 545

MIKRIAKOV, V. R. (1969). *Trudȳ Inst. Biol., Vodokhran.* **19(22)**, 70-72

MITROVIĆ, V. V. (1963). Uticaj fenolnih otpadnih voda no makroinvertebrata dna reke Pestan. (The effect of phenolic waste waters upon bottom macroinvertebrates of the River Peshtan.) Thesis, Zagreb

MITROVIĆ, V. V., BROWN, M., SHURBEN, D. G. and BERRYMAN, M. H. (1968). Some pathological effects of sub-acute and acute poisoning of rainbow trout by phenol in hard water. *Wat. Res.* **2**, 249-254

MOSEVICH, N. A., GUSEV, G. A., DRAGULIN, G. M., KUSHNAROVA, S. V., MOSEVCH, V. M. and NIKIFOROV, D. N. (1952). *Izv. Vses. nauchno-Issled. Inst. Ozern. rechn. ryb. Khoz.* **31**, 13-41

MÜLLER, H. (1962). Die Wirkung der Abwassereinleitungen auf den Fischbestand der fliessender und stehenden Gewässer in der DDP. *Wissenzchaft. Z. Karl Marx Univ., Leipz.* **11**, 153-157

MÜLLER, H. and ANWAND, K. (1967). Fischsterben in der Deutschen Demokratischen Republik wahrend des Abflussjahres 1966. *Dt. Fischwirtschaftztg.* **14**, 361-364

NOLTE, E. (1933). Phenol bestimmung im Flusswasser. *Chem. Ztg.* **57**, 654

OCHYNSKI, F. W. (1960). The absorptiometric determination of phenol. *Analyst, Lond.* **85**, 278-281

PATRICK, R., CAIRNS, J. Jr. and SCHEIER, A. (1968). The relative sensitivity of diatoms, snails, and fish to twenty common constituents of industrial wastes. *Prog. Fish Cult.* **30**, 137-140

PICKERING, P. H. and HENDERSON, C. (1966). Acute toxicity of some important petrochemicals to fish. *J. Wat. Pollut. Control Fed.* **38**, 1419-1429

REICHENBACH-KLINKE, H. H. (1965). Die Temperaturabhängigkeit der Fische. In *Der Fisch in Wissenschaft und Praxis*. Festschr. anl. d. 50 jähr. Bestehens d. Teichwirtschaftl. Abteilung Wielenbach der Bayr. Biol. Versuchsanstalt München. München, Obpacher

SCHULZE, E. (1961). Zur geschmacklichen Beeinflussungen von Fischen durch Phenolhaltige Abwasser. *Int. Rev. Gesamten Hydrobiol. Hydrogr.* **46**, 84-90

SHEANON, M. J. and TRAMA, F. B. (1972). Influence of phenol and temperature on the respiration of a freshwater snail (*Helisoma trivolvis*). *Hydrobiologia* **40(3)**, 321-328

SHELFORD, V. E. (1917). An experimental study of the effects of gas wastes upon fishes with special reference to stream pollution. *Bull. Ill. State Lab. Nat. Hist.* 11, 381–412

SOLLMANN, T. (1949). Correlation of the aquarium goldfish toxicities of some phenols, quinones, and other benzene derivatives with their inhibition of auto-oxidative reactions. *J. gen. Physiol.* 32, 671–679

SOMMERFELT, R. C. and LEWIS, W. M. (1967). Repulsion of green sunfish by certain chemicals. *J. Wat. Pollut. Control Fed.* 39, 2030–2038

SOUTHGATE, B. A., PENTELOW, F. T. K. and BASSINDALE, R. (1933). The toxicity to trout of potassium cyanide and *p*-cresol in water containing different concentrations of dissolved oxygen. *Biochem. J.* 27, 983–985

SPRAGUE, J. B. and DRURY, E. (1969). Avoidance reactions of salmonid fish to representative pollutants. *Adv. Wat. Pollut. Res.* 4, 169–179

STEPANOV, B. C. and FLEROV, B. A. (1969). *Trudy Inst. Biol. Vodokhran.* 19(22), 60–61

SYMONS, G. and SIMPSON, R. (1938). Report on fish destruction in the Niagara River in 1937. *Trans. Am. Fish. Soc.* 68, 246–255

THAYSEN, A. C. and PENTELOW, F. T. K. (1936). The origin of earthy or muddy taint in fish. 2. The effect on fish of the taint produced by an odoriferous species of actinomyces. *Ann. appl. Biol.* 23, 105–109

U.K., MINISTRY OF TECHNOLOGY (1968). In *Water Pollution Research, 1967*, p. 63. London, H.M.S.O.

U.K., MINISTRY OF TECHNOLOGY (1969). In *Water Pollution Research, 1968*, pp. 65–66. London, H.M.S.O.

U.K., MINISTRY OF TECHNOLOGY (1971). In *Water Pollution Research, 1970*, p. 59. London, H.M.S.O.

U.K., MINISTRY OF TRANSPORT AND MINISTRY OF AGRICULTURE, JOINT COMMITTEE ON DAMAGE TO FISHERIES. (1930). *Detailed biological and chemical reports on tar used for road surfacing.* London, H.M.S.O.

VESELOV, E.`A. (1957). *Uch. Zap. Petrozavodsk. Univ.* 7, 3

VOLODIN, V. M., LUKANENKO, V. I. and FLEROV, B. A. (1966). *Trudy Inst. Biol. Vodokhran.* 10(13), 300–310

WALUGA, D. (1966a). Zmiany anatomo-histologiczne u leszcza pod wplywem fenolu. (Phenol effects on the anatomico-histopathological changes in bream (*Abramis brama* L.).) *Acta Hydrobiol.* 8, 55–78

WALUGA, D. (1966b). Zmiany we krwi obwodowej leszczy pod wplywem fenolu. (Phenol-induced changes in the peripheral blood of the bream (*Abramis brama* L.).) *Acta Hydrobiol.* 8, 87–95

WEIGELT, C., SAARE, O. and SCHWAB, L. (1885). Die schädigung der Fischerei und Fischzucht durch Industrie- und Hausabwasser. *Arch. Hyg.* 3, 38–117

WOLVERTON, B. C. and McKOWN, M. M. (1976). Water hyacinths for removal of phenols from polluted waters. *Aquatic Bot.* 2(3), 191–201

WUHRMANN, K. and WOKER, H. (1950). Beitrage zur Toxicologie der Fische. 5. Die Giftigkeit von Phenol fur verschiedene Fischarten. *Schweiz. Z. Hydrol.* 12, 271–287

6

DISSOLVED OXYGEN

Foreword

The preparation of the original report on dissolved oxygen and inland fisheries on which this chapter is based was accomplished largely by the Water Pollution Research Laboratory, Stevenage (now forming part of the Water Research Centre, U.K.) which prepared a draft for review by members of the EIFAC Working Party on Water Quality Criteria for European Freshwater Fish. The basis for this draft was the thorough and critical review by Doudoroff and Shumway (1970) which covered most of the work then known on freshwater fish. Since that time there have been further reviews on the dissolved-oxygen requirements of fish, notably by Warren, Doudoroff and Shumway (1973), Davies (1975), McKim *et al.* (1975) and Brungs *et al.* (1977). In this chapter references already covered by Doudoroff and Shumway (1970) are not generally cited, but a selection of the more recent papers is referred to, together with some unpublished data.

6.1 Summary

Sensitivity of fish to low concentrations of dissolved oxygen (DO) differs between species, between the various life stages (eggs, larvae, and adults), and between the different life processes (feeding, growth, and reproduction, which in turn may depend on swimming ability, and specialized behaviour which may also be influenced by DO). Any DO standards set for fisheries must take all these into account, bearing in mind the type of fishery, the times and places the fish occur, and the likely impact on the fishery of impairment of each part of the life cycle.

Although there is a considerable volume of laboratory data on the effects of DO on fish life processes, much of it is incomplete in terms of the distribution of the responses within fish populations at given physiological and behavioural states, and difficult to interpret in terms of ecological significance. However, the general pattern which emerges is that, providing other environmental factors (including the absence of poisons) are favourable, a minimum constant value of 5 mg/ℓ would be satisfactory for most stages and activities in the life cycle in that some processes, such as juvenile growth, fecundity, hatch of eggs, larval morphology and survival, upstream movement of migratory salmon, and schooling behaviour of some species, including shad, are not particularly susceptible to levels of DO above 5 mg/ℓ. However, this value may be unnecessarily high merely to ensure satisfactory survival of the fish and adequate growth of the juveniles.

Difficulties arise in formulating DO criteria for fisheries because of the widely different patterns of DO fluctuations which can exist in inland waters even when unpolluted and the uncertainty of predicting their effect even when adequately described, unless the levels are so low as to be directly lethal to fish or so high as to have no effect on them. There have been few experiments made which attempt to simulate natural conditions, most being made at constant DO levels; furthermore, field data are generally inadequate in that either the fish populations present or the DO regime are poorly described, and their interpretation is complicated by the presence of other poisons. In these circumstances, only tentative criteria can be put forward.

Because DO levels in a river normally fluctuate, it is inappropriate to put forward criteria based on a single minimum value never to be violated or even as several minima each not to be violated at a certain time of year, but they should be expressed as a minimum percentile distribution (e.g., a minimum 5- and 95-percentile value) over a year or part of a year, or, with estuarine fisheries, part of a tidal cycle.

From the limited data available it is suggested that for resident populations of moderately tolerant freshwater species, such as roach, the annual 50-percentile and 5-percentile DO values should be greater than 5 mg/ℓ and 2 mg/ℓ respectively and for salmonids the percentiles should be 9 mg/ℓ and 5 mg/ℓ respectively.

These values are to be regarded as being for general guidance only, because there are special circumstances where more consideration should be given to the seasonal distribution of DO, for example in estuaries through which migrant salmonids pass. Moreover, all these minimum values might need to be considerably increased in the presence of high temperature or poisons.

To enable more satisfactory criteria to be formulated, further laboratory studies are required which would reflect natural DO regimes, and more field observations are required on the status of fish populations where the DO is lowered and on the movements of adults and young of migratory species. These should be coupled with more complete analytical data on the DO, both where the fish populations are only marginal and where they are well established. The consequences of reduced fecundity, growth and reproduction, and of changed behaviour patterns, on population dynamics and production of fish and of fisheries should also be appraised.

6.2 Introduction

Dissolved oxygen (DO) is essential, and in some cases even the limiting factor, for maintaining aquatic life; its depletion in water is probably the most frequent general result of certain forms of water pollution, and its effects on aquatic organisms, especially at low concentrations, have therefore been very extensively studied.

Sensitivity to low dissolved-oxygen concentrations differs between species, between the various life stages (eggs, larvae, and adults), and between the different life processes (feeding, growth and reproduction, which may depend on swimming ability, and specialized behaviour which may also be influenced by DO) so that the DO requirements for fisheries must take this into account, bearing in mind the type of fishery, the times and places the fish occur, and the likely impact on the fishery of impairment of each part of the life cycle.

The effect of DO on fish is influenced by several other factors, including temperature, which affects the solubility of oxygen in water and also the metabolic rate of poikilotherms.

6.3 Direct lethal action on fish

6.3.1. AGE OF FISH

Sensitivity of young salmonids is greatest around the time of hatching, high mortalities resulting, for example, from sudden reduction of DO to 2–3 mg/ℓ for six days. Newly-hatched pike larvae (*Esox lucius*) can survive for one hour in the absence of oxygen but free-swimming larvae for only a few minutes.

Survival of the fry of fathead minnow (*Pimephales promelas*) after 30 days was only 5 per cent at 3 mg/ℓ, increasing to 66 per cent at 5 mg/ℓ (Brungs, 1971).

Mature-sized fish can probably survive in DO levels in excess of 3 mg/ℓ when other conditions are favourable, and lethal levels are often much lower than this. Generally, the maximum exposure period required to produce acute anoxia under constant conditions would be about a day for European freshwater species. Young fish tend to be less resistant, but the patterns of change in resistance with age are variable, especially in the first month. A survey of Slavonic literature published during the period 1970–1976 (A. Lysak, personal communication) shows that lethal levels of DO for salmonid species range between 0.95 and 3.4 mg/ℓ, and those for non-salmonid species, from 0.42 to 3.0 mg/ℓ. The data of Klyashtorin (1976) for various species of sturgeon also support this conclusion.

6.3.2 TEMPERATURE

Seasonal variation in resistance independent of temperature has not been demonstrated; in general the minimum DO that fish are able to tolerate increases with rise in temperature, particularly near the upper lethal thermal limit.

6.3.3 ACCLIMATION

Experiments to determine acute lethal DO values for fish have usually involved their direct transfer from well-oxygenated water to the test solutions. However, there is abundant evidence that acclimation to low DO can take place, the length of time required increasing with decreasing temperature; at low temperatures acclimation may not take place. However, it is well known that Crucian carp

(*Carassius carassius*) can withstand anaerobic conditions for some months at temperatures close to freezing point. Acclimation for periods up to ten days to low DO can reduce the 'tolerance threshold' of fish to 50 per cent of that obtained by direct transfer from the air saturation value (ASV). Alabaster, Shurben and Mallett (1979) have shown that some acclimation of smolts of Atlantic salmon to low DO occurs within a few hours, and also that acclimation to increased salinity increases resistance to low DO, the median threshold concentration for survival in fresh water and 30–80 per cent sea water being about 3.3 and 2.6 mg/ℓ respectively.

R. Lloyd and D. J. Swift (personal communication) suggest that acclimation of rainbow trout (*Salmo gairdneri*) to 3 mg/ℓ DO at 17 °C occurs in two stages; the first, involving diuresis, reduced blood volume, and increased haematocrit, taking about 6 h; the second, involving increased blood volume, and erythropoesis, taking a further 16 h. However, such DO levels also increase the permeability of rainbow trout to water. The breakdown in osmoregulatory ability in rainbow trout brought about by lack of oxygen and manifested by elevated levels of plasma electrolytes has been described by Landless (1976).

6.3.4 SUPERSATURATION

Oxygen-supersaturated water resulting from phytoplankton activity is generally unlikely to be lethal except when gas-bubble disease is caused by the sum of the partial pressures of all dissolved atmospheric gases being greatly in excess of the hydrostatic pressure, or when accompanied by high pH values. Superabundant oxygen in water can produce definite improvement in the period of survival of goldfish (*Carassius auratus*) at a fixed lethal temperature, or in the lethal temperature reached as a result of heating. No further improvement in thermal tolerance was found at dissolved-oxygen pressures over 500 kPa. (Weatherley, 1970.)

6.3.5 INTERACTION WITH POISONS AND CARBON DIOXIDE

At lowered concentration of DO the rate at which water is pumped over the gills of fish may be increased, so increasing the amount of poison in contact with the gill surface where it is absorbed. For several common poisons the LC50 at a DO of 5 mg/ℓ would be roughly half that at 10 mg/ℓ, and a similar effect has recently been confirmed with a more complex waste (Hicks and De Witt, 1971) and with hydrogen sulphide (Adelman and Smith, 1972). Also Cairns and Scheier (1957) found that the 4-day LC50 of zinc chloride, naphthenic acid, and potassium cyanide to bluegill sunfish (*Lepomis macrochirus*) in soft water at 18 °C with the dissolved-oxygen concentration fluctuating over several hours between 9 and 2 mg/ℓ was approximately 0.2, 0.3 and 0.4 of the value when the fluctuations were between 9 and 5 mg/ℓ. Other examples are given in Chapters 4, 5 and 7-10.

Sudden exposure to a moderately high concentration of CO_2 causes a normally tolerable low DO to be rapidly fatal, but prior acclimation to the CO_2 level removes much of this additional effect. In nature, however, acclimation to increasing CO_2 is likely to occur before the concomitant decreasing DO reaches a critical low level. Effects of CO_2 on DO requirements are not considered to be ascribable to decrease in pH. However, increase in temperature, CO_2, and hydrogen-ion concentration, either independently or together, cause rainbow trout blood to have a lowered affinity for oxygen (Eddy, 1971).

Interesting as this information is, it is of limited value in choosing satisfactory water quality criteria for fisheries. It would seem, however, that where conditions are otherwise favourable, acutely lethal effects on fish would probably be avoided by maintaining DO levels above 3 mg/ℓ, though for some species this limit could be much lower (Brungs, 1971), and for many species lower concentrations could be tolerated for short periods. This conclusion is embodied in the summary in *Table 6.1* (see Section 6.7).

6.4 Sublethal action on fish

6.4.1 FERTILIZATION AND FECUNDITY

Levels of DO which might affect fertilization appear to be largely unknown, but ova of pike have been fertilized in the absence of oxygen (and at temperatures between 0 and 30 °C).

There is little information on the effect of low DO on fecundity, but Brungs (1971) has reported on experiments in which fathead minnow reared for 11 months at 1 mg/ℓ failed to spawn, while those at 2 mg/ℓ or more produced proportionately more eggs per female with increase in DO up to 5 mg/ℓ. Control results at 8 mg/ℓ seem spurious and are perhaps attributable to the slightly different experimental arrangements involved.

6.4.2. EMBRYONIC DEVELOPMENT

With salmonids any reduction of DO from the air saturation value (ASV) or supersaturation can retard development and embryonic growth, reduce size at the time of hatching, or delay hatching, but most will hatch successfully at between 2 and 3 mg/ℓ to produce relatively small and underdeveloped larvae that are viable and not deformed. Observations by Gulidov (e.g. 1971) reported by A. Lysak (personal communication) show that embryonic development of *Leucaspius delincatus*, tench (*Tinca tinca*), roach (*Rutilus rutilus*), Crucian carp, pike and loach (*Misgurnus fossilis*) is adversely affected at supersaturated concentrations within the range 34–41.2 mg/ℓ.

Embryos of some non-salmonid species can develop to produce undeformed larvae at DO below 2 mg/ℓ but it has been shown (Dudley, 1969) that production of normal larvae of largemouth bass (*Micropterus salmoides*) is possible only at concentrations greater than 2, 2.5 and 3.5 mg/ℓ at incubation temperatures of 15, 20 and 25 °C. However, other species, including sturgeon (*Acipenser güldenstaedti*), bream (*Abramis brama*), *Vimba vimba*, and pike, apparently require well above 4–5 mg/ℓ at their normal temperatures; those of the last species continuously exposed to 2.0 mg/ℓ from 6 to 24 h after fertilization showed a statistically significant reduction in percentage hatch compared with that at 6 mg/ℓ

(Adelman and Smith, 1970). Siefert, Spoor and Syrett (1973) concluded that while 33 per cent ASV was not adequate for the survival and development of embryos and larvae of northern pike at 15 and 19 °C, 50 per cent ASV was satisfactory. Peterka and Kent (1976) found that the survival of embryos of northern pike exposed to 0.6 mg/ℓ for 8 h did not differ from the controls, but larval survival was reduced by exposure for 2 h to 0.8 mg/ℓ and required concentrations of 2 mg/ℓ or higher, while for an 8-h exposure they required 4 mg/ℓ or higher. Field observations showed that the average concentrations on a spawning ground varied from morning to afternoon from 4.8 to 8.1 mg/ℓ during the embryo stage, from 3.3 to 6.6 mg/ℓ during the sac larval stage and from 2.8 to 5.3 mg/ℓ during the free-swimming larval stage; water temperatures were in the range 6–10.3 °C. The hatch of eggs of scale carp (*Cyprinus carpio communis*) kept at 25 °C was reduced at 6 mg/ℓ and lower (Kaur and Toor, 1978).

Under hypoxic conditions hatching is often delayed, but in some species such as chum salmon (*Oncorhynchus keta*) it may be advanced (Trifonova, 1937); in both cases the newly hatched larvae tend to be smaller than under favourable conditions.

6.4.3 RESPIRATION AND METABOLISM

The considerable respiratory and cardio-vascular adaptive responses of fish to changes in DO, given special attention by Doudoroff and Shumway (1970) and Satchell (1971), are not necessarily indicative of impairment of ecologically important functions, and probably should not be used as a basis for judgements on DO requirements. For example, diel fluctuations in DO in water were reflected four hours later by corresponding changes in tissue oxygen tension in trout (Garey and Rahn, 1970). Levels of DO that depress ordinary metabolic rates of normally feeding fish in nature have not been determined, but they might perhaps be ecologically meaningful. However, the 'energy balance' method has been used to show that average metabolic rates of large-mouth bass (*Micropterus salmoides*) may be nearly independent of prey in its natural environment at favourable temperatures. Since similar amounts of energy can be expended in either seeking prey or in digestion and growth, DO requirements for metabolism may be independent of food consumption and growth rate, indicating that moderately reduced DO levels could affect growth rates at any level of food availability.

6.4.4 LARVAL GROWTH

Neither reduction in DO to about 5 mg/ℓ nor moderately wide diurnal fluctuations about this level has much effect on growth of salmonid alevins. At 3 mg/ℓ there may be only slight reduction of growth and, when the yolk sac has been fully absorbed, a reduction in size of about 25 per cent, unless temperatures are unfavourably high. There is little information on other species, but somewhat similar results have been reported for fathead minnow (Brungs, 1971). However, since this stage is generally short, retardation of post-larval (juvenile) growth is perhaps of more importance for fish production.

6.4.5 JUVENILE GROWTH

Any reduction in DO even to 50 per cent ASV can depress food consumption and growth rate of juvenile fish, even when all other conditions are favourable. It has been shown for the pike that while food conversion is not affected at 3 mg/ℓ, growth shows a slight decrease at 3-4 mg/ℓ and a much greater decrease at lower values (Adelman and Smith, 1970). Also, Japanese data (Itazawa, 1971) suggest that the minimum level of DO for maintaining maximum feeding, growth and efficiency of food conversion is 4-4.5 mg/ℓ for rainbow trout at about 10.5 °C, and 3 mg/ℓ for common carp at about 21.5 °C.

With carp weighing 40-250 g kept at 23 °C and offered food at a rate of 5 per cent of their body weight per day in nine portions, the ratio of weight of food offered to increase in weight of fish (conversion ratio) was almost 1 : 1 at a concentration of DO of 7 mg/ℓ, 2 : 1 at about 3 mg/ℓ, and 3 : 1 at about 1 mg/ℓ (Huisman, 1970); it was thought likely that the ratio would have been higher with a lower rate of feeding.

It has been found that 4-10-month-old brook trout (*Salvelinus fontinalis*) subjected to fluctuating levels of DO (2.4-10.6 mg/ℓ) do not grow as well as those exposed continuously to 10.6 mg/ℓ (Dorfman and Whitworth, 1969). Moreover, large diel fluctuations of DO down to minima of 2-3 mg/ℓ impair growth and appetite almost as much as do conditions of continuous low DO.

Carbon dioxide may also affect growth adversely. This is relevant where fluctuations may be caused by photosynthetic activity of aquatic plants.

If, in laboratory tests, growth rates of abundantly fed fish are low and apparently dependent on DO only at levels well below saturation, other factors such as low temperature, or nutritionally-deficient or unattractive food, which may not be important under natural conditions, though they may be so in artificial intensive culture, may have been the primary cause of the depressed growth rate.

Under natural conditions growth is usually limited by the availability of food, and increased exploitation of food may require excessive expenditure of energy. However, organic enrichment which often causes low DO can also help sustain a greater biomass of potential food organisms, thus reducing the metabolism required for foraging. Laboratory tests seldom simulate the bioenergetics of a natural system and therefore it is almost impossible to establish limiting levels of DO at which food consumption and growth might become dependent on oxygen under natural conditions. Nevertheless, they might be close to those restricting growth when food is unrestricted in the laboratory when ecosystems are used.

On the present limited information, it appears that at moderately high temperatures the critical or limiting DO levels for natural rates of growth and metabolism may be near the ASV.

6.4.6 SWIMMING PERFORMANCE

While swimming continues at near-lethal low levels of DO, maximum sustainable swimming speeds of salmonids normally decline with any reduction of DO below saturation. Even at cruising speeds there may be an increased tendency to fatigue as suggested by the results of recent experiments carried out by Smith *et al.* (1971) on adult migrant coho salmon (*Oncorhynchus kisutch*); these fish continued to swim at about 560 mm/s for an hour at 5-6.6 mg/ℓ DO and for a further hour at 4.5-5 mg/ℓ whereas those exposed for the second hour to 4-4.5 mg/ℓ became fatigued. Swimming of some warm-water fish, however, is affected only by concentrations near or below 5 mg/ℓ. Acclimating goldfish to DO deficiency does not change the effect of low DO on moderate swimming activity. The effects of reduced DO on 'burst' speeds and on the frequency with which these can be repeated have not yet been studied.

One can envisage that cruising speeds, maximum sustainable speeds, and 'bursts' would all have survival value for fish on migration and when foraging for food, but to what extent reduction in any of these abilities would affect fish stocks and catches is not known.

6.4.7 BEHAVIOUR AND AVOIDANCE

Activity can increase or decrease at reduced DO, but if the first occurs it is often followed by the second. Brook trout for example (Dandy, 1970), showed increased activity within minutes when the DO concentration was dropped from 11 to 8 or 6 mg/ℓ, reaching a peak within an hour and then gradually waning. An incidental result of increased activity may be avoidance of low DO concentrations, but some laboratory studies suggest deliberate avoidance of concentrations of about 1 mg/ℓ, for example those of Stott and Cross (1973) using roach (*Rutilus rutilus*). This avoidance level was raised slightly when the lowered DO (reduced over a period of 4 h) was accompanied by an increased CO_2, and reduced slightly when the roach were acclimated overnight to 3 mg/ℓ DO. A similar effect has been observed (Eddy, 1972; Warren, Doudoroff and Shumway, 1973) in juvenile chinook salmon exposed to a concentration of 20 mg/ℓ CO_2 in the presence of 2.5 mg/ℓ DO. There is, however, considerable variation in the levels avoided by fish reported by different workers; to some extent this may reflect the experimental technique used, in particular the nature of the DO gradient and the existence of other superimposed behaviour patterns which may be important under natural conditions. While many species occur at, and do not avoid, DO levels only slightly above lethal, successful avoidance has been observed when better oxygenated water is accessible, and this is supported by field observations. Serns (1976) demonstrated that batches of rainbow trout deposited into the epilimnion and hypolimnion of a lake in September moved in both directions through the 1-2 m layer in between in which the concentration of dissolved oxygen was 0.5-0.7 mg/ℓ.

Avoidance behaviour of fish under laboratory conditions raises the possibility that regions of low concentrations in estuaries could form a barrier to the movement of migratory fish. During an 11-year study, the upstream migration of adult chinook salmon (*Oncorhynchus tshawysha*) and coho salmon through a fish pass was apparently inhibited by DO below 5 mg/ℓ, but in an exceptional year the fish proceeded even at 3 mg/ℓ; however, the possible effects of other germane factors, such as water temperature and flow, were not taken into account.

American shad (*Alosa sapidissima*) have been reported to pass through an estuarine zone at 2 mg/ℓ and Chittenden (1973) found that the threshold concentration for migration through polluted zones was 2.5–3.0 mg/ℓ. On the other hand there appears to be no information on whether smolts can be prevented by low DO from migrating downstream.

Other behavioural reactions of fish of possible survival value for the species are also affected by reduced DO. Schooling behaviour can be altered when DO is lowered to 7 mg/ℓ (Moss and McFarland, 1970), and for the American shad this occurs when it is less than 4.5 mg/ℓ. Another example is the tendency of the walleye (*Stizostedion vitreum vitreum*) to remain quiet under cover; this behaviour is progressively changed with reduction in concentration of DO from 6 to 2 mg/ℓ, being finally replaced by abnormally active swimming in the open (Scherer, 1971) when it is 1–2 mg/ℓ.

6.5 Direct effect on fish food organisms

While some food organisms may be harmed by reduced DO levels too high to harm fish, others thrive in waters enriched by oxygen-absorbing organic material.

Larvae of the ephemeropteran (*Cloeon dipterum*), a species widespread in Europe at low altitude, lived longer at low concentrations of DO than the plecopteran (*Perlodes intricata*), which is confined to mountainous areas, whether these concentrations were arrived at gradually or suddenly; they were able to exhaust the DO in an enclosed vessel down to 0.02 mg/ℓ at 5.5 °C, whereas *P. intricata* died almost immediately when transferred suddenly to 26 per cent ASV at 5.5 and 15.5 °C (Kamler, 1971). Also, the rheotactic response of *Gammarus*, which is at a maximum under laboratory conditions at a water velocity of 50 mm/s, has been shown to be greatest at a DO of 2.7, 3.3 and 5.3 mg/ℓ for *G. pulex*, *G. roeseli* and *G. fossarum* respectively (Vobis, 1972). Other examples are given by Nebeker (1972), the 30-day LC50 for ephemeroptera and chironomids ranging from 0.6 to 5.0 mg/ℓ. Surber and Bessey (1974) measured the minimum concentration in which a large number of invertebrate species survived for 12 h after the concentration had been successively reduced by about 1 mg/ℓ at 12-h intervals; the values ranged from 3.5 to 2.5 for some trichoptera, ephemeroptera, plecoptera and odonata, to less than 1 mg/ℓ for the most resistant ephemeroptera, odonata, amphipoda and *Sialis* sp. The filtering rate of *Daphnia pulex* was measured by Kring and O'Brien (1976) and decreased sharply on sudden exposure to DO concentrations lower than 3 mg/ℓ; however, after exposure for up to 15 days to 1.5 mg/ℓ the filtering rate increased progressively until it exceeded normal rates.

Overall food resources are therefore unlikely to be impaired by organic wastes which merely reduce the DO level. Thus the oxygen requirements of fish food organisms need not necessarily be evaluated when estimating the DO levels necessary for the protection of fish or fisheries. Some organisms, however, may be of special importance because they may also comprise commercial fisheries, for example the crayfish (*Astacus fluviatilis*), and in this case little is known of its oxygen requirements though Höglund (1961) reported that it responded to gradients of DO under laboratory conditions.

6.6 Field observations

6.6.1 RIVERS

A good mixed fish fauna has been found in inland waters having DO levels below 4-5 mg/ℓ and in polluted waters even where for a long time they had not exceeded 4 mg/ℓ. However, a heavy mortality of salmon (*Salmo salar*) occurred in the R. Don, Scotland, in 1971 at DO levels of about 4 mg/ℓ when minimum temperatures were 18 °C and maximum values about 23 °C (E. McGregor Weir, personal communication). This is in agreement with laboratory data which indicate a higher lethal DO level at elevated temperatures (p. 129, para. 6). Brooker, Morris and Hemsworth (1977) recorded a heavy mortality among adult Atlantic salmon in the R. Wye, U.K., when the daily minimum concentration of DO had fallen over a period of 4-5 days from 5 mg/ℓ to about 1.0 mg/ℓ, while the maximum daily temperatures had increased over this period from about 23 °C to 27.6 °C and the minimum from about 21 to 25.2 °C. However, some mortality had also occurred at the beginning of this period. Shad (*Alosa falax*) were also affected (Welsh National Water Development Authority, 1976). Bergheim, Snekvik and Sivertsen (1978) have collected published data on fish kills of young and adult salmon and trout in rivers in Norway and generally found that they occurred when the DO was between 0.9 and 2.8 mg/ℓ at 16-20°C. Bergheim, Snekvik and Sivertsen (1978) conclude that concentrations of DO of 2-3 mg/ℓ in these rivers seem to be critical for young as well as adult salmon and trout.

Further data obtained from examination of concentrations found during daylight hours in the years 1968-1970 at places where fisheries are known to occur in the catchment area of the R. Trent, described by Alabaster (1973), show that trout fisheries occur where the median and 5-percentile of the annual distribution of DO are greater than 8.7 and 4.8 mg/ℓ respectively and that coarse fisheries occur where the median and 5-percentile are greater than 3.7 and 2.1 mg/ℓ respectively. It should be pointed out, though, that the status of these fisheries is not known, only that fish are present; there is no evidence that these populations are resident and therefore the critical levels for a permanent fishery may be higher. On the other hand, other pollutants were present in these waters, including heavy metals, which may cause an error in the opposite direction. Also, without further consideration of the sequence of changes in DO which make up the overall annual distribution found, it would be unwise to assume that these criteria would apply to other situations.

6.6.2 LAKES

In Onondaga Lake (Onondaga County, Syracuse, New York, 1971), which is saline, studies have shown that for substantial periods of time (weeks) much of the water, sometimes the whole water column, contains less than 4-5 mg/ℓ DO and yet the fisheries appear to be unharmed. According to Brodde (1972), the anaerobic region that developed near the bottom of L. Ivösjön at the end of the summer of 1969 was apparently successfully avoided by vendace (*Coregonus albula*), burbot (*Lota lota*), and ruffe (*Acerina cernua*). On the other hand, larvae of pollan (*Coregonus lavaretus*) hatched from eggs collected in 1968-1969 from L. Constance where the minimum DO was 4.3 mg/ℓ showed malformations absent in former years when the DO was much higher; also there was a high mortality of eggs in the lake in 1969-1970 (Nümann, 1972). However, it is possible that these results are partly attributable to the toxic effect of hydrogen sulphide leached from anaerobic bottom deposits (Smith and Oseid, 1972). In L. Titicaca where, because of the altitude, the ASV does not exceed about 5 mg/ℓ, the introduced rainbow trout apparently thrive (Everett, 1973).

6.6.3 ESTUARIES

Examination of data given by Wheeler (1969) for roach collected on the intake screens of electricity generating stations using the tidal Thames for cooling purposes shows that in the period November 1967-October 1968, where the average DO was about 78 per cent ASV, catches were about 14 per month, while where the average was less than 25 per cent they were less than 5 per month.

Information relating to the disappearance of fisheries from the Thames Estuary at the turn of the century and the return of some species over the last decade has been examined by Alabaster (1973). It suggests that for lampern (*Lampetra fluviatilis*), flounder (*Platichthys flesus*) and smelt (*Osmerus eperlanus*), values of at least 30-50 per cent ASV are necessary for their presence. However, shad (*Alosa fallax*) had not then reappeared and may have somewhat higher requirements for DO. Some of these fish have since become further established with the maintenance of improved conditions (Gameson and Wheeler, 1977).

Examination of data supplied by the Northumberland River Authority on salmon catches in the R. Tyne for the year 1967 suggests that the fish were passing upstream through a zone in the estuary during March and early April where the calculated minimum DO was probably oscillating between 4.5 and 6.8 mg/ℓ (J. S. Alabaster and M. J. Barrett, personal communication). However, it is not possible to conclude from the data what minimum would have inhibited the migration.

6.7 Summary of data

Laboratory data point to certain levels of DO associated with impairment or alteration of fish survival, growth, reproduction, swimming ability and behaviour; incomplete as the data are, with respect to the distributions of the responses within fish populations in given physiological and behavioural states, they must form the present basis of any DO criteria for fish and fisheries, and have had to be used to derive the tentative minimum steady levels proposed here for normal successful fulfilment of the life cycle, assuming other environmental factors are favourable including the absence of poisons (*Table 6.1*).

They suggest that, in general, a minimum of 5 mg/ℓ would be a satisfactory limit for most of the processes required for a successful fish life cycle, though it may be unnecessarily high merely to ensure satisfactory survival of the fish and growth of the juveniles. Consequently fluctuations about 5 mg/ℓ or any reduction below 5 mg/ℓ could have a greater effect on some processes than on others; the greater effect of fluctuations in DO on juvenile growth as compared with that on growth of larvae has already been mentioned, but clearly fecundity, hatch of eggs, and larval morphology and survival, as well as the upstream

Table 6.1   TENTATIVE MINIMUM SUSTAINED DO FOR MAINTAINING THE
NORMAL ATTRIBUTES OF THE LIFE CYCLE OF FISH UNDER
OTHERWISE FAVOURABLE CONDITIONS

Attribute	DO (mg/ℓ)	Page
Survival of juveniles and adults for one day or longer	3	130
Fecundity, hatch of eggs, larval survival	5	131
10 per cent reduction in hatched larval weight	7	
Larval growth	5	132
Juvenile growth (could be reduced 20 per cent)	4	
Growth of juvenile carp (*Cyprinus carpio*)	3	
Cruising swimming speed (maximum sustainable speed could be reduced 10 per cent)	5	133
Upstream migration of Pacific salmon (*Oncorhynchus* spp.) and Atlantic salmon (*Salmo salar*)	5	134
Upstream migration of American shad (*Alosa sapidissima*)	2	
Schooling behaviour of American shad	5	135
Sheltering behaviour of walleye (*Stizostedion vitreum vitreum*)	6	

movement of migratory salmon and schooling behaviour of some species, including shad, would also be adversely affected by levels below 5 mg/ℓ that would not
necessarily affect either the survival of individuals or the upstream migration of
shad. This is consistent with the mere presence of fish observed in polluted rivers
and estuaries where the DO is well below saturation and exhibits a wide variation
within a year (p. 136, para. 2 to p. 137, para. 3); this would suggest minimum
acceptable values (for ranges of variation) of much less than 5 mg/ℓ—probably
less than 1 mg/ℓ, for example, for coarse fish in the R. Trent.

6.8 Tentative DO criteria

Difficulties arise in formulating DO criteria for fisheries because of the widely
differing patterns of DO fluctuations which can exist in a river. Even in an
unpolluted river there can be a considerable fluctuation with peak DO values after
noon and low DO values before sunrise. This pattern can be similar, though at a
generally lower level, in a polluted river and on this can be superimposed a seasonal variation and changes associated with flow. Low DO values attained for
1-2 h each day will have less effect than the same value sustained for several
days or even weeks. The true DO regime in a river is likely to be shown not by
infrequent sampling during daylight hours but only where automatic monitoring
stations exist.

However, even where the DO regime is known with some certainty, it will be
difficult to predict the effect which this is likely to have on fish and fisheries,
unless the levels are so low as to be lethal to fish or so high as to have no effect
on them. Although there is an extensive literature on the DO requirements of

fish, few experiments have been made which even approach natural conditions, most being made at constant DO levels; further, field data are either inadequate in describing the fish populations present or the DO regime, or are complicated by the presence of other poisons.

In these circumstances, only tentative criteria can be put forward. It is obvious that these cannot be based on a single minimum value never to be violated or even as several minima each not to be violated at a certain time of year, but rather as a minimum percentile distribution over a year or perhaps part of a year, or, with some fisheries, part of a tidal cycle. This idea is inherent in the criteria for monohydric phenols, suggested by the EIFAC Working Party on Water Quality Criteria for European Freshwater Fish (Chapter 5) though it was not expressed as a percentile distribution.

From the limited data available it is tentatively suggested, pending further information, that for resident populations of moderately tolerant freshwater species, such as roach, the annual 50- and 5-percentile DO values should be greater than 5 mg/ℓ and 2 mg/ℓ respectively and for salmonids the percentile should be 9 mg/ℓ and 5 mg/ℓ respectively.

These values are to be regarded as of general guidance only because there are special circumstances where more consideration should be given to the seasonal distribution of DO. For example, for adult migrant salmonids the values for the 50- and 5-percentiles for periods of low water during the summer months in the region of an estuary where the DO is lowest, should be 5 and 2 mg/ℓ respectively, although with an extensive deoxygenated zone (more than a few kilometres in length) higher concentrations at these percentiles might be necessary. Moreover, because lower levels are particularly dangerous to the young stages of fish (p. 129, para. 3-4 and p. 131) they should not occur when such stages are present.

However, all these minimum values might need to be considerably increased in the presence of high temperature (p. 129, para. 6; pp. 133, 136) or poisons (p. 130, para. 4).

To enable more satisfactory criteria to be formulated, more laboratory studies are required which reflect natural DO regimes and more field observations are required on the status of fish populations and on the movements of adults and young of migratory species. These should be coupled with more complete data on the DO, both where the fish populations are only marginal and where they are well established. The consequences of reduced fecundity, growth and reproduction and of changed behaviour on population dynamics and production of fish and of fisheries should also be appraised.

6.9 References

ADELMAN, I. R. and SMITH, L. L. (1970). Effect of oxygen on growth and food conversion efficiency of northern pike. *Prog. Fish Cult.* **32 (2)**, 93-96

ADELMAN, I. R. and SMITH, L. L. (1972). Toxicity of hydrogen sulphide to goldfish (*Carassius auratus*) as influenced by temperature, oxygen and bio-assay technique. *J. Fish. Res. Bd Can.* **29 (9)**, 1309-1311

ALABASTER, J. S. (1973). Oxygen in estuaries; requirements for fisheries. In *Mathematical and hydraulic modelling of estuarine pollution. Wat. Pollut. Res. Tech. Pap, Lond.* **13**

ALABASTER, J. S., SHURBEN, D. G. and MALLETT, M. J. (1979). The survival of smolts of salmon (*Salmo salar*) at low concentrations of dissolved oxygen. *J. Fish. Biol.* **15**, 1–8

BERGHEIM, A., SNEKVIK, E. and SIVERTSEN. (1976). Effluents from grass silos as a pollution problem in rivers in the southwestern part of Norway. *Vatten* **34**, 33–43

BRODDE, A. (1972). Ivösjön—en kulturpåverkad sjö. *Vatten* **2**, 102–114

BROOKER, M. P., MORRIS, D. L. and HEMSWORTH, R. J. (1977). Mass mortalities of adult salmon (*Salmo salar*) in the River Wye, 1976. *J. appl. Ecol.* **14**, 409–417

BRUNGS, W. A. (1971). Chronic effects of low dissolved oxygen concentrations on the fathead minnow (*Pimephales promelas*). *J. Fish. Res. Bd Can.* **28 (8)** 1119–1123

BRUNGS, W. A., McCORMICK, J. H., NEIHEISEL, T. W., SPEHAR, R. L., STEPHAN, C. E. and STOKES, G. N. (1977). Effects of pollution on freshwater fish. *J. Wat. Pollut. Control Fed.* **49 (6)**, 1425–1493

CAIRNS, J. and SCHEIER, A. (1957). The effect of periodic low oxygen upon the toxicity of various chemicals to aquatic organisms. *Proc. Ind. Waste Conf. Purdue Univ., (Engng Ext. Ser.)* **12(94)**, 165–176

CHITTENDEN, M. E. (1973). Effects of handling on oxygen requirements of American shad *Alosa sapidissima. J. Fish. Res. Bd Can.* **30 (1)**, 105–110

DANDY, J. W. T. (1970). Activity response to oxygen in the brook trout (*Salvelinus fontinalis* Mitchell). *Can. J. Zool.* **48 (1)**, 1067

DAVIES, J. C. (1975). Minimal dissolved oxygen requirements of aquatic life with emphasis on Canadian species: a review. *J. Fish. Res. Bd Can.* **32 (12)**, 2295–2332

DORFMAN, D. and WHITWORTH, W. R. (1969). Effects of fluctuations of lead, temperature and dissolved oxygen on the growth of the brook trout. *J. Fish. Res. Bd Can.* **26**, 2493–2501

DOUDOROFF, P. and SHUMWAY, D. L. (1970). Dissolved oxygen requirements of freshwater fishes. *FAO Fish. Tech. Pap.* **86,**

DUDLEY, R. G. (1969). Survival of largemouth bass embryos at low dissolved oxygen concentrations. M.Sc. Thesis, Cornell University

EDDY, F. B. (1971). Blood gas relationships in the rainbow trout *Salmo gairdneri. J. exp. Biol.* **55**, 695–711

EDDY, R. M. (1972). The influence of dissolved oxygen concentration and temperature on the survival and growth of chinook salmon embryos and fry. M. S. Thesis, Oregon State University

EIFAC (1972). European Inland Fisheries Advisory Commission Working Party on Water Quality Criteria for European Freshwater Fish. Monohydric phenols and inland fisheries. *EIFAC Tech. Pap.* **(15)**

EVERETT, G. V. (1973). Rainbow trout, *Salmo gairdneri* (Rich.), fishery of Lake Titicaca. *J. Fish. Biol.* **5**, 429–440

GAMESON, A. L. H. and WHEELER, A. (1977). Restoration and recovery of the Thames Estuary. In *Recovery and restoration of damaged ecosystems* (Ed. by J. Cairns, K. L. Dickson and E. E. Herricks) pp. 72–101. University Press of Charlottesville, Virginia, USA

GAREY, W. F. and RAHN, H. (1970). Gas tensions in tissues of trout and carp exposed to diurnal changes in oxygen tension of the water. *J. exp. Biol.* **52**, 575–582

GULIDOV, M. V. (1971). Characteristics of the embryonic development of certain Cyprinidae in relation to oxygen conditions during incubation. *Dokl. Akad. Nauk. SSR Ser. Biol.* **197 (2)**, 497-500

HICKS, D. B. and DE WITT, J. W. (1971). Effects of dissolved oxygen on kraft pulp mill effluent toxicity. *Wat. Res.* **5 (9)**, 693-701

HÖGLUND, L. B. (1961). The reactions of fish in concentration gradients. *Rep. Inst. Freshwat. Res. Drottningholm* **43**

HUISMAN, E. A. (1970). Een onderzoek naar de kweekmogelijkheid van de karper in doorstroonbekkens. In *Jversl. Org. Verbet. Binnenviss.* **1968-69**

ITAZAWA, Y. (1971). An estimation of the minimum level of dissolved oxygen in water required for normal life of fish. *Bull. Jap. Soc. Sci. Fish.* **37 (4)**, 273-276

KAMLER, E. (1971). Reactions of two species of aquatic insects to the changes of temperature and dissolved oxygen. *Polsk. Arch. Hydrobiol.* **18(3)**, 303-323

KAUR, K. and TOOR, H. S. (1978). Effect of dissolved oxygen on the survival and hatching of eggs of scale carp. *Prog. Fish. Cult.* **40(1)**, 35-37

KLYASHTORIN, L. B. (1976). The sensitivity of young sturgeons to oxygen deficiency. *J. Ichthyol.* **16 (4)**, 677-682

KRING, R. L. and O'BRIEN, W. J. (1976). Effect of varying oxygen concentrations on the filtering rate of *Daphnia pulex. Ecology* **57 (4)**, 808-814

LANDLESS, P. J. (1976). Acclimation of rainbow trout to sea water. *Aquaculture* **7**, 173-179

McKIM, J. M., BENOIT, D. A., BRESINGER, K. E., BRUNGS, W. A. and SIEFERT, R. E. (1975). Effects of pollution on freshwater fish. *J. Wat. Pollut. Control Fed.* **47 (6)**, 1711-1768

MOSS, S. A. and McFARLAND, W. N. (1970). The influence of dissolved oxygen and carbon dioxide on fish schooling behaviour. *Mar. Biol.* **5**, 100-107

NEBEKER, A. V. (1972). Effect of low oxygen concentration on survival and emergence of aquatic insects. *Trans. Am. Fish. Soc.* **101**, 675-679

NÜMANN, W. (1972). The Bodensee: effects of exploitation and eutrophication on the salmonid community. *J. Fish. Res. Bd Can.* **29 (6)**, 833-847

ONONDAGA COUNTY, SYRACUSE, NEW YORK (1971). Onondaga Lake study. *Wat. Pollut. Control Res. Ser., Wash.* (11060 FAE 4/71)

PETERKA, J. J. and KENT, J. S. (1976). Final report. Dissolved oxygen, temperature, survival of young at fish spawning sites. Environmental Protection Agency, Washington (EPA/600/3-76-113)

SATCHELL, G. H. (1971). Circulation in fishes. *Cambr. Monogr. exp. Biol.* **18**

SCHERER, E. (1971). Effects of oxygen depletion and carbon dioxide build-up on the photic behaviour of the walleye (*Stizostedion vitreum vitreum*). *J. Fish. Res. Bd Can.* **28 (9)**, 1303-1307

SERNS, S. L. (1976). Movement of rainbow trout across a metalimnion deficient in dissolved oxygen. *Prog. Fish. Cult.* **38 (1)**, 54

SIEFERT, R. E., SPOOR, W. A. and SYRETT, R. F. (1973). Effects of reduced oxygen concentrations on northern pike *Esox lucius* embryos and larvae. *J. Fish. Res. Bd Can.* **30**, 849-852

SMITH, L. L. and OSEID, D. M. (1972). Effects of hydrogen sulphide on fish eggs and fry. *Wat. Res.* **6 (6)**, 711-720

SMITH, L. S., *et al.* (1971). Response of teleost fish to environmental stress. *Wat. Pollut. Control. Res. Ser., Wash.* (18050 EBK 02/71)

STOTT, B. and CROSS, D. G. (1973). The reactions of roach (*Rutilus rutilus*) to changes in the concentration of dissolved oxygen and free carbon dioxide in a laboratory channel. *Wat. Res.* 7 (5)

SURBER, E. W. and BESSEY, W. E. (1974). Minimum oxygen levels survived by stream invertebrates. *Bull. natl. tech. Inf. Serv., U.S.* 81

TRIFONOVA, A. N. (1937). La physiologie de la différenciation et de la croissance. 1. L'équilibre Pasteur-Meyerhof dans le développement des poissons. *Acta Zool., Stockh.* 18 , 375–445

VOBIS, H. (1972). Rheotaktisches Verhalten von *Gammarus pulex, Gammarus roeseli* und *Gammarus fossarum* bei verschiedenem Sauerstoffgehalt des Wassers. Thesis. Landsstelle für Gewasserkunde und Wasserwirtschaftliche Planung Baden-Württemberg, Karlsruhe

WARREN, C. E., DOUDOROFF, P. and SHUMWAY, D. L. (1973). Development of dissolved oxygen criteria for freshwater fish. *Ecol. Res. Ser., Wash.* (EPA-R3-73-019)

WEATHERLEY, A. H. (1970). Effects of superabundant oxygen on thermal tolerance of goldfish. *Biol. Bull. Mar. Biol. Lab., Woods Hole* 139, 229–238

WHEELER, A. C. (1969). Fish-life and pollution in the lower Thames: a review and preliminary report. *Biol. Conserv.* 2 (1), 25

WELSH NATIONAL WATER DEVELOPMENT AUTHORITY, U.K. (1976). Wye River Division, Fisheries Department; Annual Report, p. 1

7

CHLORINE

Foreword

The preparation of the original report on chlorine and freshwater fish was accomplished largely by the Water Pollution Research Laboratory, Stevenage, U.K. (now part of the Water Research Centre) which prepared the basic manuscript for review by the members of the Working Party on Water Quality Criteria for European Freshwater Fish. In updating the original report, minimal consideration has been given to data in papers (e.g. Heath, 1977; Brooks and Seegert, 1977) dealing primarily with the effect of short-term exposure to high concentrations, which are mainly relevant to the effects of intermittent chlorination of cooling waters and sewage effluents.

7.1 Summary

Chlorine as hypochlorous acid and chloramines is toxic to aquatic life. Coarse fish species, invertebrate organisms and plants are generally more resistant to chlorine than salmonids, although the production of young *Daphnia* is reduced at a concentration of $3.5~\mu g/\ell$ ($0.4-1.4~\mu g~HOCl/\ell$).

From the limited data available, it seems that concentrations of chlorine greater than $8~\mu g~HOCl/\ell$ could be harmful or lethal within four days to both salmonid and coarse fish, whereas $4~\mu g~HOCl/\ell$ has been endured by sensitive species of fish for five days, although with some decline in the normal activity.

The toxicity of chlorine to fish is increased by a reduction in the concentration of dissolved oxygen, and little changed by increase in salinity up to 50 per cent sea water, but there are few or no data available on the effect of temperature, pH, and water hardness.

Avoidance behaviour of rainbow trout under experimental conditions has been slight at a concentration of chlorine of $1~\mu g/\ell$ ($2-8~\mu g~HOCl/\ell$) and marked at $1-8~\mu g~HOCl/\ell$, in which range adverse changes in the blood may occur.

Chlorine is too reactive to persist for long in most streams and therefore the upper limit for fish survival might be set closer to the lethal levels than might otherwise be the case, especially as avoidance behaviour and acclimation to chlorine are likely to afford additional protection to the fish from regions of high concentration. Consequently it is tentatively suggested that an acceptable upper limit would be 4 μg HOCl/ℓ, because it should result in little or no mortality of fish, perhaps have only a minor effect on fish behaviour and blood physiology and not be high enough to be damaging to the majority of fish food organisms. The amount of total chlorine corresponding to this concentration varies according to the temperature and pH value of the water, as shown in *Table 7.2* (p. 155). Since chlorine may react with thiocyanide to produce lethal concentrations of hydrogen cyanide and/or cyanogen chloride and concentrations of chlorine as low as 1 μg/ℓ in the presence of phenols are likely to produce taints in the flesh of fish, an upper limit of less than 4 μg/ℓ might be necessary in the presence of these other poisons.

7.2 Introduction

Chlorination (by elemental chlorine (Cl_2), hypochlorites, or chloramines) is used in disinfecting and removing unwanted tastes and odours from drinking water. Sufficient chlorine (defined on p. 146, para. 4) is added to give a small excess for the destruction of pathogenic bacteria, but this excess can make municipal tap waters unsuitable for fish-keeping purposes. Chlorination is also used in the textile and paper-pulp industries for bleaching and slimicidal purposes, and in sewage treatment to reduce either odour, the density of 'ponding' algae on filter beds, or the numbers of bacteria in effluents discharged to surface waters. The amount of chlorine added to sewage is insufficient to oxidize the waste completely (i.e. the chlorine 'demand' is not fully satisfied) and there is no excess chlorine to impair the biological processes essential for treatment, or the life in the waters to which the effluent is discharged. Chlorine is also added to cooling waters, and other industrial waste waters, to reduce or eliminate growths of algal or bacterial 'slimes' in cooling towers and associated systems, and to swimming pools for the purpose of disinfection. Literature on the effects of chlorine on fish has been summarized previously by Southgate (1948), Doudoroff and Katz (1950), Liebmann (1960), McKee and Wolf (1963), Jones (1964), Zillich (1972) and Brungs (1973; 1977), and that on various freshwater organisms by Evins (1975), Mattice (1975) and Brooks and Seegert (1975; 1977).

7.3 Chemistry of chlorine in water

When elemental chlorine or hypochlorite compounds, e.g. calcium hypochlorite, are added to water at pH values above about 5, rapid reactions occur, resulting in the formation of hypochlorous acid (HOCl) in equilibrium with hypochlorite ions (OCl^-) as shown by the following two sets of equations:

(i) $Cl_2 + H_2O \leftrightharpoons HCl + HOCl$

$HOCl \leftrightharpoons H^+ + OCl^-$

(ii) $Ca(OCl)_2 \rightarrow Ca^{++} + 2OCl^-$

$H^+ + OCl^- \leftrightharpoons HOCl$

(The presence of the extremely fugitive elemental chlorine (Cl_2) can be ignored for the purpose of the present review.)

Since the toxic chemical species in solution in chlorine poisoning is probably hypochlorous acid, a weak acid, the toxicity of any solution containing chlorine will depend on the pH of the solution, because it markedly influences the degree of dissociation. Ionization constants (pK_a) for temperatures from 0 to 30 °C are given in *Table 7.1*, and the proportions of HOCl and OCl in solution at 5–25 °C at pH values between 5 and 9 are shown in *Figure 7.1*.

Table 7.1   IONIZATION CONSTANTS (pK_a) FOR HYPOCHLOROUS ACID AT TEMPERATURES BETWEEN 0 and 30 °C (SILLÉN AND MARTELL, 1964)

Temp. (°C)	0	5	10	15	20	25	30
pK_a	7.83	7.75	7.69	7.63	7.58	7.54	7.50

Below pH 7.5, therefore, at all temperatures at which the majority of European fish species are likely to be found, the greater part of any chlorine present will be in a toxic form. When chlorine (as HOCl) is added to water containing ammonia it will, in the absence of other oxidizable substances, initially form monochloramine (NH_2Cl), dichloramine ($NHCl_2$), trichloramine or nitrogen trichloride (NCl_3), or a mixture of these compounds. Formation of the more

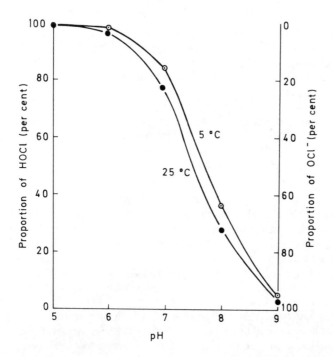

Figure 7.1. Proportion of HOCl and OCl⁻ in solution at temperatures of 5 °C and 25 °C and pH values between 5 and 9

highly substituted derivatives is favoured by increased acidity of solution and increased gravimetric ratio of chlorine to ammoniacal nitrogen according to Palin (1950) who describes the following reactions as taking place:

$$NH_4^+ + HOCl \rightarrow NH_2Cl + H_2O + H^+$$

$$NH_2Cl + HOCl \rightarrow NHCl_2 + H_2O$$

$$NHCl_2 + HOCl \rightarrow NCl_3 + H_2O$$

In non-acidic waters further addition of chlorine gives as main products probably chloride ion and elemental nitrogen. The concentration at which any particular compound will be present is difficult to predict, although probably at the normal pH values of natural waters only relatively small amounts of nitrogen trichloride (a poison known to have chronic systemic effects) are formed. However, it appears that chloramines slowly reach equilibrium with a small concentration of hypochlorous acid which possibly accounts for their toxicity to fish.

Since sewage effluents almost always contain ammonia the effects of chlorine should not be considered without taking into account the effects of chloramines, which though less toxic than chlorine are more persistent. Hypochlorous acid and hypochlorite ion decompose slowly in solution forming chloride ion and oxygen, a process accelerated in the presence of sunlight, and they are more readily removed by organic matter than chlorine and chloramines.

7.3.1 TERMINOLOGY

When chlorine is present in water in a form in which it is available to act as an oxidant it may be described in the literature as 'free', available', 'active', or 'residual' chlorine, or by some combination of these adjectives. When present as chloramines it may also be referred to as 'bound' chlorine. These forms can conveniently be classified as:

(a) *Free available chlorine*, that present as an equilibrium mixture of hypochlorite ions (OCl^-) and hypochlorous acid (HOCl),

(b) *Combined available chlorine*, that present in chloramines or other compounds with an N-Cl link, and

(c) *Total available chlorine*, essentially the sum of (a) and (b).

For brevity in this chapter the term 'chlorine' is used to refer to the total available chlorine when this cannot be, or does not need to be, more closely defined. It does not, however, include elemental chlorine (Cl_2). Specific compounds are named whenever possible. It should be noted that some of these, e.g. dichloroisocyanurates (used for the disinfection of swimming-bath waters), may react as free available chlorine in commonly used methods of chemical analysis.

Where possible the concentration at which hypochlorous acid may be present has been estimated, but this cannot always be done because many reports fail to give adequate details of the chlorine source and of temperature and pH of the solutions.

7.4 Toxicology of chlorine in water

7.4.1 MODE OF ACTION AND SYMPTOMS OF ACUTE POISONING

Various authors have described how fish exposed to chlorine solution become restless before losing equilibrium and dying. No direct information on the chemical basis of chlorine toxicity to fish is available, but enzymes within the cell contain sulphydryl (—SH) groups essential to their activity and these become oxidized almost immediately by chlorine in both animals and plants, enzymatic activity being irreversibly abolished (Green and Stumpf, 1946) because of the strength of the covalent bond formed (Albert, 1965). This may explain why, once equilibrium has been lost, the fish do not recover when placed in clean water (Panikkar, 1960; Pike, 1971); yellow perch (*Perca flavescens*) tested at 10 °C appears to be a rare exception (Brooks and Seegert, 1977).

Damage to gill epithelium has been reported by Penzes (1971), Valenzuela (1976) and Bass, Berry and Heath (1977), and inferred by Rosenberger (1971). However, Fobes (1971), who found no effect on the respiration rate of isolated gill tissue excised from white sucker (*Catostomus commersoni*) exposed to 1 mg/ℓ chlorine, concluded that the gills were not the primary site of chlorine toxicity. Acutely toxic concentrations of chlorine have increased the concentrations of various elements in the plasma of rainbow trout, especially that of potassium, and reduced the concentration of sodium (Zeitoun, Hughes and Ullney, 1977). In fathead minnow (*Pimephales promelas*) the acute toxicity of monochloramine has been ascribed to anoxia resulting from the production of methaemoglobin (Groethe and Eaton, 1975). Furthermore, young coho salmon (*Oncorhynchus kisutch*) showed a slight increase in methaemoglobin in the blood and reduction in haemoglobin and a temporary increase in the percentage of circulating erythrocytes when exposed to chlorine at a concentration of 0.07 mg/ℓ in sewage effluent diluted with sea water (Buckley, 1976), and mild to severe symptoms of haemolytic anaemia after 12 weeks exposure to concentrations in the range 3-5 μg/ℓ (Buckley, 1977).

7.4.2 LETHAL EFFECTS ON FISH

Embryos, larvae and fry

Blake (1930) showed that eyed ova of brown trout (*Salmo trutta*) incubated at 3-5 °C and exposed to 10 mg/ℓ of chlorine for 30 min showed a slight increase in mortality on hatching (1.2 per cent compared with 0.6 per cent among controls).

In general, newly-hatched larvae are more susceptible than eggs. Grande (1966) reported that in a very soft water (14 mg/ℓ as $CaCO_3$) at 9 °C and a pH of 6.4 a chlorine concentration of 0.07 mg/ℓ was not lethal within 3 days to salmon (*Salmo salar*) fry exposed immediately after completion of absorption of the yolk. At 0.1 mg/ℓ, however, the mean period of survival was 1.2 days, at 0.13 mg/ℓ it was 8 h, and at 0.3 mg/ℓ only 3 h. (The maximum concentration of HOCl under these conditions would be about 94 per cent of the given chlorine concentration.) Scheuring and Stetter (1950-51) also report that trout died in 16-24 h at a concentration of 0.1 mg/ℓ at 10-12 °C.

M. Grande (personal communication) also reported mortality of fry of brown trout, rainbow trout (*Salmo gairdneri*), Arctic char (*Salvelinus alpinus*), and Atlantic salmon in chlorinated tap water at about 0.1 mg/ℓ of chlorine (equivalent to about 0.09 mg/ℓ of HOCl) over a period of several days. Larson, Hutchings and Schlesinger (1977) found that the fry and alevins of brook trout (*Salvelinus fontinalis*) had a similar sensitivity to chloramine (present mainly as monochloramine), the 4-day LC50 values being 0.082 and 0.088 mg/ℓ respectively. 'Trout' fry were killed in 2 days by 0.05–0.06 mg/ℓ of 'chlorine' but 0.01 mg/ℓ did not prove fatal over a period of two weeks (Coventry, Shelford and Miller, 1935).

Fingerling and adult salmonids

Rainbow trout fingerlings and yearlings died in 2 h at 0.3 mg/ℓ and in 4–5 h at 0.25 mg/ℓ (Taylor and James, 1928). At a dissolved-oxygen concentration of 10–11 mg/ℓ, temperature of 15 °C, and pH of either 6.3 or 7.0, a mixture of HOCl, NH_2Cl and $NHCl_2$ in which the former predominated, was more toxic than one in which either NH_2Cl or a mixture of mono- and dichloramines predominated, the concentration at which the mixture containing predominantly HOCl killed rainbow trout in a given time interval being about one third of that in which NH_2Cl predominated. The 7-day LC50 for rainbow trout of a solution containing chlorine (mainly as NH_2Cl) was 0.08 mg/ℓ (Merkens, 1958) and under field conditions the 4-day LC50 was 0.014–0.029 mg/ℓ chlorine (Michigan Department of Natural Resources, 1971; reported in U.S. Environmental Protection Agency, 1976).

Studies with 4-month-old coho salmon (*Oncorhynchus kisutch*) showed that 76 per cent of the fish were killed at pH 7.6 by 0.2 mg/ℓ chlorine ($\equiv$ 0.1 mg/ℓ HOCl) in about 19 h (Department of Fisheries, Washington, 1960); the 4-day LC50 for chlorine has been reported as 0.1 mg/ℓ for this species and, in the presence of 4 per cent sewage effluent, as 0.07 mg/ℓ (Buckley, 1976). Pike (1971) found that brown trout (125–180 mm long) were all killed within 1 day by exposure for only 2 min to chlorine concentrations greater than 0.04 mg/ℓ at 11 °C. With continuous exposure the median period of survival at 0.03 mg/ℓ was less than 7.5 h, at 0.02 mg/ℓ less than 10.5 h, and at 0.01 mg/ℓ (8 μg HOCl/ℓ) less than 45.5 h. Under field conditions a concentration of 0.05 mg/ℓ chlorine has been found to be lethal to brown trout (Basch and Truchan, 1975). Dandy (1972) showed that at 0.35, 0.08 and 0.04 mg/ℓ chlorine (3.4 μg HOCl/ℓ) survival times of brook trout (*Salvelinus fontinalis*) were 9, 18 and 48 h respectively, while at 5 μg/ℓ (4 μg HOCl/ℓ) the fish survived at least 7 days.

Fingerling and adult coarse fish

Zimmerman and Berg (1934) observed that goldfish (*Carassius auratus*) were killed within 8 h by exposure to water containing 1.0–1.5 mg/ℓ of chlorine and replaced at a rate of 4 ℓ/min; at a pH of 7.9, a temperature of 25 °C, and a concentration of 2 mg/ℓ (0.64 mg HOCl/ℓ) they were killed within 17–48 h. Wakabayashi and Imaoka (1968) reported that goldfish were killed by unrenewed solutions having initial concentrations of 0.6–0.7 mg/ℓ chlorine. At 1 mg/ℓ chlorine (0.32 mg HOCl/ℓ) some were killed in 4 days (Ellis, 1937), and at 0.1-0.2 mg/ℓ chlorine they survived for an 'extended' period (Schaut, 1939). Taylor and James (1928) also report that they were not affected in 42 h by 0.25 mg/ℓ.

Ebeling (1931) observed the mortality of six species of fish over a period of four days in ponds having a temperature of 4.5-7 °C, pH of 7.2-7.3, and a nominal concentration of chlorine of about 1.0 mg/ℓ (0.7 mg HOCl/ℓ), the dissolved-oxygen concentration being 'constant'; pike (*Esox lucius*) died within 30 h, rainbow trout within 37-40 h, rudd (*Scardinius erythrophthalmus*) within 41-82 h, and about 80 per cent of the common carp (*Cyprinus carpio*), 20 per cent of the tench (*Tinca tinca*), and one of the eels (*Anguilla anguilla*) died after 100 h. Zimmerman and Berg (1934) also observed that 1.2 mg/ℓ killed large common carp. Scheuring and Stetter (1950-51) report that at a constant concentration of 0.15 mg/ℓ trout were killed within 14 days, whereas tench, common carp, Crucian carp (*Carassius carassius*), pike and pikeperch (*Stizostedion lucioperca*) survived between 6-37 days without apparent harm. A marked difference between rainbow trout and common carp in sensitivity to (intermittent) exposure to free chlorine has also been reported by Heath (1977).

Thus coarse fish appear to be much more resistant to high concentrations of chlorine than salmonids.

7.4.3 EFFECTS OF ENVIRONMENTAL FACTORS

Dissolved oxygen

The median period of survival of rainbow trout in a given concentration of chlorine (added as sodium hypochlorite) was found to be shorter at low concentrations of dissolved oxygen than it was at high (Department of Scientific and Industrial Research, 1958). Trout in solutions at pH 7.4 containing about 0.1 mg/ℓ chlorine (the lowest concentration tested, and equivalent to a maximum HOCl concentration of about 0.06 mg/ℓ) were killed in 1000 min at a dissolved-oxygen concentration of 90 per cent of the air saturation value (ASV) compared with 80 min at 40 per cent ASV. At pH 6.3 (when the concentration would be about 0.09 mg HOCl/ℓ) the survival times were 700 and 53 min respectively. Some of the chlorine may have reacted with ammonia excreted by the trout and been present as chloramines.

pH

No information is available on the effects of pH on the toxicity to fish of a given concentration of molecular HOCl, but the data of Merkens (1958) on the toxicity of mixtures of chlorine and chloramines to rainbow trout suggest that there is no effect.

Temperature

Little information is available on the effect of temperature on the toxicity of chlorine but studies using short-term (Stober and Hanson, 1976) or intermittent exposure of fish to chlorine (Brooks and Seegert, 1977; Heath, 1977) show that there is a tendency for toxicity to be greatest at high temperature, although there appears to be a range of temperature for a given species over which there may be little or no effect.

Hardness

There appears to be no information on the effect of hardness on the toxicity of chlorine to fish.

Salinity

At a concentration of total halogen (some of which would be bromine displaced by chlorine) of 1.34 mg/ℓ total chlorine and 0.95 mg/ℓ 'free chlorine' (0.19 mg HOCl/ℓ), rainbow trout in 50 per cent seawater (salinity 16.7 g/ℓ) at a pH of 8.3 had a median period of survival of 52 min (Department of Scientific and Industrial Research, 1958). It was concluded that the toxicity of the halogens resulting from the addition of chlorine to 'sea water' was only slightly less than that of chlorine in freshwater. 'Critical' (presumably lethal) levels of chlorine in sea water were found to be 0.05 mg/ℓ for chinook salmon (*Oncorhynchus tshawytscha*) and pink salmon (*O. gorbuscha*), while 0.09 mg/ℓ killed silver salmon within nine days (Department of Fisheries, Washington, 1960). Valenzuela (1976) showed that chlorine caused minimal gill damage and lowest mortalities in mosquitofish (*Gambusia affinis*) when tested in 25 per cent seawater, which was closest ionically to the body fluids, an observation confirmed by Cohen (1977).

7.4.4 SUBLETHAL EFFECTS ON FISH

Behaviour

Fish may avoid or be attracted to waters containing low concentrations of chlorine; Sprague and Drury (1969) found that rainbow trout showed a slight degree of avoidance of water containing chlorine at a concentration of 0.001 mg/ℓ but that this reaction became more marked at 0.01 mg/ℓ (12-day LC50), and strong at 1 mg/ℓ (4-h LC50); however, at 0.1 mg/ℓ (4-day LC50) preference was shown for the chlorinated water. Since the reported variation in pH of the test solutions was 7.0–8.4, the percentage of HOCl present could have been between 80 and 20 per cent of the nominal chlorine concentration. The reason for this behaviour is unknown, but Dandy (1972), who measured the activity of brook trout in the presence of chlorine, found that activity increased at 0.35 mg/ℓ (9-h LC50) and 0.08 mg/ℓ (18-h LC50), and suggested this would increase the possibility of fish moving randomly into fresh water given the choice, whereas at 0.04 mg/ℓ (0.034 mg HOCl/ℓ) (2-day LC50) activity was depressed, which would reduce the chances of movement into clean water. There was also a greater decline in activity than found in controls in fish kept for at least five days at 5 μg/ℓ (4 μg HOCl/ℓ) which was not lethal to fish within seven days. Avoidance of gradually increasing concentrations of chlorine in the range 0.005–0.45 mg/ℓ has also been observed by R. B. Bogardus and his colleagues (reported by Brungs, 1977) for American species. Katz and Harder (1976) quoted evidence of the senior author that chlorine reacts with ammonia excreted from the gill of fish to form chloramine, and suggested that breakpoint chlorination occurred at the gill at a concentration of 0.1 mg/ℓ of chlorine, which might explain why, in the experiments reported by Sprague and Drury (1969), salmon were apparently attracted by this concentration whereas they avoided concentrations of 1, 0.01 and 0.001 mg/ℓ. In one study (Cherry *et al.*, 1977) the avoidance response of the fish was more closely associated with the calculated concentration of HOCl than the total concentration of residual chlorine.

Spawning

The only precise data on the effects of chlorine on spawning are the unpublished results of Arthur and Eaton (quoted by Zillich, 1972) who found that chloramines at concentrations as low as 0.085 mg/ℓ nearly eliminated spawning of the fathead minnow (*Pimephales promelas*) and that at 0.043 mg/ℓ the number of spawnings per female and the number of eggs per spawning were reduced. A. R. Carlson (cited by Brungs, 1977) found no change in the reproductive behaviour of stickleback (*Gasterosteus aculeatus*) over a 3½ month period in concentrations of chloramine up to 0.014 mg/ℓ.

Taste and odour

There is no evidence that the presence of chlorine on its own can produce taints in the flesh of fish, but when present with phenols the resulting chlorinated phenols can produce taints at concentrations as low as 1 μg/ℓ (Chaper 5).

Acclimation

Increased resistance to chlorine has been demonstrated for the fathead minnow after acclimation to sublethal concentrations of chlorine (De Graeve and Ward, 1977); for example, fish exposed for three succeeding weeks to approximately 0.1, 0.2 and 0.5 of the 4-day LC50 respectively were able to survive for a further week at a concentration of about 1.5 times the 4-day LC50 and also lived at least 1.5 times longer than unacclimated fish when exposed to a concentration of about 4 times the 4-day LC50.

Other effects

The minimum concentration of residual chlorine (probably mainly present as monochloramine) in sewage effluent diluted with seawater, at which abnormalities in the blood (including anaemia) of coho salmon were observed after a 12-week exposure period, was between 3 and 9 μg/ℓ (Buckley, Whitemore and Masuda, 1976; Buckley, 1977).

7.4.5 EFFECTS OF MIXTURES OF CHLORINE WITH OTHER POISONS

Schaut (1939) found that following chlorination of solutions containing potassium thiocyanide at a concentration of 6 mg/ℓ, 'minnows' were as affected as by 3.6 mg/ℓ of sodium cyanide, and considered this to be a consequence of hydrogen cyanide production:

$$KCNS + 3Cl_2 + 4H_2O \rightarrow HCN + KHSO_4 + 6HCl$$

Allen, Blezard and Wheatland (1948) studied the same phenomenon and concluded that the poison was more likely to be cyanogen chloride:

$$KCNS + 4Cl_2 + 4H_2O \rightarrow CNCl + KCl + H_2SO_4 + 6HCl$$

Both investigations showed, however, that fish which had lost equilibrium in such mixtures recovered in poison-free water, which suggests that the effect was not produced by chlorine, which typically has an irreversible reaction (p. 147, para. 1) but rather by cyanide (a poison whose reaction is reversible).

Chlorine can combine with a wide variety of organic substances to form stable chloro-organic compounds (Jolley, 1973) some of which have been shown to be harmful to fish at concentrations as low as 1 μg/ℓ (e.g. Gehrs *et al.*, 1974).

There is no information on the effect of chlorine in the presence of other poisons with which it does not react chemically.

7.4.6 EFFECTS ON AQUATIC INVERTEBRATES AND PLANTS

Much of the information available on invertebrates will not be quoted because it relates to organisms that are not important as food for fish and to nominal concentrations that are rapidly lethal (Evins, 1975).

In soft water *Daphnia magna* was killed in three days at 0.5 mg/ℓ chlorine (Ellis, 1937). *Cyclops* sp. were stunned but recovered after exposure for one day to 1 mg/ℓ chloramines (Phillips, 1966), but 4-day LC50s of 0.089 mg/ℓ monochloramines, and of 0.069 mg/ℓ of a mixture of HOCl and monochloramines, have been reported for *C. thomasi* and *C. biscupedatus* by Beeton, Kovacic and Brooks (1975). For *Gammarus pseudolimnaeus* exposed to chlorine for a period of 15 weeks at 23 °C, pH of 7.2–8.6, dissolved-oxygen concentration of 5.2–10.4 mg/ℓ, and total hardness of 44–48 mg/ℓ, there was marked reduction in survival and no production of young at 0.035 mg/ℓ and reduction in the number of young produced per female at 3.5 μg/ℓ (0.4–1.4 μg HOCl/ℓ) (Arthur and Eaton, 1971). *Asellus* sp. were stunned but recovered after exposure for one day to 2 mg/ℓ chloramine, yet were apparently unaffected by exposure for this period to 2 mg/ℓ free chlorine (Phillips, 1966). Copulation of *A. aquaticus* was inhibited by 0.5 mg/ℓ (Holland, 1956). 'Crayfish'were killed by 1.2 mg/ℓ chloramines (Coventry, Shelford and Miller, 1935). The 1-day LC50 of monochloramines for the rotifer *Keratella cochleari* has been reported as 0.0135 mg/ℓ at 15 °C (Grossnickle, 1974).

There was an 85 per cent kill of *Chironomus* spp. larvae in one day at a concentration of chlorine of 0.65 mg/ℓ (Buchmann, 1932).

Among the molluscs, *Potamopyrgus jenkinsi* appeared dead after exposure to 100 mg/ℓ for one day, but some recovered when transferred to fresh water (English, 1958). With *Anculosa* species the 3-day LC50 was less then 0.04 mg/ℓ chlorine even with a daily exposure period of less than 2 h (Dickson *et al.*, 1977).

Little information is available on the effects of chlorine on higher plants on which fish may feed, but Zimmerman and Berg (1934) reported that *Cabomba caroliniana* and *Elodea canadensis* became slightly chlorotic after six days exposure to a chlorine concentration of 3 mg/ℓ (but not at lower concentrations). However, the concentrations fell to as little as 5 per cent of the nominal values within 3 h of preparation, suggesting that the plants may be more susceptible than these tests indicate. Initial concentrations of 0.25–0.3 mg/ℓ of chlorine have controlled the growth of algae (McKee and Wolf, 1963). With phytoplankton, Brook and Baker (1972) report an EC50 of 0.32 mg/ℓ of chlorine for reduction in photosynthesis and respiration, while Toetz, Varga and Pierce (1977) found effective concentrations of 0.11 and 0.028 mg/ℓ chlorine (as initial concentrations in the test solutions) for reduction in rates of uptake of nitrate and ammonia respectively.

It is therefore clear that the resistance of most species of invertebrate and some plants to acutely lethal levels of chlorine is greater than that of fish.

7.5 Field observations

Chlorine was reported to have caused the deaths of many fish in the R. Spree (Ebeling and Schräder, 1929) and was strongly implicated in the elimination of populations of most species in rivers immediately downstream of discharges of chlorinated effluent containing about 1 mg/ℓ chlorine (Tsai, 1968).

Basch *et al.* (1971) described the lethal effects on caged rainbow trout of chlorinated effluents from municipal waste water treatment plants serving small populations (and presumably, therefore, largely domestic in origin). Without chlorination no deaths occurred over a test period of 4–5 days, but with chlorination there was more than 60 per cent mortality within this period, 90–100 per cent being killed in one stream where the average chlorine concentration was 0.07 mg/ℓ, and 55 per cent where the average was 0.014 mg/ℓ; however all survived an average of 0.002 mg/ℓ. The estimated 90-h LC50 values in two of the streams were 0.014 mg/ℓ and 0.029 mg/ℓ respectively (although these findings conflict with the data presented which apparently contain errors). Similar experiments (J. S. Alabaster, personal communication) with this species in the chlorinated effluent from synthetic resin manufacture gave an estimated 1-day LC50 of 0.07 mg/ℓ (0.05 mg HOCl/ℓ). More recent data have shown that a concentration of 0.05 mg/ℓ chlorine was lethal to brown trout (Basch and Truchan, 1975) and that the 4-day LC50 to rainbow trout was 0.014–0.029 mg/ℓ chlorine (U.S. Environmental Protection Agency, 1976).

No data are available on the effects of chlorine or chlorinated effluents on fisheries (potential, catchability, or yields) in areas where such wastes are discharged except that, as indicated earlier, fishery sites may be lost or displaced very locally.

7.6 Summary of data

Chlorine as hypochlorous acid and chloramines is toxic to aquatic animals and, in contrast to some other poisons, for example HCN, once fish have lost their equilibrium they do not recover when placed in clean water (p. 147, para. 1). On the other hand, there is evidence that fish can acclimate to sublethal concentrations of chlorine and thereby become more resistant to lethal levels (p. 151, para. 4).

The lowest concentration of chlorine reported as lethal to trout is 0.01 mg/ℓ (0.008 mg HOCl/ℓ) under laboratory conditions (p. 148, para. 3) and 0.014 mg/ℓ in the field (p. 153, para. 5). The highest non-lethal concentrations having no apparent adverse effect on sensitive species of fish within five days are 5 μg/ℓ (4 μg HOCl/ℓ) for brook trout in the laboratory (p. 148, para. 3), though there was some decline in normal activity at this concentration (p. 150, para. 4), between 3 and 9 μg/ℓ chlorine (mainly as monochloramine) for the development of blood abnormalities in coho salmon (p. 151, para. 5) and 2 μg/ℓ for brown trout under field conditions (p. 153, para. 5). Field data are, however, very scant.

Acutely lethal levels of chlorine are reduced by reduction in the concentration of dissolved oxygen, little changed by increase in salinity up to 50 per cent sea water, but there is little or no information available on the effect of temperature, pH, and water hardness.

Slight avoidance behaviour of rainbow trout under experimental conditions has been found at a concentration of chlorine of 1 μg/ℓ (0.2-0.8 μg HOCl/ℓ) (p. 150, para. 4).

Coarse fish species (p. 148, para. 4 and p. 149, para. 2), fish food invertebrate organisms (p. 152, para. 6), and plants (p. 153, para. 2) are generally more resistant to chlorine than salmonids, although the production of young *Daphnia* was reduced at a concentration of 3.5 μg/ℓ (0.4-1.4 μg HOCl/ℓ) (p. 152, para. 6).

Chlorine may react with thiocyanide to produce lethal concentrations of hydrogen cyanide and/or cyanogen chloride (p. 152, p. 1).

Concentrations of chlorine as low as 1 μg/ℓ in the presence of phenols are likely to produce taints in the flesh of fish (p. 151, para. 3).

7.7 Tentative water quality criteria

From the limited data available, it seems that concentrations of chlorine greater than 8 μg HOCl/ℓ could be harmful or lethal within 4 days to salmonids and that a concentration as low as 1 μg/ℓ can produce marked avoidance reactions and physiological changes in the blood.

On the other hand a concentration of 4 μg HOCl/ℓ has been endured by sensitive species of fish for five days, though there was some decline in the normal activity.

Chlorine is too reactive to persist for long in most streams and therefore the upper limit for fish survival might be set closer to the lethal levels than might otherwise be the case, especially as avoidance behaviour and acclimation by fish to chlorine are likely to protect them from areas of high concentration. Consequently it is tentatively suggested that an upper limit might be set at 4 μg HOCl/ℓ, which should result in little or no mortality, perhaps have only a minor effect on

Table 7.2 APPROXIMATE TOTAL CONCENTRATION OF CHLORINE
CORRESPONDING TO 4 µg HOCl/ℓ

Temperature (°C)	Concentration (µg/ℓ)			
	pH 6	pH 7	pH 8	pH 9
5	4	5	11	75
25	4	5	16	121

behaviour and blood composition and not be high enough to be damaging to the majority of fish food organisms.

The amount of total chlorine corresponding to a concentration of 4 µg HOCl/ℓ varies according to the temperature and pH value of the water, as shown in *Table 7.2*.

7.8 References

ALBERT, A. (1965). Selective toxicity. *Surv. Munic. City Engr* **105**, 298

ALLEN, L. A., BLEZARD, N. and WHEATLAND, A. B. (1948). Formation of cyanogen chloride during chlorination of certain liquids; toxicity of such liquids to fish. *J. Hyg.* **46**, 184–193

ARTHUR, J. W. and EATON, J. G. (1971). Chloramine toxicity to the amphipod *Gammarus pseudolimnaeus* and the fathead minnow (*Pimephales promelas*). *J. Fish. Res. Bd Can.* **28**, 1841–1845

BASCH, R. E. N. and TRUCHAN, M. E. (1975). Toxicity of chlorinated power plant condenser cooling waters to fish. *Ecol. Res. Ser., Wash.* (EPA R800700)

BASCH, R. E. N., TRUCHAN, M. E., FETTEROLF, J. G. and CARLOS, M. (1971). Chlorinated municipal waste toxicities to rainbow trout and fathead minnows. *Wat. Pollut. Control Res. Ser.* (19050 G22, 10/71)

BASS, M. L., BERRY, C. R. and HEATH, A. G. (1977). Histopathological effects of intermittent chlorine exposure on bluegill (*Lepomis macrochirus*) and rainbow trout (*Salmo gairdneri*). *Wat. Res.* **11 (18)**, 731–735

BEETON, A. M., KOVACIC, P. K. and BROOKS, A. S. (1975). Effects of residual chlorine and sulphite reduction on Lake Michigan invertebrates. *Ecol. Res. Ser., Wash.* (EPA-600/3-76-036)

BLAKE, I. (1930). The external disinfection of fish ova with reference to prophylaxis of furunculosis. *Rep. Fish. Bd Scotl. Salm. Fish.* **11**

BROOK, A. J. and BAKER, A. L. (1972). Chlorination at power plants; impact on phytoplankton production. *Science, Wash.* **176 (4042)**, 1414–1415

BROOKS, A. S. and SEEGERT, G. L. (1975). The toxicity of chlorine to freshwater organisms under varying environmental conditions. In *Proceedings of the Conference on Environmental Impact of Water Chlorination* (Ed. by R. L. Jolley), Oak Ridge, Tenessee, Oak Ridge National Laboratory

BROOKS, A. S. and SEEGERT, G. L. (1977). The effects of intermittent chlorination on the biota of Lake Michigan. *Spec. Rep. Cent. Great Lake Stud.* **31**

BRUNGS, W. A. (1973). Effects of residual chlorine on aquatic life. *J. Wat. Pollut. Control Fed.* **45 (10)**, 2180-2193

BRUNGS, W. A. (1977). General considerations concerning the toxicity to aquatic life of chlorinated condenser effluent. In *Biofouling and Control Procedures; Technology and Ecological Effects* (Ed. by L. D. Jensen), pp. 109-113. New York, Marcel Dekker

BUCHMANN, W. (1932). *Chironomus* control in bathing establishments, swimming pools and water supplies by means of chlorine and copper. *Z. Gesundheitstech. Städtehyg.* 24, 235-242 (in German) (abstract in *J. Am. Wat. Works Ass.* 25, 1317)

BUCKLEY, J. A. (1976). Acute toxicity of residual chlorine in wastewater to coho salmon *Oncorhynchus kisutch* and some resultant haemolytic changes. *J. Fish. Res. Bd Can.* 33 (12), 2854-2856

BUCKLEY, J. A. (1977). Heinz body haemolytic anaemia in coho salmon *Oncorhynchus kisutch*, exposed to chlorinated sea water. *J. Fish Res. Bd Can.* 34 (2), 215-224

BUCKLEY, J. A., WHITEMORE, C. M. and MATSUDA, R. I. (1976). Changes in blood chemistry and blood cell morphology in coho salmon (*Oncorhynchus kisutch*) following exposure to sublethal levels of total residual chlorine in municipal waste water. *J. Fish. Res. Bd Can.* 33 (3), 776-782

CHERRY, D. S., LARRICK, S. R., DICKSON, K. L., HOEHN, R. C., and CAIRNS, J. Jr. (1977). Significance of hypochlorous acid in free residual chlorine to the avoidance response of spotted bass *Micropterus punctulatus* and rosyface shiner *Notropis rubellus*. *J. Fish. Res. Bd Can.* 34 (9), 1365-1372

COHEN, G. M. (1977). The influence of cations on chlorine toxicity. *Bull. envir. Contam. Toxicol.* 18 (2), 131-137

COVENTRY, F. L., SHELFORD, V. E. and MILLER, L. F. (1935). The conditioning of a chloramine-treated water supply for biological purposes. *Ecology* 16, 60-66

DANDY, J. W. T. (1972). Activity response to chlorine in the brook trout *Salvelinus fontinalis* (Mitchill). *Can. J. Zool.* 50, 405-410

DEPARTMENT OF FISHERIES, WASHINGTON (1960). Toxic effects of organic and inorganic pollutants on young salmon and trout. *Res. Bull. Wash. St. Dep. Fish.* (5)

DEPARTMENT OF SCIENTIFIC AND INDUSTRIAL RESEARCH, U.K. (1958). *Water Pollution Research 1957*, p. 25. London, H.M.S.O.

DE GRAEVE, G. M. and WARD, R. W. (1977). Acclimation of fathead minnows and lake trout to residual chlorine and bromine chloride. *J. Wat. Pollut. Control Fed.* **49 (10)**, 2172-2178

DICKSON, K. L., CAIRNS, J. Jr., GREGG, B. C., MESSENGER, D. I., PLAFKIN, J. L. and VAN DER SCHALIE, W. H. (1977). Effects of intermittent chlorination on aquatic organisms and communities. *J. Wat. Pollut. Control Fed.* 37, 35-44

DOUDOROFF, P. and KATZ, M. (1950). Critical review of literature on the toxicity of industrial wastes and their components to fish. 1. Alkalies, acids, and inorganic gases. *Sewage Ind. Wastes* 22, 1432-1458

EBELING, G. (1931). Einfluss der abwasserchlorung auf Fischgewasser. *Vom Wasser* 5, 201-212

EBELING, G. and SCHRÄDER, T. (1929). Free active chlorine in water and its effect on fish and other water organisms. *Z. Fisch.* **27**, 417–457

ELLIS, M. M. (1937). Detection and measurement of stream pollution (related principally to fish life). *Fish. Bull. U.S. Bur. Fish.* **48**, 365–437

ENGLISH, E. (1958). Biological problems in distribution systems; infestations of mains water. *Proc. Soc. Wat. Treatm. Exam.* **7**, 127

EVINS, C. (1975). The toxicity of chlorine to some freshwater organisms. *Tech. Rep. Wat. Res. Cent.* **TR8**

FOBES, R. L. (1971). Chlorine toxicity and its effect on gill tissue respiration of the white sucker *Catostomus commersoni* (Lacepede). Thesis, Michigan State University, East Lansing

GEHRS, C. W., EYMAN, L. D., JOLLEY, R. L. and THOMPSON, J. E. (1974). Effects of stable chlorine-containing organics on aquatic environments. *Nature, Lond.* **249**, 675–676

GRANDE, M. (1966). Om bruk av klorert vann i fiskeanlegg. (Use of chlorinated water in fish hatcheries.) *Jakt-Fiske Friluftsliv.* **95**, 507–508

GREEN, D. E. and STUMPF, P. K. (1946). The mode of action of chlorine. *J. Am. Wat. Works Ass.* **38**, 1301–1305

GROETHE, D. R., and EATON, J. W. (1975). Chlorine-induced mortality in fish. *Trans. Am. Fish. Soc.* **104**, 800–802

GROSSNICKLE, N. E. (1974). The acute toxicity of residual chloramine to the rotifer *Keratella cochlearis* (Gosse) and the effect of dechlorination with sodium sulphite. M. S. Thesis, University of Wisconsin, Milwaukee

HEATH, A. G. (1977). Toxicity of intermittent chlorination to freshwater fish: influence of temperature and chlorine form. *Hydrobiologia* **56**, 39–47

HOLLAND, G. J. (1956). The eradication of *Asellus aquaticus* from water supply mains. *J. Inst. Wat. Engr* **10**, 221–241

HOLLAND, G. A., LASATER, J. E., NEWMANN, E. D. and ELDRIDGE, W. E. (1960). Toxic effects of organic and inorganic pollutants on young salmon and trout. *Res. Bull. Wash. St. Dep. Fish.* **5**, 198–214

JOLLEY, R. L. (1973). Chlorination effects on organic constituents in effluents from domestic sanitary sewage treatment plants. *Oak Ridge Natl. Lab.* (ORNL-RM-4290)

JONES, J. R. E. (1964). *Fish and river pollution.* London, Butterworths

KATZ, B. M. and HARDER, U. M. (1976). The attraction of fish. *J. Wat. Pollut. Control Fed.* **48** (3), 592

LARSON, G. L., HUTCHINS, F. E. and SCHLESINGER, D. A. (1977). Acute toxicity of inorganic chloramines to early life stages of brook trout *Salvelinus fontinalis.* *J. Fish. Biol.* **11**, 595–598

LIEBMANN, H. (1960). *Handbuch der Frischwasser- und Abwasser-biologie, Volume 2.* München, Ouldenbourg

MATTICE, J. S. (1975). Method of estimating the toxicity of chlorinated discharges. Paper presented to the *Workshop on impact of power plants on aquatic systems*, Pacific Grove, California, U.S.A., 28 September, 1975. Oak Ridge, Tennessee, Union Carbide Corporation

McKEE, J. E. and WOLF, H. W. (1963). Water quality criteria. *Publ. Calif. St. Wat. Qual. Control Bd* **3-A**

MERKENS, J. C. (1958). Studies on the toxicity of chlorines and chloramines to the rainbow trout. *Wat. Waste Treatm.* **7**, 150

PALIN, A. T. (1950). A study of the chloro-derivatives of ammonia and related compounds with special reference to their formation in the chlorination of natural or polluted waters. Paper presented to the *Public Works Municipal Services Congress*, 1950, Paper 18

PANIKKAR, B. M. (1960). Low concentrations of calcium hypochlorite as a fish and tadpole poison applicable for use in partly drained ponds and other small bodies of water. *Prog. Fish-Cult.* **22**, 117-120

PENZES, B. (1971). The effect of water treated with chlorine on living fish. *Allatorv. Közl.* **58**, 87

PHILLIPS, J. H. (1966). The discovery and control of live organisms in the Great Yarmouth water supply. *J. Inst. Wat. Engng* **20**, 207

PIKE, D. J. (1971). Toxicity of chlorine to brown trout *Salmo trutta* Linn. *N. Z. Wildl.* **1971 (33)**

ROSENBERGER, D. R. (1971). The calculation of acute toxicity of free chlorine and chloramines to coho salmon by multiple regression analysis. Thesis, Michigan State University, East Lansing

SCHAUT, G. G. (1939). Fish catastrophes during droughts. *J. Am. Wat. Works Ass.* **31**, 771-822

SCHEURING, L. and STETTER, H. (1950-1951). Versuche über die Wirkung von Chlor auf Fische und andere Wassertiere. *Vom Wasser* **18**

SILLÉN, L. G. and MARTELL, A. E. (1964). Stability constants. *Spec. Publ. Chem. Soc., Lond.* **17**

SOUTHGATE, B. A. (1948). *Treatment and disposal of industrial waste waters.* London, H.M.S.O.

SPRAGUE, J. B. and DRURY, D. E. (1969). Avoidance reactions of salmonid fish to representative pollutants. *Adv. Wat. Pollut. Res.* **2 (1)**, 169-179

STOBER, Q. J. and HANSON, C. H. (1974). Toxicity of chlorine and heat to pink salmon *Oncorhynchus gorbusha* and chinook salmon *Oncorhynchus tshawytscha. Trans. Am. Fish. Soc.* **103**, 569-576

TAYLOR, R. S. and JAMES, M. C. (1928). Treatment for removal of chlorine from city water for use in aquaria. U.S. Bureau of Fisheries, Doc. No. 1045. *Rep. U.S. Comm. Fish.* **App. 7**, 322-327

TOETZ, D., VARGA, L. and PIERCE, M. (1977). Effects of chlorine and chloramine on uptake of inorganic nitrogen by phytoplankton. *Wat. Res.* **11**, 253-258

TSAI, C. (1968). Effects of chlorinated sewage effluents on fish in the upper Patuxent River, Maryland. *Chesapeake Sci.* **9**, 83-93

U.S. ENVIRONMENTAL PROTECTION AGENCY (1976). *Quality criteria for water.* Washington D.C. (EPA-440/9-76-023), pp. 61-68

VALENZUELA, J. M. (1976). A fine structural examination of the gill in the mosquito fish *Gambusia affinis* after exposure to chlorine. Master's Thesis, Florida Institute of Technology, Melbourne

WAKABAYASHI, T. and IMAOKA, M. (1968). Effect of residual chlorine in tap-water on goldfish. *Yamanashi Daigaku Kogakubu Kepkyu* **19**, 118-122

ZEITOUN, I. H., HUGHES, L. D. and ULLNEY, D. E. (1977). Effect of shock exposure of chlorine on the plasma electrolyte concentrations of adult rainbow trout (*Salmo gairdneri*). *J. Fish. Res. Bd Can.* **34 (7)**, 1034-1039

ZILLICH, J. A. (1972). Toxicity of combined chlorine residuals to freshwater fish. *J. Wat. Pollut. Control Fed.* **44**, 212-220

ZIMMERMAN, P. W. and BERG, R. O. (1934). Effects of chlorinated water on land plants, aquatic plants, and goldfish. *Contrib. Boyce Thompson Inst.* **6**, 39-49

8

ZINC

Foreword

The preparation of the original report on zinc and freshwater fish was accomplished largely by Mr M. Grande who prepared the basic manuscript for review by the members of the Working Party on Water Quality Criteria for European Freshwater Fish; he also provided much of the input for the present revision.

8.1 Summary

There are extensive amounts of data on the toxicity of zinc to fish under laboratory conditions, supported to some extent by field data on fish kills, but there are virtually no field observations to indicate the concentrations of zinc that are not inimical to fish populations or fisheries, mainly because the analytical data are too meagre, information on water hardness—perhaps the most important factor affecting the toxicity of zinc to aquatic animals—is missing and details of the status of the fish population are not given. For these reasons only tentative criteria can be suggested which may have to be revised when more adequate field data become available.

The toxicity of solutions containing zinc is mainly attributable to the zinc ion and perhaps also to particulate zinc present as the basic carbonate or the hydroxide held in suspension. It is modified by water quality, being reduced in particular by an increase in hardness and also temperature, salinity and suspended solids, and increased by a decrease in dissolved oxygen. The effect of pH, however, is uncertain.

The acute toxicity of zinc in the presence of other heavy metals and other common pollutants seems to be largely simply additive but there is no evidence that the chronic toxicity of different poisons in a mixture is also additive. The effect of zinc is modified, and can be reduced, by acclimation and by the age of the fish.

A low but significant mortality has been found among rainbow trout exposed continuously for 4 months to constant concentrations of 0.2 of the 5-day LC50 and among rudd exposed for 8½ months to 0.3 of the 7-day LC50.

Laboratory studies of avoidance reactions have shown that Atlantic salmon and rainbow trout may avoid concentrations of zinc in soft water which are

159

0.14–0.01 of the 7-day LC50. Avoidance reactions have also been observed at 0.35–0.43 of the 7-day LC50 by migrating Atlantic salmon in a river polluted with copper and zinc. Carp and goldfish show avoidance of 0.3–0.45 of lethal concentrations under laboratory conditions.

Field observations show that brown trout populations were present when the concentration of zinc was less than 0.06 of the 2-day LC50 to rainbow trout or when the annual 50 and 95 percentiles were up to 0.05 and 0.19 of the LC50 respectively; coarse fish were present when the corresponding percentiles were 0.02 and 0.11 of the 5-day LC50 to roach.

Because concentrations of zinc in freshwaters fluctuate, being distributed approximately lognormally over a period of a year, tentative criteria are expressed as annual 50- and 95-percentile values.

Pending the availability of more information, it is tentatively recommended that for the maintenance of thriving populations of fish the annual 95 percentile of concentration of zinc should be no greater than 0.1 of the appropriate 7-day LC50 at 15 °C; thus the criteria in terms of concentration of zinc would depend upon water hardness and type of fish as shown in *Table 8.1*.

Table 8.1   MAXIMUM ANNUAL 95-PERCENTILE CONCENTRATIONS OF 'SOLUBLE' ZINC (mg Zn/ℓ)

Water hardness (mg/ℓ as CaCO$_3$)	Coarse fish except minnow	Salmonids
10	0.3	0.03
50	0.7	0.2
100	1.0	0.3
500	2.0	0.5

The concentration of 0.03 mg Zn/ℓ for salmonids in very soft water may be too severe if brown trout only are present, since this species appears to survive successfully at higher concentrations; in such cases a 95-percentile concentration of 0.2 of the 7-day LC50 (0.06 mg Zn/ℓ) may be more appropriate. For the minnow it might be more appropriate to set a more stringent standard but further data would be desirable to support and explain the existing laboratory findings.

The values of the corresponding annual 50 percentiles would be approximately 0.25 of the proposed 95 percentiles unless the distribution was much wider in range than has hitherto been found or was not lognormal, resulting in a larger ratio between the 95 percentile and higher percentiles, in which cases more stringent standards would be appropriate. Where other poisons are present and dissolved-oxygen concentrations are below the air-saturation value, allowance should also be made for their contribution to the toxicity.

8.2 Introduction

Zinc is an essential trace element in living organisms, being involved in nucleic acid synthesis and occurring in many enzymes. It occurs widely in nature as the sulphide, carbonate and hydrated silicate ores, frequently accompanied by other metals, mainly iron and cadmium. It is used for galvanizing, in brass and other alloys, and some of its compounds, including the oxide, chloride, chromate, and sulphide, are widely used in other industries. Consequently, it can be an important pollutant from both mining and other industrial processes.

Background values of zinc in natural inland surface waters may vary from 0.001 to 0.2 mg Zn/ℓ or even higher, e.g. O'Connor (1968). Wastes containing zinc are often acidic and may also have a high content of copper, iron, cadmium, and other heavy metals. Zinc may occur in water as the free cation or as soluble zinc complexes, or can be adsorbed on suspended matter.

Zinc wastes can have a direct toxicity to aquatic life, and fisheries can be affected by either zinc alone, or more often together with copper and other metals.

Effects of zinc on fish have been critically reviewed, for example by Doudoroff and Katz (1953), Skidmore (1964), and Kemp, Abrams and Overbeck (1971). Rarely are references earlier than 1953 cited in this chapter.

8.3 Direct lethal action on fish

8.3.1 SYMPTOMS OF POISONING AND MODE OF ACTION

Early workers reported that zinc salts precipitated the mucus on the gills of fish, causing them to die from suffocation, although calcium salts inhibited precipitation. However, Lloyd (1960) and Mount (1966) observed little or no precipitation of mucus of rainbow trout (*Salmo gairdneri*) at low, lethal concentrations, and histological examinations showed that the epithelial cells of the gill secondary lamellae became swollen, separated from the pillar cells and finally sloughed off (Parry, in Lloyd, 1960). Skidmore (1970) and Skidmore and Tovell (1972) concluded that under such conditions the fish died from asphyxia, rather than osmotic stress, an hypothesis supported by the increased concentrations of lactic acid and glycogen utilization (Hodson, 1976), and reduced concentration of pyruvic acid in the tissues of trout killed by high concentrations of zinc (Burton, Jones and Cairns, 1972), and by increases in ventilatory and coughing frequency and response to anoxia of trout exposed to high concentrations of zinc (Hughes and Adeney, 1977). Other symptoms observed have been darkening in colour and increased swimming activity (Affleck, 1952) and a curvature of the backbone in the minnow (*Phoxinus phoxinus*) after chronic exposure (Bengtsson, 1972). Vertebral damage was found by Bengtsson (1974a) in adult minnow after 30 days exposure to concentrations of zinc nitrate as low as 0.2 mg Zn/ℓ (0.06 of the 4-day LC50), and the nervous system seemed to be affected in yearling and underyearling fish exposed for 108 days to even lower concentrations (0.16 mg Zn/ℓ and 0.06 mg Zn/ℓ respectively), as judged by the ability of the fish to maintain their vertical position in a rotating cylinder of water (Bengtsson, 1974e).

The ratio of zinc in the gill to that in the operculum is diagnostic for death of many American species caused by high concentrations of zinc under experimental conditions, the ratio being close to unity in controls and up to 100 : 1 in poisoned fish; however, ratios close to unity have not been found in the wild among carp (*Cyprinus carpio*) and goldfish (*Carassius auratus*) (Mount, 1964). Lewis and Lewis (1971) found that zinc affected channel catfish (*Ictalurus punctatus*) and golden shiner (*Notemigonus crysoleucas*), causing a drop in the salt concentration in the blood serum, and they suggested that this might be a primary cause of death. More recently Katz (1977) has demonstrated increased sodium efflux in *Gambusia affinis* within a few hours in the presence of high concentrations of zinc (5 mg Zn/ℓ) and a decrease in the efflux of ammonia with increase in concentration of zinc. Binding of zinc has decreased the macromolecular synthesis of proteins (Van Coillie *et al.*, 1975) which may be responsible for an increased mortality just after hatching.

Little is known of sublethal physiological effects except that, after six months exposure to 1.6-2.0 mg Zn/ℓ, rudd (*Scardinius erythrophthalmus*) had very low levels of fat and glycogen in the liver (Ministry of Technology, 1966); also stickleback (*Gasterosteus aculeatus*) show an increase in the number and activity of the 'chloride cells' of the gills (Matthiessen and Brafield, 1973).

8.3.2 FACTORS AFFECTING ACUTELY LETHAL LEVELS

Under given constant environmental conditions the period of survival of test batches of fish increases with decrease in the concentration of zinc in solution, lines relating survival time to concentration often being such that there is little difference between concentrations lethal at one day and those lethal at several days; a curvilinear relation thus exists between the logarithm of zinc concentration and the logarithm of median period of survival of fish. However, changes in some environmental factors can alter the shape and position of these curves, giving a series of curves which converge toward a common asymptotic ('threshold') concentration, or which diverge to give different threshold concentrations, or in some cases causing the curves to cross each other. However, the inherent variability in response within the population from which test batches are taken leads to uncertainty in the precision and accuracy of the values observed; for example with the 5-day LC50 of zinc measured using batches of 10 fish, the 95 per cent confidence limits are often roughly between ±10 and ±20 per cent, depending upon the species (Ball, 1967); furthermore, the limits are even wider for concentrations corresponding to a percentage response lower than 50, as shown recently for salmonids (Nehring and Goettl, 1974).

Temperature

Lloyd (1960) demonstrated that an increase in temperature from 13.5 °C to 21.5 °C decreased the survival time of rainbow trout in solutions of zinc sulphate in a hard water, the Q_{10} for concentrations of 5-10 mg Zn/ℓ being about 2.4; the 5-day LC50 (3.5 mg Zn/ℓ) was not, however, appreciably altered. Similar experiments (Ministry of Technology, 1968) showed that the 2-day LC50 at 2 °C could be as high as 4 mg/ℓ compared with 2 mg/ℓ at 12 °C. Sprague (1964a) found values of Q_{10} of 4 and 10 for Atlantic salmon (*Salmo salar*) tested in concentrations of 0.6-3 mg/ℓ in a soft water, but the 8-day LC50 at 5 and 15 °C was at least 0.9 and 0.6 mg Zn/ℓ respectively; later work at 4, 11 and 15 °C (J. B. Sprague and W. G. Carson, personal communication) indicates that while the 2-day LC50 was about 0.6 mg Zn/ℓ the 8-day was about 0.16, 0.26, and 0.6 mg Zn/ℓ at the three temperatures respectively. On the other hand the effect on threshold LC50 values of temperature in the range 3–19 °C was negligible in water having a hardness of 320–350 mg/ℓ as $CaCO_3$ (Hodson and Sprague, 1975).

Thus a reduction in temperature below about 15 °C may increase the period of survival of rainbow trout and salmon at acutely lethal concentrations of zinc yet reduce the lethal threshold value such that the 7-day LC50 for salmon at 5 °C is reduced to almost a quarter (i.e. toxicity is increased nearly four-fold). There is no information available on the effect of temperature on the toxicity of zinc to coarse fish.

Dissolved oxygen

Lloyd (1960), using rainbow trout unacclimated to low dissolved oxygen prior to testing, found that the 1-day LC50 was reduced by about 30 per cent by a reduction from 100 to 40 per cent of the air-saturation value. However, when the fish were acclimated beforehand to the level of dissolved oxygen used in the tests the 1-day LC50 was similar (about 3 mg Zn/ℓ) at 9.5, 6.3 and 3.7 mg/ℓ dissolved oxygen, though periods of survival at 4–12 mg Zn/ℓ were slightly lower at the lowest concentrations of dissolved oxygen. Cairns and Scheier (1957a) studied bluegill (*Lepomis macrochirus*) and found that when the dissolved oxygen concentration was fluctuating over several hours between 9 and 5 mg/ℓ, the 4-day LC50 for zinc chloride was 8.0 mg Zn/ℓ, and when the fluctuations were between 9 and 2 mg/ℓ it was 4.9 mg Zn/ℓ.

Thus a reduction in dissolved oxygen can reduce the LC50 of zinc for rainbow trout unacclimated to low dissolved oxygen beforehand, but not for those that are acclimated.

pH value

The solubility of zinc salts in natural waters decreases with an increase in pH value above about 7, though delay in reaching equilibrium can result in super-saturated solutions. However, in hard water, precipitated zinc held in suspension at about pH 8 seems to be about as toxic to rainbow trout as zinc ions in solution (Lloyd, 1960). On the other hand, Sprague (1964a) found an increase in survival time of Atlantic salmon parr in soft water when the pH was increased from 7.1–7.5 to 7.9–9.3, which he considered was accounted for by the reduced amount of zinc calculated to be in solution. Further preliminary results (J. B. Sprague and U. Zitko, personal communication) show that the 5-day LC50 values were about 2 mg Zn/ℓ at pH 4–5.5 and 0.4–0.7 mg Zn/ℓ at pH values 6–8. Mount (1966), using fathead minnow (*Pimephales promelas*), found that at a given hardness (50, 100 or 200 mg/ℓ as $CaCO_3$) the 4-day LC50 of zinc was always lower at a pH of about 7.6 than at 6.7 and tentatively suggested that zinc in suspension may be more toxic than zinc in solution.

Thus, no definite conclusion can be arrived at for the effect of pH on the toxicity of zinc solutions.

Hardness

Concentrations of zinc acutely lethal to fish are higher in hard than in soft water as shown by Jones (1938) for stickleback, Lloyd (1960) for rainbow trout, and Tabata (1969a) for grass carp (*Ctenopharyngodon idella*). Jones (1938), Affleck (1952), Sreenivasan and Raj (1963), and Tabata (1969a) showed that the addition of the calcium ion (as sulphate or chloride) reduced the toxicity of zinc. Tabata (1969a) found that the addition of sodium ions also reduced toxicity, whereas potassium ions had no effect when added to a natural water.

Lloyd (1960) observed that the concentration of zinc that was lethal to rainbow trout in 2½ days in a water of total hardness 320 mg/ℓ as $CaCO_3$ was approximately eight-fold higher than in water of total hardness 12 mg/ℓ. For the

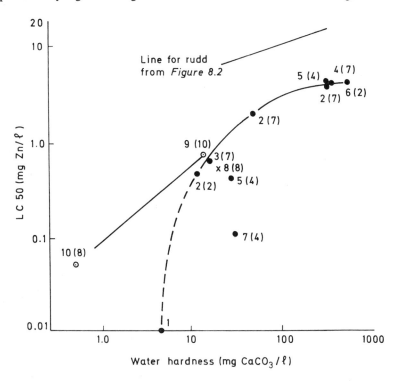

Figure 8.1   Median lethal concentration of zinc to salmonid fish (time in days shown in parentheses). Line for rudd from Figure 8.2 shown for comparison

● Rainbow trout	(*Salmo gairdneri*)	1. Affleck (1952)
		2. Lloyd (1960)
		3. Lloyd (1961)
		4. Ball (1967)
		5. Goettl (personal communication)
		6. Solbé (personal communication)
		7. Chapman (personal communication)
✕ Salmon	(*Salmo salar*)	8. Sprague (1964a)
⊙ Brook trout	(*Salvelinus fontinalis*)	10. Schofield (1965)

three levels of hardness tested, 12, 50 and 320 mg/ℓ as $CaCO_3$, the 2½-day LC50s were approximately 0.5, 2 and 4 mg Zn/ℓ, and Lloyd and Herbert (1962) suggested that a linear relation existed between the logarithm of LC50 and the logarithm of total hardness. Recent work (J. F. de L. G. Solbé, personal communication) tends to confirm this in that, for a hardness of 504 mg/ℓ as $CaCO_3$, the 2-day LC50 for rainbow trout was 4.8 mg Zn/ℓ. However, steelhead trout (*Salmo gairdneri*) (G. A. Chapman, personal communication) have recently been shown to have a greater sensitivity than expected from other published results with rainbow trout. All these tests were carried out with fish acclimated to water of the appropriate hardness. Lloyd (1965) showed that rainbow trout reared in soft water were more sensitive to zinc poisoning in soft water than those reared in hard water and tested following immediate transfer to soft water. It was also found that the fish that had been kept in hard water had to be maintained in soft water for at least 5 days before they became as sensitive as those reared in soft water (see also p. 167, para. 3).

The relation between LC50s at different time intervals and hardness is illustrated in *Figure 8.1* for rainbow trout, rudd and brook trout (*Salvelinus fontinalis*), the only other species for which comparable data are available.

Salinity

Herbert and Wakeford (1964) showed that the 2-day LC50 of zinc sulphate for yearling rainbow trout and Atlantic salmon smolts was at a maximum in 35 and 40 per cent seawater, being about 15 and 13 times greater than in freshwater for the two species respectively, while in 72 per cent seawater it was respectively about 6 and about 8 times greater. They suggest that maximum resistance occurs when the water is approximately isotonic (= 31 per cent seawater) with the blood of Atlantic salmon smolts acclimated to 100 per cent seawater.

Organic matter

Experiments have shown that the acute lethal effect of zinc on salmonids is reduced when chelating materials such as NTA (nitrilotriacetic acid) and EDTA (ethylenediaminetetra-acetic acid) are added to the water at neutral pH values (Sprague, 1968b, Grande, 1967). Humic substances, amino acids, polypeptides and other soluble organic matter may complex zinc sufficiently to influence the toxicity of total concentration of the metal to fish, although the toxicity of sewage effluents containing zinc could be predicted accurately from their total zinc content together with those of other poisons present (Lloyd and Jordan, 1964).

Suspended solids

The toxicity of mine water containing heavy metals is reduced when it is mixed with wastes from the flotation process, which contain high concentrations of finely ground silica quartz or other minerals capable of adsorbing heavy metals (Svenska Gruvföreningen, 1960). Also, preliminary studies with rainbow trout

(Ministry of Technology, 1971) suggest that the 2-day LC50 for total concentration of zinc is increased from about 3 mg Zn/ℓ to about 4 mg Zn/ℓ with increase in concentration of either organic or inorganic suspended solids from 10 to 400 mg/ℓ.

Age and size

Rainbow trout fry at the beginning of the free-feeding stage were somewhat more vulnerable than adult fish, while eyed eggs were the most tolerant, the 5-day LC50 being at least four times higher than that of adults (Edwards and Brown, 1966). Goodman (1951) found an increase in resistance in this species between the ages of 2 and 10 weeks, but this may have been partly attributable to their having been hatched and reared in water containing 1 mg Zn/ℓ. J. P. Goettl (personal communication) found that the 4-day LC50 was approximately 1.2 and 4.5 mg Zn/ℓ in hard water (325 mg/ℓ as $CaCO_3$) for fish weighing on average 2 g and 28.3 g respectively, and 0.2 and 0.4 mg Zn/ℓ in soft water (30 mg/ℓ as $CaCO_3$) for those of 4.9 g and 30.5 g respectively. With Atlantic salmon, Grande (1967) obtained only a 30 per cent hatch of eggs in soft water (hardness 14 mg/ℓ as $CaCO_3$) containing 0.04 mg Zn/ℓ, which was less than 0.1 of the 21-day LC50 for yolk-sac fry and fingerlings.

Bengtsson (1974d) found a significantly increased mortality among newly hatched minnow compared with adults at concentrations of zinc nitrate of 0.08 mg Zn/ℓ (0.025 of the 4-day LC50 of adults); underyearlings and yearlings were of intermediate sensitivity. Bengtsson (1972) also found in long-term studies at 0.13, 0.2, and 0.31 mg Zn/ℓ in soft water (mean hardness of 70 mg/ℓ as $CaCO_3$) that the percentage mortality of juvenile minnow was 10, 22, and 50, but for mature minnow it was only 0, 10, and 30 respectively. On the other hand, Jones (1938) found no difference in resistance to zinc between juvenile (18–20 mm) and mature (45–50 mm) stickleback. With minnow exposed to solutions containing zinc, older (larger) fish were better able to compensate for torque in a rotating water current than younger individuals (Bengtsson, 1974e). Zitko and Carson (1977) found that the incipient lethal level of zinc to juvenile Atlantic salmon during the period from September (stage 0+) to July the following year (stage 1+) increased from 0.5 to 1.0 mg Zn/ℓ during the first year and then decreased to 0.15 mg Zn/ℓ in the following spring. The authors related the lowered tolerance in the second year to the parr–smolt transformation of the salmon.

Acclimation to zinc

Goodman (1951) observed that the period of survival of fingerling rainbow trout in 6 and 10 mg Zn/ℓ increased after acclimation for 40 days in water containing 2 mg Zn/ℓ. Similar results were obtained by Affleck (1952) with both rainbow and brown trout, and by Lloyd (1960) and Edwards and Brown (1966) with rainbow trout. Lloyd (1960) found a significant, almost two-fold, increase in survival time among rainbow trout which had survived solutions containing 2.5

and 3.5 mg Zn/ℓ for 14 days and had then been exposed to a concentration of 10 mg Zn/ℓ, as compared with fish that had been kept beforehand in clean water. Edwards and Brown (1966) found a 40 per cent increase in the 2-day LC50 of fish kept at 0.5 of the 2-day LC50 for 60 days, but not of those kept at 0.6 of the 2-day LC50. Data of J. B. Sprague (personal communication) indicate that with acclimation to sublethal concentrations for several months the 7-day LC50 of zinc for Atlantic salmon may be increased two- or three-fold.

Pickering and Vigor (1965) found that one-day-old eggs of fathead minnow exposed to 1.1 mg Zn/ℓ hatched and the fry lived for at least three days, whereas all the newly-hatched fry not previously exposed to zinc died within one day of being exposed to this concentration; the duration of this tolerance was not, however, investigated. Edwards and Brown (1966) observed that rudd which had survived long exposure to 25 mg Zn/ℓ could live longer at 40–60 mg Zn/ℓ than a similar batch previously held in clean water.

These results are supported by field experiments (Schofield, 1965) during the summer in Honnedga Lake, U.S.A. (hardness 1–3 mg/ℓ as $CaCO_3$), when the concentration of zinc was 0.01–0.15 mg Zn/ℓ; caged brook trout transferred from Cortland hatchery (hardness about 80 mg/ℓ as $CaCO_3$), where the maximum concentration of zinc was 0.01 mg Zn/ℓ, died whereas almost all those from Cornell hatchery (hardness about 60 mg/ℓ as $CaCO_3$) in which the concentration was up to 1.52 mg Zn/ℓ, survived the transfer for nine days. Furthermore the mortality among the Cortland fish was reduced with prior acclimation for six days to Cornell hatchery water.

In another experiment rainbow trout were acclimated to a sublethal concentration (0.8 mg Zn/ℓ) and then exposed to surfactant (alkylbenzene sulphonate) alone and to mixtures of zinc and surfactant. The toxicity of the surfactant tested alone was similar for control and treated fish, but when tested in the presence of 0.8 mg Zn/ℓ the mixture was more toxic to the fish previously exposed to zinc (Brown, Mitrovic, and Stark, 1968).

Thus, some species of salmonids and coarse fish survive longer at lethal concentrations of zinc when previously exposed as eggs or juvenile fish to sublethal concentrations; under the most favourable conditions of acclimation to zinc the 7-day LC50 may be increased two- or three-fold. However, exposure to sublethal concentrations of zinc can reduce the resistance of trout to subsequent additional exposure to a surfactant.

Inbreeding

Rachlin and Perlmutter (1968) found a ten-fold increase in tolerance to zinc in an inbred strain of platyfish (*Xiphophorus maculatus*).

Joint action of zinc and other heavy metals

Lloyd (1961) studied the survival of rainbow trout in zinc and copper sulphates and in mixtures of the two in a hard borehole water and in an artificial soft water (total hardness 320 mg/ℓ and 14–20 mg/ℓ respectively as $CaCO_3$). By expressing the concentrations of the metals in the mixtures as proportions of their individual 3-day LC50 in hard water and 7-day LC50 in soft water, median periods of survival were related to concentrations of the two metals when present together. He postulated that copper and zinc exerted their acute toxic action in a similar way and that their toxicity in relatively low lethal concentrations was simply additive. Higher acutely lethal concentrations of the mixture in soft water, however, exhibited synergism, in that survival times were much shorter than with the equivalent amount of either heavy metal alone—an effect also found by Doudoroff (1952) using fathead minnow in soft water.

Sprague and Ramsay (1965) tested juvenile Atlantic salmon in zinc and copper sulphates and in mixtures of the two in a water with a total hardness of 14 mg/ℓ as $CaCO_3$. The 7-day LC50 of the mixture could be accounted for by simple addition of the corresponding LC50s of the separate metals as described above.

The 2-day LC50 to rainbow trout of mixtures of copper, zinc and nickel has also been found (Brown and Dalton, 1970) to be adequately predicted by summation of the fractional 2-day LC50 values of the separate poisons.

Joint action of zinc and other poisons

The toxicity to fathead minnow of solutions containing sodium cyanide and zinc sulphate was related mainly to the level of molecular cyanide present (Doudoroff, Leduc and Schneider, 1966).

Herbert and Shurben (1964) tested rainbow trout in solutions of ammonium chloride and zinc sulphate in both hard and soft water and also in the presence of reduced dissolved oxygen, and found that 50 per cent of the fish were killed in two days when the sum of the proportions of the 2-day LC50 of each poison reached approximately 1.0. Similar results have been found for mixtures of phenol and zinc sulphate (Herbert and Vandyke, 1964), zinc, copper and phenol (Brown and Dalton, 1970), and zinc and surfactant (alkylbenzene sulphonate) (Brown, Mitrovic, and Stark, 1968).

Brown, Jordan, and Tiller (1969) varied the proportion of zinc, ammonia, and phenol in mixtures tested with rainbow trout, and found that when zinc predominated the toxicity of the mixtures was less than expected, assuming simple addition of the fractional toxicities of the three poisons; it is possible that when zinc predominated the amount of ammonia and/or phenol present was too low to exert any effect on the fish.

Several sewage effluents were studied by Lloyd and Jordan (1963, 1964). The toxicity to rainbow trout of one containing a considerable amount of zinc in addition to other heavy metals, ammonia, surfactant, phenol, and cyanide, when tested in hard and soft water, was similar to that predicted from the concentration of zinc and other poisons present. Similar results were found (Herbert, Jordan and Lloyd, 1965) for some fishless rivers in England containing zinc, copper, ammonia and phenol.

In general the effect of zinc in the presence of other common poisons on the 2-day LC50 of the mixture to rainbow trout can be calculated by simple addition of the fractional 2-day LC50 of the individual poisons.

8.3.3 SUMMARY OF TOXICITY DATA

Acutely lethal values

Salmonid eggs   Concentrations reported to be lethal to salmonids vary from about 0.01 to more than 10 mg Zn/ℓ, depending mainly on the water hardness and species of fish (*Figure 8.1*) and stage in the life-cycle and also the duration of tests. Some results which give no details of these relevant factors are therefore not considered in this chapter.

Rainbow trout eggs failed to hatch in a soft water (4.3 mg/ℓ as $CaCO_3$) containing 0.04 mg Zn/ℓ (Affleck, 1952). Yet J. P. Goettl (personal communication) found that the eyed eggs showed no ill effects when kept for 100 and 140 days respectively in a soft water (25 mg/ℓ as $CaCO_3$) containing 0.1 mg Zn/ℓ and in a hard water (340 mg/ℓ as $CaCO_3$) containing 0.4 mg Zn/ℓ.

With brown trout eggs (Ministry of Technology, 1966) there was no significant mortality at 0.06, 0.2 and 0.6 mg Zn/ℓ in water having hardnesses equivalent to 12.5, 50 and 200 mg/ℓ as $CaCO_3$ respectively; the 5-day LC50 was lowest at the early eyed stage, being about 0.5 mg Zn/ℓ and 2.5 mg Zn/ℓ at the extreme values of hardness. Corresponding values for eggs of rainbow trout at the late eyed stage were 3 mg Zn/ℓ and > 10 mg Zn/ℓ in the soft and hard water respectively.

Schofield (1965) found 80–85 per cent survival of batches of eggs of brook trout in waters having hardnesses of 1–3 mg/ℓ as $CaCO_3$ and containing 0.02–0.04 mg Zn/ℓ.

On the other hand, the hatch of salmon was only 30 per cent at a concentration of 0.04 mg Zn/ℓ in water having a temperature of 10 °C, a hardness of 14 mg/ℓ as $CaCO_3$, and a pH of 6.4 (Grande, 1967), though Brånin and Paulsson (1971) found that in a water of similar quality (about 13 mg/ℓ as $CaCO_3$ and a pH of 6.1–6.4) they developed successfully even at 0.1 mg Zn/ℓ, while there was about 90 per cent mortality at 1.0 mg Zn/ℓ.

Salmonid fry, juveniles and adults   The results of tests with rainbow trout are shown in *Figure 8.1* (as closed circles) together with those for two other species. The line relating the logarithm of LC50 for rainbow trout to logarithm of water hardness appears to be curvilinear only if the results of Affleck (1952), G. A. Chapman (personal communication), and further unpublished data by Chapman and by G. Holcomb and D. A. Benoit quoted by the U.S. Environmental Protection Agency (1976), are given the same weight as the other points.

Affleck (1952) obtained a complete kill of rainbow trout but a complete survival of brown trout at 0.1 mg Zn/ℓ. The greater resistance of brown trout is confirmed by Goodman (1951), Grande (1967) and Nehring and Goettl (1974). Sprague's data (1964a) suggest that salmon are slightly more sensitive than rainbow trout, a conclusion also supported by Grande (1967). Brook trout on the other hand appear to be slightly more resistant than rainbow trout (Sprague, 1964a; Schofield, 1965; compared with Affleck, 1952 and Nehring and Goettl, 1974).

Coarse fish   Little work has been reported with young stages of coarse fish. There is a brief report (Sabodash, 1974) suggesting that 5 mg Zn/ℓ reduced the size of larvae of grass carp (*Ctenopharygodon idella*) in soft water but not in hard. For juvenile minnow (Bengtsson, 1972), the 10-day LC50 values in soft water (1.5–2.5 mg Zn/ℓ) appear to be slightly higher than those of salmonid fish. The most resistant species appear to be rudd (Ball, 1967) and goldfish (*Carassius auratus*) (Pickering and Henderson, 1964), and data for these and other species are shown in *Figure 8.2.*

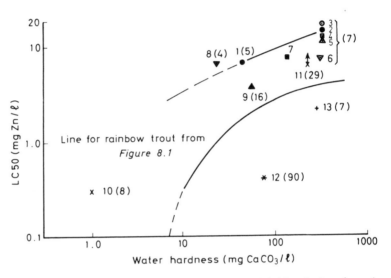

Figure 8.2.   Median lethal concentration of zinc to coarse fish (time in days shown in parentheses). Line for rainbow trout from Figure 8.1 *for comparison*

● Rudd	(*Scardinius erythrophthalmus*)	1. Ministry of Technology, U.K. (1967)
		2. Ministry of Technology, U.K. (1966b)
⊙ Roach	(*Rutilus rutilus*)	3. Ball (1967)
⊡ Perch	(*Perca fluviatilis*)	4. Ball (1967)
△ Bream	(*Abramis brama*)	5. Ball (1967)
▽ Gudgeon	(*Gobio gobio*)	6. Ball (1967)
■ Common carp	(*Cyprinus carpio*)	7. Nehring (1964)
▼ Goldfish	(*Carassius auratus*)	8. Pickering and Henderson (1964)
▲ Crucian carp	(*Carassius carassius*)	9. Weatherley *et al.* (1966)
X Stickleback	(*Gasterosteus aculeatus*)	10. Jones (1938)
		11. Brafield and Matthiessen (1976)
★ Minnow	(*Phoxinus phoxinus*)	12. Bengtsson (1972)
+ Stoneloach	(*Nemacheilus barbatulus*)	13. Solbé and Flook (1975)

Long-term lethal values

Edwards and Brown (1966) kept rainbow trout for about four months in hard water (320 mg/ℓ as $CaCO_3$) containing 0.6, 1.6 and 2.0 mg Zn/ℓ (equivalent to about 0.2, 0.5 and 0.6 of the 5-day LC50 respectively); the percentage mortality at six days was 0, 5 and 7, and at four months 16, 18 and 22 respectively.

Somewhat similar experiments have recently been carried out with rudd in hard water at 8–15 °C (V. M. Brown and T. L. Shaw, personal communication). The LC50 was 24 mg Zn/ℓ at five days and 10.5 mg Zn/ℓ at 8½ months; at the end of this period there was 10 per cent mortality at a concentration of 7 mg/ℓ (0.3 of the 5-day LC50) and none at 4 and 2 mg Zn/ℓ.

Minnow were kept for about three months in soft water (hardness about 70 mg/ℓ as $CaCO_3$) containing low concentrations of zinc (Bengtsson, 1972); the 90-day LC50 for juvenile fish was estimated at 0.3 mg Zn/ℓ. Stickleback survived 29 days at 6.0 mg Zn/ℓ in water having a hardness of 280 mg/ℓ as $CaCO_3$ (Matthiessen and Brafield, 1973).

8.4 Sublethal effects on fish

8.4.1 UPTAKE AND LOSS OF ZINC

Eggs and fry

Experiments by Wedemeyer (1968) on eggs of coho salmon (*Oncorhynchus kisutch*) indicate that uptake of zinc from the water is mainly by adsorption on the chorion (70 per cent), the remainder being by diffusion into the egg (26, 2, and 1 per cent being in the perivitelline fluid, the yolk, and the embryo respectively). However, in experiments with eggs of Atlantic salmon and brook trout, Van Coillie *et al.* (1975) found that there was also a considerable (up to 41-fold) accumulation of zinc within the embryo.

Vladimirov (1971) found that the net uptake of zinc within one month by the fry of common carp was higher in those exposed to 5 mg $ZnSO_4$/ℓ than in those exposed to 0.05 and 0.5 mg/ℓ.

Adults

Zinc is taken up by fish directly from the water, especially by the mucus and gills (Skidmore, 1964). Considerable amounts are also found in the eye, kidney, bone and the gastro-intestinal tract, with lower amounts in liver, spleen, and muscle (Saiki and Mori, 1955; Joyner, 1961; Mount, 1964). High concentrations have also been found in the gonads (Nazarenko, 1972). By plugging the oesophagus of brown bullhead (*Ictalurus nebulosus*) Joyner (1961) showed that swallowed water did not contribute to the zinc in the gastro-intestinal tract. On the other hand, after a 16-h exposure of stickleback to solutions containing zinc, the highest tissue concentrations were found in the gills, and the lowest in the gonads (Matthiessen and Brafield, 1977).

Nazarenko (1972) found that an initial high rate of uptake was followed by a decline after about 12 h. On the other hand Slater (1961) found that the rate of accumulation over 48 h was approximately constant in salmonids and was highest in brown trout, lowest in rainbow trout, and intermediate in cutthroat trout (*Salmo clarki*). Observations by Nazarenko (1972) suggest that in bream (*Abramis brama*) the accumulation of zinc is greater than in roach (*Rutilus rutilus*) and is greater in summer than in winter.

Cairns and Scheier (1957a) conclude from their results that accumulation of zinc may be faster in soft water than in hard but that temperature probably has no appreciable effect. However, Hodson (1975) showed that, with Atlantic salmon exposed to a concentration of 14 mg Zn/ℓ, the rate of uptake of zinc into the gill, and the concentration of zinc in the gill at death, increased from a minimum at 3 °C to a maximum at 19 °C.

Joyner and Eisler (1961) found that most of the zinc taken up within one day by fingerling chinook salmon (*Oncorhynchus tshawytscha*) exposed to solutions of 0.2 mg Zn/ℓ was retained when the fish were kept in flowing water for 63 days, during which time there was a gradual redistribution of zinc to the vertebral column, head and viscera at the expense of other tissues. On the other hand, Joyner (1961) observed that nearly half the zinc that accumulated in brown bullhead during prolonged exposure to 6 mg Zn/ℓ was lost during the first day after transfer of the fish to flowing freshwater, and the rate of loss was reduced later.

Mechanisms for redistribution would account for the ratio of zinc in the gill to that in the operculum being higher in fish poisoned by high concentrations of zinc than in those exposed to sublethal concentrations, and excretion and differences in exposure would account for the variation in concentrations found by Mount (1964) between different samples of fish from the wild.

8.4.2 REPRODUCTION

Brungs (1969) found that reproduction in fathead minnow was almost totally inhibited at zinc concentrations that had no effect on survival, growth and maturation. The number of eggs produced per female at 0.18 mg Zn/ℓ was only 17 per cent of that produced at 0.03 mg Zn/ℓ. The 4-day LC50 was 8.4–10 mg Zn/ℓ, and 15 per cent mortality occurred at 2.8 mg Zn/ℓ in the 10-month test period.

No experiments have been carried out on the effect of zinc on the reproduction of European species of fish, although Bengtsson (1974c) found that spawning occurred at concentrations of zinc that had adverse effects on the survival of fry and adults.

8.4.3 GROWTH

In tests lasting about four months, during which rainbow trout were exposed to concentrations of 0.6–2.0 mg Zn/ℓ (0.2–0.6 of the 5-day LC50) in hard water (Edwards and Brown, 1966), there was a small but significant mortality among the fish, and while growth rates, and weights of liver and kidney (expressed as percentage of total body weight) were apparently similar at all concentrations and for the control, consumption of pelleted food (but not that of maggots) per fish was reduced by almost 20 per cent at 2.0 mg Zn/ℓ.

Rudd, when tested over a period of 8½ months (V. M. Brown and T. L. Shaw, personal communication), also showed no marked tendency for a lower production of biomass at concentrations up to 4 mg Zn/ℓ (0.17 of the 5-day LC50).

Results for other species have been somewhat different. Pickering (1968), using bluegill over a 20-day period, found that growth was enhanced at 1 mg Zn/ℓ and reduced at 4 mg Zn/ℓ (the 20-day LC50 was 7.2-12 mg Zn/ℓ). Bengtsson (1972) however did not find such a stimulating effect of low concentrations on the growth of minnow. Indeed, Bengtsson (1974d) found that minnows exposed to zinc ate fewer tubificids and growth was suppressed within a month, yearlings being affected at lower concentrations than were adults; the fish could not compensate by increasing their growth within a further period of four months. Brungs (1969) found that the growth of fathead minnow was reduced when they were exposed to a concentration of 2.8 mg Zn/ℓ for 30 days (approximately 0.3 of the 4-day LC50), but not at lower concentrations.

Thus the growth of rainbow trout and rudd is apparently unaffected at up to 0.6 and 0.17 respectively of the 5-day LC50, while stimulation of growth at lower fractions of the LC50 has been found in bluegill but not in minnow or fathead minnow.

8.4.4 BEHAVIOUR

Sprague (1964b) used Atlantic salmon parr in a soft water (hardness 18 mg/ℓ as $CaCO_3$) in an avoidance trough in the laboratory. The lowest concentrations causing the average fish to show significant avoidance (EC50) were 0.053 mg Zn/ℓ for zinc sulphate alone and 6 μg Zn/ℓ for zinc in the presence of 0.4 μg Cu/ℓ. These were equivalent to 0.14 and 0.07 of the 7-day LC50 respectively when the natural metal contents in the test water (2 μg Cu/ℓ and 3 μg Zn/ℓ) were included.

Studies of salmon passing through a salmon counting fence in the Northwest Miramichi River, Canada (Sprague, Elson and Saunders, 1965; Saunders and Sprague, 1967) showed that downstream returns during the upstream migration rose from 1-3 per cent during six years before pollution by mine wastes to 10-22 per cent during four years of pollution, and runs to the head-waters were delayed and reduced in number. This apparent avoidance seemed to occur at about 0.35-0.43 of the 7-day LC50 of copper and zinc, while a level of 0.8 of the LC50 may have blocked all upstream movement. Of the salmon returning downstream prematurely about 31 per cent re-ascended. There was little or no difference between avoidance reactions of fish that had been previously exposed to pollution as smolts and those not so exposed. Data provided by P. F. Elson (personal communication) suggest that a lower proportion (1.05 per cent) of hatchery-reared Atlantic salmon smolts was recaptured as grilse, after having been exposed as smolts for 24 h at 10 or 15 °C to waters containing both copper and zinc, each at concentrations equivalent to about 0.35 of the median threshold value, than control fish exposed to a mixture of copper and zinc in which the corresponding proportions of the threshold were about 0.14 and 0.05 respectively; however the total numbers of fish involved were small (11 recaptures from 1046 treated smolts and 22 out of 1130 controls) and no difference in recapture rate was found between treated and untreated wild smolts (2864 of each), perhaps because the latter must have been exposed to low concentration of zinc and copper while living in the river before the test was made.

The EC50 for rainbow trout avoidance of zinc under laboratory conditions at 9.5 °C and 17 °C was 5 μg Zn/ℓ (0.01 of the 7-day LC50) and was not changed when acclimation levels were increased from 3 to 13 μg Zn/ℓ (Sprague, 1968a). Syazuki (1964) and Ishio (1966) report avoidance at 0.3 and 0.45 of concentrations lethal to common carp (*Cyprinus carpio*) and goldfish; Jones (1947), however, found that stickleback (*Pygosteus pungitius*) showed avoidance only of lethal concentrations.

Thus salmon show avoidance of concentrations of zinc equivalent to 0.14 of the 7-day LC50 under laboratory conditions and 0.35–0.43 of the LC50 in the field. In the laboratory rainbow trout react to 0.01 of the LC50 and coarse fish to 0.3–0.45.

Bloom, Perlmutter and Seeley (1978) have shown that adult female zebrafish exposed to a sublethal concentration of zinc (5 mg Zn/ℓ) for nine days did not respond as did control fish to pheromone-containing water. Hyperactivity and a change in the distribution of hourly activity over the whole day was induced in a shoal of minnows by increasing the concentration of zinc to about 0.4 mg Zn/ℓ over a period of six days (Bengtsson, 1974b).

8.4.5 RESISTANCE TO DISEASE

Observations by Pippy and Hare (1969) suggest that in the Miramichi River, Canada, a surge of copper and zinc pollution in late June 1967, accompanied by unusually high river temperatures, may have encouraged an infection in Atlantic salmon caused by the bacterium, *Aeromonas liquefaciens (A. punctata)*. However, peak concentrations of copper and zinc when the mortality started were 1.1 times the 7-day LC50.

Hiller and Perlmutter (1971) found that the amount of virus causing IPN (infectious pancreatic necrosis) in tissue cultures of rainbow trout gonad increased significantly when cultured at 10 mg Zn/ℓ but not at 7.5 mg Zn/ℓ. Sarot and Perlmutter (1976) found that the immune response of zebrafish (*Brachydanio rerio*) against injected pathogens was suppressed by zinc in the case of *Proteus vulgaris* but not with IPN.

8.5 Field observations on fish

There are many reports of fish kills in rivers polluted by water from mining industries, but because of the complexity of the wastes and paucity of analytical data it is usually difficult to identify the effect of zinc alone. However, some data are available from experiments with fish held in cages, from fish farms supplied with zinc-contaminated water and from surveys of the status of fish populations in natural waters containing zinc.

8.5.1 CAGED FISH EXPERIMENTS

Hasselrot (1965) found high mortality among caged yearling salmon and adult minnow in a polluted river in Sweden when mean and maximum concentrations were 0.15–0.28 and 0.25–0.95 mg Zn/ℓ respectively, the water hardness being 21–48 mg/ℓ as $CaCO_3$. His conclusion that the zinc was mainly responsible for killing the fish, with possibly some contribution from low concentrations of copper and other metals, accords with laboratory data for salmonids (p. 169, para. 6 and 7). The adult minnow were slightly more resistant than the yearling salmon.

Similarly, the R. Molonglo in New South Wales, Australia, has been polluted by mining activities (Weatherley, Beevers and Lake, 1967). Complete mortalities occurred within 16 days among caged rainbow trout (size range 39–59 mm) and a partial mortality among brown trout (45–94 mm), when the total zinc concentration fluctuated between 0.1 and 0.5 mg Zn/ℓ, with a total hardness of 10–13 mg/ℓ as $CaCO_3$. The difference in resistance between the two species is consistent with laboratory data (p. 169, para 7); the seemingly higher toxicity of zinc is perhaps attributable to the presence of copper. Crucian carp (*Carassius carassius*) were more resistant than trout, a 40 per cent mortality occurring in 16 days when the total zinc fluctuated between 2 and 7 mg Zn/ℓ, total copper fluctuated between 0.04 and 0.08 mg Cu/ℓ, and the hardness was 57 mg/ℓ as $CaCO_3$.

8.5.2 FISH FARMS

Brook trout were reared in Cornell hatchery (hardness 44–123 mg/ℓ as $CaCO_3$) where concentrations reached 1.52 mg Zn/ℓ (Schofield, 1965). These maxima are close to median lethal concentrations found under laboratory conditions (p. 169, para. 7).

8.5.3 FISH POPULATION SURVEYS

When the R. Ystwyth, U.K. contained up to 0.8 mg Zn/ℓ and a trace of lead at normal water level, and up to 1.4 mg Zn/ℓ during droughts with a pH of about 6.4 and a calcium content equivalent to about 11.0 mg/ℓ as $CaCO_3$, brown trout, which were plentiful above the sources of pollution, died soon after being washed into the main river during floods; sea trout (*Salmo trutta*) which occasionally ascended the lower reaches were also sometimes found dead or dying (Jones, 1940). Later (Jones, 1958) when concentrations were reduced to 0.2–0.7 mg Zn/ℓ (approximately 0.5–1.75 of the 2-day LC50 for rainbow trout) and amounts of lead were negligible, brown trout were present in small numbers, sea lamprey (*Petromyzon marinus*) occurred occasionally but other species, including minnow, stickleback and bullhead (*Cottus gobio*), were absent.

Another, preliminary, survey of small streams in Wales, U.K., from which single samples for analysis were taken in December, February and July, showed that in those in which the concentration of zinc (expressed as a proportion of the 2-day LC50 to rainbow trout) was less than 0.06, brown trout were present at a density of 11–46/100 m², where the proportion was between 0.06 and 0.09 the density was 7/100 m², and where it was between 0.14 and 0.48 the density was 0.4–4/100 m² (from data supplied by Cremer and Warner, personal communication).

Data have also been made available (P. Toner, personal communication) for the R. Kilmastualla, Ireland, in which samples have been taken at approximately fortnightly intervals during 1972; these show that at two stations where there was a self-sustaining population of brown trout, together with some salmon, annual 50 and 95 percentiles for concentrations of zinc expressed as proportions of the 2-day LC50 to rainbow trout were about 0.054 and 0.19 respectively at one station, and about 0.038 and 0.19 at the other. Zinc accounted for about 81 and 66 per cent of the predicted 2-day LC50 at the two stations respectively, there being some contribution from other heavy metals and ammonia. In L. Burley in the R. Molonglo system in Australia where Weatherley (1975) reports that concentrations of zinc were frequently 0.1 mg Zn/ℓ and could reach 0.4 mg Zn/ℓ (hardness 10-13 mg/ℓ $CaCO_3$), rainbow trout and brown trout survived but showed gill damage similar to that of trout exposed to zinc in acute toxicity experiments, and the proportion of fish in older age groups appeared abnormally low.

In Norway, soft-water lakes and rivers (hardness 2-20 mg/ℓ as $CaCO_3$) contain self-sustaining populations of salmonids in the presence of concentrations of zinc up to 0.15 mg Zn/ℓ (M. Grande, 1967; E. Snekvik, personal communication). Where higher concentrations have been observed brown trout, Atlantic salmon, and Arctic char (*Salvelinus alpinus*) are absent, but in most cases copper and other metals are also present. These observations are consistent with the laboratory findings of Lloyd (1960), Sprague (1964a, b) and J. P. Goettl (personal communication), but not with those of Affleck (1952).

Sprague, Elson and Saunders (1965) found that the concentration of zinc and copper in a tributary of the Miramichi River, Canada, averaged 0.24 of the 7-day LC50 in 1962, the maximum value being 0.6 of the 7-day LC50; salmon parr populations were much lower than in unpolluted parts of the river, perhaps partly because the number of available spawning fish was reduced in previous years. Higher concentrations were present in the other years studied.

Schofield (1965) has reported that brook trout occurred in Honnedga Lake, U.S.A. (hardness up to 3 mg/ℓ as $CaCO_3$) where concentrations of zinc ranged from 0.02 to 0.17 mg Zn/ℓ. Migratory salmonids appear to have been able to pass through a length of about 5 km of the R. Orkla, Norway, where the median and 95 percentile concentrations of zinc were about 0.1 and 0.4 mg Zn/ℓ respectively and the hardness was about 39 mg/ℓ as $CaCO_3$; copper was also present with corresponding percentile values of about 35 and 100 μg Cu/ℓ (Arnesen *et al.*, 1977).

In the Willow Brook, U.K., a stream of unusually high hardness, much present as chloride (504 mg/ℓ as $CaCO_3$) and receiving wastes (from a steel works) containing mainly zinc (Solbé, 1973), roach, tench (*Tinca tinca*) and stickleback were present in the upper reaches, where the annual 50- and 95-percentile concentrations were 0.9 and 3.7 mg Zn/ℓ (0.04 and 0.19 of the 5-day LC50 for roach), whereas roach, chub (*Leuciscus cephalus*), minnow, stickleback, eel (*Anguilla anguilla*) and stoneloach (*Nemacheilus barbatulus*) were present in the lower reaches where the corresponding percentiles were 0.4 and 2.2 mg Zn/ℓ (0.02 and 0.1 of the 5-day LC50 for roach).

In the R. Aire, U.K., which contains a variety of poisons, roach, chub, minnow and stickleback were present in limited reaches where the water was well oxygenated, when the 6-yearly 50-percentile and 95-percentile concentrations of zinc were equivalent to 0.02 and 0.05 respectively of the 5-day LC50 to roach (from data supplied by D. Woodhead, personal communication).

Thus, concentrations of zinc that are lethal to fish in the field are generally similar to those found lethal in the laboratory. Also, field observations show that salmon parr may be present in polluted rivers when the concentration of zinc is no more than 0.15 of the 7-day LC50, but that numbers are much reduced when annual mean and maximum concentrations of zinc and copper are as high as

0.24 and 0.6 of the 7-day LC50 respectively (p. 176, para. 3). A few species of coarse fish may occur where the annual median and 95-percentile concentration of zinc is 0.04 and 0.19 of the 5-day LC50 of roach and several species may be present where these values are 0.02 and 0.1 of the 5-day LC50 or lower (p. 176, para. 4 and 5).

8.6 Summary of data on aquatic vegetation and invertebrates

8.6.1 AQUATIC VEGETATION

Whitton (1970a) reviewed the little that is known about the toxicity of zinc to freshwater algae. Williams and Mount (1965) found that adding 1 mg Zn/ℓ or more to natural periphytic communities in four outdoor channels supplied with running water reduced the number of dominant species. Fungi and myxo-bacteria produced a large standing crop at the highest concentration (6.5 mg Zn/ℓ), apparently by utilizing the killed incoming phytoplankton. Organisms highly tolerant of 6.5 mg Zn/ℓ include the bacteria *Sphaerotilus natans*, *Zoogloea ramigera*, and *Beggiatoa* sp., the fungi *Alternaria tenuis* and *Leptomitus lacteus*, the algae *Anacystis* sp., *Lyngbya* sp., *Schizothrix calcicola*, *Oscillatoria*, *Oocystis lacustris*, *Spirogyra* sp., *Chlamydomonas snowii*, *Euglena acus*, *Trachelomonas volvocina*, and *Chrysococcus major* and the diatoms *Cymbella tumida*, *Nitzchia linearis* and *Synedra ulna*.

Whitton (1970b) studied the toxicity of zinc to 25 species of Chlorophyta from flowing water. *Cladophora glomerata* was among the most sensitive; *Ulothrix*, *Microspora*, *Spirogyra* and *Mougeotia* were relatively resistant; while all the *Oedogonium* spp. taken from the wild were of intermediate sensitivity. However *Oedogonium* and *Mougeotia* obtained from a zinc-enriched laboratory tank were highly resistant. Values for zinc causing a slight inhibition of growth ranged from 0.2 to 6.0 mg Zn/ℓ (or to 9.0 mg/ℓ if the algae from a zinc-enriched tank are included). The hardness was not given but is estimated at approximately 20 mg/ℓ as $CaCO_3$. Whitton also concluded (1970a) that *Lemanea* was relatively resistant. *Stigeoclonium tenue* has been found in field situations where concentrations of zinc were as high as 20 mg Zn/ℓ; such high resistance has been largely attributable to increased genetic adaptation in *Stigeoclonium* (Harding and Whitton, 1976) and in *Hormidium rivulare* (Say, 1977; Say, Diaz and Whitton, 1977). Reduction in the toxicity of zinc to algae has been associated with increases in pH and in concentrations of calcium, magnesium and phosphate (Harding and Whitton, 1977; Say and Whitton, 1977).

Extensive observations on benthic diatoms by Besch, Ricard and Cantin (1972) in parts of the Miramichi river system affected by mining operations tend to confirm that *Synedra ulna* and particularly *Achnanthes microcephala* and *Eunotia exiqua* are relatively resistant to zinc; macrophytes most affected were submerged species, followed by riparian dicotyledons, monocotyledons and *Equisetum arvense* (Besch and Roberts-Pichette, 1970). Concentrations of zinc in the range 0.08–0.1 mg/ℓ are stimulatory to some bacteria and floating plants (Albright, Wentworth and Wilson, 1972; Bartlett, Rabe and Funk, 1974; Hutchinson and Czyrska, 1972; Rachlin and Farran, 1974; Whitton 1970b).

8.6.2 INVERTEBRATES

Laboratory tests

There are relatively few data on the effects of zinc on invertebrates, especially those that include information on water quality. However, Brkovic-Popovic and Popovic (1977) carried out tests with *Tubifex tubifex* at 20 °C in waters having a total hardness of 0.1, 34.2 (without phosphate buffer), 34.2 (with phosphate buffer) and 261 mg/ℓ as $CaCO_3$ and found 2-day LC50 values of about 0.1, 3.0, 2.6 and 60.2 mg Zn/ℓ respectively. The 4-day LC50 for the ramshorn snail (*Helisoma campanulatum*) was 1.27 mg Zn/ℓ and 0.87 mg Zn/ℓ in hard and soft water respectively, and for young specimens of the pond snail (*Physa hetero-tropha*) 0.4 mg Zn/ℓ and 0.3 mg Zn/ℓ in hard and soft water (100 mg/ℓ and 20 mg/ℓ total hardness respectively) (Wurtz, 1962), values that are markedly lower than those found by Cairns and Scheier (1957b). He suggests that snails containing haemoglobin (*Helisoma* spp.) are more tolerant of zinc than those containing haemocyanin (*Physa* spp.) and also stresses that molluscs would be the first animals to be eradicated when a stream became overloaded with metals. Herbst (1967), in tests lasting up to 25 days in a water with a hardness of 80 mg/ℓ as $CaCO_3$, found that the larvae of Plecoptera, Trichoptera and Ephemeroptera all survived a concentration of 20 mg Zn/ℓ or more, while species of Hirudinea, Turbellaria and gastropods survived only 3 mg Zn/ℓ. The most sensitive species were the crustaceans *Gammarus pulex* and *G. roeselii*, which showed a 60 and 30 per cent mortality respectively at a concentration of less than 0.5 mg Zn/ℓ.

There is evidence that the resistance of the snail (*Limnaea stagnalis*) to acutely lethal concentrations of zinc is reduced when it is parasitized (Guth, Blankespoor and Cairns, 1977).

Bringmann and Kühn (1959) have reported a 2-day LC50 for young daphnids of 1.8 mg Zn/ℓ in hard water (215 mg/ℓ as $CaCO_3$) a result close to those of Tabata (1969b) which cover a wide range of hardness and are slightly lower than the corresponding values for trout. Anderson (1948), however, reports an EC50 for immobilization of *Daphnia magna* as low as 0.07 mg Zn/ℓ in water of hardness 100 mg/ℓ as $CaCO_3$ and Biesinger and Christensen (1972) using the same species report a 2-day LC50 of 0.16 mg Zn/ℓ at 18 °C in water having a hardness of 45 mg/ℓ expressed as $CaCO_3$. Similar results have been reported for *D. hyalina* (Baudouin and Scoppa, 1974).

Warnick and Bell (1969) studied the effect of zinc on insects in water having a hardness of 44 mg/ℓ and a pH of 7.25. The 10-day LC50 for the mayfly *Ephemerella subvaria* was 16 mg Zn/ℓ, whereas the 11- and 14-day LC50 for the caddisfly *Hydropsyche betteni* and the stonefly (Plecoptera) *Acroneuria lycorias* respectively was 32 mg Zn/ℓ; thus they are considerably more resistant to concentrations lethal within a few days than the fish that have been studied (Section 8.3.3).

Field observations

Field investigations from zinc-polluted waters have given some information on the tolerance of invertebrates to zinc although it is often difficult to interpret because of the presence of other pollutants. In L. Burley, where zinc concentrations were often 0.1 mg Zn/ℓ and could reach 0.4 mg Zn/ℓ, the benthic fauna contained only one molluscan species, and was poor in species of Crustacea, Odonata and Ephemeroptera (Weatherley, Dawson and Peuridge, 1975). In the R. Ystwyth where concentrations of 0.7-1.2 mg Zn/ℓ and 0.05 mg Pb/ℓ were normally present, mollusca, crustaceans, worms (Oligochaeta) and leeches (Hirudinea) were all absent (Jones, 1940), and in a small tributary containing nearly 57 mg Zn/ℓ there was still a considerable number of insect larvae. When concentrations in the main river fell some years later to 0.2-0.7 mg Zn/ℓ the fauna was still almost entirely made up of lithophilic insects (Jones, 1958), *Rhitrogena semicolorata, Heptagena lateralis, Baetis rhodani, Chloroperla tripunctata* and *Esolus parallelopipedus* being the chief species. Sprague, Elson and Saunders (1965) found that caddisflies (Trichoptera) and midges (Chironomidae) were not affected by copper-zinc pollution in the Northwest Miramichi River where concentrations were at least 1.5 times the 7-day LC50 for salmon. Mayflies were more sensitive, and few were present when concentrations were about 60 per cent higher. However studies in 1969 (W. Besch, personal communication) showed there was no hatch of caddisflies, including *Hydropsyche,* and mayflies, and that there was a marked reduction in gallery-building midges; furthermore larvae of the caddisfly *Glossosoma* spp. were absent where the concentrations of zinc were about 0.1 of the 7-day LC50 for salmon. In the Molonglo River, Weatherley, Beevers and Lake (1967) found that the number of animals was markedly reduced and that the fauna consisted mostly of bugs (Hemiptera), beetles (Coleoptera), caddisflies, Diptera, and stoneflies in the zinc-polluted part of the river. However, this may also have been due to indirect effects of the pollution. In the R. Sulz and its tributaries (hardness 80 mg/ℓ as $CaCO_3$), which were heavily polluted by zinc, Herbst (1967) observed that *Gammarus pulex* and *Lymnea ovata* were present only where zinc concentrations were 0.25 mg Zn/ℓ or lower. A great variety of insect larvae was found in areas where the concentrations were 0.8-6.5 mg Zn/ℓ, while larvae of *Baetis* were observed at 25 mg Zn/ℓ and those of the trichopteran (*Rhyacophila* sp.) at 29 mg Zn/ℓ.

8.7 Summary and conclusions

Zinc is a common pollutant in fresh water and occurs in wastes from a variety of industries and other sources. It is often accompanied by copper and other heavy metals and affects freshwater fisheries, presumably mainly by its direct effects on fish but possibly too on some fish-food organisms such as mayflies and *Daphnia* (Section 8.2.6).

Its mode of toxic action is not yet fully understood, but its toxicity is mainly attributable to the zinc ion, though particulate zinc as the basic carbonate or the hydroxide held in suspension may also be toxic (p. 163, para. 4).

In acutely toxic concentrations zinc may kill fish by destroying gill epithelial tissue (p. 161, para. 5). There may also be chronic effects on various organs and enzyme systems (Section 8.3.1).

There are few data on the confidence limits for concentrations reported as having lethal or other effects, but those that are available suggest that they are between ± 10 and 20 per cent of the LC50. The limits widen progressively as the percentage response departs from 50. There is thus some uncertainty about the precise levels that are lethal to fish and other organisms.

Nevertheless it is clear that the toxicity of zinc is modified by water quality, in particular being reduced by an increase in hardness (p. 164, para. 1-2, p. 165). An increase in temperature may shorten the period of survival of fish at concentrations that are rapidly lethal, yet increase it at lower concentrations such that the 7-day LC50 may be increased (p. 162, para. 4 and p. 163, para. 2). Furthermore, toxicity is increased by a decrease in dissolved-oxygen content (p. 163, para. 3) and decreased by an increase in salinity (p. 165, para. 3) and suspended solids (p. 165, para. 5) but probably not to a large extent by organic matter (p. 165, para. 4). The effect of pH is uncertain (p. 163, para. 4 and 5). The acute toxicity of zinc in the presence of other heavy metals and other common pollutants seems to be largely simply additive (p. 167, para. 7 to p. 168, para. 3). However, there is no evidence that the chronic toxicity of different poisons in a mixture is also simply additive. The effect of zinc is modified, and can be reduced, by acclimation and by the age of the fish (p. 166, para. 2-5).

The concentrations of zinc that are rapidly lethal to fish under laboratory conditions and their dependence upon the hardness of the water are fairly well defined for rainbow trout in the range 10-500 mg/ℓ $CaCO_3$ and for some other salmonids at the lower end of the range of hardness, the LC50 values at several days being about 0.4 and 5 mg/ℓ Zn at the two extremes of hardness (p. 164, para. 2 and *Figure 8.1*). However, the very high toxicity to rainbow trout in water containing less than 30 mg/ℓ $CaCO_3$ (p. 169, para. 7) needs confirmation and explanation.

Data for coarse fish are fewer, but they too indicate that toxicity is reduced with increase in water hardness and that the fish are generally more resistant than trout, LC50 values at 320 mg/ℓ $CaCO_3$ ranging from 8 to 17 mg Zn/ℓ (p. 164, para. 1 and *Figure 8.1*). The stoneloach and minnow, however, appear to be more sensitive than trout (p. 170, and *Figure 8.2*).

A low but significant mortality has been found among rainbow trout exposed continuously for four months to constant concentrations of 0.2 of the 5-day LC50 and among rudd exposed for 8½ months to 0.3 of the 7-day LC50 (p. 171, para. 1 and 2); although food consumption of the trout is reduced under laboratory conditions at 0.6 or more of the LC50, growth is not apparently affected (p. 170, para. 1). The 3-month LC50 for the minnow is 0.12-0.2 of the approximate 10-day LC50 (p. 170, para. 1 and p. 171, para. 3).

There is some evidence that resistance to disease (p. 174, para. 4 and 5) and reproduction (p. 172, para. 5) may be affected in sublethal concentrations of zinc, but little systematic work has been done to illuminate these problems or to study their effects in the field.

Laboratory studies of avoidance reactions have shown that Atlantic salmon and rainbow trout may avoid concentrations of zinc in soft water which are 0.01-0.14 of the 7-day LC50 (p. 173, para. 5 and p. 174, para. 1). Avoidance reactions have also been observed at 0.35-0.43 of the 7-day LC50 by migrating Atlantic salmon in a river polluted with copper and zinc (p. 173, para. 6). Carp and goldfish show avoidance of 0.3-0.45 of lethal concentrations under laboratory conditions (p. 174, para. 2).

The resistance of aquatic plants and invertebrates to zinc varies widely. Algae are adversely affected at concentrations of 0.2-9.0 mg Zn/ℓ (p. 177, para. 3). Larvae of some caddisflies and midges are highly resistant to zinc, while those of some mayflies may be about as sensitive as salmon. Mollusca, crustaceans, oligochaetes, and leeches appear to be most sensitive (p. 178, para. 2 to 5).

Field observations of fish mortalities generally confirm the laboratory studies of lethal concentrations (p. 174, para. 7 to p. 175, para. 2). Few, however, adequately describe the conditions in rivers and lakes containing zinc and thriving populations of fish. Good populations of brown trout were present in streams when the concentration of zinc was less than 0.06 of the 2-day LC50 to rainbow trout (p. 175, para. 5) and the fish were also present when the annual 50 and 95 percentiles of the 2-day LC50 were up to 0.05 and 0.19 respectively (p. 175, para. 6). Salmon were present when the concentration of zinc was no more than 0.15 of the 7-day LC50 (p. 176, para. 2) but were much reduced in numbers at annual mean and maximum concentrations of 0.24 and 0.6 of the 7-day LC50 (p. 176, para. 3); a mixed population of coarse fish species, including the minnow, was found in a river of high hardness where the annual median and 95-percentile concentrations of zinc were 0.02 and 0.11 of the 5-day LC50 for the most resistant coarse fish tested, whereas few species were found when the annual median and 95 percentile were 0.04 and 0.19 of the 5-day LC50 (p. 176, para. 5 and 6).

8.8 Tentative water quality criteria

There are extensive data on the toxicity of zinc to fish under laboratory conditions, supported to some extent by field data on fish kills, but there are virtually no field observations to indicate the concentrations of zinc that are not inimical to fish populations or fisheries, mainly because the analytical data are too meagre, information on water hardness—perhaps the most important factor affecting the toxicity of zinc to aquatic animals—is missing, and details of the status of the fish population are not given. For these reasons only tentative criteria can be suggested which may have to be revised when more adequate field data become available.

Because it is known that concentrations of zinc, and indeed of many other natural and artificial constituents of freshwaters containing fish, fluctuate, it is unrealistic to express criteria as single values that should not be exceeded for long periods. Instead they could be expressed as one or more values each relating to a percentile distribution for a defined period, distributions that in practice appear to be approximately lognormal. In the case of zinc the appropriate period might be taken as one year, since there is no reason to expect marked seasonal differences in the effect of this poison on fish, although for salmon the 7-day LC50 at 5 °C is about a quarter (0.26) of that at 15 °C.

Pending the availability of more information, it is tentatively suggested that for the maintenance of thriving populations of fish the annual 95-percentile concentration of 'soluble' zinc should be no greater than 0.1 of the appropriate

Table 8.2   MAXIMUM ANNUAL 95-PERCENTILE CONCENTRATIONS OF 'SOLUBLE' ZINC (mg Zn/ℓ)

Water hardness (mg/ℓ as CaCO₃)	Coarse fish except minnow*	Salmonids
10	0.3	0.03†
50	0.7	0.2
100	1.0	0.3
500	2.0	0.5

*See p. 182, para. 3 †But see p. 182, para. 2

7-day LC50 at 15 °C; thus the criteria in terms of concentration of zinc would depend upon water hardness and type of fish as shown in *Table 8.2*.

The concentration of 0.03 mg Zn/ℓ for salmonids in very soft water may be too severe if brown trout only are present, since this species appears to survive successfully at higher concentrations; in such cases a 95-percentile concentration of 0.2 of the 7-day LC50 (0.06 mg Zn/ℓ) may be more appropriate.

For the minnow it might be more appropriate to set a more stringent standard but further information from the field would be desirable to support and explain the existing laboratory data.

The values of the corresponding annual 50 percentiles would be approximately 0.25 of the proposed 95 percentiles were the distributions referred to in p. 175, para. 6 and p. 176, para. 5 and 6 regarded as typical. However, if the distribution was much wider in range or was not lognormal, so that the ratio between the 95 percentile and higher percentiles was much larger, more stringent standards would be appropriate.

Furthermore, where other poisons are present and dissolved-oxygen concentrations are below the air-saturation value, allowance should be made for their contribution to the toxicity.

8.9 References

AFFLECK, R. J. (1952). Zinc poisoning in a trout hatchery. *Aust. J. Mar. Freshwc Res.* 3, 142-169

ALBRIGHT, L. J., WENTWORTH, J. W. and WILSON, E. M. (1972). Technique for measuring metallic salt effects upon the indigenous heterotrophic microflora of a natural water. *Wat. Res.* 6, 1589-1596

ANDERSON, B. G. (1948). The apparent thresholds of toxicity to *Daphnia magna* for chlorides of various metals when added to Lake Erie water. *Trans. Am. Fis Soc.* 78, 96-113

ARNESEN, R. T., GRANDE, M., EVERSEN, E. R. and BAALSRUD, K. (1977). *Overvåkingsundersøkelser i nedre del av Orklavassdraget.* Blindern, Oslo, Norsk Institutt for Vannforskning

BALL, I. R. (1967). The relative susceptibilities of some species of freshwater fish to poisons. 2. Zinc. *Wat. Res.* 1, 777-783

BARTLETT, L., RABE, F. W. and FUNK, W. H. (1974). Effects of copper, zinc and cadmium on *Selanastrum capricornutum. Wat. Res.* 8, 179-185

BAUDOUIN, M. F. and SCOPPA, P. (1974). Acute toxicity of various metals to freshwater zooplankton. *Bull. envir. Contam. Toxicol.* 12(6), 745-751

BENGTSSON, B-E. (1972). Effekten av långtidsexponering i zink på overlevnad och tillväxt hos elritsa (*Phoxinus phoxinus* L.). In *Rapport från Ricklea fältstation,* Umeå universitet

BENGTSSON, B-E.(1974a). Vertebral damage to minnows (*Phoxinus phoxinus*) exposed to zinc. *Oikos* 25(2), 134-139

BENGTSSON, B-E.(1974b). Effect of zinc on the movement pattern of the minnow (*Phoxinus phoxinus* L.). *Wat. Res.* 8, 829-833

BENGTSSON, B-E.(1974c). The effects of zinc on the mortality and reproduction the minnow (*Phoxinus phoxinus* L.). *Arch. envir. Contam. Toxicol.* 2(4), 342-355

BENGTSSON, B-E. (1974d). Effect of zinc on growth of the minnow (*Phoxinus phoxinus*). *Oikos* 25(3), 370-373

BENGTSSON, B-E.(1974e). The effect of zinc on the ability of the minnow *Phoxinus phoxinus* L. to compensate for torque in a rotating water current. *Bull. envir. Contam. Toxicol.* **12(6)**, 654-658

BESCH, K. W. and ROBERTS-PILCHETTE, P. (1970). Effects of mining pollution on vascular plants in the northwest Miramichi River system. *Can. J. Bot.* **48(9)**, 1647-1656

BESCH, W. K., RICARD, M. and CANTIN, R. (1972). Benthic diatoms as indicators of mining pollution in the northwest Miramichi River system, New Brunswick, Canada. *Int. Rev. Ges. Hydrobiol.* **57(1)**, 39-74

BIESINGER, K. E. and CHRISTENSEN, G. M. (1972). Effects of various metals on survival, growth and reproduction and metabolism of *Daphnia magna. J. Fish. Res. Bd Can.* **29(12)**, 1691-1700

BLOOM, H. D., PERLMUTTER, A. and SEELEY, R. J. (1978). Effect of a sublethal concentration of zinc on an aggregating pheromone system in the zebrafish (*Brachydanio rerio* (Hamilton-Buchanan)). *Envir. Pollut.* **17**, 127-131

BRAFIELD, A. E. and MATTHIESSEN, P. (1976). Oxygen consumption by stickle-backs (*Gasterosteus aculeatus* L.) exposed to zinc. *J. Fish. Biol.* **9**, 359-370

BRANIN, B. and PAULSSON, C. (1971). Långtidsförsök med tungmetaller på de första utvecklingsstadierna hos lax. *Medd. Laxforskningsinst.* **2**

BRINGMANN, G. and KÜHN, R. (1959). Wasser-toxikologische Untersuchungen an Bakterien, Algen, und Kleinbrebsen. *Gesundheitsingenieur* **80**, 115-120

BRKOVIC-POPOVIC, I. and POPOVIC, M. (1977). Effects of heavy metals on survival and respiration rate of tubificid worms. 2. The effects on survival. *Envir. Pollut.* **13(1)**, 65-72

BROWN, V. M. and DALTON, R. A. (1970). The acute lethal toxicity to rainbow trout of mixtures of copper, phenol, zinc and nickel. *J. Fish. Biol.* **2**, 211-216

BROWN, V. M., JORDAN, D. H. M. and TILLER, B. A. (1969). The acute toxicity to rainbow trout of fluctuating concentrations and mixtures of ammonia, phenol and zinc. *J. Fish. Biol.* **1**, 1-9

BROWN, V. M., MITROVIC, V. V. and STARK, G. T. C. (1968). Effects of chronic exposure to zinc on toxicity of a mixture of detergent and zinc. *Wat. Res.* **2**, 255-263

BRUNGS, W. A. (1969). Chronic toxicity of zinc to the fathead minnow (*Pimephales promelas* Rafinesque). *Trans. Am. Fish. Soc.* **98**, 272-279

BURTON, D. T., JONES, A. H. and CAIRNS, J. (1972). Acute zinc toxicity to rainbow trout (*Salmo gairdneri*) in confirmation of the hypothesis that death is related to tissue hypoxia. *J. Fish. Res. Bd Can.* **29(10)**, 1463-1466

CAIRNS, J. Jr. and SCHEIER, A. (1957a). The effects of temperature and hardness of water upon the toxicity of zinc to the common bluegill (*Lepomis macrochirus* Raf.). *Not. Nat. Acad. Nat. Sci. Phil.* **299**

CAIRNS, J. Jr. and SCHEIER, A. (1957b). The effects of periodic low oxygen upon the toxicity of various chemicals to aquatic organisms. *Proc. 12th Ind. Waste Conf., Purdue Univ. Engng Extn. Ser.* **94**, 165-176

DOUDOROFF, P. (1952). Some recent developments in the study of toxic industrial wastes. *Proc. Pac. Northwest. Ind. Waste Conf.* **4**, 21-25

DOUDOROFF, P. and KATZ, M. (1953). Critical review of literature on the toxicity of industrial wastes and their components to fish. 2. The metals, as salts. *Sewage Ind. Wastes* **25**, 802-839

DOUDOROFF, P., LEDUC, G. and SCHNEIDER, C. R. (1966). Acute toxicity to fish of solutions containing complex metal cyanides, in relation to concentrations of molecular hydrocyanic acid. *Trans. Am. Fish. Soc.* **95**, 6-22

EDWARDS, R. W. and BROWN, V. M. (1967). Pollution and fisheries: A progress report. *J. Inst. Wat. Pollut. Control, Lond.* **66**, 63-78

EIFAC, WORKING PARTY ON BIOLOGICAL MONITORING. (1977). The effect of zinc and copper pollution on the salmonid fisheries in a river and lake system in Central Norway. *EIFAC Tech. Rep.* **29**

GOETTL, J. P. Jr., SINLEY, J. R. and DAVIES, P. H. (1972). Water Pollution Studies. Denver, Department of Natural Resources, Colorado Division of Wildlife. Job progress report, Federal Aid Project F-33-R-7

GOODMAN, J. R. (1951). Toxicity of zinc for rainbow trout (*Salmo gairdneri*). *Calif. Fish Game* **37**, 191-194

GRANDE, M. (1967). Effect of copper and zinc on salmonid fishes. *Adv. Wat. Pollut. Res.* **3(1)**, 97-111

GUTH, D. J., BLANKESPOOR, H. D. and CAIRNS, J. Jr. (1977). Potentiation of zinc stress caused by parasitic infection of snails. *Hydrobiologia* **55**, 225-229

HARDING, J. P. C. and WHITTON, B. A. (1976). Resistance to zinc of *Stigeoclonium tenue* in the field and the laboratory. *Br. phycol. J.* **11**, 417-426

HARDING, J. P. C. and WHITTON, B. A. (1977). Environmental factors reducing the toxicity of zinc to *Stigeoclonium tenue*. *Br. phycol. J.* **12**, 17-21

HARGREAVES, J. W., LLOYD, E. J. H. and WHITTON, B. A. (1975). Chemistry and vegetation of highly acidic streams. *Freshwat. Biol.* **5**, 563-576

HASSELROT, T. B. (1965). A study of remaining water pollution from a metal mine with caged fish as indicators. *Vattenhygien* **21**, 11-16

HERBERT, D. W. M. and SHURBEN, D. G. (1964). The toxicity to fish of mixtures of poisons. 2. Copper-ammonia and zinc-phenol mixtures. *Ann. appl. Biol.* **53**, 415-421

HERBERT, D. W. M. and VANDYKE, J. M. (1964). The toxicity to fish of mixtures of poisons. 2. Copper-ammonia and zinc-phenol mixtures. *Ann. appl. Biol.* **53**, 415-421

HERBERT, D. W. M. and WAKEFORD, A. C. (1964). The susceptibility of salmonid fish to poisons under estuarine conditions. 1. Zinc sulphate. *Int. J. Air Wat. Pollut.* **8**, 251-256

HERBERT, D. W. M., JORDAN, D. H. M. and LLOYD, R. (1965). A study of some fishless rivers in the industrial Midlands. *J. Proc. Inst. Sewage Purif.* **64**, 569-582

HERBST, H. V. (1967). Experimentelle Untersuchungen zur Toxizität des Zinks. *Gewässer und Abwässer* **(44/45)**, 37-47

HILLER, J. M. and PERLMUTTER, A. (1971). Effect of zinc on viral-host interactions in a rainbow trout cell line, RTG-2. *Wat. Res.* **5**, 703-710

HODSON, P. V. (1975). Zinc uptake by Atlantic salmon (*Salmo salar*) exposed to a lethal concentration of zinc at 3, 11 and 19 °C. *J. Fish. Res. Bd Can.* **32(12)**, 2552-2556

HODSON, P. V. (1976). Temperature effects on lactate-glycogen metabolism in zinc-intoxicated rainbow trout (*Salmo gairdneri*). *J. Fish Res. Bd Can.* **33(6)**, 1393-1397

HODSON, P. V. and SPRAGUE, J. B. (1975). Temperature-induced changes in acute toxicity of zinc to Atlantic salmon (*Salmo salar*). *J. Fish. Res. Bd Can.* **32(1)**, 1-10

HUGHES, G. M. and ADENEY, R. J. (1977). The effects of zinc on the cardiac and ventilatory rhythms of rainbow trout (*Salmo gairdneri*, Richardson) and their responses to environmental hypoxia. *Wat. Res.* **11(12)**, 1069-1077

HUTCHINSON, T. C. and CZYRSKA, H. (1972). Cadmium and zinc toxicity and synergism to floating aquatic plants. *Wat. Pollut. Res. Can.* 7, 59-65

ISHIO, S. (1966). Behaviour of fish exposed to toxic substances. *Adv. Wat. Pollut. Res.* 2(1), 19-33

JONES, J. R. E. (1938). The relative toxicity of salts of lead, zinc and copper to the stickleback (*Gasterosteus aculeatus* L.) and the effect of calcium on the toxicity of lead and zinc salts. *J. exp. Biol.* 15, 394-407

JONES, J. R. E. (1940). A study of the zinc-polluted river Ystwyth in North Cardiganshire, Wales. *Ann. appl. Biol.* 27, 368-378

JONES, J. R. E. (1947). The reactions of *Pygosteus pungitius* (L.) to toxic solutions. *J. exp. Biol.* 24, 110-122

JONES, J. R. E. (1958). A further study of the zinc-polluted river Ystwyth. *J. Anim. Ecol.* 27, 1-14

JOYNER, R. (1961). Exchange of zinc with environment solutions by the brown bullhead. *Trans. Am. Fish. Soc.* 90, 444-448

JOYNER, T. and EISLER, R. (1961). Retention and translocation of radio-active zinc by salmon fingerlings. *Growth* 25, 151-156

KATZ, B. M. (1977). Mechanism of entry of metals in the fish gill. In *Proc. 49th Ann. Conf. Int. Wat. Pollut. Control Fed.*, 3-8 October 1976

KEMP, H. T., ABRAMS, J. P. and OVERBECK, R. C. (1971). Effects of chemicals on aquatic life. In *Water Quality Criteria Data Book, Vol. 3 Wat. Pollut. Control Res. Ser., Wash.* (18050TWV05/71)

LEWIS, S. D. and LEWIS, W. M. (1971). The effect of zinc and copper on the osmolality of blood serum of the channel catfish *Ictalurus punctatus* Rafinesque, and golden shiner *Notemigonus crysoleucas* Mitchill. *Trans. Am. Fish Soc.* 100, 639-643

LLOYD, R. (1960). The toxicity of zinc sulphate to rainbow trout. *Ann. appl. Biol.* 48, 84-94

LLOYD, R. (1961). The toxicity of mixtures of zinc and copper sulphates to trout (*Salmo gairdneri* Richardson). *Ann. appl. Biol.* 49, 535-538

LLOYD, R. (1965). Factors that affect the tolerance of fish to heavy metal poisoning. *Biological Problems in Water Pollution. Publ. Hlth Serv., Wash.* 99-WP-25, 181-187

LLOYD, R. and HERBERT, D. W. M. (1962). The effect of the environment on the toxicity of poisons to fish. *Inst. publ. Hlth Engrs J.* 61, 132-145

LLOYD, R. and JORDAN, D. H. M. (1963). Predicted and observed toxicities of several sewage effluents to rainbow trout. *J. Proc. Inst. Sewage Purif.* 1963 (2), 167-173

LLOYD, R. and JORDAN, D. H. M. (1964). Predicted and observed toxicities of several sewage effluents to rainbow trout: a further study. *J. Proc. Inst. Sewage Purif.* 1964 (2), 3-6

MATTHIESSEN, P. and BRAFIELD, A. E. (1973). The effects of dissolved zinc on the gills of stickleback *Gasterosteus aculeatus* (L). *J. Fish. Biol.* 5(5), 607-613

MATTHIESSEN, P. and BRAFIELD, A. E. (1977). Uptake and loss of dissolved zinc by the stickleback (*Gasterosteus aculeatus* L.). *J. Fish Biol.* 10, 399-410

MINISTRY OF TECHNOLOGY, U.K. (1966). In *Water Pollution Research 1965*, pp. 142-143 London, H.M.S.O.

MINISTRY OF TECHNOLOGY, U.K. (1967). In *Water Pollution Research 1966*, p. 61. London, H.M.S.O.

MINISTRY OF TECHNOLOGY, U.K. (1968). In *Water Pollution Research 1967,* p. 63. London, H.M.S.O.

MINISTRY OF TECHNOLOGY, U.K. (1971). In *Water Pollution Research 1970,* p. 63. London, H.M.S.O.

MOUNT, D. I. (1964). An autopsy technique for zinc-caused fish mortality. *Trans. Am. Fish. Soc.* **93**(2), 174-182

MOUNT, D. I. (1966). The effect of total hardness and pH on acute toxicity of zinc to fish. *Int. J. Air. Wat. Pollut.* **10**, 49-56

NAZARENKO, L. D. (1972). Soderzhanie medi i cynka i sezonnaia dinamika ikh v organakh i tkaniakh u nekotorykh promyslovykh ryb Kuivyshevkogo vodo-khranilishcha (Copper and zinc content and their seasonal changes in the organs and tissues of some commercial fish from Kuibyshev reservoir). *Trudy Ulianovsk. Selsko-khoz. Inst.* **17**(8), 167-179

NEHRING, D. (1964). Die Schadwirkung von Kupfersulfat, Zinksulfat, Kalium-zyanid, Ammoniak und Phenol gegenüber Karpfen (*Cyprinus carpio*) vom Wasser her und nach peroraler Applikation. *Z. Fisch.* **12**, 717-721

NEHRING, R. B. and GOETTL, J. P. (1974). Acute toxicity of a zinc-polluted stream to four species of salmonids. *Bull. envir. Contam. Toxicol.* **12**, 464-469

O'CONNOR, J. T. (1968). Fate of zinc in natural surface waters. *Univ. Ill. Bull. Dep. Civ. Engng Sanit. Engng Ser.* **49**

PICKERING, Q. H. (1968). Some effects of dissolved-oxygen concentrations upon the toxicity of zinc to the bluegill, *Lepomis macrochirus,* Raf. *Wat. Res.* **2**, 187-194

PICKERING, Q. H. and HENDERSON, C. (1964). The acute toxicity of some heavy metals to different species of warm-water fishes. *Int. J. Air Wat. Pollut.* **10**, 453-463

PICKERING, Q. H. and VIGOR, W. N. (1965). The acute toxicity of zinc to eggs and fry of the fathead minnow. *Prog. Fish-Cult.* **27**, 153-157

PIPPY, J. H. A. and HARE, G. M. (1969). Relationship of river pollution to bac-terial infection in salmon (*Salmo salar*) and suckers (*Catostomus commersoni*). *Trans. Am. Fish. Soc.* **98**, 685-690

RACHLIN, J. W. and PERLMUTTER, A. (1968). Response of an inbred strain of platyfish and the minnow to zinc. *Prog. Fish-Cult.* **30**, 203-207

RACHLIN, J. W. and FARRAN, M. (1974). Growth response of the green algae *Chlorella vulgaris* to selective concentrations of zinc. *Wat. Res.* **8**, 575-577

SABODASH, V. M. (1974). Survival rate of grass carp larvae after exposure to zinc sulphate. *Hydrobiol. J.* **10**(6), 77-80

SAIKI, M. and MORI, R. (1955). Studies on the distribution of administered radioactive zinc in the tissues of fishes. 1. *Bull. Jap. Soc. Sci. Fish.* **21**, 945-949

SAROT, D. A. and PERLMUTTER, A. (1976). The toxicity of zinc to the immune response of the zebrafish (*Brachydanio rerio*), injected with viral and bacterial antigens. *Trans. Am. Fish. Soc.* **105**(3), 456-459

SAUNDERS, R. L. and SPRAGUE, J. B. (1967). Effects of copper-zinc mining pollution on a spawning migration of Atlantic salmon. *Wat. Res.* **1**, 419-432

SAY, P. J. (1977). Microbial ecology of high zinc level streams. Ph.D. Thesis, University of Durham

SAY, P. J., DIAZ, B. M. and WHITTON, B. A. (1977). Influence of zinc on lotic plants. 1. Tolerance of *Hormidium* species to zinc. *Freshwat. Biol.* **7**, 357-376

SAY, P. J. and WHITTON, B. A. (1977). Influence of zinc on lotic plants. 2. Environmental effects on toxicity of zinc to *Hormidium rivulare*. *Freshwat. Biol.* **7**, 377-384

SCHOFIELD, C. L. Jr. (1965). Water quality in relation to survival of brook trout (*Salvelinus fontinalis* Mitchill). *Trans. Am. Fish. Soc.* **94**, 227-235

SKIDMORE, J. F. (1964). Toxicity of zinc compounds to aquatic animals with special reference to fish. *Q. Rev. Biol.* **39**, 227-248

SKIDMORE, J. F. (1970). Respiration and osmoregulation in rainbow trout with gills damaged by zinc sulphate. *J. exp. Biol.* **52**, 481-494

SKIDMORE, J. F. and TOVELL, P. W. A. (1972). Toxic effects of zinc sulphate on the gills of rainbow trout. *Wat. Res.* **6**, 217-230

SLATER, J. V. (1961). Comparative accumulation of radioactive zinc in young rainbow, cutthroat and brook trout. *Copeia* **1961** (2), 158-161

SOLBÉ, J. F. de L. G. (1973). The relation between water quality and the status of fish populations in Willow Brook. *J. Soc. Wat. Treat. Exam.* **22**, 44-61

SOLBÉ, J. F. de L. G. and FLOOK, V. A. (1975). Studies on the toxicity of zinc sulphate and of cadmium sulphate to stone-loach *Noemacheilus barbatulus* in hard water. *J. Fish. Biol.* **7**, 631-637

SPRAGUE, J. B. (1964a). Lethal concentrations of copper and zinc for young Atlantic salmon. *J. Fish. Res. Bd Can.* **21**, 17-26

SPRAGUE, J. B. (1964b). Avoidance of copper-zinc solutions by young salmon. *J. Wat. Pollut. Control Fed.* **36**, 990-1004

SPRAGUE, J. B. (1968a). Avoidance reactions of rainbow trout to zinc sulphate solutions. *Wat. Res.* **2**, 367-372

SPRAGUE, J. B. (1968b). Promising anti-pollutant: Chelating agent NTA protects fish from copper and zinc. *Nature, Lond.* **200**, 1345-1346

SPRAGUE, J. B. and RAMSAY, B. A. (1965). Lethal levels of mixed copper-zinc solutions for juvenile salmon. *J. Fish. Res. Bd Can.* **22**(2), 425-432

SPRAGUE, J. B., ELSON, P. F. and SAUNDERS, R. L. (1965). Sublethal copper-zinc pollution in a salmon river—a field and laboratory study. *Int. J. Air Wat. Pollut.* **9**, 531-543

SREENIVASAN, A. and RAJ, R. S. (1963). Toxicity of zinc to fish. *Curr. Sci., Bangalore* **32**, 363

SVENSKA GRUVFÖRENINGEN (1960). Vattenföroreningar från gruvor och anrikningsverk. Forskningsuppgi 196/1960, Delrapport 1-5 avseende adsorption av metalljoner på gråbergsmineral. Institutt för mineralberedning (anrikning) KTH, Stockholm (1961-1966). (mimeo)

SYAZUKI, I. (1964). Studies on the toxic effects of industrial waste on fish and shell fish. *J. Shimonoseki Coll. Fish.* **13**, 157-211

TABATA, K. (1969a). Studies on the toxicity of heavy metals to aquatic animals and the factors to decrease the toxicity. 2. The antagonistic action of hardness components in water on the toxicity of heavy metal ions. *Bull. Tokai Reg. Fish. Res. Lab.* **58**, 215-232

TABATA, K. (1969b). Studies on the toxicity of heavy metals to aquatic animals and the factors to decrease the toxicity. 4. On the relation between the toxicity of heavy metals and the quality of environmental wastes. *Bull. Tokai Reg. Fish. Res. Lab.* **58**, 255-265

U.S. ENVIRONMENTAL PROTECTION AGENCY. (1976). Quality Criteria for Water. Washington DC, U.S. Environmental Protection Agency EPA 440/9-76-023)

VAN COILLIE, R., JONES, G., POIRIER, D. and GONSPIL, M. (1975). Effets sublethaux du cuivre et du zinc chez les oeufs de salmonides. In *Programme and abstracts of papers presented at the International Conference on Heavy Metals in the Environment,* Section C: pp. 21-23. Toronto, Ontario, Canada, 27-31 October 1975

VLADIMIROV, V. I. (1971). Izmienienie intensivnosti nakaplenia cynka pod vlijaniem ego dobavok na rannych stadiakh embriogeneze i rhizniestoikosti lichinok karpa *Cyprinus carpio.* (Changes of the intensity of zinc accumulation under the influence of its additions, and changes of vital resistance of carp *(Cyprinus carpio)* fry in the early stages of embriogenesis.) *Vop. Ikhthiol.* **11(6),** 1115-1117

WARNICK, S. L. and BELL, H. L. (1969). The acute toxicity of some heavy metals to different species of aquatic insects. *J. Wat. Pollut. Control Fed.* **41,** 280-284

WEATHERLEY, A. H. (1975). Ecology of zinc pollution of a river/lake system. In *Programme and abstracts of papers presented at the International Conference on Heavy Metals in the Environment,* Section C: pp. 308-310. Toronto, Ontario, Canada, 27-31 October 1975

WEATHERLEY, A. H., BEEVERS, J. R. and LAKE, P. S. (1967). The ecology of a zinc-polluted river. In *Australian inland waters and their fauna: Eleven studies,* pp. 252-278. Canberra, Australian National University Press

WEATHERLEY, A. H., DAWSON, P. and PEURIDGE, L. (1975). Assessment and eradication of heavy metal pollution in a planned urban environment. *Verh. int. Verein. theor. angew. Limnol.* **19(3),** 2112-2120

WEDEMEYER, G. (1968). Uptake and distribution of Zn-65 in the coho salmon egg *(Oncorhyncus kisutch). Comp. Biochem. Physiol.* **26,** 271-279

WHITTON, B. A. (1970a). Toxicity of heavy metals to freshwater algae: a review. *Phykos* **9,** 116-125

WHITTON, B. A. (1970b). Toxicity of zinc, copper and lead to Chlorophyta from flowing waters. *Arch. Mikrobiol.* **72,** 353-360

WILLIAMS, L. G. and MOUNT, D. I. (1965). Influence of zinc on periphytic communities. *Am. J. Bot.* **52,** 26-34

WURTZ, C. (1962). Zinc effects on fresh-water molluscs. *Nautilus* **76,** 53-61

ZITKO, V. and CARSON, W. G. (1977). Seasonal and developmental variation in the lethality of zinc to juvenile Atlantic salmon *(Salmo salar). J. Fish. Res. Bd Can.* **34,** 139-141

9

COPPER

Foreword

The original report on copper and freshwater fish was prepared by combining contributions from individual members of the Working Party on Water Quality Criteria for European Freshwater Fish and very little revision has been necessary to update it for the present volume. No attempt has been made to incorporate all the recent literature but particular attention has been given to several papers which underline the problem of defining the form in which copper exerts its toxicity and the role of hardness, alkalinity and pH value (e.g. Howarth and Sprague, 1978) and the difficulty of predicting the toxicity of copper under field conditions (e.g. EIFAC, 1977). A useful annotated list of references updated up to the summer of 1975 has been produced by Black et al. (1976).

9.1 Summary

Copper is a common pollutant in surface waters; its mode of action on aquatic organisms is not clear but toxicity is largely attributable to Cu^{2+}. The cupric form of copper (which is the species commonly found) is readily complexed by inorganic and organic substances and is adsorbed on to particulate matter. For this reason, the free ion rarely occurs except in pure acidic soft waters. The analytical techniques commonly used do not distinguish between toxic ionic copper and non-toxic soluble copper complexes and are not accurate at low concentrations, making the interpretation of field data difficult; where possible, copper concentrations are expressed in this chapter as 'soluble copper', i.e., that which passes through a millipore filter of average porosity 0.45 μm.

Toxicity is increased (median lethal concentrations, or LC50 values, are decreased) by reduction in water hardness, temperature, and dissolved oxygen, and decreased in the presence of chelating agents such as EDTA and NTA, humic acids, amino acids, and suspended solids, but little is known of the effects of pH and alkalinity.

Acutely lethal concentrations (i.e., 2- or 4-day LC50s) of copper to European species of fish in hard water range over 1½ orders of magnitude. No reliable comparative data are available for different species in soft water, for the young stages, or for sublethal effects.

Significant adverse effects on growth of some species, including rainbow trout, occur at about 0.1 of the 4-day LC50.

Aquatic plants and algae and invertebrates are generally more resistant than fish and there is no evidence that fisheries in waters containing copper have been adversely affected because of a reduction in food organisms.

The toxicity of copper in natural waters, except soft water free from organic matter and suspended solids, is less than that predicted from laboratory tests in clean water, probably because of the presence of non-toxic complexes and insoluble precipitates. Sewage effluents containing copper are also less toxic than would be predicted from laboratory data. The presence of non-toxic complexes may partly explain the existence of brown trout populations where the annual 50 and 95 percentile values of soluble copper were 0.17 and 0.38 of the 2-day LC50 to rainbow trout, and of some non-salmonid species where the corresponding values were 0.17 and 0.66 respectively.

Only tentative water quality criteria can be formulated at present because there are virtually no field observations that indicate unequivocally the concentrations of copper that are not inimical to fish populations or fisheries. This is mainly because analytical methods for determining low concentrations are inadequate and the methods commonly used do not distinguish between toxic and non-toxic soluble forms. Also, quantitative data on the size and structure of the fish populations are not available and other poisons are frequently present with copper. Only meagre qualitative data are available for non-salmonid species.

In the absence of data on the precise effects of copper on natural fish populations, considerable reliance has to be placed on laboratory data; it is suggested that the maximum safe concentrations should be based on annual 50 and 95 percentile values of soluble copper of 0.05 and 0.2 respectively of the threshold LC50 to rainbow trout, taking into account the effect of water hardness as shown in *Table 9.1*. Peak concentrations (> 0.5 of the threshold LC50) may be more damaging in the winter than in the summer.

The presence of organic matter might allow the values in *Table 9.1* to be increased up to 3-fold. The values should be decreased to allow for low tempera-

Table 9.1   APPROXIMATE MAXIMUM ANNUAL 50 and 95 PERCENTILE CONCENTRATIONS OF SOLUBLE COPPER FOR RAINBOW TROUT (μg Cu/ℓ)*

Water hardness (mg/ℓ as CaCO$_3$)	50 percentile	95 percentile
10	1.0[†]	5.0[†]
50	6.0	22.0
100	10.0	40.0
300	28.0	i12.0

*Adjustments can be made for the presence of organic matter, low temperature, harmful substances and other species (see pp. 191–212).
[†]Higher values occurring naturally where fish are present may indicate the predominance of soluble organo-copper complexes.

ture and for the presence of other poisons and also adjusted to allow for the different sensitivities of other species of fish, as illustrated in the appropriate sections of the chapter.

9.2 Introduction

Copper is found in natural waters as a trace metal, i.e., usually at concentrations of < 5 $\mu g/\ell$, but can also be present at much higher concentrations (several mg/ℓ), as a result of mining activities and other industrial processes, to the detriment of fish; it is often present with other heavy metals (especially zinc) at potentially harmful concentrations and with other poisons, making it difficult to distinguish the effect attributable to copper. It is also used as an algicide and molluscicide.

9.2.1 CHEMISTRY OF COPPER IN FRESH WATER

In the aerobic conditions normally prevailing in natural surface fresh waters the only stable oxidation state of copper is the cupric form. This has a great tendency to form complexes (i.e., the stability constants of its complexes are large), and the chemistry of copper in water is dominated by this tendency. The proportion of the total dissolved copper present as the free ion has been found to be about 1 per cent, but would be much smaller in waters with heavy organic loads and those of high pH (> 7.5). Only in water of unusually low pH, or very soft water, could a significant proportion be present as the free ion.

Complexation in fresh water has been thoroughly investigated by Stiff (1971b). The complexes usually present are those with the carbonate and hydroxide ions and amino acids and, in waters receiving domestic and industrial wastes, cyanide and synthetic chelating agents such as the detergent builders polyphosphate and nitrilotriacetic acid (NTA). The stability constants of all these complexes are known (Sillen and Martell, 1964) and the extent of complexation can be calculated if the pH and concentration of the complexing agent are also known. Another important class of copper compounds found in natural waters is that containing humic substances, for which few accurate stability constants are known.

Most copper complexes are labile and equilibria are rapidly established. Certain of the humic complexes, however, appear to be inert (Chau and Lum-Shue-Chan, 1974) and once formed, probably by slow rearrangement of a labile humic complex, their subsequent response to changes in the composition of the water which would lead toward dissociating the complex will be slow.

The least soluble copper salt formed under normal aerobic conditions in natural fresh waters containing bicarbonate salts is the basic carbonate, malachite. At a bicarbonate concentration of 5×10^{-3} mol/ℓ the equilibrium of free cupric ion is 8×10^{-8} mol/ℓ (or 5 $\mu g/\ell$) at pH 7, and 3×10^{-9} mol/ℓ (or 0.16 $\mu g/\ell$) at pH 8. Because of complexation, however, total dissolved copper concentrations in excess of this are thermodynamically stable and establishment of equilibrium is in any case a slow process.

There has been discussion of the role of the chemical speciation of copper in accounting for differences in the toxicity of the metal in water of different chemical composition (Stiff, 1971a, 1971b; Calamari and Marchetti, 1974 and Pagenkopf, Russo and Thurston, 1974). It has been suggested (p. 195, para. 5) that the toxicity can be related to the total concentration of soluble copper, i.e. Cu^{2+} and $CuCO_3$ (Shaw and Brown, 1974), but recent work in the U.S.A. (Andrew, 1976) appears to demonstrate adequately that it is the copper ion which is the most important form, although one or more of the hydroxides may also be toxic (Howarth and Sprague, 1978).

Like other trace metals, copper is also readily adsorbed on to solid particles suspended in water and on to container surfaces. Substantial proportions of the total copper present in unfiltered natural water samples, therefore, can be associated with particulate material (Stiff, 1971b; Nachšina and Feld'man, 1971).

The more common methods for measuring copper in fresh water (atomic absorption spectrophotometry, activation analysis, mass spectrometry, and most colorimetric methods) measure the total concentration of copper in the sample after suitable pretreatment. The concentration of copper associated with particulate material can readily be obtained by filtration, but the differentiation and identification of even only some of the complexes present requires more elaborate procedures involving the copper specific ion electrode and colorimetric reagents (Stiff, 1971a) and possibly other methods. Anodic stripping voltammetry can also be used to a limited extent to measure complexation (Chau and Lum-Shue-Chan, 1974), and after the release of copper from inert complexes provides an alternative method of determining the total dissolved metal concentration. Complete analytical identification cannot be made, however, and because of the low concentrations at which the ionic form (the most important state) is present, this is very difficult to determine at levels of interest with regard to aquatic life.

It will be evident from the foregoing paragraphs that the value of much of the published data on the toxicity of copper to aquatic life is severely limited by the inadequacy of analytical information on water quality, especially in early publications, and the fact that conditions in the field are more complex than these produced in the laboratory. This is discussed again on p. 194, para. 4 to p. 196, para. 3 and on p. 205, para. 1 to p. 207, para. 4.

9.3 Direct lethal action on fish

9.3.1 MODE OF ACTION

The toxicity of copper salts to fish was attributed by early workers, for example, Ellis (1937), to the precipitation of mucus on the gills thereby causing suffocation, and also to direct damage of the gill. Certainly, acutely lethal concentrations of copper cause a temporary reduction in the number of mucus cells in common carp (*Cyprinus carpio*) (Labat, Pequignot and Chantelet, 1974) and rainbow trout (*Salmo gairdneri*) (Pequignot, Labat and Chantelet, 1975) and extensive breakdown of the gill of the latter, the lamellae tending to collapse and overlie each other and showing hypertrophy and hyperplasia (Department of Scientific and Industrial Research, 1961). Effects on the gills of lower concentrations are less severe (Dabrowska, 1976), the epithelial layer showing thickening of the apical cells, vacuolization, and containing myelin-like bodies and increased numbers of chloride cells (Baker, 1969).

Bilinski and Jonas (1973) found that the exposure of rainbow trout to rapidly lethal levels of copper reduced the capacity of excised gills to oxidize lactate, but with exposure to concentrations causing 33 per cent mortality in 96 h there was no reduction in oxidation rate. Therefore the hypothesis that fish die from asphyxiation is probably an oversimplification, metabolic pathways involving other enzymes probably being implicated. For example, hepatic and renal disorders have been reported for the winter flounder (*Pseudopleuronectes americanus*) (Baker, 1969) and for killifish (or mummichog) (*Fundulus heteroclitus*) (Gardner and La Roche, 1973), and changes in the activity of some liver enzymes have been found in mummichog following exposure to the 4-day LC50 of copper (Jackim, Hamlin and Sonis, 1970). *In vitro* measurements of the effect of copper on the plasma lactate dehydrogenase (PLDH) and plasma glutamic oxalacetic transaminase (PGOT) activity in white sucker (*Catostomus commersoni*) showed inhibition by 65 and 130 mg Cu/ℓ respectively (Christensen, 1971), but these levels are certainly higher than those likely to be found in the plasma of fish exposed to copper solutions (see p. 200, para. 5). However, with brook trout (*Salvelinus fontinalis*) PGOT activity was reduced at levels of copper that were detrimental to survival and growth (McKim and Benoit, 1971).

Little is known of the significance of enhanced concentrations of copper in the blood, gill, liver and kidney of trout treated with sublethal concentrations (Calamari and Marchetti, 1973) and in whole fish exposed to lethal concentrations (Kariya, Haga and Tsunda, 1967). Increased levels occurred in the gill, liver and kidney but not in the opercula, red blood cells and blood plasma of brown bullhead (*Ictalurus nebulosus*) exposed to sublethal concentrations of copper (Brungs, Leonard and McKim, 1973); and somewhat similar results were found for bluegill (*Lepomis macrochirus*) (Benoit, 1975). Tissue levels in brown bullhead when killed by further exposure to lethal concentrations were higher than those of controls kept beforehand in clean water. Other relevant data are given in Sections 9.4.2 and 9.4.3.

It may therefore be concluded that little of the harmful mode of action of copper on fish is known with certainty.

9.3.2 FACTORS AFFECTING ACUTELY LETHAL LEVELS

The curve relating the logarithm of median period of survival to the logarithm of copper concentration can be used to estimate the median asymptotic or threshold LC50; the shape, and more importantly, the asymptotic values of the curves, are affected by environmental factors such as water hardness, dissolved-oxygen concentration, pH value, and temperature, and are different for different species and stages in the life history. Since these concentration–response curves may cross each other, one curve may indicate a shorter period of survival at high concentrations than another and yet indicate a higher threshold median lethal concentration, i.e., a lower toxicity (p. 194, para. 2).

Temperature

Liepolt and Weber (1958) found that in hard water (250 mg/ℓ as CaCO$_3$), the threshold concentration for rainbow trout was 0.5 mg Cu/ℓ at both 15 °C and 10 °C although the survival times at concentrations higher than the threshold were shortest at the highest temperature.

Similarly, the 8-day LC50 of 0.5 mg Cu/ℓ for this species found by the Department of the Environment (1971) in water having a hardness of about 250 mg/ℓ as $CaCO_3$ and a temperature of 11.5 °C was close to that obtained by Calamari and Marchetti (1973) in water having a hardness of 290–310 mg/ℓ as $CaCO_3$ and a temperature of 15.0–15.6 °C.

On the other hand, for juvenile rainbow trout (length 30 mm) acclimated to the test temperature for at least 14 days in hard water (250–260 mg/ℓ as $CaCO_3$) at a dissolved-oxygen concentration of over 70 per cent of the air-saturation value and at a pH value 7.0–7.5, the 6-day LC50 at 6 °C and 2 °C was about 0.3 and 0.5 of the value at 15 °C (Department of the Environment, 1973). Thus for rainbow trout at 6 °C, as compared with 15 °C, survival time at acutely lethal concentrations can be increased but the 6-day LC50 reduced by two thirds, providing an example of crossing over of the concentration–response curves. Reduction in the survival time of goldfish (*Carassius auratus*) acclimated to the test temperature and exposed to 1.5 mg Cu/ℓ in very soft water has been found at 27 °C as compared with 14 °C (Marchetti, 1962). Similar results have been found for the minnow (*Phoxinus phoxinus*) though the 7-day LC50 was unchanged (Liepolt and Weber, 1958). Rehwoldt *et al.* (1972) also found no differences in 4-day LC50 values for six North American species tested at 17 °C and 28 °C.

Dissolved oxygen

Low concentrations of dissolved oxygen increase the toxicity of poisons to fish (Lloyd, 1961a), and for copper the 2-day LC50 is reduced by about one-third with a reduction in the dissolved-oxygen concentration from 100 per cent to 40 per cent of the air-saturation value.

pH value

There are few data on the effects of pH on the toxicity of copper, but it is known that copper is precipitated in hard water at alkaline pH values. For example, for a nominal concentration of 5 mg Cu/ℓ at pH 7.45, 2.94 mg Cu/ℓ were in solution after 24 h, whereas at pH 8 only 1 mg/ℓ was in solution after 2 h (Department of the Environment, 1971). It is not known whether the precipitate is toxic.

Liepolt and Weber (1958) found that in hard water (250 mg/ℓ as $CaCO_3$) the threshold concentration for rainbow trout was 0.5 mg Cu/ℓ at pH values of both 5.6 and 6.4 although the survival time was reduced at the lower pH value. Also, Shaw and Brown (1974) found that the median period of survival for rainbow trout was similar for equal concentrations of copper (Cu^{2+} and $CuCO_3$) at pH values of 6.5 and 7.5 in hard water. On the other hand, Howarth and Sprague (1978) have shown that at a given hardness the toxicity of dissolved copper to this species tends to be reduced with increase in pH value especially in hard water.

Hardness

Copper has been shown to be more toxic in soft than in hard water (Department of Scientific and Industrial Research, 1962); tests made with rainbow trout at three different levels of hardness (12, 42 and 320 mg/ℓ as $CaCO_3$) to which the fish were acclimated beforehand showed that the 7-day LC50 was about 0.03, 0.08 and 0.5 mg Cu/ℓ respectively.

Tabata (1969) also found with both rainbow trout and carp that the 1-day LC50 increased almost three-fold with an eight-fold increase in hardness effected by the addition of calcium chloride and magnesium sulphate. Lloyd and Herbert (1962) suggested that a linear relation exists between the logarithm of threshold LC50 of copper for rainbow trout and the logarithm of total water hardness. However, the data of Howarth and Sprague (1978) (and of C. Chakoumakos, R. C. Russo and R. V. Thurston (submitted to *Envir. Sci. Technol.*) which they mention) indicate much more complex relationships dependent also upon alkalinity and pH value.

Salinity

With juvenile pompano (*Trachinotus carolinus*) acclimated to different salinities the toxicity of solutions containing copper sulphate decreased with increase in salinity (Birdsong and Avault, 1971), the 4-day LC50 being 1.42 mg Cu/ℓ at 10 g/ℓ and 1.97 mg Cu/ℓ at 30 g/ℓ.

Organic substances

Some organic substances of low toxicity to fish such as ethylenediaminetetra-acetic acid (EDTA), NTA, citric acid, humic substances, and natural amino acids, can reduce the acute toxicity of copper (Sprague, 1968; Nishikawa and Tabata, 1969; Ministry of Technology, 1970).

Grande (1967) found an increased survival of Atlantic salmon fingerlings (*Salmo salar*) in soft water containing 1 mg Cu/ℓ after addition of an amount of EDTA sufficient for a complete chelation of the metal. Shaw and Brown (1974) observed a 50 per cent mortality of rainbow trout in eight days at 0.5 mg Cu/ℓ in the absence of NTA, but no mortality with 4 mg Cu/ℓ in the presence of 12 mg NTA/ℓ under otherwise the same test conditions. In the presence of up to 2 mg Cu/ℓ survival time of rainbow trout was progressively increased by increase in the concentration of humic acid (Brown, Shaw and Shurben, 1974).

Zitko, Carson and Carson (1973) also found that the presence of humic acid reduced the toxicity of copper; the 4-day LC50 for juvenile Atlantic salmon in water having a hardness of 14 mg/ℓ as $CaCO_3$ and a temperature of 3.8-4.8 °C was 0.09 and 0.165 mg Cu/ℓ in the presence of 5 and 10 mg/ℓ of humic acid respectively, and about 0.02 mg Cu/ℓ in its absence, i.e. a reduction in toxicity of 0.22 and 0.12 respectively. Cook and Côte (1972), using a slightly harder water (24-96 mg/ℓ as $CaCO_3$), found a somewhat smaller reduction in toxicity, being about 0.3, 0.2 and 0.14 of control values in the presence of 10, 20 and 30 mg/ℓ humic acid respectively.

Increasing the concentration of glycine can also reduce the toxicity of copper sulphate solutions, and at a concentration of 10 mg glycine/ℓ the 1-, 2- and 3-day LC50 values for rainbow trout were seven to ten times higher than in the absence of the amino acid. The survival time of this species in the presence of 2 mg Cu/ℓ was increased from 8 h in solutions containing no sewage effluent to 80 h in those consisting of only sewage effluent (Brown, Shaw and Shurben, 1974) (see p. 205, para. 1).

The above observations suggest that these organo-copper complexes have little if any, acutely toxic effect on fish but no information is available on long-term effects. However, some organic substances containing copper may be toxic (p. 209, para. 5).

Suspended solids

Investigations of Svenska Gruvföreningen (1960) and observations of the Norwegian Institute of Water Research (M. Grande, personal communication) indicate that the toxicity of copper and zinc is reduced when the metals are mixed with wastes from flotation processes. These wastes contain high levels of finely ground materials which may absorb heavy metals. A three-fold increase in the 2-day LC50 of *total* copper to rainbow trout was shown in the presence of organic or inorganic solids at a concentration of 50 mg/ℓ (Brown, Shaw and Shurben, 1974). However, in terms of *soluble* copper, the toxicity of such solutions appears to increase with increase in the concentration of solids, the 2-day LC50 in the presence of 100 mg/ℓ organic solids being about half of that observed when no solids are present.

Age and size of fish

In a hard water (260-280 mg/ℓ as $CaCO_3$) a copper concentration of 1 mg/ℓ did not affect fertilization of rainbow trout eggs although it did increase the rate of development, all copper-exposed eggs hatching before any of the controls (Shaw and Brown, 1971).

Experiments with eggs of rainbow trout at 10 °C and in water having a hardness of 14 mg/ℓ as $CaCO_3$ showed that at 0.02, 0.04 and 0.06 mg Cu/ℓ there was 25, 70, and 100 per cent mortality respectively, compared with 10 per cent in the controls (Grande, 1967). Mortality among eggs of Atlantic salmon under the same conditions was 82, 92 and 100 per cent respectively, compared with 15 per cent in the controls. These concentrations had less effect on yolk-sac fry and fingerlings of Atlantic salmon for which the 21-day LC50 was 0.04 mg Cu/ℓ. However, damage to the fish at 0.02 mg Cu/ℓ was indicated by their unwillingness to eat food. Thus, there was relatively little difference in tolerance between eggs, yolk-sac fry and fingerling Atlantic salmon, but salmon eggs were more sensitive than those of rainbow trout.

Yearling and fingerling rainbow trout had a similar resistance to acutely lethal levels of copper in the range 0.8-1.0 mg/ℓ in water having a hardness of 320 mg/ℓ as $CaCO_3$ (Department of Scientific and Industrial Research, 1961).

Hazel and Meith (1970) found that eggs of chinook salmon (*Oncorhynchus tshawytscha*) were more resistant to copper than fry; eyed eggs exposed to a concentration of 0.08 mg Cu/ℓ at 13-14 °C and a hardness of 44 mg/ℓ as $CaCO_3$

hatched successfully, but 0.04 mg/ℓ was acutely toxic to fry and 0.02 mg/ℓ caused a mortality of 33 and 12 per cent among the swim-up stages and the sac fry respectively, compared with a mortality of 23 per cent and 4 per cent respectively in the controls. McKim and Benoit (1971) reported that 17 µg Cu/ℓ did not adversely affect the survival of adult brook trout or the hatchability of the eggs but severely reduced the survival of the alevin/juveniles during eight-month experiments in water having a hardness of 45.4 mg/ℓ as $CaCO_3$ and temperature ranging from 6 °C in March to 16 °C in September; the 4-day LC50 for adults was 0.1 mg Cu/ℓ. Thus it appears that the early stages of some salmonids are more sensitive to copper than other stages in the life cycle.

Mount and Stephan (1969) found that no fathead minnow fry survived a 30-day exposure to water having a hardness of 31.4 mg/ℓ as $CaCO_3$ at 19 °C and containing 18 µg Cu/ℓ, whereas the 4-day LC50 for adults was 75 µg/ℓ. Gardner and LaRoche (1973) found that the emergence of larval mummichog was greatly reduced in the presence of 0.25 mg Cu/ℓ and that only 57 per cent of the hatched individuals survived whereas the 2-day LC50 for the larvae was 1.2 mg/ℓ. These studies suggest that for some non-salmonid fish also the early larval stages are less tolerant of copper than eggs or adults.

Acclimation to copper

There are no specific studies known to us on the effect of acclimation to copper on the resistance of fish, but in a three-month experiment with brook trout alevins McKim and Benoit (1971) found that the mortality of those from parents not previously exposed to copper was similar to that of the progeny from parents exposed for eight months to copper. Results with fathead minnow (Mount and Stephan, 1969) in soft water were similar. On the other hand, Paul (1952) observed that fish were resident in the Sacramento River despite the presence of a concentration of copper high enough to prevent the survival of introduced hatchery-reared fish.

Rainbow trout exposed to surfactant, after being kept for one week at 0.5 of the 14-day LC50 of copper, during which time they accumulated abnormally high concentrations of metal in some organs, survived about as long as those not previously exposed to copper (Calamari and Marchetti, 1973).

Acclimation to other poisons

Oseid and Smith (1972) found that the period of survival of bluegill in solutions containing copper was two- to four-fold higher among fish acclimated to high concentrations of hydrogen sulphide (5–15 µg/ℓ) than it was among those acclimated to low concentrations 1.5 µg/ℓ).

Joint effect of copper and other heavy metals

Doudoroff (1952) found that whereas fathead minnow (*Pimephales promelas*) usually survived an 8-h exposure to solutions containing either 8 mg Zn/ℓ or 0.2 mg Cu/ℓ in soft water, most succumbed within this period in a mixture of copper and zinc at one-eighth of these concentrations respectively. Lloyd

(1961b) obtained somewhat similar results with rainbow trout in soft water (hardness 14 mg/ℓ as $CaCO_3$) but found that at relatively low concentrations, corresponding to less than the 3-day and 7-day LC50 of copper and zinc respectively, the effect of the mixtures was simply additive in both the soft and a hard water (hardness 320 mg/ℓ as $CaCO_3$). Sprague and Ramsay (1965), who used these metals in water having a hardness of 14 mg/ℓ as $CaCO_3$, also found that the toxicity of mixtures to juvenile Atlantic salmon could be accounted for by the simple addition of the fractions of the corresponding LC50 of the separate metals.

D. Calamari and R. Marchetti (personal communication) obtained similar data in terms of fractions of the 4-day LC50 values for rainbow trout with copper and mercury tested at 15 °C in a water having a hardness of 320 mg/ℓ as $CaCO_3$.

The 2-day LC50 to rainbow trout exposed to mixtures of copper, zinc and nickel has also been found to be adequately predicted by summation of the fraction of the 2-day LC50 values of the separate poisons (Brown and Dalton, 1970).

Eaton (1973) reported that the 4-day LC50 for fathead minnow was only 0.8 of that predicted for a mixture containing mainly copper and zinc in hard water (hardness 200 mg/ℓ as $CaCO_3$). On the other hand, Eisler and Gardner (1973) found increased mortality of mummichog when non-lethal concentrations of cadmium were present with lethal concentrations of copper and zinc.

Thus it can be concluded that the acute lethal toxicity of mixtures of copper and other heavy metals can be largely accounted for by summation of the individual toxicities of the metals expressed as fractions of the threshold LC50.

Joint action of copper and other poisons

Herbert and Vandyke (1964) tested rainbow trout in solutions containing ammonium chloride and copper sulphate in hard water and found that the estimated value for the threshold concentration of the mixture was close to the value predicted from the sum of the fractions of the threshold concentrations of the individual poisons. Similar results have been found for mixtures of copper and phenol, and for copper, zinc and phenol (Brown and Dalton, 1970). Cairns and Scheier (1968) also report an additive effect on bluegill of a mixture of acetic acid, acetaldehyde, acetone and copper in soft water. Calamari and Marchetti (1973) tested rainbow trout in mixtures of copper and surfactants and found that with the non-ionic nonyl phenol ethoxylate the survival time was longer than that expected, but with the anionic ABS or LAS the survival time was greatly reduced; the 4-day LC50, expressed as a sum of the fractions of the individual LC50 values, was about 0.8 of that predicted assuming a simply additive effect, i.e. the mixture was slightly more toxic than expected.

Thus the acute lethal toxicity of a number of common poisons tested in mixtures with copper demonstrate a simple additive effect which could be largely predicted on the basis of the sum of the fractions of the 2-day LC50 values of the individual poisons.

Uptake in food

An oral dose of 400 mg Cu/kg was reported as lethal to common carp after three days (Nehring, 1964) but no information is apparently available on chronic effects.

9.3.3 SUMMARY OF TOXICITY DATA

Acutely lethal values

Concentrations from 0.02 to over 10 mg/ℓ of copper are reported to be lethal to fish, the difference being attributed mainly to different water hardness, species of fish, duration of test and stage in the life cycle. However, as is clear from Section 9.2.1 and pp. 194-196 there is considerable uncertainty as to the amount and speciation of soluble copper especially at low concentrations, and often the data relate to the total concentration of copper apparently in solution.

Salmonid eggs   Concentrations of 0.02-0.04 mg Cu/ℓ impaired the hatch of rainbow trout and Atlantic salmon in very soft water (14 mg/ℓ as $CaCO_3$), while in slightly harder water (44 mg/ℓ as $CaCO_3$) 0.08 mg Cu/ℓ did not affect the hatching success of chinook salmon (p. 196, para. 7). In harder water (260-280 mg/ℓ as $CaCO_3$), 1 mg Cu/ℓ increased the rate of development of rainbow trout eggs (p. 196, para. 4).

Salmonid fry, juveniles and adults   The early stages of the life cycle of sal-monids are more sensitive to copper than the adult (p. 196, para. 5). Brook trout appear to be less sensitive and Atlantic salmon more susceptible than rainbow trout (McKim and Benoit, 1971; Sprague, 1964a; Zitko, Carson and Carson, 1973; Lloyd and Herbert, 1962).

For adult rainbow trout in soft water (14-45 mg/ℓ as $CaCO_3$) the 4-day LC50 is 0.02-0.1 mg Cu/ℓ whereas in hard water (200-300 mg/ℓ as $CaCO_3$) the values are 0.5-1 mg Cu/ℓ.

Coarse fish   No work has been reported for the young stages of European coarse fish but studies on other non-salmonid species (p. 196, para. 7 and p. 197, para. 2) show that these stages are more sensitive than adults.

The 4-day LC50 for adult goldfish in a hard water (hardness about 220 mg/ℓ as $CaCO_3$) was found to be 0.46 mg Cu/ℓ by Calamari and Marchetti (1970). In soft water (53 mg/ℓ as $CaCO_3$) the values were less than 1 mg Cu/ℓ for this species and common carp while for other species including the eel (*Anguilla rostrata*) they were 0.81 and 6.4 mg Cu/ℓ under static conditions (Rehwoldt, Bida and Nerri, 1971). Values were about 3 mg/ℓ for pike (*Esox lucius*) and 4 mg/ℓ for eel (*Anguilla anguilla*) at 10 °C in tests in a hard water (250 mg/ℓ as $CaCO_3$) and continuous flow conditions, and for rudd (*Scardinius erythrophthalmus*), common carp, and perch (*Perca fluviatilis*) tested concurrently they were about 0.6, 0.6 and 0.3 mg Cu/ℓ respectively, compared with 0.9 mg Cu/ℓ for rainbow trout (Department of the Environment, 1971). For stone loach (*Nemacheilus barbatulus*) in water of the same hardness at 12 °C the 4-day LC50 was 0.76 mg Cu/ℓ (Solbé and Cooper, 1976). In a slightly softer water (about 100 mg/ℓ as $CaCO_3$) the lethal threshold for tench (*Tinca tinca*) at 16 °C and pH 7.7 was 0.08-0.15 mg Cu/ℓ (Haider, 1966).

Long-term lethal values

Salmonids   A mortality of 24 per cent was found among rainbow trout kept for 17 weeks in a hard water (250–260 mg/ℓ as $CaCO_3$) containing 0.28 mg Cu/ℓ (about 0.6 of the 4-day LC50) but little or no mortality was found at lower concentrations (Department of the Environment, 1973). McKim and Benoit (1971) kept brook trout for eight months in soft water (hardness 45 mg/ℓ as $CaCO_3$) containing copper; with adults there was a 57 per cent mortality at 32 μg Cu/ℓ (0.32 of the 4-day LC50) and no mortality at 17 μg Cu/ℓ but with the alevins there was a complete mortality at the lower concentration. With the same species in water of the same hardness McKim, Christensen and Hunt (1970) found a mortality of 10 per cent at 69 μg Cu/ℓ in 21 days and 60 per cent mortality at 32 μg Cu/ℓ in 337 days.

Coarse fish   With fathead minnow in hard water (198 mg/ℓ as $CaCO_3$) (Mount, 1968; Mount and Stephan, 1969), there was in one test a low mortality and in another a complete survival after 11 months at 33 μg Cu/ℓ and a 30 per cent kill at 95 μg Cu/ℓ (0.2 of the 4-day LC50). On the other hand, in soft water (30 mg/ℓ as $CaCO_3$) there was a low mortality or complete survival at 11 μg Cu/ℓ and 50 per cent kill at 18 μg Cu/ℓ (0.24 of the 4-day LC50). Fry from exposed and unexposed parents survived equally well when kept for one month at 10 μg Cu/ℓ but all died at 18 μg Cu/ℓ.

In replicate tests Calamari and Marchetti (1970) found a 50 per cent mortality among goldfish at 20 and 30 days respectively at a concentration of 0.12 mg Cu/ℓ (0.26 of the 4-day LC50) in water having a hardness of about 220 mg/ℓ as $CaCO_3$ and a temperature of 15.5 °C. Also the 50-day LC50 for the stone loach was found to be 0.29 mg Cu/ℓ in water having a hardness equivalent to 250 mg/ℓ as $CaCO_3$ (Solbé and Cooper, 1976).

9.4 Sublethal effects on fish

9.4.1 ENZYMES

The few enzymes that have been studied (p. 193, para. 1) have been inhibited only at concentrations of copper that are either rapidly or potentially lethal to fish. With brown bullhead (Christensen, McKim and Brungs, 1972), as with brook trout (McKim and Benoit, 1971), the only measured long-term effect was a reduced level of PGOT at above 27 μg Cu/ℓ (0.15 of the 4-day LC50).

9.4.2 TISSUE RESIDUE ANALYSES

No accumulation of copper occurred in the opercula, red blood cells, or blood plasma of brown bullhead exposed for up to 20 months to copper levels up to 104 μg/ℓ in water of total hardness 202 mg/ℓ as $CaCO_3$ (4-day LC50, 170–190 μg Cu/ℓ) (Brungs, Leonard and McKim, 1973). However, gill and liver levels increased with exposure to concentrations greater than 27–53 μg Cu/ℓ (0.16–0.31 of the 4-day LC50) and kidney levels increased at 104 μg/ℓ within 30 days, but not at 27 μg/ℓ within 20 months. Also, brown bullhead exposed to sub-lethal concentrations of copper had higher levels of copper in their tissues when killed by copper solutions than those so killed after having previously been held in clean water. After 24 months exposure in the laboratory to copper solutions in L. Superior water (total hardness 45 mg/ℓ as $CaCO_3$), bluegill showed increased copper levels in the gills at concentrations above 40 μg Cu/ℓ, and higher liver and kidney levels were measured at 162 μg Cu/ℓ and above (Benoit, 1975). However, survival was reduced at levels higher than 40 μg/ℓ for fry and 77 μg/ℓ for adults. McKim and Benoit (1974) found that progeny of brook trout which had been exposed to 4.5 and 9.4 μg Cu/ℓ (total hardness 44 mg/ℓ as $CaCO_3$) were not more susceptible, nor did they accumulate copper in their tissues,when exposed to these copper levels.

Increased copper in fish tissues, especially the gill, has also been observed in one-year-old common carp fed on a diet enriched with copper (Iozepson, 1971). Prolonged feeding of this species with a copper ammonium compound caused elevated levels of copper in the tissues, especially the liver, disturbed protein synthesis and reduced serum globulins (Semčuk and Avdošev, 1972).

Elevated levels of copper in the tissues (gill and liver) of some species have therefore been associated with adverse physiological effects.

9.4.3 BLOOD ANALYSES

When channel catfish (*Ictalurus punctatus*) were exposed to 2.5 mg Cu/ℓ for four days (total hardness 206–236 mg/ℓ as $CaCO_3$), a non-lethal level, the serum osmolarity decreased during the first two days, followed by a recovery to normal levels (Lewis and Lewis, 1971). However, exposure to 5 mg Cu/ℓ was lethal in two days. Similar results were obtained with golden shiner (*Notemigonus crysoleucas*) and in both species the effects were eliminated by the addition of 235 mOsm NaCl to the solution. At these copper concentrations both species were coated with precipitated mucus.

Measurements of red blood cells, haematocrit and haemoglobin levels of brook trout exposed to 24, 39 and 67 μg Cu/ℓ (total hardness 46 mg/ℓ as $CaCO_3$) showed a transient increase, and chloride a decrease, during the first 21 days, but after 337 days there was no measurable difference between fish exposed to up to 32.5 μg Cu/ℓ and the controls (McKim, Christensen and Hunt, 1970). Higher levels were detrimental to survival and growth of this species (McKim and Benoit, 1971). Similar experiments with brown bullhead exposed to 3.4–104 μg Cu/ℓ for up to 20 months showed that glucose and haematocrit increased within six days at 104 μg/ℓ, the highest concentration, and that at levels above 49 μg Cu/ℓ (0.26 of the 4-day LC50), chloride, haematocrit, haemoglobin and glucose increased at 30 days (Christensen, McKim and Brungs, 1972).

Transient increases in cortisol and cortisone during a 1-day period were observed in sockeye salmon (*Oncorhynchus nerka*) exposed to 6 μg Cu/ℓ in water having a hardness of 12 mg/ℓ as $CaCO_3$; levels of 0.6 mg Cu/ℓ were lethal within 1 day (Donaldson and Dye, 1975).

Thus transient changes only have been observed in blood analyses of some species exposed to concentrations of copper lower than 0.5–0.26 of the 4-day LC50.

9.4.4 LIFE CYCLE STUDIES

Several long-term studies have been made on the effects of chronic exposure to copper solutions on the survival, growth and spawning success of species of North American fish. McKim and Benoit (1971) found that, in the laboratory in L. Superior water (hardness 45 mg/ℓ as $CaCO_3$, pH 6.9-8.0 and seasonal temperature 4-21 °C) the growth and survival of yearling brook trout was affected at a copper concentration of 32.5 µg/ℓ over an eight-month exposure period, although spawning was successful at this level. However, this concentration affected the hatching success of the eggs, and copper levels above 17.4 µg/ℓ affected the growth and survival of alevins, both from exposed and non-exposed parents, over a three-month period. A transient effect of copper on growth rate was noted at copper concentrations of 3.4-32.5 µ/ℓ, but after 23 weeks the growth rate of brook trout was equal to that of the controls at concentrations up to 9.5 µg/ℓ. It was concluded that the maximum concentration of copper which did not significantly affect brook trout under these experimental conditions was 0.1-0.17 of the 4-day LC50 values. Subsequently, McKim and Benoit (1974) showed that the progeny from brook trout exposed as above to 4.5 and 9.5 µg Cu/ℓ were not more susceptible to these concentrations and concluded that a single life-cycle experiment gave results which were probably applicable to exposure for many generations. McKim, Eaton and Holcombe (1978) exposed several species during the embryonic stage and for 30-60 days after hatching and found significant effects on the larval standing crop at concentrations of copper and in the range 31.7-43.5 µg Cu/ℓ for brook trout, rainbow trout and brown trout (*Salmo trutta*) and at 104 µg Cu/ℓ for the more resistant Northern pike, in a water having a hardness of 45.4 mg/ℓ as $CaCO_3$.

Tests with bluegill over a 24-month exposure period showed that survival was reduced at copper levels greater than 40 µg/ℓ and that growth was retarded at 77-162 µg/ℓ (Benoit, 1975). Growth of larvae was slightly reduced at 77 µg/ℓ and survival was less at 40 and 70 µg/ℓ (water hardness 45 mg/ℓ as $CaCO_3$ and a seasonal range of temperature of 13-28 °C). The level of 40 µg Cu/ℓ was 0.04 of the 4-day LC50 value for this species under these conditions.

Similar tests with fathead minnow exposed for 11 months to copper solutions in a soft water (hardness 31.4 mg/ℓ as $CaCO_3$; temperature 19-25 °C) showed that spawning potential was reduced at 18.4 µg/ℓ Cu but that at levels up to 10.6 µg/ℓ growth and reproduction were normal (Mount and Stephan, 1969); these levels were 0.22 and 0.13 of the 4-day LC50 respectively. However, tests in a hard water (198 mg/ℓ as $CaCO_3$) showed that growth and fecundity were unaffected below the range 14.5-33.0 µg Cu/ℓ which was 0.03-0.07 of the 4-day LC50 value of 450 µg/ℓ (Mount, 1968).

Comparable data are not available for European species but Grande (1967) found that salmon fry were unwilling to feed when held in solutions containing 20 µg Cu/ℓ in soft water which was equivalent to 0.4 of the 21-day LC50 (p. 196, para. 5). Decreased food intake has been observed in roach (*Rutilus rutilus*) during a 7-day exposure to sublethal concentrations of copper (0.5 mg Cu/ℓ in water having a hardness of 250 mg/ℓ as $CaCO_3$), and for 5 days subsequently when held in clean water (Morrice, 1977), and depressed feeding and growth was observed initially in rainbow trout when exposed to sublethal concentrations (0-0.3 mg Cu/ℓ in water having a hardness of 365 mg/ℓ as $CaCO_3$), although the effects disappeared within 40 days (Lett, Farmer and Beamish, 1976). On the other hand, rainbow trout kept for 17 weeks at concentrations of 0.05–0.16 mg Cu/ℓ (about 0.1–0.32 of the 4-day LC50) grew less rapidly in the higher than in the lower concentrations and controls (Department of the Environment, 1973).

Thus long-term tests have shown that the highest levels of copper that failed to produce adverse effects on fish were (expressed as fractions of the 4-day LC50) between 0.1 and 0.17 for the growth of brook trout and rainbow trout and 0.13 and 0.07 for the growth and reproduction of fathead minnow in soft and hard water respectively; growth and survival of bluegill, however, were affected at 0.04. No comparable data are available for European species.

9.4.5 BEHAVIOUR

Experiments on the effects of heavy metals on the palatal chemo-receptors of common carp showed that a concentration of 6.4 mg Cu/ℓ (10^{-4} mol/ℓ) depressed the response of the sugar and salt receptors (Hidaka, 1970). Also olfactory responses of sockeye salmon, coho salmon (*Oncorhynchus kisutch*) and rainbow trout to food extracts, amino acids and hand rinses were extinguished after more than 12 h exposure of the fish to a concentration of 40 μg Cu/ℓ (Hara, 1972). However, the nature of the dilution was not given in either of these studies. The 'cough frequency' of brook trout was found to increase within the range 6–15 μg Cu/ℓ (water hardness 45 mg/ℓ as $CaCO_3$, pH 7.5–7.7 and temperature 8.5 °C), reaching a peak 5–20 h after exposure and decreasing thereafter (Drummond, Spoor and Olson, 1973). A similar, though more prolonged, transitory response was found by Morgan and Kühn (1974) who found that largemouth bass (*Micropterus salmoides*) exposed to 100 μg Cu/ℓ (water hardness 54 mg/ℓ as $CaCO_3$, temperature 25 °C) increased their respiratory frequency during the first three days of exposure with a gradual return to normal in the following four days. Reduction in heart rate within a few hours exposure to concentrations of 0.5–1.5 mg Cu/ℓ in a water having a hardness of 120 mg/ℓ as $CaCO_3$ has been observed in common carp (Labat, Chantelet and Kugler, 1976).

Increase in activity of fish exposed to sublethal copper solutions is well known; for example, brook trout exposed to copper solutions of 6–115 μg/ℓ (Drummond, Spoor and Olson, 1973) increased their activity to 4–6 times that of the controls during the first 8 h of exposure; activity patterns returned to normal after three days in those fish exposed to up to 12 μg Cu/ℓ. Similarly, brook trout exposed to copper levels greater than 17 μg/ℓ stopped feeding and at 12 μg/ℓ an initial reduced feeding rate returned to normal (albeit sluggishly) after four days; these levels were similar to those at which the survival and growth of brook trout began to be affected (McKim and Benoit, 1971) (p. 202, para. 1).

Sprague (1964b) showed that in the absence of other stimuli Atlantic salmon parr could detect levels of copper in a soft water (20 mg/ℓ as $CaCO_3$) as low as 2.4 μg/ℓ, which was 0.05 of the threshold lethal concentration; in these laboratory experiments the fish were given a choice of clean or polluted water in a short tube with a sharp interface between the two solutions. Rainbow trout apparently avoided even lower concentrations (0.1 μg Cu/ℓ) in a Y-shaped maze in water having a hardness of 89.5 mg/ℓ as $CaCO_3$ (Folmar, 1976). However, field observations at a counting fence (Saunders and Sprague, 1967) showed that adult salmon migrating upstream were turned back only by much higher concentrations, equivalent to 0.35-0.43 of the joint lethal threshold concentration for the mixtures of zinc and copper present in the river. Data provided by P. F. Elson (personal communication) suggest that a lower proportion (1.05 per cent) of hatchery-reared Atlantic salmon smolts was recaptured as grilse after having been exposed as smolts for one day at 10 or 15 °C to waters containing both copper and zinc, each at concentrations equivalent to about 0.35 of the median threshold value, as compared with control fish exposed to a mixture of copper and zinc in which the corresponding proportions of the threshold were about 0.14 and 0.05 respectively; however the total numbers of fish involved were small (11 recaptures from 1046 treated smolts and 22 out of 1130 controls), and no difference in recapture rate was found between treated and untreated wild smolts (2864 of each), perhaps because the latter were exposed to these metals in the river before the tests were made. However, the downstream migration of yearling coho salmon was adversely affected by exposure to sublethal concentrations of copper (Lorz and McPherson, 1976). Kleerekoper, Waxman and Matis (1973) found that goldfish, which avoided water with a copper concentration of 10 $\mu g/\ell$ (total hardness 5.4 mg/ℓ as $CaCO_3$), were attracted to this water when the temperature was increased by 1.0-1.4 °C above the acclimation temperature and this interaction between temperature and copper provided a stronger attractant than temperature alone. In other experiments, Timms, Kleerekoper and Matis (1972) found that the characteristics of the copper gradient were more important in behaviour studies than the actual copper levels present and that goldfish, channel catfish and largemouth bass displayed only slight changes of behaviour in such solutions; a concentration of 50 μg Cu/ℓ was a slight attractant in water of total hardness 5 mg/ℓ as $CaCO_3$ for goldfish and channel catfish.

9.4.6 MIXTURES OF POISONS

Although mixtures of copper and other heavy metals are approximately additive in their acute lethal toxicity at combined lethal levels (p. 197, para. 6 to p. 198, para. 5), Eaton (1973) found that the specific sublethal effects of copper on fathead minnow—reduced growth and inhibition of secondary sexual characteristics—were only slightly enhanced in the presence of sublethal levels of cadmium and zinc which produced other specific sublethal effects.

9.4.7 SUMMARY

Much of the work summarized in this section is fragmentary, and only very general conclusions can be made. Several authors indicate that the sublethal effects measured in copper solutions are transitory and persist for a few days only, which could imply that some acclimation takes place. Except for work on the long-term effects of copper solutions on the fathead minnow (Mount, 1968) and bluegill (Benoit, 1975) in hard waters, concentrations below 0.1 of the threshold or 4-day LC50 appear to exert no measurable effect.

9.5 Field observations on fish

9.5.1 TOXICITY IN NATURAL WATERS AND SEWAGE EFFLUENTS

The majority of the laboratory experiments reported so far in this review have determined the toxicity of soluble copper to fish in the absence of organic matter. But, as shown earlier (p. 195, para. 4 to p. 196, para. 3), the toxicity of copper can be reduced if it is precipitated or complexed with organic compounds, both of which can occur in field situations, so that values of total copper usually measured may or may not be greater than the actual toxic amount present. For example, Brungs, Geckler and Gast (1976) found that for fathead minnow the 4-day LC50 for total copper in a natural stream water containing sewage effluent varied between 1.6 and 21.0 mg/ℓ (using static tests), whereas the corresponding values for 'dissolved' copper (after filtration to remove particles > 0.45 μm) were 0.60 and 0.98 mg/ℓ. The water hardness varied between 88 and 352 mg/ℓ as $CaCO_3$ and the pH value between 7.5 and 8.5; considerable precipitation occurred at the higher hardness and pH values. Chronic tests showed that the maximum level of no observed effect was between 0.07 and 0.13 of the 4-day LC50 value for 'dissolved' copper, and these values were higher than those given by Mount (1968) for this species, as were the 4-day LC50 values themselves (cf. p. 200, para. 2).

Laboratory tests on sewage effluents containing trade waste residues (Lloyd and Jordan, 1964) showed that when copper was present in relatively high concentrations the observed toxicity was less than that predicted from the poisons present. Further experiments with sewage effluents showed that the toxicity of copper present was not reduced by a constant proportion but varied with the total amount of copper present (R. Lloyd, personal communication). These 'sliding values' were used in the prediction of copper in river waters containing copper-bearing sewage effluents, but the general validity of such an approach is doubtful. Zitko, Carson and Carson (1973) showed that the presence of 10 mg/ℓ humic acid increased four-fold the 4-day LC50 of copper in soft water (14 mg/ℓ as $CaCO_3$) for Atlantic salmon parr; these authors, as well as Montgomery and Stiff (1971), recommend the use of a specific ion electrode for the calculation of copper toxicity. Stiff (1971a) has added amino acids and polypeptides to the list of soluble organic compounds capable of complexing copper. Similar complexing effects of humic acid have also been reported by Grande (1967) (p. 195, para. 5).

Wilson (1972) found that the 4-day LC50 for copper to Atlantic salmon parr in water taken from the Exploits River, Newfoundland (total hardness 8–10 mg/ℓ as $CaCO_3$) was 125 μg/ℓ, compared with about 30 μg/ℓ as predicted from laboratory experiments of Sprague and Ramsay (1965). The humic acid content of this water was 4.5–5.0 mg/ℓ, and an addition of spent sulphite liquor (SSL) increased the 4-day LC50 still further, so that, in the presence of 450 mg/ℓ SSL, there was only a 10 per cent mortality at 250 μg/ℓ copper. Wilson (1972) concludes that it is impossible to predict the toxicity of copper in natural waters; even with a specific ion electrode there is some interference with other ions at low copper concentrations. This difficulty has been demonstrated by Zitko, Carson and Carson (1973).

Recently, Pagenkopf, Russon and Thurston (1974) have presented theoretical calculations to support the conclusion that, in the absence of organic matter, only ionic copper (Cu^{2+}) is toxic to fish, and that increasing alkalinity reduces the proportion of copper ions present. However, in experimental studies Shaw and Brown (1974) observed that the concentrations of both copper carbonate and copper ions were related to the lethal toxicity of copper to rainbow trout. Calamari and Marchetti (1974) kept rainbow trout in cages in L. Orta, Italy, in the presence of copper and found that the 2-day LC50 derived from data relating to 5-12 °C, pH 5.5-6.4 and hardness of 21-26 mg/ℓ as $CaCO_3$ was 70 µg Cu/ℓ (95 per cent confidence limits of 60-82 µg/ℓ), which is in reasonable agreement with laboratory data (p. 195, para. 1 and 2).

9.5.2 COMPARISON OF FIELD OBSERVATIONS WITH LABORATORY DATA

Because of the factors discussed above, it is unrealistic to expect to find a close correlation between field observations of the relation between toxicity or fisheries and total copper concentration except in very pure, soft water, free from organic compounds; the position is complicated further by the fact that rivers and lakes which contain copper also frequently contain zinc, and sometimes other metals such as cadmium, and it is very difficult to separate their individual contributions when present in low concentrations.

Grande (1967) found that salmonids were present in some Norwegian lakes when the copper concentrations may have been as high as 60 µg/ℓ (total hardness 2-15 mg/ℓ as $CaCO_3$), even in the presence of considerable concentrations of zinc; this copper concentration is at the upper limit of the 21-day LC50 of 40-60 µg Cu/ℓ obtained by this author for a soft water (14 mg/ℓ as $CaCO_3$). A more detailed study in Norway (EIFAC, 1977) showed that the standards proposed for copper (EIFAC, 1976; *Table 9.1*) and for zinc (*Table 8.2*) are not seriously in error, and the apparent over-estimation of toxicity in the field can be accounted for by a combination of the annual distribution of heavy metal concentrations, a higher-than-predicted combination of soluble organic material with copper, and acclimation of fish. Similar conclusions about the cause of over-estimation of toxicity in the field were drawn from a study of a stream in the U.S.A. which contained sewage effluent and to which copper was added over a long period (Geckler *et al.*, 1976). In streams in North Wales containing copper and zinc and studied intensively for a year from August 1973 (Cremer and Warner, personal communication), moderate populations of brown trout were present when the 50 and 95 percentile values for the concentrations of copper were 0.17 and 0.38 of the 2-day LC50 for rainbow trout (in the presence of zinc at concentrations equivalent to 0.16 and 0.28 for the corresponding percentiles); fish were virtually absent where the corresponding percentiles for copper were 0.34 and 0.78 (in the presence of zinc equivalent to 0.01 and 0.02 for the corresponding percentiles).

Observations on the R. Churnet, England, showed that brown trout, bullhead (*Cottus gobio*), three-spined stickleback (*Gasterosteus aculeatus*) and minnow were present where the annual 50 and 95 percentile values for the concentration of copper were 34 and 83 µg/ℓ (equivalent to 0.12 and 0.30 respectively of the predicted 2-day median lethal concentration to rainbow trout). The median and 95 percentile for the sum of all pollutants were 0.16 and 0.33 of the LC50, the difference being largely attributable to zinc. The average concentration of organic carbon was 11.3 mg/ℓ and a single sample of soluble copper at this site had the following percentage composition: labile copper complexes 61; $CuCO_3$, 24; strong copper complexes 10; inert humic complexes 3; and free cupric ion 3 (J. F. de L. G. Solbé, personal communication). In the R. Ouse in Yorkshire, England, which contains sewage and industrial wastes, data supplied by the Yorkshire Ouse River Authority from 1966 to 1973 indicated that minnow, stickleback, roach and chub (*Leuciscus cephalus*) were present where the 50 and 95 percentile concentrations of copper were 50 and 130 μg Cu/ℓ respectively, equivalent to 0.17 and 0.66 of the predicted 48-h LC50 to rainbow trout (I. C. Hart and J. S. Alabaster, personal communication).

There exists the possibility of natural fish populations becoming acclimatized to copper as suggested by the observations of Paul (1952) in the Sacramento River (p. 197, para. 3).

Numerous reports exist in the literature on the use of copper sulphate as an algicide in fish-bearing waters; in general the concentrations applied are higher than those which would be predicted to kill or harm fish, but in practice the amounts actually remaining in solution as the toxic cupric ion and copper carbonate would be small after adsorption and complexation by organic matter, and precipitation (Section 9.6.1).

It is clear that considerably more research effort should be given to the analysis of copper ions in natural waters, so that a realistic estimate can be made of their potential toxicity to fish. Until this is achieved, water quality objectives based on total copper concentrations will necessarily be more severe than perhaps warranted. All that can be stated at present is that there are no known instances where the toxicity of copper in a field situation is apparently greater than that predicted from laboratory tests.

9.6 Summary of data on algae and invertebrates

9.6.1 ALGAE

Toxic effects of copper on algae are usually thought to be caused by ionic copper (Steeman-Nielsen and Wium-Andersen, 1970) although insoluble copper in contact with algae in culture may also be toxic (Fitzgerald and Faust, 1963). However, under field conditions more copper is required for the treatment of blooms in hard water, where much precipitation of basic copper carbonate occurs, than in soft waters, but no precise information is available. Higher concentrations of copper are generally required to kill algae in culture than to control their growth in reservoirs, possibly because in the latter the ratio of copper to algal biomass is greater, the excess chelating capacity lower, and only an algistatic effect is required.

The effects of copper on algae have been reviewed by Whitton (1970a). The growth of most genera is checked at 0.1-0.4 mg Cu/ℓ (e.g. Prescott, 1948; Maloney and Palmer, 1956; Whitton, 1970b) but concentrations of 0.4-2.0 mg Cu/ℓ are tolerated by some natural populations (Butcher, 1946; Whitton, 1970a; Besch, Ricard and Cantin, 1972). Copper inhibits photosynthesis (Greenfield, 1942; Steeman-Nielsen, Nielson and Wium-Anderson, 1969; Hassall, 1963) and respiration (Hassal, 1962) of cultured algae, the extent of the response appearing to increase with increase in the concentration of copper per unit of biomass (e.g. McBrien and Hassall, 1967) and with increase in light intensity (Nielson, 1969).

Temperature is also important, work by Windle-Taylor (1965) showing that algal growth in a reservoir was more effectively checked at temperatures above 6.5 °C than at those below it. Horne and Goldman (1974) also showed that with the blue-green algae *Aphanizomenon* and *Anabaena* nitrogen fixation as well as photosynthesis was inhibited in lake waters on the addition of small amounts of copper (5-10 μg/ℓ), however, rates in the lake waters without added copper but already containing either 2-3 μg Cu/ℓ or 60-70 μg Cu/ℓ were neither inhibited by, nor related to, the indigenous concentration of copper, suggesting that these background levels were largely chelated and that there was little excess chelating capacity available. Chelation can arise from the presence of organic as well as inorganic ligands, some of which might be produced by algae. For example, *Anabaena cylindrica* produces polypeptide in culture able to bind about 0.3 mg Cu/mg total peptide nitrogen (Fogg and Westlake, 1953); in the absence of polypeptide 0.5 mg Cu/ℓ reduced cell movement and 4 mg Cu/ℓ was lethal whereas in its presence the corresponding concentrations were 2.25 and 32 mg/ℓ.

In lakes treated for algal blooms, concentrations of copper in the water are not necessarily uniform and soon decline following treatment (Whitton, 1970a) and. in practice fish are seldom adversely affected. However, in rivers polluted continuously by wastes containing copper, the fauna are more severely affected than the flora (Butcher, 1946). At a concentration of 50 μg Cu/ℓ in L. Orta, fish and zooplankton were absent but algal production on stones was high (D. Calamari, personal communication). Thus, levels for the protection of fisheries should not necessarily be based upon those that allow algae to thrive.

9.6.2 INVERTEBRATES

Acutely lethal values

There is abundant information on the effect of copper on aquatic invertebrates, much of which has been discarded because details of the test conditions, particularly on the water quality, are not given. Water hardness, for example, clearly has a marked effect on the toxicity of copper to invertebrates, as well as to fish, as shown by Boch (1951) for the leech (*Piscicola geometra*) and by Brkovic-Popovic and Popovic (1977) with *Tubifex tubifex*; for the latter the 2-day LC50 at 20 °C was about 6.4, 210, 210 and 890 μg Cu/ℓ in water having a total hardness of 0.1, 34.2 (without phosphate buffer), 34.2 (with phosphate buffer) and 261 mg/ℓ as $CaCO_3$. For *Daphnia magna* the 2-day LC50 is 90 μg Cu/ℓ (Malăceă and Gruia, 1965) at 21 °C in water having a hardness of 196 mg/ℓ as $CaCO_3$, and 40 μg Cu/ℓ, as interpolated from the results of Anderson (1944), for tests at 25 °C in water having a hardness of 90 mg/ℓ as $CaCO_3$; these values are consistent with those (50-100 μg Cu/ℓ) found by Ivekovič (1932) to be acutely toxic to *Daphnia pulex* at 20 °C in water having a hardness of 215 mg/ℓ as $CaCO_3$ and are between 0.17 and 0.25 respectively of the corresponding values for rainbow trout. *D. longispina* appears to be more resistant than the other two species of *Daphnia* (Weber, 1932; Deschiens, Floch and Floch, 1964) while *D. hyalina* appears to be quite sensitive (Baudouin and Scoppa, 1974). Winner and Farrell (1976) found reduced survival for four species of cultured *Daphnia* maintained over periods of up to 19 weeks at concentrations of copper greater than 40 μg Cu/ℓ in water having a hardness of 130-160 mg/ℓ as $CaCO_3$

and a pH value 8.2–9.5; adverse effects on population growth and brood size were found at a similar or higher concentrations, depending upon species. Andrew, Biesinger and Glass (1977) have shown that the toxicity to *Daphnia* of solutions containing copper are related to the activity of cupric and hydroxyl ions and their results indicate that increasing the pH value increases the toxicity of cupric ion. With *Gammarus pseudolimnaeus* six weeks exposure to 280 μg Cu/ℓ at a hardness of 44 mg/ℓ as $CaCO_3$ was fatal and a reduction in survival was evident at 15 μg Cu/ℓ (Arthur and Leonard, 1970).

Some other invertebrates are exceptionally sensitive to copper. The leech, *Piscicola geometra*, is adversely affected by a concentration of 8 μg Cu/ℓ at a hardness of 300 mg/ℓ as $CaCO_3$ and is killed within 24 h at 40 μg Cu/ℓ (Boch, 1951). The naid worm, *Chaetogaster diaphanus* and the planktonic crustacean, *Bythotrephes longimanus*, are both killed by a concentration of 4 μg Cu/ℓ, in water having a hardness of about 50 mg/ℓ as $CaCO_3$; for *Planaria gonocephala* the threshold for acute toxicity in water of the same hardness is 4–40 μg Cu/ℓ (Weber, 1932; data on water quality furnished by R. Gächter, personal communication). For a number of organisms the lethal concentrations of copper are similar to those for rainbow trout. Thus, the survival of the snail, *Physa integra* and *Campeloma decisum*, at 15 °C in water having a hardness of 45 mg/ℓ as $CaCO_3$ was reduced during a 6-week exposure to 15 μg Cu/ℓ and was nil or very low at 28 μg Cu/ℓ (Arthur and Leonard, 1970); for the larval mayfly, *Ephemerella subvaria*, the 2-day LC50 was 0.32 mg Cu/ℓ at 18 °C in water having a hardness of 44 mg/ℓ as $CaCO_3$ (Warnick and Bell, 1969) and for *Heptagenia lateralis* the 7-day LC50 was about 0.5 mg Cu/ℓ at 10 °C in water having a hardness of 109 mg/ℓ as $CaCO_3$ (Liepolt and Weber, 1958); the 60-day LC50 for the worm, *Nais communis*, was 0.06 mg Cu/ℓ at 20 °C in water having a hardness of 320 mg/ℓ as $CaCO_3$, *N. variabilis* and *N. elingis* being somewhat more sensitive (Learner and Edwards, 1963).

Other organisms for which there are relevant data appear to be more resistant than trout, e.g. the 2-day LC50 for the stonefly, *Acroneuria lycorias*, was 8.3 mg Cu/ℓ and the 14-day LC50 of the larvae of the caddis, *Hydropsyche betteni*, was 32 mg Cu/ℓ at 18 °C in water having a hardness of 44 mg/ℓ as $CaCO_3$ (Warnick and Bell, 1969). However, the normal net-building of *H. instabilis* ceased after exposure to 1 mg Cu/ℓ in water of a hardness of 351 mg/ℓ as $CaCO_3$ (Decamps, 1973). Tubificid worms are less sensitive than the naid worms, the 8-day LC50 being > 8 mg Cu/ℓ in water having a hardness of 50 mg/ℓ as $CaCO_3$ (Weber, 1932).

Some planktonic crustacea, for example *Cyclops strenuus*, are particularly resistant. The decapod crustacean *Orconectes rusticus* was killed in 13 days at a concentration of 1 mg Cu/ℓ at 20 °C with a hardness of 112 mg/ℓ as $CaCO_3$ (Hubschman, 1967) and *Astacus leptodactylus* is probably somewhat more sensitive to this concentration (Chaisemartin, 1973); a characteristic delayed mortality of a week or a month after exposure to copper could lead to an underestimation of the sensitivity of this group.

Toxicity of organic compounds containing copper

Kapkov (1972), using several molluscan species, investigated complexes of copper with pyridine, α- and β-picoline, and 2,6-lutidine and found them to be more toxic than copper ion alone.

Chronically lethal and sublethal values

Levels lower than those that are acutely lethal have been shown to be damaging to some invertebrates; exposure of *Gammarus pseudolimnaeus* from one generation to another showed that no young survived a concentration of 8 μg Cu/ℓ (0.29 of the acutely lethal value) although there were more young produced at 2.8 μg Cu/ℓ than in the controls (Arthur and Leonard, 1970); Biesinger and Christensen (1972) found a 16 per cent reduction in reproduction in *Daphnia magna* after a three-week exposure to 22 μg Cu/ℓ (approximately 0.5 of the 2-day LC50 estimated by extrapolation from the value given on p. 208, para. 3). Biesinger *et al.* (unpublished; cited in National Academy of Sciences, 1973) indicated that the 'safe' level for reproduction and growth was 6 μg Cu/ℓ at a hardness of 45 mg/ℓ as $CaCO_3$, which is probably equivalent to about 0.7 of the 2-day LC50.

Field observations

Few data are available for situations where copper is the main poison present. In L. Orvsjøen, Norway, in which the hardness was about 11 mg/ℓ as $CaCO_3$ and the concentrations of copper and zinc were 0.13 and 0.4 mg/ℓ respectively, chironomid larvae and a few planktonic crustaceans were present while *Gammarus lacustris*, snails, insect life and fish were absent. In the R. Skorovasselv, containing 35 μg Cu/ℓ and 150 μg Zn/ℓ, brown trout and salmon (abundant in tributaries), snails and most ephemeroptera were absent but stickleback and other fauna and flora were present (M. Grande, personal communication). In streams in North Wales containing copper at between 50 and 99 per cent of the total concentration of copper plus zinc, each expressed as the fraction of its respective 2-day LC50 to rainbow trout, and in which the biomass of brown trout was markedly reduced and related to the concentrations of copper and zinc, the invertebrate biomass was not affected (Cremer and Warner, personal communication).

Summary

Invertebrates vary widely in their resistance to copper, a few organisms being at least ten times and *Daphnia* and *Gammarus* being about five times as sensitive as rainbow trout (p. 208, para. 3 and p. 209, para. 2) but the majority are either similar to or much more resistant than trout (p. 209, para. 3 and 4). Thus, while the presence of copper would be expected to produce changes in the species composition this should not necessarily adversely affect the food supply of fish. Indeed, there is no evidence that fisheries in waters containing copper are adversely affected because of a reduction in fish food organisms; on the contrary, reduction in trout biomass has been observed with increase in concentration of copper even though invertebrate biomass is unchanged (p. 210, para. 2).

9.7 Summary and conclusions

Copper is commonly present in polluted surface water often together with zinc, cadmium and other poisons, making it difficult to distinguish its contribution to any adverse effects found in fish populations.

Under aerobic aqueous conditions the cupric form of copper that is present tends to form compounds and complexes with carbonate and hydroxide ions, humic and amino acids (p. 191, para. 3-6) and is also readily adsorbed on to particulate material (p. 192, para. 2), very little being present as the free ion (Cu^{2+}) except in very pure soft waters low in pH value.

Toxicity to fish seems to be attributable to the combined effect of the inorganic forms of copper, mainly Cu^{2+} and $CuCO_3$, at least in hard borehole water in the pH range 6.5-7.5 (p. 192, para. 1 and p. 194, para. 5). However, analytical methods do not enable Cu^{2+} to be measured directly at very low concentrations and therefore in this chapter, unless otherwise stated, concentrations are expressed as 'soluble' copper, i.e., that which passes through a millipore filter of average porosity 0.45 μm.

The mode of action of copper on fish is not clear but acutely lethal concentrations damage the gill (p. 192, para. 5), may affect cell processes (p. 191, para. 5 and p. 192, para. 6) and enzyme activity, cause liver and kidney disorders (p. 200, para. 4), effects which may also be associated with chronic toxicity and with elevated levels of copper in the tissues (Section 9.4.1).

Toxicity to aquatic organisms is modified by water quality and, in particular, the lethal toxicity to fish (p. 195, para. 1 and 2), invertebrates (p. 208, para. 2) and algae (p. 207, para. 4) is reduced by increase in water hardness. The relationship is best described for rainbow at 15 °C, the 7-day LC50 at a total hardness of 10, 50, 100 and 300 mg/ℓ as $CaCO_3$ being 0.024, 0.11, 0.2 and 0.56 mg Cu/ℓ respectively.

Increase in temperature may shorten the period of survival of fish at concentrations that are rapidly lethal yet increase it at lower concentrations; however, the LC50 is decreased by reduction in temperature (p. 193, para. 5 and p. 194, para 2), the value for rainbow trout at 6 °C being 0.3 of that at 15 °C. There is little information on the effect of pH but at a value of 5.6 the period of survival, though not the threshold concentration, may be lower than at 7.5 (p. 194, para. 5). Toxicity is increased by reduction in dissolved oxygen (p. 194, para. 3) and decreased by chelating agents such as EDTA and NTA (p. 195, para. 5), humic acids (p. 195, para. 6) and amino acids (p. 196, para. 1); thus organo-copper complexes appear to have little, if any, acute toxicity. Toxicity of total copper is reduced but that of the soluble copper is increased in the presence of organic and inorganic solids (p. 196, para. 3).

The early larval stages of some fish tend to be the most sensitive period in the life cycle (p. 196, para. 5 to p. 197, para. 2).

While acclimation to copper has not been observed in the laboratory there is one report suggesting that acclimatization might have occurred in a polluted river (p. 197, para. 3).

Data from short-term tests in hard water show that some fish species are more sensitive to copper than salmonids. For example, the 4-day LC50 values for stone loach, rudd, common carp and perch are 0.8, 0.7, 0.7 and 0.3 respectively of the corresponding value for rainbow trout. Tench also appear to be more sensitive than trout. For pike and eels the values are about six and eitht times respectively that of trout (p. 199, para. 6). Tests lasting several weeks show that the LC50 values for stone loach and goldfish are about 0.6 and 0.24 respectively of that of trout (p. 200, para. 3). No reliable data for comparing the sensitivity of trout and other species are available relating to soft water, to the young stages, or to sublethal effects.

A significant (24 per cent) mortality was found among rainbow trout kept for 17 weeks at 0.6 of the 4-day LC50 (p. 200, para. 1). Salmon fry were unwilling to feed at 0.4 of the 21-day LC50 (p. 196, para. 5) and growth of rainbow trout was adversely affected over a period of 17 weeks at concentrations in excess of 0.1 of the 4-day LC50 (p. 202, para. 4). These values are close to those adversely affecting the growth of brook trout and the survival, growth and reproduction of some North American species (p. 202, para. 1 to 3 and p. 203, para. 2); no comparable data, however are available for the growth and reproduction of European species.

Data on behavioural changes induced by exposure to copper are fragmentary and difficult to relate to field conditions. There is some evidence that depression of the response of chemo-receptors, increase in cough frequency, respiration (p. 203, para. 3) and activity, and reduction in feeding (p. 203, para. 4) observed at sublethal concentrations are only transitory. Laboratory studies have demonstrated avoidance by Atlantic salmon of concentrations of copper in soft water of 0.05 of the 7-day LC50 but under field conditions adult migrating fish were turned back only by much high concentrations equivalent to 0.35–0.43 of the combined LC50 of copper and zinc (p. 203, para. 5). A concentration of 0.01 mg Cu/ℓ in soft water (close to the 4-day LC50 to rainbow trout) was avoided by goldfish under laboratory conditions unless the temperature was slightly higher than the acclimation temperature, when it was attractive (p. 203, para. 5).

Aquatic algae and invertebrates vary widely in their resistance to copper but under field conditions are generally less severely affected than fish (p. 207, para. 6 and p. 208, para. 2). While the presence of copper may alter the invertebrate species composition this should not necessarily affect the food supply of fish and there is no evidence that fisheries in water containing copper have been adversely affected because of a reduction in their food.

Measurements of the toxicity of sewage effluents, except in soft water free from organic matter and suspended solids, and of natural waters show that acute toxicity is less than that predicted from laboratory tests in clean water, probably because of the presence of non-toxic complexes and insoluble precipitates (p. 195, para. 4 to p. 196, para. 3 and p. 205). This may partly explain why natural fish populations have been found where the measured concentrations of copper approach the values found lethal in laboratory tests. Even in the presence of other poisons moderate populations of brown trout have been found where the annual 50 and 95 percentile values were 0.17 and 0.38 of the 2-day LC50 to rainbow trout, and some non-salmonid species have been reported where the corresponding values were 0.17 and 0.66 respectively (Section 9.5.2). These values would be somewhat higher expressed as fractions of the threshold median concentration rather than as fractions of the 2-day LC50.

There is a clear need for the development of more refined analytical techniques to measure the chemical states of soluble copper compounds at low concentrations in natural waters to enable better comparisons to be made between laboratory and field data.

9.8 Tentative water quality criteria

There are fairly extensive data on the toxicity of copper to salmonid fish but in general toxicity under field conditions is less than that predicted from laboratory tests except in water low in organic matter and suspended solids; there are no comparable data for non-salmonid species. Furthermore, there are virtually no field observations that indicate unequivocally the concentrations of copper that are not inimical to fish populations or fisheries. This is mainly because of deficiencies in the analytical data on water quality, an absence of quantitative data on the size and structure of the fish populations, and the fact that other poisons are not inimical to fish populations or fisheries. This is mainly because of deficiencies in the analytical data on water quality, an absence of quantitative data able for other species.

Since the concentrations of copper in fresh water fluctuate both seasonally and within shorter time intervals, and fish populations are likely to be adversely affected by particular levels at particular times of the year, some account should be taken of this in water quality criteria for fish. However, in the absence of data on the precise effects of copper on fish populations, the variations in concentrations of copper are arbitrarily expressed as the annual percentile distribution. It is possible, however, that peak values could be more damaging in the winter than in the summer if, as found in laboratory tests with rainbow trout, copper is more toxic at low temperatures (the 6-day LC50 at 6 °C was 0.3 of that at 15 °C for rainbow trout) and because the sensitive young stages of salmonid species are present at low temperatures.

Field and laboratory data for which analyses are given only for concentrations of total copper can be misleading because much of the copper may be present as insoluble particles or may be adsorbed onto particulate organic or inorganic matter; analyses of the various forms of copper would be the most relevant, but methods are not available for the very low concentrations important in soft water. The criteria are therefore expressed as 'soluble' copper, i.e., the portion that passes through a millipore filter having an average porosity of 0.45 μm, although it is recognized that this may also lead to errors because it could include non-toxic cupro-organic complexes of low toxicity.

Considering all the data available, it is proposed that the criteria should be based upon an annual percentile distribution of water quality expressed as the 50 and 95 percentile concentrations of soluble copper, and it is suggested that these should be 0.05 and 0.2 of the threshold LC50 respectively. Such criteria must take into account the hardness of the water. *Table 9.1* shows the 50 and 95 percentiles for rainbow trout for different hardness values for which there are well-founded data, and these criteria may be generally applicable to other salmonid species.

The presence of organic matter might allow the values in *Table 9.1* to be increased perhaps up to 3-fold. The values should be decreased to allow for low temperatures (p. 211, para. 6) and for the presence of other poisons (p. 198, para. 5 and 7) and also adjusted to allow for the different sensitivity of various species of fish (p. 211, para. 9).

9.9 References

ANDERSON, B. G. (1944). The toxicity thresholds of various substances found in industrial wastes as determined by the use of *Daphnia magna. Sewage Wks J.* **16**, 1156-1165

ANDREW, R. W. (1976). Toxicity relationships to copper forms in natural waters. In *Toxicity to biota of metal forms in natural water*, pp. 127-143 Proceedings of the Workshop, Duluth, Minnesota, Oct. 1975. Sponsored by the International Joint Commission, Great Lakes Division, Standing Committee on the Scientific Basis of Water Quality Criteria, Windsor, Ontario

ANDREW, R. W., BIESINGER, K. E. and GLASS, G. E. (1977). Effects of inorganic complexing on the toxicity of copper to *Daphnia magna. Wat. Res.* **11**, 309-315

ARTHUR, J. W. and LEONARD, E. N. (1970). Effects of copper on *Gammarus pseudolimnaeus, Physa integra* and *Campeloma decisum* in soft water. *J. Fish. Res. Bd Can.* **27**(7), 1277-1283

BAKER, J. T. P. (1969). Histological and electron microscopical observations on copper poisoning in the winter flounder (*Pseudopleuronectes americanus*). *J. Fish. Res. Bd Can.* **26**(11), 2785-2793

BAUDOUIN, M. F. and SCOPPA, P. (1974). Acute toxicity of various metals to freshwater zooplankton. *Bull. envir. Contam. Toxicol.* **12**, 745-751

BENOIT, D. A. (1975). Chronic effects of copper on survival growth, and reproduction of the bluegill (*Lepomis macrochirus*). *Trans. Am. Fish. Soc.* **104**, 353-358

BESCH, W. K., RICARD, M. and CANTIN, R. (1972). Benthic diatoms as indicators of mining pollution in the Northwest Miramichi River System, New Brunswick, Canada. *Int. Revue ges. Hydrobiol.* **57**, 39-74

BIESINGER, K. E. and CHRISTENSEN, G. M. (1972). Effects of various metals on survival, growth, reproduction and metabolism of *Daphnia magna. J. Fish. Res. Bd Can.* **29**(12), 1691-1700

BILINSKI, E. and JONAS, R. R. E. (1973). Effects of cadmium and copper on the oxidation of lactate by rainbow trout (*Salmo gairdneri*) gills. *J. Fish. Res. Bd Can.* **30**(10), 1553-1558

BIRDSONG, C. L. and AVAULT, J. W. Jr. (1971). Toxicity of certain chemicals to juvenile pompano. *Prog. Fish-Cult.* **33**, 76-80

BLACK, G. A. P., HINTON, D. J., JOHNSTON, H. C. and SPRAGUE, J. B. (1976). Annotated list of copper concentrations found harmful to aquatic organisms. *Tech. Rep. Fish. Mar. Serv. Can.* **603**, 44

BOCH, J. (1951). Versuche über die Bekämpfung des Fischegels (*Piscicola geometra*) mit Hilfe von Kupferverbindungen. München, Dissertation

BRKOVIC-POPOVIC, I. and POPOVIC, M. (1977). Effects of heavy metals on survival and respiration rate of tubificid worms. 1. The effects of survival. *Envir. Pollut.* **13** (1), 65-72

BROWN, V. M. and DALTON, R. A. (1970). The acute lethal toxicity to rainbow trout of mixtures of copper, phenol, zinc and nickel. *J. Fish. Biol.* **2**, 211-216

BROWN, V. M., SHAW, T. L. and SHURBEN, D. G. (1974). Aspects of water quality and the toxicity of copper to rainbow trout. *Wat. Res.* **8**, 797-803

BRUNGS, W. A., LEONARD, E. N. and McKIM, J. M. (1973). Acute and long-term accumulation of copper by the brown bullhead *Ictalurus nebulosus. J. Fish. Res. Bd Can.* **30** (30), 583-586

BRUNGS, W. A., GECKLER, J. R. and GAST, M. (1976). Acute and chronic toxicity of copper to the fathead minnow in a surface water of variable quality. *Wat. Res.* **10**, 37-43

BUTCHER, R. W. (1946). The biological detection of pollution. *J. Proc. Inst. Sewage Purif.* **2**, 92-97

CAIRNS, J. and SCHEIER, A. (1968). A comparison of the toxicity of some common industrial waste components tested individually and combined. *Prog. Fish-Cult.* **30**, 3-8

CALAMARI, D. and MARCHETTI, R. (1970). L'analisi tossicologica nel controllo delle acque: interazioni fra inquinanti. *Ig. Mod.* **63**, 455-471

CALAMARI, D. and MARCHETTI, R. (1973). The toxicity of mixtures of metals and surfactants to rainbow trout (*Salmo gairdneri* Rich.). *Wat. Res.* **7**, 1453-1464

CALAMARI, D. and MARCHETTI, R. (1974). Predicted and observed acute toxicity of copper and ammonia to rainbow trout (*Salmo gairdneri* Rich.). *Prog. Wat. Technol.* **7**, 569-577

CHAISEMARTIN, C. (1973). Analyse expérimentale comparée de la toxicité du cuivre de l'eau chez les Astacidae. Paper presented to the Conference 98e Congrès National des Sociétés Savantes, Avril 1973: St. Etienne (France). (Manuscript)

CHAU, Y. K. and LUM-SHUE-CHAN, K. (1974). Determination of labile and strongly bound metals in lake water. *Wat. Res.* **8**, 383-388

CHRISTENSEN, G. M. (1971). Effects of metal cations and other chemicals upon the *in vitro* activity of two enzymes in the blood plasma of the white sucker, *Catostomus commersoni* (Lacépède). *Chem. Biol. Interactions* **4**, 351-361

CHRISTENSEN, G. M., McKIM, J. M. and BRUNGS, W. A.(1972). Changes in the blood of the brown bullhead (*Ictalurus nebulosus* (Lesuer)) following short- and long-term exposure to copper (III). *Toxic. appl. Pharmacol.* **23**, 417-427

COOK, R. H. and CÔTE, R. P. (1972). The influence of humic acids on the toxicity of copper and zinc to juvenile Atlantic salmon as derived by the toxic unit concept. *Manusc. Rep. Envir. Protect. Serv. Can.* **72-75**

DABROWSKA, H. (1976). *Zesz. nauk. ART Olszt* **6**, 63-72

DECAMPS, H. (1973). Untersuchungen für Verwendung der Larven der 6a Hung Hydropsyche (*Trich. Insecta*) zu Toxizitats. Landesanstalt für Umweltschutz (Unpublished manuscript)

DEPARTMENT OF SCIENTIFIC AND INDUSTRIAL RESEARCH, U.K. (1961). In *Water Pollution Research 1960*, pp. 82-88. London, H.M.S.O.

DEPARTMENT OF SCIENTIFIC AND INDUSTRIAL RESEARCH, U.K. (1962). In *Water Pollution Research 1961*, pp. 88-89. London, H.M.S. O.

DEPARTMENT OF THE ENVIRONMENT, U.K. (1971). In *Water Pollution Research 1970*, pp. 58-64. London, H.M.S.O.

DEPARTMENT OF THE ENVIRONMENT, U.K.(1973). In *Water Pollution Research 1972*, pp. 37-39. London, H.M.S.O.

DESCHIENS, R.; FLOCH, H. and FLOCH, T. (1964). Sur les propriétés molluscicides non piscicides du chlorure cuivreux en poudre. *Bull. Soc. Path. exot.* **57**, 377-381

DONALDSON, E. M. and DYE, H. M.(1975). Corticosteroid concentrations in sockeye salmon exposed to low concentrations of copper. *J. Fish. Res. Bd Can.* **32**, 533-539

DOUDOROFF, P. (1952). Some recent developments in the study of toxic industrial wastes. *Proc. Pac. Northwest Ind. Waste Conf.* **4**, 21-25

DRUMMOND, R. A., SPOOR, W. A. and OLSON, G. F. (1973). Some short-term indicators of sublethal effects of copper on brook trout, *Salvelinus fontinalis*. *J. Fish. Res. Bd Can.* **30 (5)**, 698-701

EATON, J. G. (1973). Chronic toxicity of a copper, cadmium and zinc mixture to the fathead minnow (*Pimephales promelas* Rafinesque). *Wat. Res.* **7**, 1723-1736

EIFAC. (1976). Report on copper and freshwater fish. *EIFAC Tech. Pap.* **27**

EIFAC. (1977). Report on the effect of zinc and copper pollution on the salmonid fisheries in a river and lake system in central Norway. *EIFAC Tech. Pap.* **29**

EISLER, R. and GARDNER, G. R. (1973). Acute toxicity to an estuarine teleost of mixtures of cadmium, copper and zinc salts. *J. Fish. Biol.* **5**, 131-142

ELLIS, M. M. (1937). Detection and measurement of stream pollution. *Bull. Bur. Fish., Wash.* **48**, 365-437

FITZGERALD, G. P. and FAUST, S. L. (1963). Factors affecting the algicidal and algistatic properties of copper. *Appl. Microbiol.* **2**, 345-351

FOGG, G. E. and WESTLAKE, D. F. (1953). The importance of extracellular products of algae in freshwater. *Verh. int. Verein. theor. angew. Limnol.* **12**, 219-232

FOLMAR, L. C. (1976). Overt avoidance reaction of rainbow trout fry to nine herbicides. *Bull. envir. Contam. Toxicol.* **15 (5)**, 509-514

GARDNER, G. R. and LA ROCHE, L. G. (1973). Copper induced lesions in estuarine teleosts. *J. Fish. Res. Bd Can.* **30 (3)**, 363-368

GECKLER, J. R., HORNING, W. B., NEIHEISEL, T. M., PICKERING, Q. H. and ROBINSON, E. L. (1976). Validity of laboratory tests for predicting copper toxicity in streams. Washington, D.C., Environmental Protection Agency (EPA-600/3-76-116)

GRANDE, M. (1967). Effect of copper and zinc on salmonid fishes. *Adv. Wat. Pollut. Res.* **3 (1)**, 97-111

GREENFIELD, S. S. (1942). Inhibitory effects of inorganic compounds on photosynthesis in *Chlorella*. *Am. J. Bot.* **29**, 121-131

HAIDER, G. (1966). Über die Empfindlichkeit der Schleie gegen Kupfersulfat. *Fischwirt* **16**, 46-47

HARA, T. J. (1972). Electrical response of the olfactory bulb of Pacific salmon *Oncorhynchus nerka* and *Oncorhynchus kisutch*. *J. Fish. Res. Bd Can.* **29**, 1351-1355

HASSALL, K. A. (1962). A specific effect of copper on the respiration of *Chlorella vulgaris*. *Nature, Lond.* **193**, 90

HASSALL, K. A. (1963). Uptake of copper and its physiological effects on *Chlorella vulgaris*. *Physiologia Pl.* **16**, 323-332

HAZEL, C. R. and MEITH, S. J. (1970) Bio-assay of king salmon eggs and sac fry in copper solutions. *Calif. Fish Game* **56**, 121-124

HERBERT, D. W. M. and VANDYKE, J. M. (1964). The toxicity to fish of mixtures of poisons. 2. Copper-ammonia and zinc-phenol mixtures. *Ann. appl. Biol.* **53**, 415-421

HIDAKA, I. (1970). The effects of transition metals on the palatal chemoreceptors of the carp. *Jap. J. Physiol.* **20**, 599-609

HORNE, A. J. and GOLDMAN, C. R. (1974). Suppression of nitrogen fixation by blue-green algae in a eutrophic lake with trace additions of copper. *Science, Wash.* **183**, 409-411

HOWARTH, R. S. and SPRAGUE, J. B. (1978). Copper lethality to rainbow trout in waters of various hardness and pH. *Wat. Res.* **12**, 455-462

HUBSCHMAN, J. H. (1967). Effects of copper on the crayfish *Orcenectes rusticus* (Girard). 1. Acute toxicity. 2. Mode of action. *Crustaceana* **12**, 33-42 and 143-150

IOZEPSON, U. P. (1971). Raspredelenije microelementov v organizme karpa v zavisimosti ot sposovov ich prymienija v iskustvennych karmach. (Disposition of microelements in carp organs depending on the ways of their addition to artificial food.) *Mat. Konf. Izuc. Vnutr. Vodoiemov Pribaltikii, Petrozav*

IVEKOVIČ, H. (1932). Versuche über die Verwendung von Kupfer und Silber zur Vernichtung der Mikro- und Makroorganismen im Schwimmbeckenwasser. *Z. GesundhTech. Städtehyg.* **24**, 251

JACKIM, E., HAMLIN, J. M. and SONIS, S. (1970). Effects of metal poisoning on five liver enzymes in the killifish (*Fundulus heteroclitus*). *J. Fish. Res. Bd Can.* **27**, 383-390

KAPKOV, V. J. (1972). Toksicnost komplekenych soedinenji medi dlja presno-vodnych moljuskov. (Toxicity of complex copper compounds to freshwater molluscs.) *Vestn. Mosk. Univ. (Biol. pochvoved.)* **26 (1971) (2)**, 34-37

KARIYA, T. Y., HAGA, H. and TSUNDA, T. (1967). Studies on the post mortem identification of the pollutant in the fish killed by water pollution. 5. Detection of copper in the fish. *Bull. Jap. Soc. scient. Fish.* **33**, 818-825

KLEEREKOPER, H., WAXMAN, J. B. and MATIS, J. (1973). Interaction of temperature and copper ions as orienting stimuli in the locomotor behaviour of the goldfish (*Carassius auratus*). *J. Fish. Res. Bd Can.* **30 (6)**, 725-728

LABAT, R., CHATELET, A. and KUGLER, J. (1976). Action toxique du cuivre sur l'électrocardiogramme de la carpe (*Cyprinus carpio*). *Bull. Soc. Hist. Nat. Toulouse* **112 (1-2)**, 188-198

LABAT, R., PEQUIGNOT, J. and CHATELET, A. (1974). Action toxique du cuivre sur les branchies de carpe (*Cyprinus carpio*). *Ann. Limnol.* **10**, 109-114

LEARNER, M. A. and EDWARDS, R. W. (1963). The toxicity of some substances to *Nais* (Oligochaeta). *Proc. Soc. Wat. Treat. Exam.* **12**, 161-168

LETT, P. F., FARMER, G. J. and BEAMISH, F. W. H. (1976). Effect of copper on some aspects of the bioenergetics of rainbow trout (*Salmo gairdneri*). *J. Fish. Res. Bd Can.* **33 (6)**, 1335-1342

LEWIS, S. D. and LEWIS, W. M. (1971). The effect of zinc and copper on the osmolality of blood serum of the channel catfish, *Ictalurus punctatus* Rafinesque, and golden shiner, *Notemigonus crysoleucas* Mitchill. *Trans. Am. Fish. Soc.* **100**, 639-643

LIEPOLT, R. and WEBER, E. (1958). Giftwirkung von Kupfersulfat auf Wasserorganismen. *Wass. Abwass.* **99**, 335-353

LLOYD, R. (1961a). Effect of dissolved-oxygen concentrations on the toxicity of several poisons to rainbow trout (*Salmo gairdnerii* Richardson). *J. exp. Biol.* **38**, 447-455

LLOYD, R. (1961b). The toxicity of mixtures of zinc and copper sulphates to rainbow trout (*Salmo gairdnerii* Richardson). *Ann. appl. Biol.* **49**, 535-538

LLOYD, R. and HERBERT, D. W. M. (1962). The effect of the environment on the toxicity of poisons to fish. *Instn publ. Hlth Engrs J.* **61**, 132-145

LLOYD, R. and JORDAN, D. H. M. (1964). Predicted and observed toxicities of several sewage effluents to rainbow trout: a further study. *J. Proc. Inst. Sewage Purif.* **2**, 183

LORZ, H. W. and McPHERSON, B. P. (1976). Effects of copper or zinc in fresh water on the adaptation to sea water and ATPase activity, and the effects of copper on migratory disposition of coho salmon (*Oncorhynchus kisutch*). *J. Fish. Res. Bd Can.* **33**, 2023-2030

MALĂCEĂ, I. and GRUIA, E. (1965). Contributii la cunosterea actuinii toxice a cuprului, zincului, plumbului si nichelului asupra unor specii di pesti si a dafnei. *Stud. Prot. Epur. Apel., Bucuresti* **6**, 391-451

MALONEY, T. E. and PALMER, C. M. (1956). Toxicity of six chemical compounds in thirty cultures of algae. *Wat. Sewage Wks* **103**, 509-513

MARCHETTI, R. (1962). *Biologia e tossicologia delle acque usate.* Milan, ETAS (Editrice Tecnica Artistica Scientifica)

McBRIEN, D. C. H. and HASSALL, K. A. (1967). The effect of toxic doses of copper upon respiration, photosynthesis and growth of *Chlorella vulgaris*. *Physiologia Pl.* **20**, 113-117

McKIM, J. M. and BENOIT, D. A. (1971). Effects of long-term exposures to copper on survival, growth, and reproduction of brook trout (*Salvelinus fontinalis*). *J. Fish. Res. Bd Can.* **28** (5), 655-662

McKIM, J. M. and BENOIT, D. A. (1974). Duration of toxicity tests for establishing 'no effect' concentrations for copper with brook trout (*Salvelinus fontinalis*). *J. Fish. Res. Bd Can.* **31**, 449-452

McKIM, J. M., CHRISTENSEN, G. M. and HUNT, E. P. (1970). Changes in the blood of brook trout (*Salvelinus fontinalis*) after short-term and long-term exposure to copper. *J. Fish. Res. Bd Can.* **27**, 1883-1889

McKIM, J. M., EATON, J. G. and HOLCOMBE, G. W. (1978). Metal toxicity to embryos and larvae of eight species of freshwater fish. 2. Copper. *Bull. envir. Contam. Toxicol.* **19**, 608-616

MINISTRY OF TECHNOLOGY, U.K. (1970). *Water Pollution Research 1969,* pp. 58-62. London, H.M.S.O.

MONTGOMERY, H. A. C. and STIFF, M. J. (1971). Differentiation of chemical states of toxic species, especially cyanide and copper, in water. International Symposium on Identification and Measurement of Environmental Pollutants, pp. 375-379. National Research Council of Canada, Ottawa, 1971

MORGAN, W. S. G. and KÜHN, P. C. (1974). A method to monitor the effects of toxicants upon breathing rate of largemouth bass (*Micropterus salmoides* Lacépède). *Wat. Res.* **8**, 67-77

MORRICE, C. P. (1977). The effects of copper sulphate ($CuSO_4 \cdot 5H_2O$) on the feeding of roach (*Rutilus rutilus* L.). *Fish Mgmt* **8** (3), 82-85

MOUNT, D. I. (1968). Chronic toxicity of copper to fathead minnows (*Pimephales promelas* Rafinesque). *Wat. Res.* **2**, 215-223

MOUNT, D. I. and STEPHAN, C. E. (1969). Chronic toxicity of copper to the fathead minnow (*Pimephales promelas*) in soft water. *J. Fish. Res. Bd Can.* **26**, 2449-2457

NACHŠINA, E. P. and FELD'MAN, M. B. (1971). The effect of certain factors on the bonding of zinc and copper by the bottom oozes in water bodies. *Hydrobiol. J.* **7** (4), 12-17 (Translation of *Gidrobiol. Zh., Kiev* **7** (4), 18-24)

NATIONAL ACADEMY OF SCIENCES, U.S. (1973). National Academy of Engineering Committee on Water Quality Criteria. Water quality criteria 1972. Washington D.C., Government Printing Office (EPA-R3-73-0337)

NEHRING, D. (1964). Die Schadwirkung von Kupersulfat, Zinksulfat, Kaliumzyanid, Ammoniak und Phenol gegenüber Karpfen (*Cyprinus carpio*) vom Wasser her und nach peroraler Application. *Z. Fisch.* **12** (8/9/10), 717-724

NIELSEN, L. K. (1969). The influence of copper on the photosynthesis and growth of *Chlorella pyrenoidosa. Dansk Tidsskr. Farm.* **43**, 249-254

NISHIKAVA, K. and TABATA, K. (1969). Studies on the toxicity of heavy metals to aquatic animals and the factors to decrease the toxicity. 3. On the low toxicity of some heavy metal complexes to aquatic animals. *Bull. Tokai reg. Fish. Res. Lab.* **58**, 233-241

OSEID, D. and SMITH, Ll. L. (1972). Swimming endurance and resistance to copper and malathion of bluegills treated by long-term exposure to sublethal levels of hydrogen sulfide. *Trans. Am. Fish. Soc.* **101**, 620-625

PAGENKOPF, G. K., RUSSO, R. C. and THURSTON, R. V. (1974). Effect of complexation on toxicity of copper to fishes. *J. Fish. Res. Bd Can.* **31**, 462-465

PAUL, R. M. (1952). Water pollution: a factor modifying fish populations in Pacific coast streams. *Sci. Monthly, N.Y.* **74**, 14-23

PEQUIGNOT, J., LABAT, R. and CHATELET, A. (1975). Action du sulfate de cuivre sur les cellules à mucus de l'alevin de truite (*Salmo irideus*). *J. Eur. Toxicol.* **8 (1)** 52-56

PRESCOTT, G. W. (1948). Objectionable algae with reference to killing of fish and other animals. *Hydrobiologia*, 1-13

REHWOLDT, R., BIDA, G. and NERRIE, B. (1971). Acute toxicity of copper, nickel and zinc ions to some Hudson river fish species. *Bull. envir. Contam. Toxicol.* **6**, 445-448

REHWOLDT, R., MENAPACE, L. W., NERRIE, B. and ALESSANDRELLO, D. (1972). The effect of increased temperature upon the acute toxicity of some heavy metal ions. *Bull. envir. Contam. Toxicol.* **8**, 91-96

SAUNDERS, R. L. and SPRAGUE, J. B. (1967). Effects of copper-zinc mining pollution on a spawning migration of Atlantic salmon. *Wat. Res.* **1**, 419-432

SEMČUK, V. R. and AVDOŠEV, B. S. (1972). Nakaplenkije medi v organach i tkanijach karpov pri skormlivani im kombikarma z dobavlenijem ammikata medi. (Copper concentration in organs and tissues of carp fed with food mixture containing copper ammicat.) *Rȳb. Khoz. Kiev.* **14**, 25-28

SHAW, T. L. and BROWN, V. M. (1971). Heavy metals and the fertilization of rainbow trout eggs. *Nature, Lond.* **230 (5291)**, 251-253

SHAW, T. L. and BROWN, V. M. (1974). The toxicity of some forms of copper to rainbow trout. *Wat. Res.* **8**, 377-392

SILLÉN, L. G. and MARTELL, A. E. (1964). Stability constants of metal-ion complexes. *Spec. Publ. Chem. Soc. Lond.* **17**

SOLBÉ, J. F. de L. G. and COOPER, V. A. (1976). Studies on the toxicity of copper sulphate to stone loach (*Noemacheilus barbatulus* (L.)). *Wat. Res.* **10**, 523-527

SPRAGUE, J. B. (1964a). Lethal concentrations of copper and zinc for young Atlantic salmon. *J. Fish. Res. Bd Can.* **21 (1)**, 17-26

SPRAGUE, J. B. (1964b). Avoidance of copper-zinc solutions by young salmon in the laboratory. *J. Wat. Pollut. Control Fed.* **36**, 990-1004

SPRAGUE, J. B. (1968). Promising anti-pollutant: chelating agent NTA protects fish from copper and zinc. *Nature, Lond.* **220**, 1345-1346

SPRAGUE, J. B. and RAMSAY, B. A. (1965). Lethal level of mixed copper-zinc solutions for juvenile salmon. *J. Fish. Res. Bd Can.* **22 (2)**, 425-432

STEEMAN-NIELSEN, E., NIELSON, L. K. and WIUM-ANDERSEN, S. (1969). The effect of deleterious concentrations of copper on the photosynthesis of *Chlorella pyrenoidosa. Physiologia Pl.* **22**, 1121-1133

STEEMAN-NIELSEN, E. and WIUM-ANDERSEN, S. (1970). Copper ions as poison in the sea and in freshwater. *Marine Biol.* **6**, 93-197

STIFF, M. J. (1971a). The chemical states of copper in polluted freshwater and a scheme of analysis to differentiate them. *Wat. Res.* **5**, 585–599

STIFF, M. J. (1971b). Copper/bicarbonate equilibria in solutions of bicarbonate ion at concentrations similar to those found in natural water. *Wat. Res.* **5**, 171–176

SVENSKA GRUVFÖRENINGEN (1960). Vattenföroreningar från gruvor och anrikningsverk. Forskningsuppgift 196/1960, Delrapport 1–5 avseende adsorption av metalljomer på grabergsmineral. Stockholm, Stensil. Institutt för mineralberedning (anrikning) KTH

TABATA, K. (1969). Studies on the toxicity of heavy metals to aquatic animals and the factors to decrease the toxicity. 2. The antagonist action of hardness components in water on the toxicity of heavy metal ions. *Bull. Tokai reg. Fish. Res. Lab.* **58**, 215–232

TIMMS, A. M., KLEEREKOPER, H. and MATIS, J. (1972). Locomotor response of goldfish, channel catfish, and largemouth bass to a 'copper-polluted' mass of water in an open field. *Wat. Resour. Res.* **8**, 1574–1580

WARNICK, S. L. and BELL, H. L. (1969). The acute toxicity of some heavy metals to different species of aquatic insects. *J. Wat. Pollut. Control. Fed.* **41**, 280–284

WEBER, H. (1932). Vergiftungversuche mit Kupfersulfat an niederen Süssvassertieren. *Revue suisse Zool.* **39**, 275–279

WHITTON, B. A. (1970a). Toxicity of heavy metals to freshwater algae: a review. *Phykos* **9**, 116–125

WHITTON, B. A. (1970b). Toxicity of zinc, copper and lead to *Chlorophyta* from flowing waters. *Arch. Mikrobiol.* **72**, 353–360

WILSON, R. C. H. (1972). Prediction of copper toxicity in receiving waters. *J. Fish. Res. Bd Can.* **29**, 1500–1502

WINDLE-TAYLOR, E. (1965). *Treatment of storage reservoirs with copper sulphate.* Forty-first Report on the Results of the Bacteriological, Chemical and Biological Examination of the London Waters for the Years 1963–1964, pp. 52–55. London, Metropolitan Water Board

WINNER, R. W. and FARRELL, M. P. (1976). Acute and chronic toxicity of copper to four species of *Daphnia. J. Fish. Res. Bd Can.* **33 (8)**, 1685–1691

ZITKO, V., CARSON, W. V. and CARSON, W. G. (1973). Prediction of incipient lethal levels of copper to juvenile Atlantic salmon in the presence of humic acid by cupric electrode. *Bull. envir. Contam. Toxicol.* **10**, 265–271

10

CADMIUM

Foreword

The original report on cadmium and freshwater fish, and the updated version for this chapter, were prepared by the Water Research Centre from contributions by individual members of the Working Party on Water Quality Criteria for European Freshwater Fish.

10.1 Summary

Cadmium is widely used in industry and small quantities are discharged to surface fresh waters; natural background concentrations are usually below 1 $\mu g/\ell$ and higher levels have been found in polluted waters. A substantial proportion of the cadmium in a river water is adsorbed onto solids in suspension but only the soluble forms of cadmium are toxic to fish. The concentrations at which soluble cadmium is present in natural and polluted waters are close to the limits of measurement and this causes difficulties in defining and interpreting field data. Little is known of the toxic action of cadmium to fish. The metal is accumulated predominantly in the gills, liver and kidney, but the significance of the levels found to the functioning of these organs is not clear, although there is some evidence that the osmoregulatory role of the gills and kidney may be impaired. Cadmium is slowly lost from the tissues when fish previously exposed to cadmium are returned to clean water, but loading can occur in a short period of time, causing death several days later.

Acute and chronic toxicity tests with sensitive species of fish have given conflicting results which may have been caused by the variable and unusual concentration–response curve or errors in measuring concentrations of soluble cadmium. Concentrations lethal after at least 10 days exposure can be up to 100-fold less than those lethal in 2–4 days, and if a threshold lethal concentration exists, it is ill-defined. Several environmental factors influence the position and shape of the concentration–response curve. A decrease in water hardness and dissolved oxygen and possibly in pH value, produces a lower LC50; changes in temperature and salinity may also affect cadmium toxicity.

The interspecific sensitivity of fish is more variable for cadmium than for other common pollutants but comparisons between data are difficult to make because of differences in water quality and exposure times. However, of the few species tested, salmonids are more sensitive than cyprinids (with the possible exception of carp), with pike occupying an intermediate position. Juvenile stages appear to be the more sensitive.

Few sublethal effects of cadmium have been observed. Minnow have been shown to develop spinal deformities and in rainbow trout the development of ova can be impaired. Increased activity of male brook trout during spawning in low concentrations of cadmium has led to increased mortality.

Salmonid fish appear to be more sensitive than those other components of the aquatic biota which have been tested. Some species of invertebrates such as *Daphnia magna* and *Gammarus fossarum* appear to be as sensitive as salmonids, but most others are much more resistant. Some species of aquatic plants grow more slowly in concentrations of cadmium which are close to the limits for the survival of fish, but the majority of plants appear to be very resistant.

Few data exist on the status of the fish fauna in surface waters polluted with cadmium, although there is some evidence that brown trout were absent from waters where the cadmium concentration was predicted to be harmful on the basis of laboratory experiments. Minnows were also found at concentrations predicted to be harmless to rainbow trout. However, rivers polluted with cadmium also contain other pollutants, especially heavy metals, and although some of these have been shown to be additive with cadmium in their joint toxic action, there is some evidence that zinc may have an antagonistic effect.

On the basis of a critical examination of the available data (summarized in Sections 10.9 and 10.10), tentative criteria for dissolved cadmium can be proposed as in *Table 10.1* (p. 245).

Values for common carp should be taken to be the same as those for rainbow trout pending further data on long-term effects. The corresponding values for brown trout and pike appear to be about twice as high as those for rainbow trout, while those for the more insensitive non-salmonid fish such as perch (*Table 10.1*) and minnow would be about 38 times higher.

The values in *Table 10.1* should be decreased to allow for low concentration of dissolved oxygen and for the presence of other poisons.

There is a need for reliable field data from polluted and unpolluted rivers and from semi-artificial experimental aquatic ecosystems, to reinforce these criteria. Such studies are particularly necessary to establish the maximum concentrations associated with flourishing populations of resistant coarse fish species, and the modifying effects of other pollutants, especially zinc, in the water.

The concentration of cadmium in the muscle of fish exposed for long periods to low concentrations of cadmium in the water under either laboratory or field conditions is highly variable and can be 1–1000 times higher (on a dry weight basis) and 0.1–100 times higher (on a wet weight basis) than that in the water, i.e., < 1 mg Cd/kg muscle (dry weight) or < 0.1 mg Cd/kg muscle (wet weight) of fish from water containing 1 μg Cd/ℓ. The reasons for these wide differences are not all known nor fully understood.

10.2 Introduction

10.2.1 SOURCE OF CADMIUM

Cadmium is a rare element and is usually found as an impurity in ores of other metals, principally those of zinc. It is obtained as a by-product in the refining of zinc and copper, but small quantities can remain as impurities in these and other metals. It is present in low concentrations in soils, sandstones and shales from which it is leached only very slowly into surface water (Bowen, 1966) and is also present in some phosphate fertilizers. Because of its many industrial applications, chief among which is electroplating, it is often present in manufacturing industrial discharges. Other sources of surface water contamination include rainfall with airborne particulate matter (e.g. from the burning of fossil fuels, including emission from vehicle exhausts), corrosion and erosion.

10.2.2 CHEMISTRY OF CADMIUM IN FRESHWATER

The chemical properties of cadmium are intermediate between those of zinc and mercury and consequently cadmium compounds are predominantly ionic in character. Cadmium occurs in the moderately electropositive oxidation state two in aqueous solution so that reduction cannot occur in water containing dissolved oxygen. The hydrated ion $(Cd(H_2O)_6{}^{2+})$ is stable in aqueous solution, is not readily hydrolysed and is far less amphoteric than the corresponding zinc ion. Organo-cadmium compounds (i.e. those with metal–carbon bonds) are known but are far less important in the environment than those of mercury, and are not stable in aqueous solution.

Cadmium can form a wide variety of soluble complexes. Complexation in freshwater has been estimated from stability constants published by Weber and Posselt (1974) and Elder (1975), and has been studied experimentally using the specific-ion electrode by Gardiner (1974a) and using anodic stripping voltammetry (ASV) by, for example, O'Shea (1972). The humic complex is usually the most important in water containing organic matter (deriving either from decayed vegetation or from sewage effluent) but complexes with the carbonate, sulphate, chloride and hydroxide, and with chelating agents such as ethylenediaminetetraacetic acid (EDTA) and nitrilotriacetic acid (NTA), may also be present. However, the free, uncomplexed ion can normally be expected to predominate over cadmium complexes especially in unpolluted soft waters of relatively low pH value (Gardiner, 1974a).

The solubility of cadmium in natural waters and the rate of precipitation have been studied by Weber and Posselt (1974) and Hem (1972). In aerobic natural waters the carbonate is usually the least soluble salt at concentrations greater than 10 μg Cd/ℓ, and precipitation may occur within the pH range of approximately 8.5–11; where soluble cadmium is present the principal route by which the metal is removed from solution is by adsorption. The tendency of cadmium to be adsorbed on naturally occurring solids has been studied by Gardiner (1974b), Neufeld, Gutiernez and Novak (1977) and Farrah and Pickering (1977). Cadmium ions are adsorbed onto solid humic materials to a far greater extent than onto clay or silica particles. The reduction in the dissolved cadmium concentration observed during biological sewage treatment (Oliver and Cosgrove, 1974) is caused by adsorption on solids, and a large proportion of the cadmium transported in rivers is carried on solid particles (Williams, 1973). The distribution of cadmium in an eutrophic lake has been studied by Mathis and Kevern (1975).

10.2.3 ANALYTICAL METHODS

The main analytical techniques used routinely for determining cadmium in natural waters are atomic absorption spectrometry (AAS) using conventional flame excitation (Kuwata, Hisatomi and Hasegawa, 1971) and preceded if necessary by solvent extraction and concentration, flameless AAS with graphite furnace (Rattonetti, 1974) and colorimetric methods (e.g. American Public Health Association, 1971). All should be capable of a detection limit of at least 0.1 $\mu g/\ell$ under favourable conditions, but normally conventional AAS would be used when the cadmium concentration is at least 5 $\mu g/\ell$ to avoid preliminary solvent extraction. Other techniques used have included: ASV (Gardiner and Stiff, 1975) which also has a detection limit of approximately 0.1 $\mu g/\ell$ but is operationally difficult; neutron activation analysis; X-ray fluorescence; fluorimetry; flame photometry; and optical emission spectrometry.

Concentrations of cadmium found in surveys of European and North American fresh waters uncontaminated by any known point sources of the metal are usually between 0.01 and 0.5 $\mu g/\ell$ (Henriksen, Balmer and Wright, 1976).

Because of difficulty both in measuring cadmium at the concentrations usually found in water and in identifying the forms relevant to its toxicity to fish and other aquatic organisms, particularly under field conditions, many of the published data on cadmium in water and on other relevant water quality characteristics are inadequate. Comparison between the results of field and laboratory studies must be made with care. In many cases the concentrations used in laboratory tests are well above the solubility and often the nominal concentrations used are not checked by chemical analysis. Also, differences in the interval between making up test solutions and introducing fish in static tests and in the mean retention time in continuous flow tests, could result in differences in the chemical conditions to which the test fish are exposed.

10.3 Accumulation of cadmium in fish tissues

10.3.1 LABORATORY EXPERIMENTS

Uptake from water

Mount and Stephan (1967), using bluegill (*Lepomis macrochirus*), found that cadmium accumulated maximally in the kidney, liver, gill and gut, to a lesser extent in the spleen but not significantly in bone or muscle. The uptake curves indicated that within 30–60 days equilibria were established between the concentrations of cadmium in the water and those in the tissues. Equilibria were also found to occur after about two months in bluegill and largemouth bass (*Micropterus salmoides*) (Cearley and Coleman, 1974) and in flagfish (*Jordanella floridae*) (Spehar, 1976).

Similar results have been obtained by Kumada *et al.* (1972) using rainbow trout (*Salmo gairdneri*). Calamari and Marchetti (1977b) exposed rainbow trout to 50 μg Cd/ℓ (water hardness 320 mg/ℓ as $CaCO_3$) for 120 days and found the metal to be accumulated in various organs with equilibrium reached after 80 days. The increase (on a wet weight basis) was about 30-fold in the blood and liver (0.12–3.4 mg Cd/kg), 80-fold in the gill and 100-fold in the kidney (0.17–16.5 mg Cd/kg). Concentrations found in the muscle were about 30 μg Cd/kg. These fish were apparently in good health. When the fish were returned to clean water the concentrations of cadmium fell by 50 per cent in the gill after 7 days and in the liver and kidney after 50 days; normal values were reached in all organs after 80 days.

V. M. Brown, D. G. Shurben and W. F. Miller (personal communication) kept rainbow trout for 65 weeks in nominal concentrations of 2, 5 and 8 μg Cd/ℓ and found a minimal degree of accumulation in muscle and no trend with time. Accumulation factors for muscle, liver and kidney (on a dry weight basis) at the end of the period were no more than about 500, 3000 and 10 000 respectively. The concentration factor in the gills of fish kept for three days at 1 mg Cd/ℓ (equivalent to the 4- to 5-day LC50 for rainbow trout) was 20 for rainbow trout and about 3 for roach (*Rutilus rutilus*) and perch (*Perca fluviatilis*) (Department of the Environment, 1973).

D. Pascoe (personal communication) kept three-spined stickleback (*Gasterosteus aculeatus*) for up to 79 days in solutions containing cadmium in a soft water (hardness 110–120 mg/ℓ as $CaCO_3$) and his data show a linear relation between log concentration of cadmium in whole fish (wet weight) and log concentration of cadmium in the water; body residues were about 0.4 mg/kg in fish exposed to 1 μg Cd/ℓ and about 1 mg/kg in those exposed to 10 μg Cd/ℓ. Tests of a few hours duration with adult mosquito fish (*Gambusia affinis*) in deionized water containing 9 g sucrose/ℓ showed that high ambient concentrations of cadmium (5–20 mg Cd/ℓ) resulted in high concentrations of cadmium in the gill, an effect that is reduced with increasing salinity until it is undetectable in 100 per cent seawater (Katz, 1977); concentrations in the gill of fish tested in 25 per cent seawater were similar to those of fish tested in the presence of calcium at a concentration equivalent to that in 25 per cent seawater.

Uptake from food

Guppy (*Lebistes reticulatus*) were fed for seven weeks on *Tubifex* worms containing 20 mg Cd/kg without showing evidence of accumulation of cadmium (L. Landner, personal communication); another group exposed for that period to 70–100 μg Cd/ℓ accumulated about 9 mg Cd/kg (wet weight) and within this group there was no significant difference in cadmium uptake between fish fed cadmium-loaded *Tubifex* and controls fed normal worms.

Somewhat similar results were found by Williams and Giesy (1978) who kept mosquitofish in flowing water containing 10 μg Cd/ℓ and fed the fish with food flakes spiked with cadmium chloride at a concentration of either 0.1 or 1.0 mg Cd/kg for between six and eight weeks; however, concentrations of cadmium in the fish receiving 1 mg Cd/kg in the food (but not those in fish receiving 0.1 mg

Cd/kg) increased significantly from about 0.03 mg Cd/kg to about 0.07 mg Cd/kg (dry weight). Kumada *et al.* (1973) also found that the amount of cadmium accumulated was greater than that from aqueous exposure to cadmium alone when dace (*Leuciscus leuciscus*) were fed with cadmium-contaminated food.

On the other hand Rehwoldt and Karimian-Teherani (1976) who fed zebrafish (*Brachydanio rerio*) on fish food spiked with 10 mg Cd/kg (as acetate) over a six-month period, and did not expose them to cadmium in the water, found rapid accumulation in whole fish with a levelling-off after a few months to 12.7 and 5.1 mg Cd/kg (dry weight) in females and males respectively (coupled, incidentally, with a marked reduction in the number of offspring produced and, by the end of the period, less defined colours and markings on the fish).

10.3.2 FIELD OBSERVATIONS

Lucas, Edgington and Colby (1970) studied trace element concentrations in various species of fish from the Great Lakes using neutron activation analysis and found a median value for cadmium of 0.094 mg Cd/kg for whole (wet) body and 0.4 mg/kg for concentrations in the (wet) liver. Uthe and Bligh (1971), using atomic absorption spectrophotometry, found less than 0.05 mg Cd/kg for whole (wet) body analyses of different species of freshwater fish with no differences between fish from industrialized and non-industrialized areas.

Fish from New York State contained about 0.02 mg Cd/kg in (wet) eviscerated body, with only a few individuals having levels up to 0.1 mg/kg (Lovett *et al.*, 1972).

Comparable surveys have not been carried out in Europe but Jaakkola *et al.* (1972) found 3 μg Cd/kg in the wet muscle of pike (*Esox lucius*) in a 'clean' area and between 4 and 13 μg/kg in fish from a 'polluted' area in Finland. Values for the liver and kidney in these fish were 0.028–0.055 mg/kg and 0.153–0.232 mg/kg respectively for the clean area and 0.034–0.113 mg/kg and 0.169–0.339 mg/kg respectively for contaminated areas.

A sample of 10 brown trout (*Salmo trutta*) from the R. Churnet, England, where the median and 95 percentile values for cadmium in membrane-filtered samples of water taken over a 44-month period were 3 and 6 μg Cd/ℓ, contained average values of 1.4, 4.0, 6.3 and 17.7 mg Cd/kg dry weight in the muscle, liver, kidney and spleen respectively (J. F. de L. G. Solbé, personal communication). Somewhat similar results (0.1, 1.1, 15.4 and 15.7 mg Cd/kg dry weight respectively) have been reported by R. Huddart and H. A. Hawkes (personal communication) for rainbow trout kept for three months in an outdoor channel containing river water in which the 50 percentile and 95 percentile concentrations of cadmium were 2 and 4 μg Cd/ℓ respectively. The concentration factor for the cadmium in the muscle on a dry weight basis is thus about 470 for the brown trout and 50 for the rainbow trout in these two studies.

In L. Ringvatnet, Norway, where the median and 95 percentile values of cadmium were 0.6 and 1.4 μg Cd/ℓ, the concentration of cadmium in the muscle of char (*Salvelinus alpinus*) and brown trout was about 0.03 and 0.075 mg/kg dry weight respectively (M. Grande and K. W. Jensen, personal communication), i.e. a concentration factor of about 50 and 125 respectively.

In the R. Elsenz, Federal Republic of Germany, where the average reported concentration of cadmium over a two-month period was 0.5 μg Cd/ℓ, the concentration of cadmium in the dry muscle was 0.04 mg/kg for a one-year-old rainbow trout and 0.05 mg/kg for two six-year-old roach; where the concentration in the water was 0.9 μg Cd/ℓ, the concentration of cadmium in the whole (dry) body of two three-spined stickleback was about 0.1 mg/kg (Prosi, 1976), a value similar to that found in Pascoe's laboratory experiments (p. 225, para. 4). Much higher concentrations were present in the kidney and liver of the fish, and in invertebrates.

In a stream in Illinois, U.S.A., studied by Enk and Mathis (1977), in which the concentration of cadmium was less than 20 μg Cd/ℓ (on one occasion a concentration of 1 μg/ℓ was found), concentrations in invertebrates were about 1 mg Cd/kg (wet weight) and in fish and sediments were about 0.15 mg Cd/kg (wet weight), suggesting a concentration factor from food organisms similar to that found by Williams and Giesy (p. 225, para. 6).

In no case has a positive correlation been noted between cadmium concentration and size or age of the fish.

The relative importance of water and food as sources of cadmium to fish may be dependent on many factors such as food quality, relative cadmium concentrations in food and water, availability of cadmium in water and food, and species of fish.

10.4 Lethal effects on fish

10.4.1 MODE OF ACTION

Calamari and Marchetti (1977b) suggested that the toxic effect of cadmium cannot be attributed to one or another of the different chemical forms of the metal in solution but that probably all the 'soluble' chemical forms (i.e. that passing through a filter having a porosity of 0.45 μm) are of similar toxicity.

Hyperplasia and necrosis of the epithelium of the secondary lamellae of the gill occurred in rainbow trout exposed to 10 mg Cd/ℓ, but gill damage was less evident at 0.01 mg Cd/ℓ (Ministry of Technology, 1970). Bilinski and Jonas (1973) observed extensive degeneration of gill structure in this species after exposure to 1.12 mg Cd/ℓ for one day in very soft water (4 mg/ℓ as $CaCO_3$). They found detachment of the epithelial layer, hypertrophy and hyperplasia of the interlamellar epithelium and also a significant (60 per cent) depression of lactate oxidation in excised gill filaments from surviving fish. Exposure to a lower concentration (11 μg Cd/ℓ which caused a 75 per cent mortality in four days) did not result in detectable reduction in the oxidative activity.

The liver, heart and brain can also be affected by cadmium (Ministry of Technology, 1970, 1973). Gardner and Yevich (1970) found pathological changes in kidney and intestinal tract and a rapid increase of eosinophil levels in the blood of mummichog (or killifish) (*Fundulus heteroclitus*) exposed to cadmium, and suggested that death was caused by impairment of respiratory and extrarenal function through reduction in respiratory surface. Marafante (1976) has detected cadmium-bound protein in the liver and kidney of goldfish (*Carassius auratus*) following intraperitoneal injection with a mixture of the chlorides of cadmium, mercury and zinc.

Changes in the activity of some liver enzymes of this species were observed by Jackim, Hamlin and Sonis (1970). *In vitro,* the alkaline phosphatase (ALP) activity was the most sensitive to cadmium, but *in vivo* this was not different from that of the control; on the other hand, the *in vivo* activity of acid phosphatase, xanthine oxidase and catalase was significantly depressed in fish surviving short exposure to the 4-day LC50. *In vitro,* cadmium is also able to interrupt energy production in the liver mitochondria of bluegill by blocking oxygen uptake at a concentration of 0.37 mg Cd/ℓ (Hiltibran, 1971). A three-month exposure of rainbow trout to 9 μg Cd/ℓ, and of brown trout to 27 μg Cd/ℓ, failed to produce any effect on 10 enzyme systems in gill and liver studied *in vitro* by Roberts *et al.* (1979) except to increase L-malate nictotinamide adenine oxide reductase activity in rainbow trout liver within two weeks. Much higher levels (420-1000 mg/ℓ) are required to induce inhibition of plasma lactate dehydrogenase (PLDH) and plasma glutamic oxalacetic transaminase (PGOT) in white sucker (*Catostomus commersoni*) (Christensen, 1971). However, the same author found a statistically significant decrease in weight, an increase in protein content, and an increase in activity of acetylcholinesterase (ACH) in alevins of brook trout (*Salvelinus fontinalis*) held in 0.7 and 3.4 μg Cd/ℓ in soft water; at the higher concentration he found an increase in activity of PGOT and ALP (Christensen, 1975).

Larsson, Bengtsson and Svanberg (1976) exposed flounder (*Platichthys flesus*) for 15 days to sublethal concentrations of cadmium and found a reduction in the size of the liver, anaemia, alteration in carbohydrate metabolism (increased blood sugar and liver glycogen and reduced blood lactate and muscle glycogen) and increased plasma Na^+, Cl^-, and Mg^{2+} and reduced plasma K^+ and Ca^{2+}. On the other hand Katz (1977) has demonstrated increased sodium efflux in *Gambusia affinis* within a few hours in the presence of 5 mg Cd/ℓ, an effect that was reduced in the presence of calcium at a concentration equivalent to 25 per cent seawater. Increased concentrations of calcium and zinc and reduced concentrations of copper in the liver, and of calcium in the bone, were found in several rainbow trout after exposure to 8 μg Cd/ℓ for 80 weeks (V. M. Brown, D. G. Shurben and W. F. Miller, personal communication); changes in the calcium concentrations suggest an alteration of calcium metabolism which might explain the suppression of maturation found in the females (Water Research Centre, 1975). Cadmium-induced ionic imbalance could also explain neuromuscular disturbances, hyperexcitability, convulsions and tetany observed in fish by various authors (Cearley and Coleman, 1974; Eaton, 1974; Benoit *et al.,* 1976; Spehar, 1976) and also perhaps the degeneration of muscle fibre (Department of the Environment, 1973) and lesions in the spinal cord (Bengtsson *et al.,* 1975). The latter authors attribute the high (30 per cent) incidence of spinal damage in minnow (*Phoxinus phoxinus*) to the continuous tension of opposing muscles brought about by prolongation of the muscle action potential caused by cadmium. Spinal deformities have also been described in a large proportion of fish ('Tribolodon') that died after nearly 15 months exposure to 5 μg Cd/ℓ (Nakamura, 1974).

Inflammation of the pancreas has been found in roach surviving exposure to 9.0 mg Cd/ℓ for 50 days (Department of the Environment, 1973), and changes in carbohydrate metabolism in flounder were attributed to pancreatic disorders (Larsson, 1975). Histological changes have been demonstrated in blood-forming tissues of rainbow trout (spleen) (Ministry of Technology, 1970) and mummichogs (head of kidney) (Gardner and Yevich, 1970). Sangalang and O'Halloran (1972) found testicular damage with extensive haemorrhagic necrosis and a reduction in *in vitro* synthesis of androgen (11 ketosterone) in brook trout.

Merlini (1978) kept immature sunfish (*Lepomis gibbosus*) for two weeks at a concentration of 22 μg Cd/ℓ, a month after they had received a single ration containing [58]Co-vitamin B_{12}, and on examination 31 days later found a depletion of radioactive vitamin B_{12} in the liver and an increase in concentration in the gall bladder, compared with controls. No changes in blood cortisol were found in sockeye salmon (*Oncorhynchus kisutch*) kept for six days at a concentration of 12 μg Cd/ℓ (53 per cent average mortality) in water having a hardness of 90 mg/ℓ as $CaCO_3$ (Schreck and Lorz; 1978), nor in those exposed (without any mortality) for 67 days to a concentration of 4.5 μg Cd/ℓ, even after transfer to seawater at 10 °C and a salinity of 30 per cent; the gonad, liver, kidney and gill tissues of the latter group of fish were histologically no different from those of the controls.

Irreversible lethal effects appear to have been caused in rainbow trout within one day when exposed to the 2-day LC50 value and within two days when exposed to the 6-day LC50 (p. 231).

Cadmium has been found in fish tissues in laboratory experiments with fish exposed to known aqueous concentrations (p. 228, para. 5 to p. 225, para. 4) and in fish caught in polluted waters (p. 226, para. 3 to p. 227, para. 2) but little is known of its significance in causing disorders or impairment in function in organs though concentrations there may be much higher than in normal tissues.

It appears that damage to the ion-regulating mechanisms by cadmium is more likely to be the cause of death than respiratory impairment or damage to the nervous system (Cearley and Coleman, 1974), but the precise toxicology of the metal to various species of fish, and the cause of the wide variation in species sensitivity, have yet to be clarified. Further information is given in Section 10.5.

10.4.2 FACTORS AFFECTING LETHAL LEVELS

Ball (1967) found that the relationship between the logarithm of the median period of survival of rainbow trout and the logarithm of the cadmium concentration was described by a sloping straight line over the range 1–64 mg Cd/ℓ, and by a horizontal line over the range 0.01–1.0 mg Cd/ℓ. Later investigation showed that the linear relation in the latter range had a slight slope, survival time being highest at low concentrations (Department of the Environment, 1972); the slope varies with environmental factors such as water hardness, dissolved-oxygen concentration (Calamari and Marchetti, 1977b) and temperature (M. Grande, personal communication) and with different species of fish; with goldfish (*Carassius carassius*) for example, the slope is such that the 2-, 4- and 10-day LC50 values are quite similar to each other (A. H. Houston and C. McCarty, personal communication). The flatness of the toxicity curve for rainbow trout, also found in another test (Ministry of Technology, 1969), may contribute to poor replication of test results. However, additional problems of defining the amount of readily available toxic material in test aquaria are caused by the low solubility of cadmium in moderately hard waters of high pH value (see p. 230, para. 4). The median asymptotic value (or median threshold concentration) for cadmium is difficult to estimate for some species because it may not be evident until after several months of exposure have elapsed. Concentrations lethal in a few days may be up to 100-fold higher than those causing mortality in long-term experiments.

Temperature

There are few data available on the effects of temperature on the toxicity of cadmium; with Atlantic salmon (*Salmo salar*) M. Grande (personal communication) found that the 5-day LC50 at 4 °C and 10 °C in a soft water was about 1000 μg Cd/ℓ and 50 μg Cd/ℓ respectively although the corresponding 1-day LC50 values were virtually identical. Greater toxicity at high temperature has also been found by Eisler (1971) (p. 231, para. 2).

Dissolved oxygen

D. Calamari and R. Marchetti (personal communication) used rainbow trout acclimated for one week to dissolved oxygen at 40 per cent of the air saturation value and found a decrease in survival time in comparison with fish held at the same cadmium concentration at 100 per cent air saturation, and a slight reduction of about one third for the LC50 values at 4-40 days.

On the other hand, Voyer (1975) found that the 1- and 4-day LC50 of cadmium to mummichog were not significantly different at levels of dissolved oxygen between 4 mg/ℓ and the air saturation value, to which the fish were acclimated for less than 2 h.

pH value

There is no information published on the effect of pH on the toxicity of cadmium but Pickering and Gast (1972) report a personal communication of R. W. Andrew who found that cadmium had the highest acute toxicity at high pH value despite the fact that in hard water with alkaline pH values cadmium is precipitated from solution (Pickering and Gast, 1972; Eaton, 1974) (see p. 223, para. 4). On the other hand, preliminary studies (V. M. Brown and D. G. Shurben, personal communication) have shown that a concentration of 4 mg Cd/ℓ is not lethal to rainbow trout within ten days at pH 8.4 but is lethal within a few days at pH 7.2 in water having a hardness of about 280 mg/ℓ as $CaCO_3$.

Hardness

Brown (1968) produced a curve showing a positive relation between the logarithm of the 2-day LC50 of cadmium to rainbow trout and the logarithm of the water hardness. Calamari and Marchetti (1977a) confirmed the relationship with alevins acclimated to the test water hardness, the 2-day LC50 being about 0.12, 0.44 and 3.8 mg Cd/ℓ at a water hardness of 20, 80 and 320 mg/ℓ as $CaCO_3$ respectively. This is in reasonable accord with the 75 per cent mortality of rainbow trout in four days at 11 μg/ℓ observed by Bilinski and Jonas (1973) at a hardness of 4 mg/ℓ as $CaCO_3$.

Recent investigations have shown that the long-term toxicity of cadmium to rainbow trout increases with decrease in hardness of the water; at a total hardness of 14 mg/ℓ (as $CaCO_3$) the 42-day LC50 was 6 μg Cd/ℓ, compared with 15 μg Cd/ℓ at a total hardness of 250 mg/ℓ as $CaCO_3$ (Department of the Environment, 1976). A marked effect of hardness on the toxicity of cadmium to gold-fish has also been demonstrated by L. McCarty and A. H. Houston (personal communication) using a static test procedure; the 10-day LC50 values were 1.78 and 40.2 mg Cd/ℓ in waters having a hardness (expressed as $CaCO_3$) of about 21 and at least 100 mg/ℓ respectively.

Salinity

Mummichog, acclimated to different salinities, were more susceptible to cadmium at 5 per cent than at 15, 25 or 35 per cent seawater (Eisler, 1971), the 8-day LC50 being about 15 mg Cd/ℓ at 5 per cent and about 30 mg Cd/ℓ at 35 per cent at 20 °C. At a lower temperature (5 °C) the lethal values were about 30 and 50 mg Cd/ℓ respectively for the two extreme salinities. Apparently, fish held at 15 per cent were generally more resistant than those acclimated at higher and lower salinities, a phenomenon also observed for other poisons which Herbert and Wakeford (1964) suggested occurs when the blood of fish is approximately isotonic with the surrounding medium.

Suspended solids

It has been determined that cadmium is as toxic in hard water (240 mg/ℓ as $CaCO_3$) at pH 8.0 without organic solids as it is in the presence of 25 mg/ℓ humus solids (containing low levels of metals and surfactant) obtained from a percolating filter treating sewage (Department of the Environment, 1972).

Intermittent exposure to potentially lethal concentrations

Rainbow trout exposed to the 2-day LC50 of cadmium for only one day exhibited similar mortalities (50 per cent) after nine days as fish continuously exposed to this concentration (Ministry of Technology, 1969), showing that irreversible lethal effects had occurred within the one-day exposure period. D. Calamari and R. Marchetti (personal communication) found that about 50 per cent of each batch of rainbow trout were killed by the 6-day LC50 of cadmium, whether the fish were exposed to the poison for an uninterrupted 6-day or for three successive 2-day periods separated by intervals of half, one, two, three or four days in clean water.

Acclimation to cadmium

The range of aqueous concentrations of cadmium, represented by the highest concentration at which the standing crop of fish (proportion of fish surviving multiplied by their weight) was not significantly different from the controls, and the lowest concentration at which it was significantly different, has been calculated by Eaton, McKim and Holcombe (1978) for two groups of brown trout acclimated to cadmium for different periods. Lower figures (1.1–3.7 μg Cd/ℓ compared with 3.8–11.7 μg Cd/ℓ) were obtained for brown trout whose exposure started only at the late eyed stage, and therefore involved only two days exposure as embryos compared with 50 days for the other group exposed as fertilized eggs. Similar results were found with coho salmon (*Onchorhynchus kisutch*). This suggests that acclimation to cadmium occurred during the embryonic stage. Spehar (1976) has found similar increased resistance of flagfish larvae which had been first exposed to cadmium as embryos and similar evidence has been produced for rainbow trout (Beattie and Pascoe, 1978). Also some acclimation seems to be possible at the alevin stage; a seven-day exposure of alevins of rainbow trout to 10 μg Cd/ℓ in water having a hardness of 104 mg/ℓ as $CaCO_3$ and a temperature of 8.5 °C, resulted in a mortality of 20 per cent, but the median period of survival of the healthy survivors in a concentration of 100 μg Cd/ℓ was about seven days compared with about two days for controls not acclimated to cadmium (D. Pascoe and J. H. Beattie, personal communication).

Fish behaviour

Larsson, Bengtsson and Svanberg (1976) exposed flounder to 10 mg Cd/ℓ and observed activity among the fish after nine to ten days and the death of a single individual (out of a batch of eight) after thirteen days. Benoit *et al.* (1976) found that males of brook trout when exposed to solutions containing cadmium, were more excitable and suffered greater mortality than did the females during spawning. Hyperactivity has also been reported for bluegill (Cearley and Coleman, 1974; Eaton, 1974), for largemouth bass (Cearley and Coleman, 1974) and for flagfish (Spehar, 1976) though there were no differences in this respect between the sexes. Ellgaard, Tusa and Malizia (1978) have also described an increase in the locomotor activity of bluegill at concentrations of cadmium of 0.1 and 0.25 mg Cd/ℓ, which were not lethal to the fish within two weeks; at 0.5 mg Cd/ℓ there was reduced activity and 30 per cent mortality. Benoit *et al.* (1976) also quote R. A. Drummond who isolated 28 yearling brook trout from each other and exposed them to 40 μg Cd/ℓ for six days and found only 14 per cent mortality, suggesting that interaction between individuals in a test container can increase the apparent toxicity of cadmium to fish.

Joint effect of cadmium and other poisons

Eisler and Gardner (1973) found increased mortality of mummichog when non-lethal concentrations of cadmium were present with lethal concentrations of copper and zinc in saline waters. On the other hand, Eaton (1973) found that the 4-day LC50 for fathead minnow (*Pimephales promelas*) in hard water was only 0.8 of that predicted for a mixture containing mainly copper and zinc with cadmium comprising only 4 per cent of the total. Tests with rainbow trout in hard water (J. F. de L. G. Solbé and V. A. Cooper, personal communication) have shown that the 2-day LC50 for zinc was about 3.8 mg/ℓ in the presence of cadmium at concentrations of up to 2 mg Cd/ℓ and that at lower concentrations of zinc down to 0.5 mg/ℓ, periods of survival were accountable by the concentration of cadmium alone. Furthermore, in another experiment in which rainbow trout yearlings were exposed for four weeks to mixtures of either 30 or 40 μg Cd/ℓ and zinc at concentrations of up to 500 μg/ℓ in a hard water (245 mg/ℓ as CaCO₃) at pH values of about 7.8, there was a tendency for mortality to be least at intermediate concentrations of zinc suggesting some antagonism between the two metals (Cooper and Solbé, 1978). Moreover, pre-exposure of the fish for five days to 109 μg Zn/ℓ, followed by intermittent exposure up to 35 μg Cd/ℓ (six two-hour periods of cadmium exposure within three days), protected all fish from the lethal effects of 33 μg Cd/ℓ in continuous exposure for 44 days. During this period there was a 50 per cent mortality of a batch of fish exposed to 35 μg Cd/ℓ, but not pretreated as above.

Disease

Pascoe and Cram (1977) kept three-spined stickleback in water having a total hardness of 110–120 mg/ℓ as CaCO₃, pH values at about 8, a temperature of 15 °C and concentrations of cadmium in the range 0.5–5.0 mg Cd/ℓ; the median period of survival was 29–33 days for non-parasitized fish and 13–29 days in fish containing the plerocercoids of *Schistocephalus solidus* at an average of almost one-third of the body weight.

10.4.3 SUMMARY OF TOXICITY DATA

The majority of the concentrations reported to be lethal to fish are in the range 10 to > 10 000 μg Cd/ℓ. The differences can be attributed mainly to duration of the experiments (p. 229, para. 5) and the shape of the concentration–response curve which causes difficulty in defining a threshold median lethal concentration even after months of exposure, water hardness (p. 230, para. 5 to p. 231, para. 5), temperature (p. 230, para. 1) dissolved oxygen (p. 230, para. 2) and fish behaviour (p. 232, para. 2). Differences attributable to pH (p. 230, para. 4), and stage in life cycle (p. 233, para. 4 to p. 234, para. 3) and disease (p. 233, para. 2) are less clearly defined.

Acutely lethal values

Salmonid alevins and fry   The 5-day LC50 of cadmium to 14-day alevins of brown trout at a hardness of 320 mg/ℓ as CaCO₃ and 10–12 °C is about 30 μg Cd/ℓ (Ministry of Technology, 1967). Alevins of rainbow trout are also quite sensitive, mortalities of 50 per cent and 33 per cent having been found during a two-day exposure to 120 and 25 μg Cd/ℓ respectively in soft water (20 mg/ℓ as CaCO₃) (Calamari and Marchetti, 1977). Similar findings are reported for swim-up fry of chinook salmon (*Oncorhynchus tshawytscha*) in soft water; the 8-day LC50 was 1.6 μg Cd/ℓ (Environmental Protection Agency, 1975), while in a 19-week test with eggs through to fry there was 27 and 18 per cent mortality at 1.9 and 1.3 μg Cd/ℓ, suggesting the possibility of some acclimation having occurred in the egg stage (see p. 231, para. 5). Alevins of both chinook salmon and steelhead trout (*Salmo gairdneri*) are markedly more resistant to cadmium than are the swim-up fry, the 8-day LC50 for both species being greater than 26 μg Cd/ℓ for alevins and about 1.4 μg Cd/ℓ for swim-up fry in water at about 12 °C and having a hardness of about 25 mg/ℓ as CaCO₃ (G. A. Chapman, personal communication).

Salmonid juveniles and adults   In very soft water (4 mg/ℓ as $CaCO_3$) there was a 75 per cent mortality of rainbow trout in four days at 11 μg Cd/ℓ (Bilinski and Jonas, 1973). In some experiments in hard water (290-320 mg/ℓ as $CaCO_3$) the 4-day LC50 was 2-3 mg Cd/ℓ (Ball, 1967; Calamari and Marchetti, 1977a) and in others (240 mg/ℓ as $CaCO_3$) as low as 50 μg Cd/ℓ for fry and adults (Ministry of Technology, 1969) or 30 μg Cd/ℓ (Department of the Environment, 1972). The reasons for these differences are not clear but they might be attributable to differences in pH value and in the equilibrium between Cd^{2+} and other forms of cadmium in the test solutions.

The resistance (8-day LC50) of parr and smolt of both chinook salmon and steelhead trout to cadmium (0.9-2.3 μg Cd/ℓ) is similar to that of swim-up fry (1.4 μg Cd/ℓ) at about 12 °C in water having a hardness of about 25 mg/ℓ as $CaCO_3$ (G. A. Chapman, personal communication) but appears to be lower than that of adult male steelhead which had a 17-day LC50 of 4.8 μg Cd/ℓ at a temperature of about 10 °C in water having a hardness of about 44 mg/ℓ as $CaCO_3$ (G. A. Chapman and D. G. Stevens, personal communication).

Grande (1972) has carried out short-term tests with Atlantic salmon under-yearlings (40-50mm in length) and found a 6-day LC50 of 45 μg/ℓ in a soft water (hardness 9.6 mg/ℓ as $CaCO_3$) and at a temperature of 9 °C. This suggests that salmon may be slightly more resistant than rainbow trout to acutely lethal concentrations. However, at 4 °C the 25-day LC50 for salmon was about 5 μg Cd/ℓ with no indication of a threshold concentration for survival at this time (M. Grande, personal communication). No significant difference in short-term survival between under-yearling brown trout and rainbow trout was found over the range 10-1000 μg Cd/ℓ in hard water (250 mg/ℓ as $CaCO_3$) at pH 7.5 and a temperature of 11 °C, the 10-day median lethal concentration being about 100 μg Cd/ℓ for both species (D. G. Shurben, personal communication).

Non-salmonid fish   The 4-day LC50 was reported as 240 μg Cd/ℓ for the common carp (*Cyprinus carpio*) in water having a hardness of 55 mg/ℓ as $CaCO_3$ (Rehwoldt *et al.*, 1972) and as 6.5 mg Cd/ℓ for the three-spined stickleback in water of hardness 110-120 mg/ℓ as $CaCO_3$ (Pascoe and Cram, 1977).

Long-term lethal values

Salmonid fish   The range of concentrations of cadmium, represented by the highest concentration at which the standing crop of fish (proportion of fish surviving multiplied by their weight) was not significantly different from that of the controls, and the lowest concentration at which it was significantly different, has been calculated by Eaton, McKim and Holcombe (1978) for several salmonid species exposed to cadmium in a soft water (45 mg/ℓ as $CaCO_3$) at pH 7.2-7.8 and at temperatures of about 10 °C during their embryonic stage and for at least 60 days during their subsequent larval stage; the ranges were 4.4-12.3 μg Cd/ℓ for lake trout (*Salvelinus namaycush*), 3.8-11.7 for brown trout and 1.1-3.8 for brook trout.

M. Grande (personal communication) has recently exposed eyed eggs of Atlantic salmon to cadmium in the range 1-88 μg Cd/ℓ in a soft water (hardness 12.6 mg/ℓ as $CaCO_3$) at a temperature of 4 °C rising to 6 and 8 °C after 78 and

97 days respectively; the duration of the experiment was 134 days and the pH value was about 6.3. The hatch was virtually complete except at 88 μg Cd/ℓ, where it was 78 per cent, but was delayed slightly (up to 2 days) compared with that of the control (0.3 μg Cd/ℓ); there was a complete mortality of fry at 5 μg Cd/ℓ and higher, and a small (10 per cent) mortality at 1 μg Cd/ℓ, compared with 2 per cent mortality in the control.

The 50-day LC50 for rainbow trout was found to be 10 μg/ℓ in water having a hardness of 240 mg/ℓ as $CaCO_3$ at a pH of about 8.0 (Department of the Environment, 1972). On the other hand, Calamari and Marchetti (1977b), using a somewhat harder water (320 mg/ℓ as $CaCO_3$), obtained a threshold of 100 μg/ℓ for yearlings of the same species in a 40-day experiment, and observed almost complete survival of adults (200 g in weight) during a 120-day period of exposure to 50 μg/ℓ under the same environmental conditions. The reasons for this difference in results with rainbow trout are not clear.

Non-salmonid fish   The range of concentrations of cadmium, represented by the highest concentration at which the standing crop of fish (proportion of fish surviving multiplied by their weight) was not significantly different from that of the controls, and the lowest concentration at which it was significantly different has been calculated by Eaton, McKim and Holcombe (1978) for pike exposed to cadmium in soft water (45 mg/ℓ as $CaCO_3$) at pH 7.2-7.8 at a temperature of about 16 °C for seven days as embryos and subsequently for 28 days as larvae; the range was 4.2-12.9 μg Cd/ℓ which is similar to that for brown trout (p. 234 para. 5).

No other data are reported on young stages and few are available for the adults of European species of coarse fish. The 60-day LC50 for stone loach (*Nemacheilus barbatulus*) in a hard water (240 mg/ℓ as $CaCO_3$) at about 12°C was approximately 2 mg Cd/ℓ (Solbé and Flook, 1975); the 7-day LC50 for stone loach was also about 2 mg Cd/ℓ, which is much higher than the corresponding value of about 0.01 mg Cd/ℓ found for rainbow trout by Ball (1967) under comparable conditions.

Bream (*Abramis brama*) all survived for six weeks at 5 mg Cd/ℓ or for 10 weeks at 0.5 mg Cd/ℓ, though pathological changes occurred in the latter test, necrosis of the liver being particularly evident (Department of the Environment, 1971). The 50-day LC50 for perch in hard water (250 mg/ℓ as $CaCO_3$) was about 0.5 mg Cd/ℓ, and for roach $>$ 9 mg Cd/ℓ (Department of the Environment, 1973); although all the roach survived 50 days at 0.5 mg Cd/ℓ, every fish showed degeneration of muscle fibres.

Bengtsson *et al.* (1975) kept minnow for 70 days in a water having an alkalinity of 40 mg/ℓ as $CaCO_3$, and a salinity of 6.7 per cent, at pH 7.8-8.0 in the presence of cadmium. The 70-day LC50 was 0.4 mg Cd/ℓ (95 per cent confidence limits of 0.15 and 1.16 mg Cd/ℓ) and there was about 30 per cent mortality at 34 μg Cd/ℓ and about 20 per cent at 7.5 μg Cd/ℓ and in the controls (up to 1 μg Cd/ℓ). A small proportion ($<$ 5 per cent) of those surviving at about 7.5 μg Cd/ℓ showed signs of spinal deformity compared with none in the controls and about 15 per cent in those surviving 34 μg Cd/ℓ. D. Pascoe (personal communication) found 50 per cent mortality among stickleback exposed to concentrations of cadmium in the range 3.2-10 μg Cd/ℓ and a median period of survival of 33 days at 1 μg Cd/ℓ in a water having a hardness of 110-120 mg/ℓ as $CaCO_3$.

10.5 Sublethal effects on fish

Some sublethal effects have already been mentioned in Section 10.4.7 in relation to the mode of action of cadmium.

Kumada *et al.* (1972) found no significant mortality, and no effect on growth of rainbow trout exposed to a concentration of 5 μg Cd/ℓ over a period of 30 weeks; the hardness of the water was not stated but from the low 10-day LC50 values it might have been very low. Long-term constant-flow tests have been carried out on under-yearling rainbow trout over a period of 65 weeks in hard water (250 mg/ℓ as $CaCO_3$) at nominal concentrations of cadmium of 0, 2, 5 and 8 μg Cd/ℓ (V. M. Brown, D. G. Shurben and W. F. Miller, personal communication). All the fish survived and their growth was apparently not affected by the cadmium, but the development of ova, the hatchability of artificially-stripped eggs and the survival of the larvae were all adversely affected at levels down to 2 μg Cd/ℓ. Spermatogenesis was adversely affected in only a single male kept at 8 μg Cd/ℓ. The fish at this concentration were exposed for a further 15 weeks without any mortality or development of ova. The observed concentration-related suppression of female maturity was confirmed by histological examination; ovaries from fish exposed to 8 μg Cd/ℓ contained only immature oocytes at an early stage of development. All control fish were easily stripped of eggs, but only three out of four fish at 2 μg Cd/ℓ, two out of four at 5 μg Cd/ℓ and none at 8 μg Cd/ℓ could be treated in this way. The mortality of eggs was 75 per cent in the controls at seven weeks and 100 per cent at 2 μg Cd/ℓ after five weeks and at 5 μg Cd/ℓ after one week. The hatch of control eggs and the survival of control larvae subsequently exposed to cadmium were not affected by levels up to 8 μg Cd/ℓ. The *in vitro* respiration of liver mitochondria of fish exposed to cadmium for 33 weeks (B. N. Zaba and E. J. Harris, personal communication) was not inhibited (cf. p. 227, para. 8), but concentrations of cadmium and copper were lowest in mitochondria from fish exposed to the highest concentrations of cadmium). The diffusing capacity (a measure of respiratory function) of the gills of the fish after exposure to 2, 5 and 8 μg Cd/ℓ for seven months was examined by Hughes (1976); the results indicate a reduction in diffusing capacity at all concentrations (Hughes, Perry and Brown, 1979). The concentration of cadmium in the control water was about 0.4 μg Cd/ℓ.

A preliminary constant-flow test in a hard water (240 mg/ℓ as $CaCO_3$) using batches of ten yearling brown trout ten weeks before the onset of sexual maturity at ambient temperatures of 7–19 °C showed that 20 per cent of the fish became mature at nominal concentrations of 3 μg Cd/ℓ, 9 μg Cd/ℓ, and in the controls, although at 27 μg Cd/ℓ 10 per cent had died and none matured. Fourteen months after the beginning of the experiment 80 per cent were sexually mature in the controls and in those at 3 μg Cd/ℓ and 9 μg Cd/ℓ; at 27 μg Cd/ℓ 60 per cent had died and three of the four remaining fish were sexually mature (V. M. Brown and D. G. Shurben, personal communication). These findings suggest that brown trout may be less sensitive to cadmium than rainbow trout.

Peterson (1976) found that juvenile Atlantic salmon acclimated to 15 °C in a soft water (13 mg/ℓ as $CaCO_3$) selected this temperature in a horizontal gradient tank and tended to select a slightly lower value (14 °C) in the presence of 2 μg Cd/ℓ, although this preference was not statistically different from that of the controls.

Whereas the 'maximum allowable toxicant concentration' (MATC) of cadmium for fathead minnow has been reported as 57–37 μg Cd/ℓ in hard water (Pickering and Gast, 1972), Sullivan *et al.* (1978) have reported a slight but significant decrease in the vulnerability of this species to predation by largemouth bass after exposure for two days to a concentration of 50 μg Cd/ℓ; with 21 days exposure at 25 and 50 μg Cd/ℓ there was a slight but significant increase in vulnerability, but not at 19 μg Cd/ℓ.

Weis and Weis (1976) found that initial healing and formation of the blastema of amputated fins of killifish was inhibited at a concentration of 10 μg Cd/ℓ which was not lethal to the fish in 14 days.

10.6 Field observations on fish

Downstream of a sewage effluent outfall in the R. Arrow, England, where concentrations of soluble cadmium ranged from 8 to 25 μg Cd/ℓ and averaged 19 μg Cd/ℓ, other poisons being present at 0.1 of the combined 2-day LC50 values for rainbow trout, the median period of survival of caged rainbow trout was eight days which is close to the results found in laboratory experiments (p. 234, para. 1). Some non-salmonid fish were resident upstream of the outfall, however, where the mean concentration of cadmium was only about 0.8 μg/ℓ (0.08 of the 10-day LC50 value) (Ministry of Technology, 1970).

It has been shown that brown trout were present upstream of an effluent outfall in the R. Tean, England (hardness 210 mg/ℓ as $CaCO_3$) where the median and 95 percentile concentrations of 'soluble' cadmium over a 44-month period were 2.6 and 6.4 μg Cd/ℓ respectively, but were absent downstream of the outfall where the corresponding values were 7 and 19 μg Cd/ℓ (V. A. Cooper and J. F. de L. G. Solbé, personal communication). The latter figure is lower than the 8-month LC50 for brown trout (30 μg Cd/ℓ); only small concentrations of other poisons, principally copper and zinc, were also present which, on average, were equivalent to only 0.06 and 0.04 of the respective predicted 2-day LC50 values to rainbow trout.

However, on 11 occasions between 1971 and 1974 samples of water for cadmium analyses were taken from the river and filtered both on site and in the laboratory and stabilized by the addition of acid; on average the cadmium contents of the former were 1.8 times those of the latter (V. A. Cooper and J. F. de L. G. Solbé, personal communication). Other species which were present under these conditions were bullhead (*Cottus gobio*), three-spined stickleback and minnow (Department of the Environment, 1973).

Similar observations (V. A. Cooper and J. F. de L. G. Solbé, personal communication) have been made in the head waters of the R. Churnet, England, where the median pH value was 7.2, the median hardness was 104 mg/ℓ as $CaCO_3$ and the 50 and 95 percentile values of soluble cadmium, where brown trout and bullhead were present, were 3 and 6 μg Cd/ℓ; median and 95 percentile values of copper and zinc were equivalent to 0.11 and 0.28 respectively of their combined predicted 2-day LC50 values to rainbow trout.

Recent studies in Norway (M. Grande and K. W. Jensen, personal communication) have shown that good brown trout fisheries were present in soft water streams (average hardness between 17 and 20 mg/ℓ as $CaCO_3$) where the median and 95 percentile values of soluble cadmium over the period March–August were about 0.3 and 0.6 μg Cd/ℓ respectively. Good char fisheries were also present in two lakes of similar hardness into which the streams discharged: L. Ringvatnet, where the corresponding percentile values were about 0.6 and 1.4 μg Cd/ℓ respectively and L. Hostovatnet, where they were about 0.5 and 1.2 μg Cd/ℓ respectively. Average concentrations of zinc in the water were up to 35 μg Zn/ℓ in the streams and up to 88 μg Zn/ℓ in the lakes; the corresponding values for copper were up to 43 μg Cu/ℓ for both streams and lakes.

In the R. Thames and its tributaries, good or very good populations of trout occurred where (in 1975, for example) concentrations of total (not 'soluble') cadmium averaged about 3.5 μg Cd/ℓ, the hardness was about 300 mg/ℓ as $CaCO_3$, and the concentrations of suspended solids were about 11 mg/ℓ (from data supplied by L. B. Wood, personal communication).

10.7 Aquatic invertebrates

10.7.1 LABORATORY TESTS

Brkovic-Popovic and Popovic (1977) carried out tests with *Tubifex tubifex* at 20 °C and found 2-day LC50 values of about 2.8, 31, 45 and 720 μg Cd/ℓ in water having a total hardness of 0.1, 34.2 (without phosphate buffer), 34.2 (with phosphate buffer) and 261 mg/ℓ expressed as $CaCO_3$. These authors report (personal communication) similar results for *Daphnia magna*. Thus it seems that water hardness has a marked effect on the acute toxicity of cadmium to these species, just as it has on the toxicity of cadmium to fish.

Some freshwater crustaceans, such as *Daphnia magna* have been shown to be among the aquatic invertebrates most sensitive to cadmium. Cebejszek and Stasiak (1960) found that the 2-, 4- and 5-day LC50 values for this species in a hard water (275-290 mg/ℓ as $CaCO_3$) at 20-22 °C were 620, 470 and 370 μg Cd/ℓ for cadmium sulphate and slightly higher for the chloride salt. Bringmann and Kühn (1959) found a much lower 2-day LC50 of 100 μg Cd/ℓ for the juvenile stages in a somewhat softer water (hardness 215 mg/ℓ as $CaCO_3$) at 23 °C, while Biesinger and Christensen (1972) obtained a 2-day LC50 of 65 μg Cd/ℓ for unfed young in a much softer water (hardness 44-53 mg/ℓ as $CaCO_3$) at 11-19 °C. Thus the young appear to be somewhat more sensitive than the adults.

However, immobilization of this organism has been observed after 64 h at 2.6 μg Cd/ℓ in water having a hardness of 100 mg/ℓ as $CaCO_3$ and a temperature of 25 °C (Anderson, 1948). Also Biesinger and Christensen (1972) found that the 21-day LC50 was only 5 μg Cd/ℓ. Furthermore, they showed that there was a 7 per cent lower weight at the end of this period at 1 μg Cd/ℓ than in the controls and that 50 per cent and 16 per cent impairment of reproduction was caused at 0.7 and 0.17 μg Cd/ℓ respectively. On the other hand in experiments with populations of *Daphnia galeata mendotae* lasting 22 weeks, Marshall (1978) found that at concentrations of 2 μg Cd/ℓ and higher, the average number of individuals, average biomass and number of populations having stable long-term average numbers of individuals were significantly reduced below those of controls, and that the average brood size, the ratio of ovigerous females to total females and the ratio of eggs to females increased above those of the controls;

the EC50 for reduction in relative mean numbers was 7.7 µg Cd/ℓ. The response of the population was less sensitive than that of the most sensitive individual attribute, namely, pre-natal mortality, which was significantly about four-fold higher at 1 µg Cd/ℓ and predicted to be about two-fold higher at 0.15 µg Cd/ℓ than in the controls.

Boutet and Chaisemartin (1973) found a 50 per cent impairment of reproduction in the crustaceans *Orconectes limosus* and *Austropotamobius pallipes* at 50 and 40 µg Cd/ℓ respectively (water hardness not stated). Another sensitive organism appears to be *Gammarus fossarum* which was killed within seven days at a concentration of 10 µg Cd/ℓ (as chloride) in a hard water (hardness 320 mg/ℓ as $CaCO_3$) and a temperature of 18-20 °C (I. Schreiber and W. K. Besch, personal communication). Significant reductions in the budding rate of *Hydra littoralis* have been found at concentrations higher than 16 µg Cd/ℓ in water having a hardness of 80 mg/ℓ as $CaCO_3$ (V. A. Cooper, personal communication).

Other invertebrates examined are either similar to *Daphnia* in their sensitivity to acutely lethal concentrations of cadmium or are more resistant. The 10-day LC50 for the chironomid (*Tanytarsus dissimilis*) was 3.4 µg Cd/ℓ while the 28-day LC50 for the snail (*Physa integra*) was 8.2 µg Cd/ℓ and for the mayfly (*Ephemerella* sp.), 1.7 µg Cd/ℓ, but no significant mortality was observed for the caddisfly (*Hydropsyche betteni*) and the stonefly (*Pteronarcys dorsata*) (Environmental Protection Agency, 1975). Schweiger (1957) found that *Carinogammarus roeseli* was not injured in seven days at 30 µg Cd/ℓ but was killed at 400 µg Cd/ℓ in a water having a hardness of 260 mg/ℓ as $CaCO_3$, and that the corresponding values for *Tubifex tubifex* were 0.3 mg/ℓ and 5 mg/ℓ respectively. Thorp and Lake (1974) tested Australian freshwater crustacea in a soft water (hardness, 10 mg/ℓ as $CaCO_3$) at 15 °C and found 4-day LC50 values of 10 µg Cd/ℓ for *Austrochiltonia subtenuis,* and 60 and 180 µg Cd/ℓ for the shrimp *Paratya tasmaniensis* for animals collected in the summer and spring respectively.

Wier and Walter (1976) found that immature specimens of the snail (*Physa gyrina*) were more sensitive than the adults, the 4-day LC50 being 0.4 and 1.4 mg Cd/ℓ respectively in water having a temperature of 20-22 °C, pH 6.7 and hardness of 200 mg/ℓ as $CaCO_3$. Ravera, Gommes and Muntau (1974) quote unpublished data for the snail *Biomphalaria glabrata* showing that the adults are more sensitive than the embryos, the median periods of survival at the lowest test concentration (0.1 mg Cd/ℓ) being 63 and 192 h respectively in water having a temperature of 20 °C, pH about 8 and containing about 20 mg/ℓ of carbonates. Eggs from adults kept at 10 µg Cd/ℓ died at the morula stage.

The 4-day LC50 at 18-20 °C of the larvae of the mayfly *Athalophebia australis* in a soft water (hardness 40 mg/ℓ as $CaCO_3$) was 0.84 mg Cd/ℓ (Thorp and Lake, 1974) and for *Ephemerella subvaria* in water of similar hardness (44 mg/ℓ as $CaCO_3$) it was 2 mg Cd/ℓ (Warnick and Bell, 1969). These latter authors also found that the 4-day LC50 of the larvae of the stonefly *Acroneuria lycorias* and the 11-day LC50 of the larvae of the caddisfly *Hydropsyche betteni,* tested under the same conditions, were both 32 mg Cd/ℓ (cf. p. 229, para. 3). W. K. Besch (personal communication) has found that the structure of nets by larvae of *Hydropsyche* was apparently normal at concentrations of cadmium in the water falling from about 2 to 0.02 mg Cd/ℓ every day in a hard water (320 mg/ℓ as $CaCO_3$). Median lethal concentrations of the same order of magnitude for larvae of several species of Diptera and Plecoptera, *Ephemerella grandis* and the caddis *Brachycentrus americanus* were found by Clubb, Gaufin and Lords (1975b) in a hard water (240 mg/ℓ as $CaCO_3$); the 4-day LC50 of small immature specimens of *E. grandis* was about 0.2 of that of mature adults. *Chironomus thummi* survived 50 mg Cd/ℓ for seven days but was killed at 150 mg Cd/ℓ (Schweiger, 1957).

Other species are even more resistant. The 4-day LC50 for the damselfly nymph *Ischnura heterostica* is 230 mg Cd/ℓ and for larvae of leptocerid caddisflies is as high as 2 g Cd/ℓ even when deprived of their cases (Thorp and Lake, 1974); the eruciform caddisfly larva of *Anabolia nervosa* is of similar sensitivity (Schweiger, 1957).

In one study with several species of insects (Clubb, Gaufin and Lords, 1975a) a higher mortality was found at high concentrations of dissolved oxygen (6–7.6 mg/ℓ) than at low concentrations (3–4.9 mg/ℓ), and since concentrations of cadmium in the insects also increased with increases in dissolved-oxygen concentration it was suggested that the increased toxicity was attributable to increase in metabolic rate at higher dissolved oxygen levels.

Laboratory tests (W. K. Besch, personal communication) in a soft water (hardness about 30 mg/ℓ as $CaCO_3$) showed that when the larvae of *Chironomus lepperi* were exposed to a concentration of 1 mg Cd/ℓ only 10 per cent survived to the adult stage, but that in the presence of mud they developed to this stage even when the mud contained a concentration of 22 mg Cd/kg wet weight, although development appeared more successful when the mud contained only 10 mg Cd/kg.

10.7.2 FIELD STUDIES

In the South Esk River, Tasmania, which is heavily polluted by mining wastes and contains about 40 µg Cd/ℓ together with 150 µg Zn/ℓ and 30 µg Cu/ℓ, crustacea, molluscs and larvae of Odonata and Plecoptera were eliminated and mayflies, beetles and caddisflies were severely affected. Further downstream, where concentrations of heavy metals were between 20 per cent and 30 per cent lower, nearly all taxa were present and crustaceans and campodeiform caddisfly larvae were even more abundant than upstream of the source of pollution (Thorp and Lake, 1974).

In an outdoor channel supplied with river water containing 75 per cent sewage-works effluent in which the median and 95 percentile concentrations of cadmium over a three-month period were 6.8 and 9.3 µg Cd/ℓ respectively, the pH value about 7, the hardness 254 mg/ℓ as $CaCO_3$, and the mortality of rainbow trout was 32 per cent, commonly occurring invertebrates were, in descending order of numerical dominance, *Asellus aquaticus, Limnaea pereger, Anatopynia notata, Pentaneura lentiginosa, Tubifex tubifex, Microspectra astrofasciatus* and *Simulium ornatum* (D. Balloch and H. A. Hawkes, personal communication). H. W. Holm (personal communication) has shown that within a few months, artificial streams in Georgia, U.S.A., containing 5 µg Cd/ℓ, had lower numbers of copepods, ostracods and cladocerans and much higher numbers of the protozoan *Paramecium bursaria* than in the controls.

These results from the field and simulated stream ecosystems show differences in sensitivity between different species of aquatic invertebrates and fish similar to those observed under laboratory conditions and suggest that where

fish faunas are adversely affected by cadmium the direct effects on fish themselves are likely to be more important than indirect effects caused by a reduction in the numbers of fish-food organisms.

10.8 Aquatic algae and macrophytes and other organisms

Cadmium interferes with photosynthesis of terrestrial plants, partly by reducing
the total concentration of chlorophyll pigments and altering their ratios (Bazzaz
and Govindjee, 1974), thereby reducing growth rates and crop yields (Haghiri,
1973; Turner, 1973). Few data are available, however, for aquatic plants particularly under field conditions.

A concentration of 300 μg Cd/ℓ in water of low hardness (15 mg/ℓ as $CaCO_3$)
was lethal to a culture of the green alga *Selenastrum capricornutum*, and 50 μg
Cd/ℓ inhibited growth (Bartlett, Rabe and Funk, 1974). However, subsequent
experiments with mixtures of heavy metals suggested that cadmium inhibited
the toxicity of copper to this species. Bumbu and Mokryak (1973) found that
the addition of $CdCl_2$ to cultures of *Scenedesmus quadricauda* at concentrations of 50 to 500 μg Cd/ℓ severely reduced growth rates. Klass, Rose and
Massaro (1974) found significant reductions in growth of this species at 6.1 μg
Cd/ℓ and severe inhibition at 61 μg Cd/ℓ in a hard water (about 270 mg/ℓ as
$CaCO_3$).

In laboratory experiments with water milfoil (*Myriophyllum spicatum*)
Stanley (1974) found 50 per cent reduction of root weight at 7.4 mg Cd/ℓ
and of shoot weight at 14.6 mg Cd/ℓ, of root length at 20.8 mg Cd/ℓ and of
shoot length at 809 mg Cd/ℓ, but gave no indication of the threshold concentrations for growth inhibition. Hutchinson and Czyrska (1972) found that at 10
μg Cd/ℓ and 50 μg Cd/ℓ the inhibition of growth of *Lemna valvidiana* was about
25 per cent and 80 per cent respectively and that of *Salvinia natans,* 50 per cent
and 90 per cent respectively; however, cadmium was more toxic to *L. valvidiana*
when grown with *S. natans* than without it, and the latter was able to grow more
rapidly and cadmium accumulation was less in the presence of *L. valvidiana* than
in its absence. Hutchinson and Czyrska (1978) also showed that the adverse
effect of 10 and 30 μg Cd/ℓ on the growth of these species could be enhanced in
the presence of either 50 or 80 μg Zn/ℓ even though these concentrations of zinc
alone were stimulatory.

Little evidence for antagonism or synergism between lead and cadmium, at
nominal initial concentrations of 100 μg/ℓ, was found in terms of the reduction
in primary production of natural communities of phytoplankton tested under
laboratory conditions, compared with control populations (Pietilainen, 1975).
However, Say (1977) demonstrated synergism between cadmium and zinc in
their combined effect on growth inhibition of *Homidium rivalare*, a threshold
response being obtained, for example, in mixtures containing 0.5 plus 0.2 of the
respective threshold concentrations of cadmium and zinc, and also at 0.1 plus 0.5
of the respective thresholds; the latter concentrations were 34 μg Cd/ℓ and 2.5 mg
Zn/ℓ respectively.

Taub (1976) has studied laboratory microcosms comprising the alga *Chlamydomonas reinhardtii*, the protozoan *Tetrahymena vorax,* a rotifer mixture predominantly *Philodina*, the ostracod *Cypridopsis vidua* and the bacterium *Serratia
marcescens* kept under static conditions for five weeks at an initial concentration

of 6.5 μg Cd/ℓ; the main observation was of a small (30 per cent), slightly significant, reduction in ostracod population. Information on the water hardness is not available and concentrations of cadmium were not measured during the course of the experiment. Although such a microcosm might demonstrate interaction between different trophic levels it lacks an effective predator.

Concentrations of 5 and 10 μg Cd/ℓ maintained over a 28-day period between April and November in artificial streams containing a soft well water (hardness about 29 mg/ℓ as $CaCO_3$; pH about 6.5) significantly reduced the colonization of tree-leaf material by fungi and bacteria and reduced leaf decomposition, compared with a control stream containing 0.02 μg Cd/ℓ (J. P. Giesy, personal communication); reductions in periphyton biomass and chlorophyll, and in productivity, were also observed.

10.9 Summary and conclusions

Cadmium occurs naturally in the environment at geochemically low levels, usually with other metals, principally zinc, and is also present with metals and other chemicals in industrial waste discharges and receiving waters (p. 223, para. 1 and p. 237, para. 4). This makes it difficult to distinguish the effects of cadmium *per se* in the aquatic environment.

Concentrations of cadmium in fresh waters uncontaminated by known sources of the metal are usually between 0.01 and 0.5 μg Cd/ℓ (p. 224, para. 3). These concentrations are difficult to measure (p. 223, para. 2 and p. 224, para. 2) as are the higher levels which adversely affect sensitive aquatic organisms; it is also difficult to measure concentrations of dissolved forms of cadmium which are believed to be mainly responsible for the toxicity. Concentrations of cadmium in natural waters vary, and the 95 percentile value over a period of a year or so has been found to be between 2.0 and 2.7 times the 50 percentile value (p. 237, para. 4 to p. 238, para. 1). Cadmium can form a wide variety of complexes with humic material, inorganic ions, and organic chelating agents but under aerobic aqueous conditions uncomplexed ionic cadmium occurs predominantly, especially in unpolluted soft water of relatively low pH value (p. 223, para. 3). Cadmium carbonate normally precipitates at pH values greater than about 8.5 but cadmium compounds may also be adsorbed, especially by humic material (p. 223, para. 4). For these reasons, and also because data on factors affecting toxicity (Section 9.4.2) are often lacking, much of the literature is difficult to interpret.

Cadmium has been found to accumulate in the tissues of aquatic organisms exposed to known aqueous concentrations but little is known of its toxicological significance (p. 224, para. 5 to p. 226, para. 2 and p. 227, para. 5 to p. 229, para. 4). It appears, however, that damage to ion-regulating mechanisms is more likely to be a cause of death than respiratory impairment or damage to the nervous system (p. 229, para. 3-4).

The concentration of cadmium in the muscle of fish exposed for long periods to low concentrations of cadmium in the water under either laboratory (p. 224, para. 5, to p. 225, para. 4) or field conditions (p. 226, para. 3 to 8) is usually < 1000 and < 100 times higher (on a dry weight and wet weight basis respectively) than that in the water i.e. < 1 mg Cd/kg muscle (dry weight) or < 0.1 mg Cd/kg muscle (wet weight) in fish from water containing 1 μg Cd/ℓ. There is no clear correlation between concentrations of cadmium in the muscle and those in the water to which the fish were exposed.

The relationship between the logarithm of median period of survival of fish and the logarithm of concentration of cadmium is unusual in that the slope of the line is shallow. Moreover the position of the line varies considerably between experiments (p. 229, para. 5), possibly because the test solutions have not come to the same chemical equilibrium, different amounts of ionic cadmium being present according to the retention time in the apparatus at the particular pH, temperature and hardness of the water used. It is also possible that the sensitivity of fish to cadmium toxicity may vary with different experimental conditions.

The acute toxicity of cadmium to fish is increased by increase in temperature (p. 230, para. 1 and p. 231, para. 2) and by reduction in dissolved oxygen (p. 230, para. 2), in water hardness (p. 230, para. 5 and 6) and in pH (p. 230, para. 4). With hardness the effect is much more marked over a period of 2–6 days than it is at 40–50 days at which time there may be a clear indication of asymptotic concentrations. There are no data on the effect of salinity on the toxicity of cadmium to European freshwater fish but toxicity might be least at salinities approximately isotonic with the blood of the fish (p. 231, para. 2). Toxicity is not apparently affected by the presence of suspended humus solids at a concentration of 25 mg/ℓ (p. 231, para. 3). Acclimation to cadmium may occur in the egg stage (p. 231, para. 5). Lethal effects may be increased by factors which increase activity such as spawning and testing of fish in batches rather than singly (p. 232, para. 2).

Irreversible lethal effects may occur at high concentrations of cadmium; in rainbow trout they occur within 24 h on exposure to the 2-day LC50 and within two days on exposure to the 6-day LC50 (p. 231, para. 4). There is some evidence that the presence of low concentrations of cadmium, which are not lethal on their own, reduce the time of survival of fish at lethal concentrations of copper and zinc (p. 232, para. 3). On the other hand, the lethal effect of low concentrations of cadmium seem to be reduced by the presence of sublethal concentrations of zinc.

Species differ in their sensitivity to cadmium. Of the species of fish found in Europe and tested to date, the most sensitive appears to be the rainbow trout, long-term experiments on which have shown that adverse effects on reproduction occur at concentrations of cadmium as low as about 2 μg Cd/ℓ (p. 236, para. 2). The 'no effect' concentration has not been measured but probably lies between 0.5 and 2 μg Cd/ℓ.

Adult brown trout appear to be similar to rainbow trout in their resistance to the acute lethal effects of cadmium (p. 234, para. 3); however, the threshold concentration for median survival is about 10 μg Cd/ℓ and 30 μg Cd/ℓ for the rainbow and brown trout respectively in hard water (p. 236, para. 2 and 3). Moreover, sexual maturity in brown trout has been observed to occur at concentrations as high as 27 μg Cd/ℓ under laboratory conditions (p. 236, para. 3).

There are few data on non-salmonid fish and none relate to experiments carried out at more than one hardness for a given species. However, common carp appear to be comparable to rainbow trout (p. 234, para. 4), whereas goldfish are much less sensitive to acutely lethal concentrations (p. 231, para. 1), while the long-term (40–70 day) lethal values for minnow (p. 235, para. 6), stone loach (p. 235, para. 4) and perch, bream and roach (p. 235, para. 5) are much higher than those of trout. With minnow, however, the lowest concentration at which significant mortality and spinal deformity occurred was 7.5 μg Cd/ℓ

(p. 235, para. 6) in a soft water (40 mg/ℓ as $CaCO_3$). Embryos and larvae of pike and brown trout are comparable in their sensitivity to cadmium (p. 235, para. 3).

Field data on the effects of cadmium on fish are scarce. Brown trout have been observed in the R. Tean in which the median and 95 percentile concentrations of cadmium were 2.6 and 6.4 µg Cd/ℓ respectively and also in the R. Churnet where the corresponding concentrations were 3 and 6 µg Cd/ℓ (p. 237, para. 4, 5 and 6). This is consistent with laboratory findings on the ability of this species to survive and become sexually mature at concentrations below 27 µg Cd/ℓ (p. 236, para. 3).

Non-salmonid fish (bullhead, stickleback and minnow) occurred in the R. Tean where the brown trout were absent and the 50 and 95 percentile concentrations of total 'soluble' cadmium were 7 and 19 µg Cd/ℓ; for the minnow this is consistent with the laboratory data (p. 235, para. 6) bearing in mind the higher water hardness in the R. Tean (210 mg/ℓ as $CaCO_3$).

There are almost no data available on the effects of sublethal concentrations of cadmium on the behaviour of fish. Hyperactivity has been observed in several species and is associated, especially in males, with increased mortality at spawning time (p. 232, para. 2). Behavioural changes induced by sublethal exposure to cadmium have been shown to increase the vulnerability of fathead minnow to predation by largemouth bass (p. 237, para. 1).

Aquatic invertebrates are generally more resistant than fish to cadmium poisoning (p. 238, para. 3 to p. 240, para. 4), although *Daphnia* and *Gammarus* appear to be particularly sensitive (p. 238, para. 3 to p. 239, para. 2). Aquatic plants do not appear to be particularly sensitive to cadmium (Section 10.8) although the absence of data on water hardness generally prevents a comparison to be made with other organisms. Thus it is likely that the direct effects of cadmium on fish would be more important than those caused indirectly through reduction in numbers of fish food organisms.

There is need for the development of sensitive methods for measuring soluble cadmium, particularly in its ionic forms at the low levels (µg/ℓ) at which it appears to exert its toxic effects on the most sensitive organisms. Relevant environmental variables should also be measured when carrying out laboratory toxicity tests and field studies, the latter being particularly important in developing water quality criteria.

10.10 Tentative water quality criteria

The data on the toxicity of cadmium to aquatic organisms are extensive but not conclusive. Fish, particularly rainbow trout, have received most attention and the threshold concentrations for median survival at different hardnesses of water and the threshold concentrations for reproductive success in a hard water have been established under laboratory conditions. However, different workers obtain different results under apparently similar conditions. Effects of other environmental variables, especially pH value and temperature, are not yet thoroughly worked out. Moreover, the measurement of cadmium, particularly in the dissolved states at concentrations which adversely affect aquatic organisms, has generally been unsatisfactory.

Salmon are similar to rainbow trout in their response to acutely lethal concentrations of cadmium in soft water while brown trout appear to be more resistant to adverse effects on reproduction in a hard water. Pike and brown trout appear to be similar in their sensitivity to cadmium at the embryonic and larval stages. Non-salmonid fish are more resistant than salmonid fish to long-term lethal effects in hard water and minnows are more resistant than salmonids to adverse effects on growth in soft water.

Field data on all species are few and relate mainly to brown trout.

Thus, any water quality criteria that are developed for cadmium must remain very tentative until further observations are available.

Concentrations of cadmium in freshwater fluctuate both seasonally and within shorter time intervals and, in the absence of precise information on the way in which fish populations are likely to be adversely affected by particular levels at certain times of the year, an arbitrary method has to be used to take such effects into account in water quality criteria for fish.

Table 10.1 APPROXIMATE MAXIMUM ANNUAL 50 AND 95 PERCENTILE CONCENTRATIONS OF SOLUBLE CADMIUM (μg Cd/ℓ) FOR RAINBOW TROUT AND PERCH*

Water hardness (mg/ℓ as CaCO$_3$)	Rainbow trout 50 percentile	Rainbow trout 95 percentile	Perch 50 percentile	Perch 95 percentile
10	0.3	0.6	10	20
50	0.4	0.9	15	30
100	0.5	1.0	19	38
300	0.75	1.5	25	50

*Adjustment should be made for the presence of other harmful substances, low concentration of dissolved oxygen, and for other species (p. 245, para. 6 and 7).

It is proposed that water quality should be expressed as annual 50 and 95 percentile concentrations of 'soluble' cadmium (i.e. that passing through a filter having a porosity of 0.45 μm) and that the maximum levels not inimical to fisheries should be taken as 0.05 and 0.1 respectively of the median threshold concentration for survival, taking into account the effect of hardness of the water. *Table 10.1* shows the values appropriate to rainbow trout and perch.

Values for common carp should be taken to be the same as those for rainbow trout pending further data on long-term effects. The corresponding values for brown trout and pike appear to be about twice as high as those for rainbow trout, while those for the more insensitive non-salmonid fish such as perch and minnow could be tentatively taken to be about 38 times higher.

The values in *Table 10.1* should be decreased to allow for low concentration of dissolved oxygen and for the presence of other poisons. The values may also have to be increased to allow for a reduction in toxicity caused by the presence of sublethal concentrations of zinc.

10.11 References

AMERICAN PUBLIC HEALTH ASSOCIATION, AMERICAN WATER WORKS ASSOCIATION AND WATER POLLUTION CONTROL FEDERATION (1971). *Standard methods for the examination of water and wastewater,* 13th edn, pp. 77, 213 and 214. New York, American Public Health Association

ANDERSON, B. G. (1948). The apparent thresholds of toxicity to *Daphnia magna* for chlorides of various metals when added to Lake Erie water. *Trans. Am. Fish. Soc.* **78**, 96-113

BALL, I. R. (1967). The toxicity of cadmium to rainbow trout (*Salmo gairdneri* Rich.). *Wat. Res.* **1**, 805-806

BARTLETT, L., RABE, F. W. and FUNK, W. H. (1974). Effects of copper, zinc and cadmium on *Selenastrum capricornutum*. *Wat. Res.* **8**, 179-185

BAZZAZ, M. B. and GOVINDJEE, A. (1974). Effects of cadmium nitrate on spectral characteristics and light reactions of chloroplasts. *Envir. Lett.* **6**, 1-12

BENGTSSON, B.-E., CARLIN, C. H., LARSSON, A. and SVANBERG, O. (1975). Vertebra damage in minnows, *Phoxinus phoxinus* L., exposed to cadmium. *Ambio* **4(4)**, 166-168

BEATTIE, J. H. and PASCOE, D. (1978). Cadmium uptake by rainbow trout (*Salmo gairdneri* Richardson), eggs and alevins. *J. Fish. Biol.* **13**, 631-639

BENOIT, D. A., LEONARD, E. N., CHRISTENSEN, G. M. and FIANDT, J. T. (1976). Toxic effects of cadmium on three generations of brook trout (*Salvelinus fontinalis*). *Trans. Am. Fish. Soc.* **105(4)**, 550-560

BIESINGER, K. E. and CHRISTENSEN, G. M. (1972). Effects of various metals on survival, growth, reproduction, and metabolism of *Daphnia magna*. *J. Fish. Res. Bd Can.* **29(12)**, 1691-1700

BILINSKI, E. and JONAS, R. E. E. (1973). Effects of cadmium and copper on the oxidation of lactate by rainbow trout (*Salmo gairdneri*) gills. *J. Fish. Res. Bd Can.* **30(10)**, 1553-1558

BOUTET, C. and CHAISEMARTIN, C. (1973). Propriétés toxiques spécifiques des sels métalliques chez *Austropotamobius pallipes pallipes* et *Orconectes limonus*. *C. R. Séances Soc. Biol.* **167**, 1933-1938

BOWEN, H. J. M. (1966). *Trace elements in biochemistry*, pp. 164, 179 and 209. New York, Academic Press

BRINGMANN, G. and KÜHN, R. (1959). Vergleichende wasser-toxikologische Untersuchungen an Bakterien, Algen und Kleinkrebsen. *Gesundheitsingenieur* **80**, 115-120

BROWN, V. M. (1968). The calculation of the acute toxicity of mixtures of poisons to rainbow trout. *Wat. Res.* **2**, 723-733

BRKOVIC-POPOVIC, I. and POPOVIC, M. (1977). Effects of heavy metals on survival and respiration rate of tubificid worms. 1. The effects of survival. *Envir. Pollut.* **13(1)**, 65-72

BUMBU, Y. V. and MOKRYAK, A. S. (1973). O vliyanii nekotorykh mikroelementov na razvitie vodoroslej *Scenedesmus quadricauda* (Trup.) Breb. (Effect of some trace elements on the development of the alga *Scenedesmus quadricauda*. *Izv. Akad. Nauk. Mold. S.S.R. (Biol. Khim. Nauk)* **1**, 82-83 (abstract only seen)

CALAMARI, D. and MARCHETTI, R. (1977a). Influence of water hardness on cadmi toxicity to *Salmo gairdneri* Rich. Paper presented to the International Workshop on Structure and Function of Fish Gills. Messina, 26-29 September 1977 (mimeo)

CALAMARI, D. and MARCHETTI, R. (1977b). Accumulo di Cadmio in *Salmo gairdneri* Rich. *N. Ann. Ig.* **28**, 425-436

CEARLEY, J. E. and COLEMAN, R. L. (1974). Cadmium toxicity and bioconcentration in largemouth bass and bluegill. *Bull. envir. Contam. Toxicol.* **11**, 146-151

CEBEJSZEK, I. and STASIAK, M. (1960). Studies on the effect of metals on water biocenosis using the *Daphnia magna* index, Part 2. *Rocz. Panstw. Zakl. Hyg.* **11**, 533-540 (in Polish)

CHRISTENSEN, G. M. (1971). Effects of metal cations and other chemicals upon the *in vitro* activity of two enzymes in the blood plasma of the white sucker, *Catostomus commersoni* (Lacepède). *Chem. Bio. Interactions* **4**, 351-361

CHRISTENSEN, G. M. (1975). Biochemical effects of methylmercuric chloride, cadmium chloride and lead nitrate on embryos and alevins of the brook trout (*Salvelinus fontinalis*). *Toxic. appl. Pharmac.* **32**, 191-197

CLUBB, R. W., GAUFIN, A. R. and LORDS, J. L. (1975a). Synergism between dissolved oxygen and cadmium toxicity in five species of aquatic insects. *Envir. Res.* **9**, 285-289

CLUBB, R. W., GAUFIN, A. R. and LORDS, J. L. (1975b). Acute cadmium toxicity studies upon nine species of aquatic insects. *Envir. Res.* **9**, 332-341

COOPER, V. A. and SOLBÉ, J. F. de L. G. (1978). Reducing the toxicity of cadmium sulphate to rainbow trout (*Salmo gairdneri*) by preliminary exposure of fish to zinc sulphate, with and without intermittent exposure to cadmium. A progress report. *Int. Lab. Rep. Wat. Res. Cent.* **750**, Jan. 1978

DEPARTMENT OF THE ENVIRONMENT, U.K. (1971). *Water Pollution Research 1970*, p.59. London, H.M.S.O.

DEPARTMENT OF THE ENVIRONMENT, U.K. (1972). *Water Pollution Research 1971*, p. 37. London, H.M.S.O.

DEPARTMENT OF THE ENVIRONMENT, U.K. (1973). *Water Pollution Research 1972*, p. 37. London, H.M.S.O.

DEPARTMENT OF THE ENVIRONMENT, U.K. (1976). *Water Pollution Research 1973*, p. 36. London, H.M.S.O.

EATON, J. G. (1973). Chronic toxicity of a copper, cadmium and zinc mixture to the fathead minnow (*Pimephales promelas* Rafinesque). *Wat. Res.* **7**, 1723-1736

EATON, J. G. (1974). Chronic cadmium toxicity to the bluegill (*Lepomis macrochirus* Rafinesque). *Trans. Am. Fish. Soc.* **103**(4), 729-735

EATON, J. G., McKIM, J. M. and HOLCOMBE, G. W. (1978). Metal toxicity to embryos and larvae of seven freshwater fish species. 1. Cadmium. *Bull. envir. Contam. Toxicol.* **19**(1), 95-103

EISLER, R. J. (1971). Cadmium poisoning in *Fundulus heteroclitus* (Pisces: Cyprinodontidae) and other marine organisms. *J. Fish. Res. Bd Can.* **28**(9), 1225-1234

EISLER, R. and GARDNER, G. R. (1973). Acute toxicology to an estuarine teleost of mixtures of cadmium, copper and zinc salts. *J. Fish. Biol.* **5**, 131-142

ELDER, J. F. (1975). Complexation side reactions involving trace metals in natural water systems. *Limnol. Oceanogr.* **20**(1), 96-102

ELLGAARD, E. G., TUSA, J. E. and MALIZIA, A. A. (1978). Locomotor activity of the bluegill (*Lepomis macrochirus* Rafinesque); hyperactivity induced by sublethal concentrations of cadmium, chromium and zinc. *J. Fish. Biol.* **1**, 19-23

ENK, M. D. and MATHIS, B. J. (1977). Distribution of cadmium and lead in a stream ecosystem. *Hydrobiologia* **52**(2/3), 153-158

ENVIRONMENTAL PROTECTION AGENCY (1975). National Water Quality

Laboratory Quarterly Research Report, March 31, 1975, Duluth, Minn., National Water Quality Laboratory

FARRAH, H. and PICKERING, W. F. (1977). Influence of clay-solute interactions on aqueous heavy metal ion levels. *Wat. Air Soil Pollut.* **8(2)**, 189-197

GARDINER, J. (1974a). The chemistry of cadmium in natural water. 1. A study of cadmium complex formation using the cadmium specific-ion electrode. *Wat. Res.* **8(1)**, 23-30

GARDINER, J.(1974b). The chemistry of cadmium in natural water. 2. The adsorption of cadmium on river muds and naturally occurring solids. *Wat. Res.* **8(3)**, 157-164

GARDINER, J. and STIFF, M. J. (1975). The determination of cadmium, lead, copper and zinc in ground water, estuarine water, sewage and sewage effluent by anodic stripping voltammetry. *Wat. Res.* **9(5/6)**, 517-523

GARDNER, G. R. and YEVICH, P. P. (1970). Histological and hematological responses of an estuarine teleost to cadmium. *J. Fish. Res. Bd Can.* **27(12)**, 2185-2196

GRANDE, M. (1972). Tungmetallenes invirkning på ferskvanns fisket. *Forskningsnytt* **17**, 31-34

HAGHIRI, F. (1973). Cadmium uptake by plants. *J. Envir. Qual.* **2**, 93-96

HENRIKSEN, A., BALMER, K. and WRIGHT, R. (1976). Heavy metals in Norwegian waters. Oslo, Norwegian Institute for Water Research. Report B2-20 (Norwegian; English summary)

HEM, J. D. (1972). Chemistry and occurrence of cadmium and zinc in surface water and groundwater. *Wat. Resour. Res.* **8(3)**, 661-679

HERBERT, D. W. M. and WAKEFORD, A. C. (1964). The susceptibility of salmonid fish to poisons under estuarine conditions. 1. Zinc sulphate. *Int. J. Air Wat. Pollut.* **8**, 251-256

HILTIBRAN, R. C. (1971). Effect of cadmium, zinc, manganese, and calcium on oxygen and phosphate metabolism of bluegill liver mitochondria. *J. Wat. Pollut. Control Fed.* **43(5)**, 818-823

HUGHES, G. M. (1976). Polluted fish respiratory physiology. *Semin. Ser. Soc. exp. Biol.* **2**, 163-183

HUGHES, G. M., PERRY, S. F. and BROWN, V. M. (1979). A morphometric study of effects of nickel, chromium and cadmium on the secondary lamellae of rainbow trout gills. *Wat. Res.* **13(7)**, 665-679

HUTCHINSON, T. C. and CZYRSKA, H. (1972). Cadmium and zinc toxicity and synergism to floating aquatic plants. Water Pollution Research in Canada 1972. In *Proceedings of the 7th Canadian Symposium on Water Pollution Research*, pp. 59-65

HUTCHINSON, T. C. and CZYRSKA, H. (1978). Cadmium and zinc toxicity and synergism to floating aquatic plants. In *Water Pollution Research in Canada, Volume 7*, University of Toronto, Institute of Environmental Science Engineering

JAAKKOLA, T., TAKAHASH, H., SOININEN, R., RISSANEN, K. and MIETTINEN, J. K. (1972). Cadmium content of sea water, bottom sediment and fish and its elimination rate in fish. *IAEA Panel Proc. Ser.* (PL-469/7 Sta-Pub./332), 69-75

JACKIM, E., HAMLIN, J. M. and SONIS, S. (1970). Effects of metal poisoning on five liver enzymes in the killifish (*Fundulus heteroclitus*). *J. Fish. Res. Bd Can.* **27(2)**, 383-390

KATZ, B. M. (1977). Mechanism of entry of metals in the fish gill. In *Proceedings of the 49th Annual Conference, International Water Pollution Control Federation*, Minneapolis, Minn. 3-8 Oct. 1976

KLASS, E., ROSE, D. W. and MASSARO, E. J. (1974). The effect of cadmium on population growth of the green alga (*Scenedesmus quadricauda*). Buffalo, N.Y., Department of Biochemistry, State University of New York at Buffalo

KUMADA, H., KIMURA, S., YOKATA, M. and MATIDA, Y. (1972). Acute and chronic toxicity, uptake and retention of cadmium in freshwater organisms. *Bull. Freshwat. Fish. Res. Lab. Tokyo* **22**, 157-165

KUWATA, K., HISATOMI, K. and HASEGAWA, T. (1971). Rapid determination of trace amounts of cadmium and copper in river and sea water by atomic absorption spectroscopy. *At. Absorpt. Newsl.* **10**, 111-115

LARSSON, A., BENGTSSON, B.-E. and SVANBERG, O. (1976). Some haematological and biochemical effects of cadmium. *Semin. Ser. Soc. exp. Biol.* **2**, 35-46

LOVETT, R. J., GUTENMANN, W. G., PAKKALA, I. S., YOUNGS, W. D., LISK, D. J. and BURDICK, G. E. (1972). A survey of the total cadmium content of 406 fish from 49 New York State fresh waters. *J. Fish. Res. Bd Can.* **29(9)**, 1283-1290

LUCAS, H. F., EDGINGTON, D. N. and COLBY, P. J. (1970). Concentrations of trace elements in Great Lake fishes. *J. Fish. Res. Bd Can.* **27**, 677-684

MARAFANTE, E. (1976). Binding of mercury and zinc to cadmium-binding protein in liver and kidney of goldfish (*Carassius auratus* L.). *Experientia* **32**, 149-150

MARSHALL, J. S. (1978). Population dynamics of *Daphnia galeata mendotae* as modified by chronic cadmium stress. *J. Fish. Res. Bd Can.* **35(4)**, 461-469

MATHIS, B. J. and KEVERN, N. R. (1975). Distribution of mercury, cadmium, lead and thallium in a eutrophic lake. *Hydrobiologia* **46(2/3)**, 207-222

MERLINI, M. (1978). Hepatic storage alteration of vitamin B_{12} by cadmium in a freshwater fish. *Bull. envir. Contam. Toxicol.* **19**, 767-771

MINISTRY OF TECHNOLOGY, U.K. (1967). In *Water Pollution Research 1966*, p. 52. London, H.M.S.O.

MINISTRY OF TECHNOLOGY, U.K. (1969). In *Water Pollution Research 1968*, p. 62. London, H.M.S.O.

MINISTRY OF TECHNOLOGY, U.K. (1970). In *Water Pollution Research 1969*, p. 62. London, H.M.S.O.

MOUNT, D. I. and STEPHAN, C. E. (1967). A method for detecting cadmium poisoning in fish. *J. Wildl. Mgmt* **31**, 168-172

NAKAMURA, M. (1974). Experimental studies on the accumulation of cadmium in the fish body (T.). *Jap. J. publ. Hlth* **21(16)**, 321-327

NEUFELD, R. D., GUTIERNEZ, J. and NOVAK, R. A. (1977). A kinetic model and equilibrium relationship for heavy metal accumulation. *J. Wat. Pollut. Control Fed.* **49(3)**, 489-498

OLIVER, B. G. and COSGROVE, E. G. (1974). The efficiency of heavy metal removal by a conventional activated sludge treatment plant. *Wat. Res.* **8(11)**, 869-874

O'SHEA, T. (1972). Anodic stripping voltammetric study of the competitive interactions between trace metals and the alkaline earths for complexing ligands in aquatic environments. Ph.D. Thesis, University of Michigan. University Microfilms, No. 73-6891

PASCOE, D. and CRAM, P. (1977). The effect of parasitism on the toxicity of cadmium to the three-spined stickleback *Gasterosteus aculeatus* L. *J. Fish. Biol.* **10**, 467–472

PETERSON, R. H. (1976). Temperature selection of juvenile Atlantic salmon (*Salmo salar*) as influenced by various toxic substances. *J. Fish. Res. Bd Can.* **33(8)**, 1722–1730

PIETILAINEN, K. (1975). Synergistic and antagonistic effects of lead and cadmium on aquatic primary production. In *Programme and abstracts of papers presented at the International Conference on Heavy Metals in the Environment,* Toronto, Canada, October 27–31, pp. 861–874

PROSI, F. (1976). Die Schwermetallbelastung der Elzenz und ihre Auswirkung und limnipche Organismen. Ph.D. Thesis, University of Heidelberg

PICKERING, Q. H. and GAST, M. H. (1972). Acute and chronic toxicity of cadmium to the fathead minnow (*Pimephales promelas*). *J. Fish. Res. Bd Can.* **29(30)**, 1099–1106

RATTONEJTI, A. (1974). Determination of soluble cadmium, lead, silver and indium in rain water and stream water with use of flameless atomic absorption. *Anal. Chem.* **46(6)**, 739–742

RAVERA, O., GOMMES, R. and MUNTAU, H. (1974). Cadmium distribution in aquatic environment and its effects on aquatic organisms. In *Problems of the contamination of man and his environment by mercury and cadmium,* pp. 317–331. Commission of the European Communities, European Colloquium, Luxembourg, 3–5 July 1973. Luxembourg, E.E.C.

REHWOLDT, R. and KARIMIAN-TEHERANI, D. (1976). Uptake and effect of cadmium on zebra fish. *Bull. envir. Contam. Toxicol.* **5(4)**, 442–446

REHWOLDT, R., MENAPACE, L. W., NERRIE, B. and ALESSANDRELLO, D. (1972). The effect of increased temperature upon the acute toxicity of some heavy metal ions. *Bull. envir. Contam. Toxicol.* **8**, 91–96

ROBERTS, K. S., CRYER, A., KAY, J., SOLBÉ, J. F. de L. G., WHARFE, J. R. and SIMPSON, W. R. (1979). The effects of exposure to sublethal concentrations of cadmium on enzyme activities and accumulation of the metal in tissues and organs of rainbow and brown trout (*Salmo gairdneri* Richardson and *Salmo trutta fario* L.). *Comp. Biochem. Physiol.* **62(C)**, 135–140

SANGALANG, G. B. and O'HALLORAN, M. J. (1972). Cadmium-induced testicular injury and alterations of androgen synthesis in brook trout. *Nature, Lond.* **240**, 470–471

SAY, P. J. (1977). Microbial ecology of high zinc level streams. Ph.D. Thesis, University of Durham

SCHRECK, C. B. and LORZ, H. W. (1978). Stress response of coho salmon (*Oncorhynchus kisutch*) elicited by cadmium and copper and potential use of cortisol as an indicator of stress. *J. Fish. Res. Bd Can.* **35(8)**, 1124–1129

SCHWEIGER, G. (1957). Die toxikologische Einwirkung von Schwermetallsalzen auf Fische und Fischnährtiere. *Arch. Fischereiwiss.* **8**, 54–78

SOLBÉ, J. F. de L. G. and FLOOK, V. A. (1975). Studies on the toxicity of zinc sulphate and of cadmium sulphate to stone loach *Noemacheilus barbatulus* (L.) in hard water. *J. Fish. Biol.* **7(5)**, 631–637

SPEHAR, R. L. (1976). Cadmium and zinc toxicity to flagfish *Jordanella floridae*. *J. Fish. Res. Bd Can.* **33(9)**, 1939–1945

STANLEY, R. A. (1974). Toxicity of heavy metals and salts to Eurasian water-milfoil (*Myriophyllum spicatum* L.). *Arch. envir. Contam. Toxicol.* **2**, 331–341

SULLIVAN, J. F., ATCHISON, G. J., KOLAR, D. J. and McINTOSH, A. W. (1978). Changes in the predator-prey behaviour of fathead minnows (*Pimephales promelas*) and largemouth bass (*Micropterus salmoides*) caused by cadmium. *J. Fish. Res. Bd Can.* **35(4)**, 446-451

TAUB, F. B. (1976). Demonstration of pollution effects in aquatic microcosms. *Int. J. Envir. Stud.* **10(1)**, 23-33

THORP, V. J. and LAKE, P. S. (1974). Toxicity bio-assays of cadmium on selected freshwater invertebrates and the interaction of cadmium and zinc on the freshwater shrimp (*Paratya tasmanensis* Ric.) *Aust. J. Mar. Freshwat. Res.* **25**, 97-104

TURNER, M. A. (1973). Effect of cadmium treatment on cadmium and zinc uptake by selected vegetable species. *J. envir. Qual.* **2**, 118-119

UTHE, J. F. and BLIGH, E. G. (1971). Preliminary survey of heavy metal contamination of Canadian freshwater fish. *J. Fish. Res. Bd Can.* **28(5)**, 786-788

VOYER, R. A. (1975). Effect of dissolved oxygen concentration on the acute toxicity of cadmium to the mummichog *Fundulus heteroclitus* (L.) at various salinities. *Trans. Am. Fish. Soc.* **104**, 129-134

WARNICK, S. L. and BELL, H. L. (1969). The acute toxicity of some heavy metals to different species of aquatic insects. *J. Wat. Pollut. Control Fed.* **41**, 280-284

WATER RESEARCH CENTRE, (1975). Annual Report 1974/5, 27

WEBER, W. J. and POSSELT, H. S. (1974). Equilibrium models and precipitation reactions for cadmium (II). In *Aqueous-environmental chemistry of metals* (Ed. by A. J. Rubin), pp. 225-289. Ann Arbor, Science Publishers

WEIS, P. and WEIS, J. S. (1976). The effects of heavy metals on fin regeneration in the killifish (*Fundulus heteroclitus*). *Bull. envir. Contam. Toxicol.* **16(2)**, 197-202

WIER, G. F. and WALTER, W. M. (1976). Toxicity of cadmium in the freshwater snail (*Physa gyrina* Say). *J. envir. Qual.* **5(4)**, 359-362

WILLIAMS, L. G., JOYCE, J. and MONK, J. T. (1973). Stream-velocity effects on the heavy metal concentrations. *J. Am. Wat. Wks Assoc.* **65(4)**, 275-279

WILLIAMS, D. R. and GIESY, J. P. (1978). Relative importance of food and water sources to cadmium uptake by Gambusia affinis (Poeciliidae). *Envir. Res.* **16**, 326-332

11

MIXTURES OF TOXICANTS

Foreword

Although the Working Party on Water Quality Criteria for European Freshwater Fish, in reviewing the literature on the environmental requirements of freshwater fish and fisheries in Chapters 1–10, concentrated its attention on various water quality characteristics considered separately, the importance of the joint effect of chemicals was recognized and relevant data reviewed in each case.

However, the present chapter now separately reviews the principles which have been proposed for the joint effect of toxicants and the evidence put forward in support of them. The relationships between toxicity to fish and naturally occurring water quality characteristics, such as pH, temperature, dissolved oxygen and water hardness, have been covered in the previous chapters on individual toxicants and are not considered further in this one.

The preparation of the original report on which this chapter is based was accomplished from drafts produced by Dr Calamari (Section 11.2), Dr Alabaster (Sections 11.3 and 11.6), Mr Lloyd (Section 11.4) and Dr Dethlefsen (Section 11.5), all of which were commented upon and discussed by the Working Party. Dr W. K. Besch, Dr S. J. Broderius, Dr G. W. Stratton, and Dr P. T. S. Wong also kindly provided unpublished or otherwise inaccessible data. Since the report was published, several relevant papers have come to hand and are reviewed in this chapter. These include Leach and Thakore (1977), Könemann (1979), Verma et al. (1981), Tsai and McKee (1980), Thompson et al. (1980) and Christensen and Zielski (1980). Further supplementary information, which supports the conclusions reached in this chapter, is given in the reviews of Alabaster (1981) and Alabaster et al. (1981).

11.1 Summary

This summary is an attempt to generalize from fragmentary information, and the conclusions reached should not be used as a basis for action without reference to the main report.

For water pollution control purposes, the concentration-addition model for describing the joint effects of mixtures of toxicants on aquatic organisms is appropriate; in this model the contribution of each component in the mixture is expressed as a proportion of the aqueous concentration producing a given response in a given time (e.g. p 96-h LC50).

Examination of available data using this model shows that for mixtures of toxicants found in sewage and industrial effluents, the joint acutely lethal toxicity to fish and other aquatic organisms is close to that predicted assuming simple addition of the proportional contribution from each toxicant. The observed median value for the joint effect of these toxicants on fish is 0.95 of that predicted; the corresponding collective value for sewage effluents, river waters and a few industrial wastes, based on the toxicity of their constituents, is 0.85, while that for pesticides is 1.3. The less than additive effect of commonly occurring toxicants in some mixtures may be partly attributable to small fractions of their respective LC50 values having little or no additional effect.

The few (unpublished) data available for the long-term lethal joint effect on fish of toxicants in mixtures, suggest that they may be markedly more than additive, a phenomenon that needs confirmation and further investigation.

On the other hand, in the few studies on the growth of fish, the joint effect of toxicants has been consistently less than additive which suggests that as concentrations of toxicants are reduced towards the levels of no effect, their potential for addition is also reduced. There appear to be no marked and consistent differences between the response of species to mixtures of toxicants.

Field studies have shown that toxicity predictions based on chemical analysis can be made if the waters which are polluted are acutely lethal to fish, and that a fish population of some kind can exist where the median Σ pt LC50s* (rainbow trout) is < 0.2. It is not known whether this condition is equivalent to a Σ p NOEC* of < 1.0 (i.e. the sum of the individual fractions of the NOEC for the species present), or to a NOEC of < 1.0 for each individual toxicant (i.e. fractions of the NOEC are not summed).

In general, the joint effect of toxicants on lethal and sub-lethal responses of fish is not explained by variations in the uptake of the individual toxicants concerned.

There is an immediate need for more empirical studies on the joint effect of mixtures of toxicants, especially on the contribution of small fractions of the toxic units of individual components, and the relation between long- and short-term lethal and non-lethal joint effects. The data obtained should be reinforced by studies on the mechanisms of interaction of toxicants. More field studies relating water quality to the structure and productivity of fish populations are also required, involving direct measurements of fractional toxicity of the river water wherever possible.

Meanwhile, the concentration-addition model appears to be adequate to describe the joint effect of commonly occurring constituents of sewage and industrial wastes, and to be used to make the tentative predictions of the joint effect on fish populations of toxicants present at concentrations higher than the EIFAC recommended values. Because concentrations lower than the EIFAC recommended values do not appear to contribute to the toxicity of mixtures of toxicants, there is no need to adjust these values downward in such situations. For toxicants not already considered by EIFAC, it might be sufficient to assume that concentrations less than 0.1 of the threshold lethal concentrations would make no substantial contribution to joint action.

*Defined on page 305

11.2 Introduction

Much of the information available on the toxicity of substances to fish and other aquatic organisms relates to materials tested singly under laboratory conditions, or considered separately in field studies. However, it is uncommon to find a river or lake which is polluted by a single toxicant and usually several harmful substances are present together in significant quantities in a polluted water. In preparing tentative water quality criteria for specific pollutants, the Working Party, in its reports, has emphasized that the presence of other pollutants in the water may modify the corresponding water quality standards set for the protection of fisheries, and in reviewing the literature gave attention to data on mixtures with other toxicants; the main purpose of the present review is to collate the information available to us on the effect of such mixtures on fish in order to determine the extent to which water quality standards should be modified for those waters receiving inputs of more than one toxicant.

11.2.1 FUNDAMENTAL CONCEPTS AND APPROACHES ADOPTED

When a potentially toxic substance is present in water, several processes may be involved before an aquatic organism shows a response. In the aquatic phase, the substance may interact with other constituents in the water; for example, pH will affect the dissociation of acids and alkalis, and humic acids will form complexes with some heavy metals, particularly copper. These reactions will not be considered explicitly in this review because they have been given attention in previous chapters. However, where such processes are inadequately understood or even unknown, and more than one potentially toxic substance is present, they may have an overriding effect on the subsequent response of the organism and lead to erroneous conclusions about the type of joint action of the substances present. It is essential, therefore, that the biological availability of the toxicant concentrations in a mixture is known before firm conclusions are reached on their combined action.

Secondly, within the organism, physiological processes, including absorption (mainly through the gills, gut and skin), transport and distribution by the circulatory system, metabolic transformation, accumulation at various sites, and excretion, may all influence the amount of toxicant and its metabolites present in the body fluids, tissues and organs, and thus the quantity available at the site or sites of action. These processes may also be affected by other water quality characteristics of the ambient environment of the organism that are not necessarily harmful in themselves.

Thirdly, where an organism is exposed to two or more potentially toxic substances, interaction between different physiological processes within the organism may occur, including (after Sjöquist and Alexanderson, 1972) those affecting the chemicals' absorption, binding to plasma proteins, distribution, transport and release from tissues, action on receptor sites, metabolism and elimination, all of which may contribute to the response of the whole organism, such as death, growth, avoidance behaviour and accumulation of chemicals in tissues and organs.

Attention to interactions at receptor sites within tissues has centred on the assumption that occupation of these sites by chemicals is regulated by the law of mass action and depends on the concentrations there. This concept has been elaborated by considering several possibilities including the effect of two biologically active substances, of a compound active if applied singly and another inactive alone but modifying the response to the first, and of two inactive compounds acting only in combination. Further elaboration arises from considering such concepts as common receptors and common sites of effects, different sites of action and a common target system, and different receptors and common sites of effects. These approaches have been developed mainly in the fields of pharmacology and pesticide research and as yet there has been little attempt to apply such fundamental concepts to the action of mixtures of common pollutants on fish and other aquatic life. This aspect is discussed briefly by Calamari and Alabaster (1980).

Nevertheless, the problem of mixtures of poison was recognized by a few early workers who carried out appropriate tests with fish and found it possible to account for the harmful effect of a mixture of chemically similar poisons in water by a summation of their individual toxic fractions (Southgate, 1932; Bucksteeg *et al.*, 1955; Cherkinsky, 1957; Friedland and Rubleva, 1958); on the other hand, some experiments indicated that more than additive effects (or 'synergism') occurred, as with mixtures of some heavy metals (Bandt, 1946; Doudoroff, 1952). This latter finding has been commonly quoted to support the setting of water quality standards for pollutants considerably more stringent than those indicated as reasonable on the basis of tests and observations made on the effects of single substances. In the last 25 years, however, a considerable amount of more detailed and longer-term work has been carried out on mixtures of toxicants on fish and to a lesser extent on other aquatic organisms. These often involved rigorous statistical test designs and treatment of data in order to develop theoretical and empirical models; such approaches were necessarily pragmatic and did not invoke a fundamental consideration of the problem at the biochemical level as outlined above. This material is critically reviewed here to examine the extent to which the effect of mixtures of toxicants on fish and other aquatic organisms can be described, modelled and predicted, and to identify areas where future research should be concentrated.

11.2.2 MODELS AND TERMINOLOGY

In dealing with the joint effects on organisms of two or more toxicants, it is necessary in the context of water pollution control to determine the extent to which the measured response is the result of additive action and also the range and limits of concentrations and proportions of the toxicants in a mixture which produce the measured effect. Various authors, including Bliss (1939), Hewlett and Plackett (1959, 1979), Plackett and Hewlett (1948), Ashford and Smith (1964, 1965), Finney (1971), Ashford and Cobby (1974), Anderson and Weber (1976) and Morse (1978), have suggested methods of modelling and data analysis to describe the types of combined effect that occur. However, the terminology is confused despite recent revisions and reviews (Ariens, 1972; Fedeli *et al.*, 1972); in this report definitions given in EIFAC (1975) will generally be used, with the exception of 'synergism' (Warren, 1971), together with a few additional terms*.

A stochastic model for a single drug was developed by Puri and Senturia

*Defined on page 305

(1972) but there were mathematical difficulties with a corresponding model for more than one drug. The other models that are considered in this report are all deterministic.

Concentration addition (Anderson and Weber, 1975a) or similar joint action (Bliss, 1939) model

In theory, the simplest explanation of an additive joint effect of toxicants in a mixture is that the mode of action of each toxicant is qualitatively identical, even though a common effect is produced by a different concentration of each.

Bliss (1939) denoted this mode of physiological interaction as a similar joint action; his method for examining this in studies of whole organisms using quantal response regressions has been applied to the results of several mixtures and their constituents, for example, Anderson and Weber (1975a). They applied the term 'concentration addition' to denote this empirical model.

If the effective concentration of each toxicant is taken as unity, then the effective concentration of a mixture will be obtained when the sum of each toxicant concentration, expressed as the fractions of the effective concentration of each toxicant, equals unity. This model of additive joint action has been used to evaluate the joint effect of mixtures using, for example, the sum of the proportions of the median threshold lethal concentration (newly designated, in this report, Σ pt LC50)* and 48-h LC50 (Lloyd, 1961; Brown, 1968) (designated here as Σ p 48-h LC50); Sprague and Ramsay (1965) coined the term 'toxic unit' (TU) for pt LC50 of individual toxicants, while Marking (1977) has suggested a somewhat similar 'additive toxicity index'. The approach can also be used for other quantal responses, such as LC10 or EC90, and for graded responses. The relationship between the toxic unit and other terminology for a two-component mixture is shown in *Figure 11.1*, but the model is also applicable to mixtures of more than two components.

The joint action for a two-component mixture (A + B) is defined in *Table 11.1*.

Table 11.1   THE JOINT ACTION FOR A 2-COMPONENT MIXTURE (A + B)

Toxic units of A + B to produce given effect (1.0 TU of mixture)	*Definition*
> 1.0 for A or B < 1.0 for both A and B with A + B > 1.0	Antagonism Less than additive joint action, or infra-additive interaction (Warren, 1971; Anderson and Weber, 1975a)
1.0 for A + B	Additive joint action
< 1.0 for A + B	More than additive joint action, or supra-additive synergism (Ariens and Simonis, 1964) or supra-additive interaction (Anderson and Weber, 1975a)

The scale of units corresponds to that on the ordinate in *Figure 11.1*. Such deviations from unity are not necessarily the same for all combinations of a

*Defined on p. 305

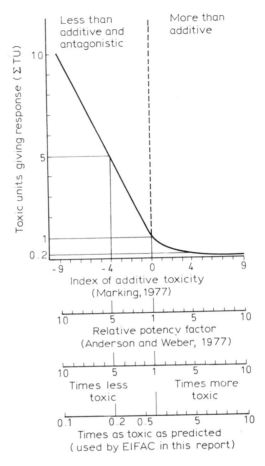

Figure 11.1 Relation between different terminology used in studies of mixtures of toxicants

particular two-component mixture of toxicants, as found, for example by Bianucci and Legnani (1973), Herbes and Beauchamp (1977) and Sprague and Logan (1979), and illustrated in *Figure 11.2* by isopleths of equal observed toxicity (Loewe, 1953 and Gaddum, 1953) for two hypothetical examples of a mixture of two toxicants. The area above and to the right of such a curve represents the conditions in which the expected mortality would be greater than 50 per cent, whereas the area below and to the left represents that in which it would be less than 50 per cent. In example 1, joint action is always less than additive, but in a mixture containing 0.5 toxic units of A and 1.5 toxic units of B (the sum of observed/predicted toxicity being 2) the particular mixture is half as toxic as expected from strictly additive joint action indicating a marked antagonism. In example 2 joint action between the toxicants is slightly more than additive at most proportions of their respective toxic units, the greatest effect (1.11 times more toxic than expected) being in a mixture of 0.4 toxic

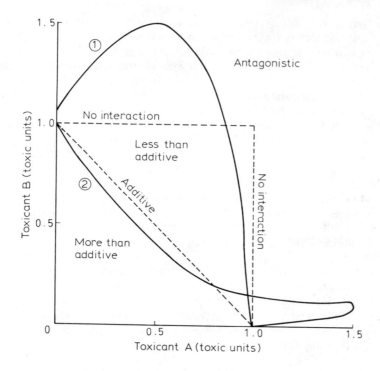

Figure 11.2 Types of joint action between two toxicants in a mixture illustrated by lines of equal observed toxicity for two hypothetical examples

units of toxicant A and 0.5 toxic units of toxicant B; however the mixture containing 1.5 toxic units of A and 0.1 units of B shows marked antagonistic joint action between toxicants.

Although toxicants may be additive in terms of a threshold median lethal concentration when present in a mixture, the shorter periods of survival at high, rapidly lethal concentrations may suggest a greater than additive effect. This has sometimes been described as 'synergism', and has been found, for example, in the case of mixtures of copper and zinc (Lloyd, 1961; Sprague and Ramsay, 1965) and copper and detergent (Calamari and Marchetti, 1970).

Response addition (Anderson and Weber, 1975a) or independent joint action (Bliss, 1939) model

In theory, another and more complicated joint effect of toxicants in a mixture is found when each constituent acts on a different physiological or biochemical system but contributes to a common response. Several authors, for example, Plackett and Hewlett (1948, 1952) and Finney (1971), have approached this problem quantitatively. The expected proportion of individuals responding to a mixture depends upon the correlation between the susceptibilities of the individual organisms to each constituent toxicant; the lowest response occurs where susceptibilities are positively correlated and the highest where they are negatively correlated, that is, acting independently. The assumption is that, since the response is log normally distributed for each component, it can be expected to be a log-normal bivariate for the joint action of the two (Plackett and Hewlett, 1948). If an organism is exposed simultaneously to two poisons A and B which act independently, it can be killed by a lethal dose of either A or B, or by a combination of both. But in order to predict the proportion of organisms expected to be killed by the mixture, it is necessary to know to what extent the tolerance of the organism to A is correlated with its tolerance to B. If there is complete negative correlation, all the organisms susceptible to A are tolerant to B and vice versa; the mixture would then be more effective than if A and B were completely or partially positively correlated. The model has been applied to the results with several mixtures, for example, by Anderson and Weber (1975a; 1976) and Broderius and Smith (1979).

Anderson and Weber (1975a) point out that parallelism between response curves for different compounds in a mixture may be a prerequisite for concentration addition, but cannot be relied upon to distinguish it from response addition.

Anderson and d'Apollonia (1978) proposed that the common response to a response-additive mixture is never greater than that predicted on the basis of the potency for threshold or above-threshold concentrations of each constituent in the mixture. Therefore, in theory, water quality criteria which set 'safe' (sub-threshold) levels for individual response-additive substances should protect organisms against their combined effects in mixtures.

Combination of concentration-addition and response-addition model
(Anderson and Weber, 1975a)

In mixtures containing more than two toxicants, the pattern of joint action between certain combinations of the respective constituents may differ. Anderson and Weber (1975a) found that the lethal effects of copper and nickel in binary mixtures were concentration additive, while those of dieldrin and pentachlorophenate in their binary mixtures were response additive. The effects of mixtures containing all four toxicants together were predicted on the assumption that copper and nickel remained concentration additive between themselves but interacted collectively as response-additive agents with the two organic constituents.

11.2.3 EXPERIMENTAL DESIGN AND DATA ANALYSIS

Difficulty in interpreting the results reported in this literature survey has often been due to lack of consistency in experimental design and lack of proper statistical analysis. Brown (1978) has discussed standard requirements for dose-effect studies in both these areas. For example, two particularly important aspects of data analysis, not always dealt with adequately by experimentalists, are the choice of appropriate transformations for dose and response and the testing of statistical significance of differences between observed and predicted results.

Various transformations have been suggested for the units of dose and response, but Finney (1964) recommends using those that appear to fit the observed data, without ignoring additional relevant information about the mechanisms of action. Brown (1978) compared the dose-response relations of three models (normal probability, logistic and sine) and while there was little difference between them over nearly three borders of magnitude of dose, extrapolations to doses three orders of magnitude lower than the median produced wide divergences. Hodson *et al.* (1977) give special attention to the need for replicate tests.

There is also a need for appropriate statistical tests for determining significant deviations from unity in a concentration-additive index. For example, one method includes in its computations the standard deviation at the median response (e.g. LC50), without consideration of the possible differences in slope of the dose-response lines of the individual constituents (Abt *et al.*, 1972). Thus, any conclusion about joint action at the median level may not apply to the full response range unless there is parallelism between the dose-response relationships.

Modifying factors

Several factors may affect the results of experiments designed to test the additivity of the effect of toxicants in a mixture. These include the type of response (i.e. whether long term or short term and whether lethal or sub-lethal), the magnitude of response, the type of and proportion between chemical constituents, and biological (e.g. life stage, size, acclimation, history, diet) and environmental (e.g. water hardness, pH) variables.

Multi-factorial studies

One approach to assessing the role of modifying factors on the toxicity of mixtures of substances is through multi-factorial studies. In theory, this approach allows for the measurement of all possible joint interactions without the necessity of examining all possible combinations. The complexities inherent in such studies have been discussed by Street *et al.* (1970). Suitable experimental designs have been described by Kempthorne (1952) and Cochran and Cox (1957) for general statistical problems, and by Finney (1964) and Das and Kulkarni (1966) for toxicity tests; these enable the size of such studies to be reduced by assuming that certain interactions between the dose and the response are negligible, although this increases the complexity of the statistical analysis. There have, however, been few attempts, (Marubini and Bonanomi, 1970; Benijts-Claus and Benijts, 1975; Gray and Ventilla, 1973) to apply purely factorial experimental design to quantitative responses. Alderdice and Forrester (1968) used a multi-factorial, response-surface approach to demonstrate the effects of concurring environmental modifying factors on the toxicity of pollutants to fish during development. However, these experiments were limited to a short exposure period.

Another approach which combines aspects of the multi-factorial approach with the quantal response approach for binary mixtures of Anderson and Weber (1975a), is that of Fedeli *et al.* (1977). They assumed that any concentration of a substance can be expressed as an equi-effective concentration of another when dealing with dose-response lines that were not parallel. Curvilinear-regression lines resulted from studying a number of mixtures and can be empirically represented by an exponential parabolic regression. The maximum attainable joint effect may be predicted at a particular ratio of the concentrations of the two components. Finally, the authors arrived at an equation for a paraboloid whose equi-effective horizontal sections are shown to correspond to a series of coaxial elipses.

In practical terms, the use of a multi-factorial model can lead to difficulties, especially where some combinations of factors may lead to long response times, and maintaining the non-variable parameters constant becomes difficult. It is sometimes simpler, and more instructive, to begin with bifactorial experiments and proceed to more complicated models when a need for such information becomes apparent.

11.2.4 CONCLUSION

The choice of the most suitable model to study the joint effects of mixtures of poisons on fish and other organisms depends on the type of information required. Response addition has been widely used in the development of pesticides where maximum lethality may be the primary aim, whereas it has been considered that for water-pollution control purposes the concentration-addition model is more relevant in the context of water quality standards. For this reason the experimental data reviewed in the subsequent sections have been derived mainly from experiments based on the concentration-addition model and, in particular, to identify deviations from an additive relationship.

11.3 Application of additive index to laboratory studies

In this part of the chapter the joint effect of toxicants in mixtures is described as being more than additive (see *Figure 11.1*) when tests carried out to measure the sum of the toxic units of individual toxicants, when tested together (Σ TU) show these to be less than unity. A factor (the reciprocal of Σ TU) is given to indicate by how much the effect is more than additive; conversely, when the sum is more than unity, a factor is given indicating by how much the effect is less than additive. Information is also provided on whether there is evidence for no physiological interaction and antagonism, as defined in Section 11.2 and shown in *Figures 11.1* and *11.2*. Where possible, the approximate ratio of the TUs of the constituent toxicants of mixtures is also given. Additionally, especially if TUs cannot be quoted or calculated, the interaction is sometimes described in terms of response addition of short-term period of survival and percentage response.

11.3.1 FISH: THE TOXICITY OF MIXTURES CONTAINING CONSTITUENTS COMMONLY PRESENT IN SEWAGE AND INDUSTRIAL WASTES

The constituents of sewage and industrial wastes are considered in the order ammonia, phenol, cyanide, copper, zinc, cadmium, nickel, chromium, mercury and other heavy metals and other substances, and mixtures are cross-referenced to appropriate pages. Data for non-European and marine species are included where information for European freshwater fish is scarce or absent and where such information appears to make a useful contribution to the present review.

Ammonia and phenols Herbert (1962) carried out tests with rainbow trout (*Salmo gairdneri*) using made-up gas liquor phenols, and ammonia, and a mixture of both at a concentration of dissolved oxygen close to the air-saturation value (ASV). Results were rather variable, perhaps because the ratio of pt LC50 of unionized ammonia to that of phenols varied during the tests from 1:1 to 1:2, but the joint effect of the two was approximately additive (between 0.7 and 1.0 times that expected from Σ pt LC50); similar results were also obtained at 33 and 66 per cent ASV.

Jenkins (1964) carried out static tests with fathead minnow (*Pimephales promelas*) using ammonium chloride and phenol separately and together in two different mixtures; from the data for 24-h LC50 values (in his Table VI), joint action was not consistent and ranged from 0.72 and 0.69 times less than additive for a ratio of p 24-h LC50 for these two toxicants of 1:0.1 and 1:0.3 at pH 8 and 8.5 respectively, to 1.19 and 1.0 times more than additive for corresponding ratios of 1:0.7 and 1:0.3 respectively.

Lloyd and Swift (1976) considered the interaction between ammonia and phenol and concluded that the rate of uptake and concentration of phenol in fish muscle was not caused by high ambient concentrations of ammonia, and that no physiological basis could be found to account for the observed additive toxic action of these two toxicants.

Ammonia and cyanide Experiments with solutions containing both ammonia and cyanide showed that the combination was more toxic than either substance alone (Wuhrmann and Woker, 1948). More recently, the acutely lethal effect on rainbow trout of un-ionized ammonia and hydrogen cyanide in mixtures, in the ratio of 1:1 of the respective p 96-h LC50 values, has been tested in a hard water (220 mg/ℓ as $CaCO_3$) at 10 °C and shown to be slightly (1.16 times) more than additive (Broderius and Smith, 1979). Similar results have been obtained using smolts of salmon (*Salmo salar*) in fresh water at ASV, and values between 0.61 and 1.25 at lower percentage ASV and higher salinity (J. S. Alabaster, D. G. Shurben and M. J. Mallett, personal communication).

Examination of Broderius and Smith's Figure 1 and data in Smith *et al.* (1979), on growth in 30 d (for both the threshold of no effect and for 50 per cent reduction, compared with controls) suggests that the effect of these toxicants in a mixture in the ratio of 1:0.7 of the respective p EC values of ammonia and cyanide is about 0.6 times less than additive.

Ammonia and copper Vamos and Tasnadi (1967) used copper sulphate to reduce the toxicity of ammonia in carp ponds, and suggested that the cupro-ammonium compounds formed are not toxic. However, Herbert and Vandyke (1964) measured the 48-h LC50 of un-ionized ammonia and copper and mixtures of the two, in the ratio 1:1 p 48-h LC50, using rainbow trout in a hard water (320 mg/ℓ as $CaCO_3$); the joint effect of the two was not significantly different from additive but, on the basis of LC25 and LC10, it was 1.2 and 1.4 times respectively more than additive. The authors pointed out that 75 per cent of the copper and 0.3 per cent of the ammonia was calculated to be present as cupram-monium ions, with $Cu(NH_3)_3^{2+}$ being predominant and suggested, therefore, that the toxicity of copper and cuprammonium ions was similar, possibly because a large proportion of the latter would dissociate to copper ions and ammonia at the gill surface.

Ammonia and zinc Herbert and Shurben (1964) measured the t LC50 of un-ionized ammonia and zinc and a mixture of the two, in the ratio of 1.0:0.5 and 1:2 of their respective pt LC50 values, using rainbow trout in a hard water (320 mg/ℓ as $CaCO_3$) at ASV and found that the joint effect of the two was 0.96 and 0.97 times less than additive; at 40 per cent ASV and with a ratio of 1:1 of the respective pt LC50 values, the effect was 0.85 times less than additive, and at ASV and the same ratio in a soft water (44 mg/ℓ as $CaCO_3$) it was 0.8 times less than additive.

Ammonia, phenol and zinc Brown, Jordan and Tiller (1969) measured the 48-h LC50 to rainbow trout of ammonia, phenol and zinc and mixtures of all three, using different ratios of the respective p 48-h LC50 values. The joint effect was additive (where the ratio of the respective p 48-h LC50 values was 1.0:1.0:0.5); 1.2 times more than additive (with a ratio of 1:7:1), 0.7 times less than additive (ratio 1:1:6, in two cases); or 0.9 times less than additive (ratio 1:0.2:0.1). The authors point out that slightly different results are obtained using 48-h LC50 values for the three toxicants from other published sources, although the joint action was still 1.4 times more than additive in the mixture in the ratio 1:7:1, and was still 0.7 times less than additive in the mixture in the ratio 1:1:6.

Ammonia, phenol and sulphide Jenkins (1964) carried out static tests with fat-head minnow using ammonium chloride, phenol and sodium sulphide separately and together in two different mixtures. From the data for 24-h LC50 values (in his Table VI), joint action between the toxicants ranged from 0.47 and 0.61 times less than additive for a ratio of p 24-h LC50 of 1:0.1:1.1 and 1:0.02:0.1 for these three toxicants at pH 8 and 8.5 respectively, to 0.6 and 0.83 times less than additive for corresponding ratios of 1:0.7:2 and 1:0.3:0.3.

Ammonia and sulphide Jenkins (1964) also carried out 24-h tests using ammonium chloride and sodium sulphide separately and together in two different mixtures; his data for LC50 values show that the joint action of the toxicants was 0.56 and 0.64 times less than additive for a ratio of p 24-h LC50 of 1:2.2 and 1:0.3 for these two toxicants at pH 8 and 8.5 respectively and 0.78 and 0.81 times more than additive for corresponding ratios of 1:11 and 1:1.4.

Ammonia and nitrate Rubin and Elmaraghy (1977) used the fry of guppy (*Poecilia reticulatus*) to test the individual and joint effect of potassium nitrate and un-ionized ammonia. The results indicate no more than 1.13 times more than additive effect except in mixtures in which the p 72-h LC50 of ammonia is below or at 0.35 when joint action was at a minimum of 0.7 times less than additive; in the latter case there appears to be no interaction between the two, that is, toxicity is entirely attributable to potassium nitrate in the mixture, with ammonia making no contribution.

Monohydric phenols Southgate (1932) measured the survival period of rainbow trout in tests lasting a few hours in the presence of p-cresol and phenol and mixtures of the two. He noticed that the behaviour of the fish was similar in the two toxicants and found that the effect of phenol and p-cresol on the short-term (11–$12\frac{1}{2}$ min) survival of rainbow trout was additive. He also carried out similar tests with p-cresol and 2,6-xylenol and mixtures of the two. In this case the behaviour of the fish in the two toxicants was different, and he found that the toxicity of p-cresol was increased in the presence of xylenol, but that the converse was not true. Calculation of the 1-h LC50 values shows that the joint action of p-cresol and 2,6-xylenol in the ratio 1:1.5 of their respective 1-h LC50 values was 1.5 times more than additive. Herbert (1962) compared the survival of rainbow trout at 9 °C in simulated spent still gas liquors from a gas works and a coke oven, made up with a variety of monohydric phenols (including 13 per cent p-cresol and 0.5 per cent 2,6-xylenol), with the survival of fish in pure phenol; in one experiment the toxicity (in terms of p 24-h LC50) was respectively about 1.3 and 1.1 times that of phenol alone, and in another it was not significantly greater.

Phenol, ammonia and zinc See Ammonia, phenol and zinc on page 264.

Phenol, ammonia and sulphide See Ammonia, phenol and sulphide on page 264.

p-cresol and cyanide Southgate (1932) also measured the short-term survival of rainbow trout in the presence of potassium cyanide and p-cresol and mixtures of the two. The toxicity of p-cresol was increased in the presence of cyanide but the converse was not true. Calculation of the 26-min LC50 values shows that the joint action of p-cresol and cyanide in the ratio of about 1:1.2 of their respective 26-min LC50 values was 1.7 times more than additive.

Phenol and copper Brown and Dalton (1970) measured the 48-h LC50 to rainbow trout of phenol and copper and mixtures of the two in a hard water (240 mg/ℓ as $CaCO_3$) in the ratio of 1:1 of their respective p 48-h LC50 values and found that their joint action was 0.85 times less than additive.

Phenol, copper and zinc Brown and Dalton (1970) measured the 48-h LC50 to rainbow trout of phenol, copper and zinc and mixtures of the three in a hard water (240 mg/ℓ as $CaCO_3$) in the ratio of 1:1:1 of the respective p 48-h LC50 values and found that their joint action was 0.9 times less than additive.

Phenol and sulphide Jenkins (1964) carried out static tests with fathead minnow using phenol and sodium sulphide separately and together in two different mixtures; from the data for 24-h LC50 values (in his Table VI) interaction between the toxicants ranged from 0.82 and 0.81 times less than additive for a ratio of p 24-h LC50 of 1:3.5 and 1:11 for these two toxicants at pH 8 and 8.5 respectively, to 0.71 and 0.85 times more than additive for corresponding ratios of 1:3 and 1:1.

Phenol and chlorine At ambient water temperature phenol reacts with chlorine to form chlorinated phenols which are more toxic than phenol; for example, the 96-h LC50 of pentachlorophenol is 0.21 mg/ℓ for goldfish (*Carassius auratus*) and fathead minnow (Adelman and Smith, 1976), and for mosquitofish (*Gambusia affinis*) the 6-d LC50 is about a third of that of phenol (Katz and Cohen, 1976).

Phenol, nickel and vanadium See nickel, vanadium and phenol on page 273.

Phenol, pentachlorophenol and dinitrophenol Verma *et al.* (1981) carried out static tests with phenol, pentachlorophenol and dinitrophenol, using the fish *Notropterus notropterus* and estimated the 96-h LC50 values. They also tested all mixtures of two and mixtures of three at several different ratios of the respective 96-h LC50 values. Examination of their data shows that on average the mixtures were 0.78 less than additive, the range being 0.34 to 1.47 (as detailed in their Table 1). In interpreting these results it should be noted that the confidence limits for individual tests differed by a factor of 1.5 on average, ranging from close to unity to 1.8.

Cyanide and ammonia See Ammonia and cyanide on page 263.

Cyanide and p-cresol See p-cresol and cyanide on page 265.

Cyanide and zinc The toxicity to fathead minnow of solutions containing sodium cyanide and zinc sulphate was related mainly to the level of molecular cyanide present (Doudoroff *et al.*, 1966).

Cairns and Scheier (1968) measured the 96-h LC50 of cyanide and zinc and a mixture of the two using bluegill (*Lepomis macrochirus*) and found that the joint action was 0.42 times less than additive. On the other hand, Broderius and Smith (1979) made similar measurements, in duplicate, with fathead minnow in a hard water (220 mg/ℓ as $CaCO_3$) at 25 °C, using mixtures in the ratio of 1:1 of the respective p 96-h LC50 values, and showed that the joint action was 1.4 times more than additive. However, examination of their Figure 1 and raw data in Smith *et al.* (1979) suggests that the effect on the growth of the fish in 30 d (threshold of no effect), of a mixture in the ratio of 1:0.6 of the respective p EC, is about 0.4 times less than additive.

Cyanide and PCB Anderson and Weber (1975a) found that in the majority of cases interaction between cyanide and PCB was response additive.

Cyanide, zinc and PCB Anderson and Weber (1975a) showed that the results of Negilski and Davies (1974) for reduction in the biomass of juvenile chinook salmon (*Oncorhynchus tshawytscha*) maintained in artificial streams and exposed to a mixture comprising 0.2 of each of the 96-h LC50 values of cyanide, zinc and PCB, when compared with the reduction found with 0.2 of the 96-h LC50 of each separately, could be accounted for by response addition. A similar conclusion can be drawn from an examination of the data on production of fish biomass (from their Table 4). However, in the stream exposed to 0.1 of the 96-h LC50 of cyanide alone production of biomass was enhanced, but if this is equated to no reduction in production, the reduction found in the stream containing all three toxicants can be shown to be about 0.6 of that expected from strict addition.

Cyanide and chromium The acutely lethal effect on fathead minnow of chromium and cyanide in mixtures in the rato of 1:1 of the respective 96-h LC50 values tested in a hard water (220 mg/ℓ as $CaCO_3$) at 25 $^\circ$C has been shown to be slightly (0.76 times) less than additive (Broderius and Smith, 1979). Their Figure 1 and raw data (Smith *et al.*, 1979) suggest that the effect on growth in 30 d (threshold of no effect) of mixtures in the ratio 1:0.8 and 1:0.1 is also slightly (0.6 to 0.8 times) less than additive.

Copper and ammonia See Ammonia and copper on page 263.

Copper and phenol See Phenol and copper on page 265.

Copper and zinc Doudoroff (1952) found that whereas fathead minnow usually survived an 8 h exposure to solutions containing either 8 mg Zn/ℓ or 0.2 mg Cu/ℓ in soft water, most succumbed within this period in a mixture of copper and zinc at one-eighth of these concentrations respectively. Lloyd (1961) obtained somewhat similar results with rainbow trout in soft water (hardness 14 mg/ℓ as $CaCO_3$), but found that at relatively low concentrations, corresponding to less than the 72-h and 7-d LC50 of copper and zinc respectively, the effect of the mixtures was simply additive in both the soft and a hard water (hardness 320 mg/ℓ as $CaCO_3$). Sprague and Ramsay (1965), who used these metals in water having a hardness of 14 mg/ℓ as $CaCO_3$, also found that the toxicity of mixtures to juvenile Atlantic salmon (*Salmo salar*) could be accounted for by the simple addition of the corresponding p 7-d LC50 of the separate metals. Recently, Thompson *et al.* (1980) reached the same conclusion using bluegill in a water having a hardness of 21 to 60 mg/ℓ as $CaCO_3$. La Roche *et al.* (1973) mentioned that histological examination of mummichog (*Fundulus heteroclitus*) exposed to mixtures of copper and zinc showed that the effects of copper on the lateral line were not aggravated by the presence of zinc.

Somewhat different results have been found for other species. Lewis (1978) measured the 96-h LC50 of copper and zinc, and a mixture of the two in a hard water (218 mg/ℓ as $CaCO_3$) using longfin dace (*Agosia chrysogaster*) and found that their joint effect was 1.2 times more than additive. Anderson *et al.* (1979a), using zebrafish (*Brachydanio rerio*) reported that, whereas the toxicity expressed as 96-h LC50 of both zinc and copper was reduced with increase in calcium and magnesium ions over a range of 20 to 300 mg/ℓ as $CaCO_3$, the toxicity of a mixture of the two remained virtually the same over this range; thus the effect of copper and zinc in the mixture was strictly additive in soft water but progressively more than additive with increase in hardness. In these experiments the pH and alkalinity were held constant, whereas these would normally increase with hardness.

Eisler and Gardner (1973) measured the percentage survival of mummichog in synthetic sea water (20 per cent salinity) in the presence of copper and zinc and mixtures of the two. Although tests were carried out under static conditions and concentrations of dissolved copper were known to have fallen considerably during the tests, the results, though not entirely consistent, suggest that the interaction between copper and zinc was several-fold more than additive.

Anderson and Weber (1975a) carried out tests using mature male guppy and found that the toxicity of a mixture of copper and zinc was 2.65 times more than additive and later (Anderson and Weber, 1976) suggested that this might be attributable to the two metals having a similar mode of toxic action, correlated perhaps with a similar affinity for sulphur-containing ligands present at high concentrations in the gill. Their tests were carried out in a water of medium hardness (126 mg/ℓ as $CaCO_3$), and they pointed out that the results of Sprague (1964) and Lloyd (1961) with these two metals in a soft water (about 20 mg/ℓ as $CaCO_3$) also showed greater than additive effects in the short term whereas in a much harder water (about 320 mg/ℓ as $CaCO_3$) (Lloyd, 1961, and Brown and Dalton, 1970) the effects were simply additive.

Copper, zinc and nickel Brown and Dalton (1970) measured the 48-h LC50 to rainbow trout of copper, zinc and nickel, and mixtures of the three, in a hard water (240 mg/ℓ as $CaCO_3$) in the ratio of 1:1:1 of their respective p 48-h LC50 values and found that the joint effect of the three was approximately additive. Marking (1977) also found that their joint action was approximately additive (unspecified LC50).

Copper and nickel Weinstein and Anderson (1978), using zebrafish, showed that copper and nickel were more than additive at both the lethal (more than two-fold) and sub-lethal levels, and also reported (Anderson *et al.*, 1979a) that this was markedly affected by the relative proportion of each in the mixture, the higher the proportion of nickel, the lower the percentage mortality. However, Muska and Weber (1977) report briefly that, in 7 d tests on the effect of copper and nickel and their mixture on the growth and food consumption of juvenile guppy at 7 °C and 25 °C, interaction between copper and nickel was slightly more than additive with a restricted ration, and approximately additive with an unrestricted ration.

Copper and cadmium Although La Roche *et al.* (1973) mentioned that histological examination of mummichog exposed to mixtures of copper and cadmium showed that the effects of copper on the lateral line were not aggravated by the presence of cadmium, Eisler and Gardner (1973) measured the percentage survival of mummichog in synthetic sea water (20 per cent salinity) in the presence of copper and cadmium and mixtures of the two, and their results suggest that interaction between the two toxicants was several-fold more than additive on both a response and concentration basis.

Hewitt and Anderson (1979), and P. D. Anderson (person communication) using zebrafish in 96 h tests, found the lethal effect of copper and cadmium in mixtures to be approximately 2-fold more than additive.

Copper, zinc and cadmium Eisler and Gardner (1973) measured the percentage survival of mummichog in synthetic sea water (20 per cent salinity) in the presence of copper, zinc and cadmium and a mixture of all three, and the results suggest that interaction between them was several-fold more than additive on a response and concentration basis, except possibly in one case where the ratio of p 96-h LC30 for the three was 1:1:0.1, where the interaction seemed to be approximately response additive.

Eaton (1973) tested the toxicity to the fathead minnow of a mixture of copper, zinc and cadmium in the ratio 1:0.1:1.2 of the 96-h LC50 of copper and the lethal threshold values of cadmium and zinc respectively, and the data show that the joint action at 96 h was 1.3 times more than additive. The author also used the same proportions of these three metals in tests lasting $12\frac{1}{2}$ months and measured several sub-lethal effects and compared them qualitatively with that for zinc he had tested separately, and those for copper and cadmium tested separately by other workers. The evidence presented (in his Figure 1) suggests that, for a reduction of 90 per cent in the number of eggs produced per female, joint action may be more than additive, but for a reduction of 50 per cent it may be less than additive, with zinc playing the predominant adverse role. In addition, reduction in the size of the fish, and inhibition of sexual development, was found at a concentration of copper in the mixture of about 0.3 of that of copper alone, suggesting a greater than additive effect, while hatchability was actually better in the mixture than in the presence of an almost identical concentration of cadmium alone, suggesting a less than additive joint action (perhaps with zinc).

Copper and mercury Work has been carried out at the Istituto di Ricerca sulle Acque (Italian Institute for Water Research) (1975) (D. Calamari and R. Marchetti, personal communication) to measure 96-h LC50 values for rainbow trout with copper and mercury, and mixtures of the two, tested at 15 °C in a water having a hardness of 320 mg/ℓ as $CaCO_3$; additive joint action was found between the two metals.

Roales and Perlmutter (1974b) measured the 96-h LC50 of copper and methyl mercury to blue gourami (*Trichogaster tricopterus*) and the percentage mortality at 96 h in mixtures of the two in tap water in which the pH was adjusted to 7.4 by the addition of sodium bicarbonate; a less than additive interaction was found where the ratio of p 96-h LC50 of copper to that of methyl mercury was between 1:0.25 and 1:1.5. These authors later showed (Roales and Perlmutter, 1977) that exposure of this species for one week to 0.1

of the 96-h LC50 of copper, or methyl mercury or a mixture of the two, produced a marked decline in immune response to antigens of infectious pancreatic necrosis virus and *Proteus vulgaris*; the response was probably too large to distinguish the type of interaction between copper and methyl mercury, although there was no evidence that it was not simply additive.

Copper and manganese Lewis (1978) measured the 96-h LC50 of copper and manganese, and a mixture of the two in a hard water (218 mg/ℓ as $CaCO_3$) using the longfin dace and found that joint action was 0.67 times less than additive.

Copper and surfactant Calamari and Marchetti (1970), measuring the 96-h LC50 to goldfish in a hard water (190 to 240 mg/ℓ as $CaCO_3$) at a temperature of 14.7 to 15.9 °C, found that the joint action of copper and sodium alkyl benzene sulphonate (ABS) was more than additive, the effect increasing with increase in the ratio of the respective p 96-h LC50 values of copper and ABS, from 1.3-fold, for a ratio of 1:0.1, to 2.1-fold for a ratio of 1:0.6. The same authors (1973) working with rainbow trout in a hard water (290 to 310 mg/ℓ as $CaCO_3$) and 15 to 15.6 °C also reported marked reductions in periods of survival compared with those predicted assuming additive interaction, with both mixtures of copper and ABS and of copper and LAS. In the latter case the joint action in terms of the Σ p 96-h LC50 was 1.25 times more than additive. However, with mixtures of copper and nonyl phenol ethoxylate joint action was slightly (probably 0.8 times) less than additive.

Tsai and McKee (1980) using goldfish found that the toxicity of mixtures of copper and LAS was additive except in the ratio 1:0.5 of the 96-h LC50 when it was twice as additive.

Copper and other substances Tsai and McKee (1980) also found that, depending upon the proportion of the toxicants present, mixtures of copper and chloramines and mixtures of copper, chloramines and LAS were between 1.3 and 1.7 more than additive.

Cairns and Scheier (1968) report an additive effect on bluegill of a mixture of acetic acid, acetaldehyde, acetone and copper in soft water.

Sun and Gorman (1973) tested the 24-h LC50 of copper sulphate and paraquat and a mixture of the two in the ratio of 1:0.25 to *Poecilia mexicana* in a soft water (hardness 32 mg/ℓ as $CaCO_3$); the joint action between copper sulphate and paraquat was 1.3 times more than additive. On the other hand, Fitzgerald (1963) found that the 24-h LC50 of copper sulphate to the bluntnose minnow (*Hyborhynchus notatus*) and several sunfish was 0.5 mg/ℓ whereas a concentration of 500 mg/ℓ in the presence of 1000 mg/ℓ of citric acid at either pH 6 or 8.5 did not kill any fish within 24 h.

Zinc and ammonia See Ammonia and zinc on page 264.

Zinc, ammonia and phenol See Ammonia, phenol and zinc on page 264.

Zinc, phenol and copper See Phenol, copper and zinc on page 265.

Zinc and cyanide See Cyanide and zinc on page 266.

Zinc, cyanide and PCB See Cyanide, zinc and PCB on page 267.

Zinc and copper See Copper and zinc on page 267.

Zinc, copper and nickel See Copper, zinc and nickel on page 268.

Zinc, copper and cadmium See Copper, zinc and cadmium on page 269.

Zinc and cadmium Tests with rainbow trout in hard water (J. F. de L. G. Solbé and V. A. Cooper, personal communication) have shown that the 48-h LC50 for zinc was about 3.8 mg/ℓ in the presence of cadmium at concentrations of up to 2 mg Cd/ℓ and that at lower concentrations of zinc (down to 0.5 mg/ℓ), periods of survival were accountable by the concentration of cadmium alone. Furthermore, in another experiment in which rainbow trout yearlings were exposed for 4 weeks to mixtures of either 30 or 40 μg Cd/ℓ with zinc at concentrations of up to 500 μg/ℓ in a hard water (245 mg/ℓ as CaCO$_3$) at pH values of about 7.8, there was a tendency for mortality to be least at intermediate concentrations of zinc, suggesting less than additive interaction between the two metals (Cooper and Solbé, 1978). Moreover, pre-exposure of the fish for 5 days to 109 μg Zn/ℓ, followed by intermittent exposure up to 35 μg Cd/ℓ (six 2-h periods of cadmium exposure within 72 h), protected all fish from the lethal effects of 35 μg Cd/ℓ in continuous exposure for 44 days. During this period there was a 50 per cent mortality of a batch of fish exposed to 35 μg Cd/ℓ, but not pretreated as above.

Spehar *et al.* (1978) exposed flagfish (*Jordanella floridae*) for 2 weeks from the day-old larval stage and for 100 days from embryos, to zinc and cadmium and mixtures of the two. Survival of larvae (not exposed as eggs) was reduced in the presence of mixtures of zinc and cadmium to an extent similar to that found in previous work they cited by R. L. Spehar with zinc alone. The authors suggested that because such fish were a sensitive indicator of toxicity it could be concluded that the chronic toxicity of mixtures of cadmium and zinc would also be largely attributable to the effect of zinc. This would agree with the findings of Eaton (1973) for the effect on the production of embryos in mixtures of zinc, copper and cadmium, which was largely attributable to the effect of zinc. With larvae of flagfish initially exposed as embryos to zinc and cadmium (Spehar *et al.*, 1978) additive interaction was not demonstrated.

Eisler and Gardner (1973) measured the percentage survival of mummichog in synthetic sea water (20 per cent salinity) in the presence of zinc and cadmium and mixtures of the two, and the results suggest that interaction was several-fold more than additive on both a response and concentration basis.

Anderson *et al.* (1979a) report that the combined toxicity of cadmium and zinc appeared to differ with the stage in the life cycle.

Gallimore and Anderson (1979) and P. D. Anderson (personal communication) found that zinc was more toxic than cadmium to eggs of zebrafish, but that the converse was true of the larval, juvenile and adult stages. However, at each stage in the life cycle, zinc and cadmium were consistently concentration additive in their joint lethal toxicity. The decreases in susceptibility of zebrafish from larvae through to adult stages exposed to zinc, cadmium and their mixtures were correlated with a decrease in weight-specific metabolic rate.

Zinc and detergent Brown, Mitrovic and Stark (1968) exposed rainbow trout to mixtures of a detergent containing 55 per cent ABS and a fixed concentration of 0.8 mg Zn/ℓ, and comparison of their results with those for zinc alone (Lloyd, 1960) shows that joint action (based upon p 72-h LC50 values in the ratio 1:3.8) was 0.9 times less than additive. They also carried out similar experiments with fish that had been acclimated for 100 days beforehand to 0.8 mg Zn/ℓ, and comparison of their results with those of Edwards and Brown (1966) for zinc alone for fish acclimated for 60 days suggests that, in this case, the joint action between zinc and detergent was 1.5 times more than additive.

Zinc and cygon Roales and Perlmutter (1974a) measured the 72-h LC50 of zinc and cygon (0,0-dimethyl-S-N-methyl) carbamylmethyl phosphorodithion-ate) to the embryos of zebrafish and the percentage mortality at 72 h in mixtures of the two in distilled water; the results indicate additive joint action with a ratio of p 72-h LC50 of zinc to that of cygon of 1:0.7 but less than additive action with a ratio of 1:4.

Cadmium and copper See Copper and cadmium on page 268.

Cadmium, copper and zinc See Copper, zinc and cadmium on page 269.

Cadmium and zinc See Zinc and cadmium on page 271.

Cadmium, chromium and nickel D. Calamari (personal communication) held large (220 g) rainbow trout in a hard water (320 mg/ℓ as CaCO$_3$) in the presence of 0.01 mg Cd/ℓ, 0.2 mg Cr/ℓ and 1.0 mg Ni/ℓ separately and together, for a period of six months after an initial period of one month in clean water, and subsequently he kept the fish for a three-month recovery period in clean water. There was no significant mortality among the fish but preliminary results indicate that adverse physiological effects (on content of sialic acid in gills, glucide in liver and proteolytic activity in liver and red blood cells) were found in all four treatments but no evidence of effects with the mixtures more marked than those with the single metal treatments. This suggests a less than additive joint sub-lethal action of the three metals.

Cadmium and mercury Anderson *et al.* (1979a) suggested that apparent safe levels of poorly accumulated toxicants, like cadmium, could enhance the acute toxicity of cumulative toxicants such as mercury. L. A. Hewitt and P. D. Anderson (personal communication) showed that while the joint lethal action of these two metals was additive at 96 h it was two-fold more than additive at 10 days.

Nickel and copper See Copper and nickel on page 268.

Nickel, cadmium and chromium See Cadmium, chromium and nickel on page 272.

Nickel and chromium Data provided by F. S. H. Abram (personal communication) for the survival of rainbow trout in mixtures of nickel and chromium in a hard water (hardness 270 mg/ℓ as $CaCO_3$) at 15 °C show that, for the 96-h LC50 in the ratio of 3:1 of the p LC50 values for chromium and nickel, there is additive joint action but for the 10-week LC50 in the same ratio, and also in the ratio 1:1, joint action was apparently 13- and 21-times more than additive respectively.

Nickel and vanadium Anderson *et al.* (1979b) found that the lethal effects of mixtures of nickel and vanadium became progressively less than additive as the proportion of vanadium increased.

Nickel, vanadium and phenol In contrast to the above results with nickel and vanadium, Anderson *et al.* (1979b) found that when the concentrations of these two metals increased in proportion to that of phenol in tertiary mixtures, the lethal effect of the mixture became progressively (2-fold) more than additive.

Chromium and cyanide See Cyanide and chromium on page 267.

Chromium and nickel See Nickel and chromium above.

Chromium and surfactant Bianucci and Legnani (1973) using alborella (*Alburnus albidus*) to test the toxicity of mixtures of potassium dichromate and sodium benzene sulphonate in a hard water (hardness 200 mg/ℓ as $CaCO_3$) at 20 °C, showed that, over a wide range of ratios of the respective fractions of the 96-h LC50 (1:17 to 1:0.8), their combined effect on the LC50 was between 0.6 and 0.7 times less than additive; similar results were obtained for 24- and 48-h LC50 values.

Mercury and copper See Copper and mercury on page 269.

Mercury and selenium   Huckabee and Griffith (1974) showed that although the presence of 1 mg/ℓ of both selenium (added as SeO_2) and mercury (added as $HgCl_2$) resulted in a reduction in the hatch of eggs of carp (*Cyprinus carpio*) of only 0.4 and 0.6 per cent respectively, a mixture of the two each at a concentration of 1 mg/ℓ (the lowest concentration tested, but unrealistically high in relation to those reported to occur in surface waters) was markedly more than additive in toxic effect, resulting in a reduction in hatch of over 80 per cent. The authors suggest that although both toxicants had an affinity for sulphydryl (SH) groups, they reacted together, when metabolized, to form less reactive complexes or compounds and might therefore be expected to interact less than additively; however their results suggest that reaction with SH groups might occur directly in the outer membrane of the egg.

Kim *et al.* (1977) however, showed that pretreatment of northern creek chub (*Semotilus atromaculatus*) for 48 h with 3 mg Se/ℓ (0.4 of the lethal concentration) resulted in a lower percentage mortality than in untreated fish when subsequently exposed for 48 h to a range of concentrations of mercury. Insufficient information is available to determine whether or not the protection afforded by this treatment resulted from the effect of selenium on the accumulation of mercury in the fish.

More recently, however, Heisinger *et al.* (1979) showed that in the presence of equimolar concentrations of selenium dioxide the 48-h LC50 of mercuric chloride to goldfish was 0.8 times less than the corresponding value in its absence, and 0.7 times less when exposure to mercury and selenium followed a 24-h pretreatment with the selenium.

Mercury and surfactant   Calamari and Marchetti (1973) measured the 96-h LC50 of mercury and LAS and reported that joint action was more than additive, but their data show that the effect was not large (1.1-fold), and probably not statistically significant.

Summary   The results of laboratory tests with fish using mixtures of toxicants commonly found in sewage and industrial wastes, summarized in *Table 11.2* show that joint action for acutely lethal concentrations range from 0.4 to 2.6 times those predicted from simple addition of the individual p LC50 values, the median value being about 0.9. Thus there is no evidence of marked antagonistic or more than additive ('synergistic') effects. However, for long-term lethal joint action of some of the heavy metals, results of a couple of unpublished experiments suggest that marked more than additive joint action might occur.

11.3.2 FISH: THE TOXICITY OF INDUSTRIAL WASTES, EFFLUENTS AND RIVER WATERS

Sewage effluents   The predictive method of estimating toxicity from Σ TU has been used to estimate the relative importance of the commonly occurring poisons (ammonia, monohydric phenols, zinc, copper and free cyanide) in sewage effluents in industrial areas in the United Kingdom, samples being taken from a variety of disposal works covering a range of treatment processes and receiving various types of industrial wastes (Lloyd and Jordan, 1963 and 1964). The toxicity of the effluents to rainbow trout was measured under controlled conditions and predicted on the assumption that the toxicity of the mixture of all five poisons could be calculated from chemical analyses in a similar manner to that used in laboratory studies. In 13 out of 18 toxic effluents the predicted toxicities were within ± 30 per cent of the observed values, and 6 effluents were correctly predicted to be non-toxic; only 2 effluents were more toxic than predicted, probably because of the presence of unidentified poisons. The factors by which the observed Σ TU differed from unity were 0.63, 0.73, 0.8, 0.81, 0.83, 0.9, 1.0, 1.06 and 1.18 (Lloyd and Jordan, 1963) and 0.48, 0.83, 0.89, 0.91, 1.04, 1.3, 1.4, 1.5 and 3.0 (Lloyd and Jordan, 1964).

Esvelt *et al.* (1973) measured the 96-h LC50 of municipal wastes discharged to San Francisco Bay in 43 tests using golden shiner (*Notemigonus crysoleucas*) and found an average value of 2.2 TU of which only 0.74 TU was not attributable, from statistical correlation, to ammonia or MBAS, that is, these two toxicants accounted for 0.66 of the observed toxicity. Too few data on other water quality characteristics were available to assess their possible contributions.

Servizi *et al.* (1978) measured the 96-h LC50 of effluent from a primary sewage treatment plant using sockeye salmon (*Oncorhynchus nerka*). They could attribute about 0.4 of the toxicity to anionic surfactants and cyanide, but further examination of their data suggests that the figure would rise to between 0.54 and 0.84 if contributions from un-ionized ammonia (0.01), zinc (0.05) and copper (0.38 to 0.08 depending upon the figure assumed for the toxicity of copper in the presence of organic matter), were also taken into account.

Thus what little evidence is available for sewage effluents containing industrial wastes shows that a large proportion of the observed acute lethal toxicity can be accounted for in terms of Σ p LC50 of commonly occurring toxicants.

Spent gas liquor Herbert (1962) using rainbow trout showed that, as expected, the toxicity of a spent liquor from a gas works was largely attributable to its content of ammonia and monohydric phenols, it being very similar to that expected from the additive effect of ammonia and phenol.

Pulp and paper effluent Compounds isolated from two acidic fractions of effluents from kraft mills were thought, by Leach and Thakore (1975), on the basis of chemical analysis and bioassays, to account for most of the toxicity of other acidic fractions of such effluents.

Later, Leach and Thakore (1977) gave examples showing that there was no clear evidence for more than additive or less than additive toxicity of constituents identified in 11 effluents from debarking, kraft pulping, caustic extraction and mechanical pulping. Measured toxicity was on average 1.03 times that predicted from chemical analysis, the range being 0.81 to 1.54 and often within the range of experimental error of the toxicity tests and chemical analyses.

Drilling fluid Sprague and Logan (1979) tested rainbow trout in three samples of used drilling fluid, whose composition was estimated rather than measured,

Table 11.2 SUMMARY OF LABORATORY DATA ON THE JOINT ACTION OF MIXTURES OF TOXICANTS ON FISH

Toxicants	Species	Exposure period and response	Ratio of toxicant EC50	Joint action	Multiple of additive joint action	Reference
Ammonia + phenol	Rainbow trout	Threshold LC50	1:1 to 1:2	Additive	0.7 to 1.0	Herbert (1962)
	Fathead minnow	24-h LC50	1.0:0.1 and 0.3	Less than additive	0.7	Jenkins (1964)
	Fathead minnow	24-h LC50	1.0:0.3 and 0.7	Additive	1.0 to 1.2	Jenkins (1964)
Ammonia + cyanide	Rainbow trout	96-h LC50	1:1	Additive	1.2	Broderius and Smith (1979)
		30-d EC50 (growth)	1.0:0.7	Less than additive	0.6	Smith et al. (1979)
Ammonia + copper	Rainbow trout	48-h LC50	1:1	Additive	1.0	Herbert and Vandyke (1964)
		LC25	1:1	More than additive	1.2	
		LC10	1:1	More than additive	1.4	
Ammonia + zinc	Rainbow trout	Threshold LC50	{ 1.0:0.5	Additive	1.0	Herbert and Shurben (1964)
		Hard water	1:2	Additive	1.0	
		Soft water	1:1	Less than additive	0.8	
Ammonia + phenol + zinc	Rainbow trout	48-h LC50	1.0:1.0:0.5	Additive	1.0	Brown, Jordan and Tiller (1969)
			1:7:1	More than additive	1.2	
			1:1:6	Less than additive	0.7	
			1.0:0.2:0.1	Additive	0.9	
Ammonia + phenol + sulphide	Fathead minnow	24-h LC50	1.0:0.1:1.1	Less than additive	0.5	Jenkins (1964)
			1.0:0.02:0.1	Less than additive	0.6	
			1.0:0.7:2.0	Less than additive	0.6	
			1.0:0.3:0.3	Less than additive	0.8	
Ammonia + sulphide	Fathead minnow	24-h LC50	1.0:2.2	Less than additive	0.6	Jenkins (1964)
			1.0:0.3	Less than additive	0.6	
			1:1	Less than additive	0.8	
			1.0:1.4	Less than additive	0.8	
Ammonia + nitrate	Guppy	72-h LC50	1.0:> 0.55	Additive	< 1.1	Rubin and Elmaraghy (1977)
			1.0:< 0.35	Less than additive	≥ 0.7	

Mixture	Species	Test	Ratio	Interaction	Value	Reference
Phenol + copper	Rainbow trout	48-h LC50	1:1	Less than additive	0.85	Brown and Dalton (1970)
Phenol + copper + zinc	Rainbow trout	48-h LC50	1:1:1	Less than additive	0.9	Brown and Dalton (1970)
Phenol + sulphide	Fathead minnow	24-h LC50	1:3.5	Less than additive	0.8	Jenkins (1964)
			1:11	Less than additive	0.8	
			1:3	Less than additive	0.7	
			1:1	Additive	0.9	
Phenol + PCP	Notopterus notopterus	96-h LC50	1:3	More than additive	1.47	Verma et al. (1981)
			1:1	Less than additive	0.61	
Phenol + DNP	Notopterus notopterus	96-h LC50	1:0.5	Less than additive	0.44	Verma et al. (1981)
			1:1.6	More than additive	1.27	
Phenol + PCP + DNP	Notopterus notopterus	96-h LC50	1:0.1:0.2	Less than additive	0.82	Verma et al. (1981)
			1:0.1:0.6	Less than additive	0.74	
			1:0.3:0.3	Less than additive	0.34	
			1:0.5:0.5	Less than additive	0.59	
			1:6.7:3.3	Less than additive	0.61	
			1:6.3:15.0	Less than additive	0.56	
PCP + DNP	Notopterus notopterus	96-h LC50	1:1.7	Less than additive	0.73	Verma et al. (1981)
			1:1.3	More than additive	1.14	
Cyanide + zinc	Bluegill	96-h LC50		Less than additive	0.4	Cairns and Scheier (1968)
	Fathead minnow	96-h LC50	1:1	More than additive	1.4	Broderius and Smith (1979)
		30-d EC50 (growth)	1.0:0.6	Less than additive	0.4	Smith et al. (1979)
Cyanide + chromium	Fathead minnow	96-h LC50	1:1	Less than additive	0.8	Broderius and Smith (1979)
		30-d EC50 (growth)	1.0:0.8	Less than additive	0.6 to 0.8	Smith et al. (1979)
			1.0:0.1	Less than additive		

Table 11.2 (*cont.*)

Toxicants	Species	Exposure period and response	Ratio of toxicant EC50	Joint action	Multiple of additive joint action	Reference
Copper + zinc	Rainbow trout	3-d LC50 (hard water)	1:1	Additive	1.0	Lloyd (1961)
	Atlantic salmon	7-d LC50 (soft water)	1:1	Additive	1.0	Lloyd (1961)
		7-d LC50 (soft water)	1:1	Additive	1.0	Sprague and Roussey (1965)
	Longfin dace	96-h LC50	1:0.75	More than additive	1.2	Lewis (1978)
	Bluegill	96-h LC50	1:1	Additive	0.8	Thompson et al. (1980)
Copper + zinc + nickel	Rainbow trout	48-h LC50	1:1:1	Additive	0.7	Brown and Dalton (1970)
Copper + nickel	Rainbow trout	Non-specified	1:1:1	Additive	(0.4 to 1.2)	Marking (1977)
	Guppy	7-d EC50 (growth, restricted ration)	?	Slightly more than additive	?	Muska and Weber (1977)
		7-d EC50 (growth, unrestricted ration)		Additive		
Copper + cadmium	Mummichog (salinity 20%)	Effect on lateral line	?	Less than additive	?	La Roche et al. (1973)
	Mummichog (salinity 20%)	96-h LC50	Various	More than additive	?	Eisler and Gardner (1973)
	Zebrafish	96-h LC50	?	More than additive	2.0	Hewitt and Anderson (1979)

Mixture	Species	Test	Ratio	Type of interaction	Value	Reference
Copper + zinc + cadmium	Mummichog (salinity 20%)	96-h LC50	Various	More than additive	?	Eisler and Gardner (1973)
	Fathead minnow	96-h LC50 (Cu) Threshold LC50 (Cd and Zn)	1.0:0.1:1.2	More than additive	1.3	Eaton (1973)
		12½ months EC50	1.0:0.1:1.2	Varied, depending on response measured		Eaton (1973)
		90% red. in no eggs	1.0:0.1:1.2	More than additive	> 1.6	
		50% red. in no eggs		Less than additive	< 0.9	
Copper + mercury	Rainbow trout	96-h LC50	?	Additive	?	D. Calamari and R. Marchetti (personal communication)
Copper + mercury (methyl)	Blue gourami	96-h LC50	1.0:0.25 to 1.0:1.15	Less than additive	?	Roales and Perlmutter (1977)
Copper + manganese	Longfin dace	96-h LC50		Less than additive	0.67	Lewis (1978)
Copper + surfactant ABS	Goldfish	96-h LC50	1.0:0.1	More than additive	1.3	Calamari and Marchetti (1970)
LAS		96-h LC50	1.0:0.6	More than additive	2.1	
	Rainbow trout	96-h LC50	1:1	More than additive	1.3	Calamari and Marchetti (1973)
Copper + nonyl phenol ethoxylate	Rainbow trout	96-h LC50	1:1	Less than additive	0.8	Lewis (1978)
Copper + LAS	Goldfish	96-h LC50	1:1	More than additive	1.06	Tsai and McKee (1980)
			1:0.5	More than additive	2.0	
			1:2	Less than additive	0.95	
Copper + chloramine	Goldfish	96-h LC50	1:1	More than additive	1.27	Tsai and McKee (1980)
			1:0.5	More than additive	1.69	
			1:2	More than additive	1.64	
Copper + paraquat	Poecilia mexicana	24-h LC50	1:0.25	More than additive	1.3	Sun and Gorman (1973)

280

Table 11.2 (cont.)

Toxicants	Species	Exposure period and response	Ratio of toxicant EC50	Joint action	Multiple of additive joint action	Reference
Zinc + cadmium (see text)				Various		
Zinc + detergent (55% ABS) See text for additional tests	Rainbow trout	72-h LC50	1:3.8	Additive	0.9	Brown, Mitrovic and Stark (1968)
Cadmium + chromium + nickel	Rainbow trout	3-month physiological	?	Less than additive	?	D. Calamari (personal communication)
Cadmium + mercury	?	96-h LC50	?	Additive	1.0	Hewitt and Anderson (personal communication)
		10-d LC50	?	More than additive	2.0	
Mercury + surfactant (LAS)	Rainbow trout	96-h LC50	Various	Additive	1.1	Calamari and Marchetti (1973)
Chromium + nickel	Rainbow trout	96-h LC50	1:0.3	Additive	0.9	F. S. H. Abram (personal communication)
	Rainbow trout	10-week LC50	1:0.3	More than additive	13	F. S. H. Abram (personal communication)
	Rainbow trout	10-week LC50	1:1	More than additive	21	F. S. H. Abram (personal communication)
Chromium + surfactant	Alborella	96-h LC50	1:17 to 1.0:0.8	Less than additive	0.6 to 0.7	Bianucci and Legnani (1973)

and found that the toxicity (based upon 96-h LC50) was 1.4, 1.2 and 0.8 times as toxic as predicted from the sum of estimated p 96-h LC50 values, although the differences from unity did not appear to be statistically different. However, they tested a simulated drilling fluid containing barium sulphate, potassium chloride, ferrochrome lignosulphonate, bentonite, an industrial xanthate gum, paraformaldehyde and potassium chromic sulphate, and found it (significantly) 0.6 times as toxic as predicted. Significant differences from predicted toxicity were also found with this fluid when other components were added singly to it. With each added component three mixtures were tested, the ratio of component to fluid being 1:0.43, 1:1 and 1:2.3, and in all cases antagonism was found with one of the three mixtures, the least toxic of which was 0.3 times that expected on the basis of simple addition. Interaction appeared to be less than additive in eight of the remaining twelve mixtures and more than additive in the other four, but none of these appeared to be significantly different from additive interaction. The authors suggested that the adsorptive capacity of the bentonite might have accounted for some of the reduction in toxicity found.

River waters   J. F. de L. G. Solbé and F. H. Davies (personal communication) tested the toxicity to rainbow trout of samples of water from the R. Churnet, UK, taken on five separate occasions when the predicted 48-h LC50 based upon the content of ammonia, phenol, cyanide, copper and zinc, was less than unity (Σ p 48-h LC50, 0.08 on average). After adding either zinc (on all occasions), nickel (4 occasions), copper or ammonia (one occasion each), to increase the predicted value above unity, the measured 48-h LC50 values were, on average, only 0.66 of those expected. For data from on-site tests with river waters see Section 11.4, Field studies on page 294.

11.3.3 FISH: THE TOXICITY OF PESTICIDES

Mixtures of pesticides   Macek (1975) measured the percentage mortality within 1 to 4 days of bluegill exposed to 29 different mixtures of pairs of pesticides at individual concentrations that were expected to produce less than 40 per cent mortality in 72 h. The results were expressed as the proportion of the total mortality in all concentrations of both chemicals tested singly, to the total mortality for all corresponding concentrations of chemicals tested together, and do not allow conventional analysis. The proportions ranged from 0.28 to 11.7 and are distributed approximately lognormally, with a median value of 1.25 and lower and upper limits of the standard deviation of 0.66 and 2.3 respectively. Six of the mixtures when also tested with rainbow trout apparently gave similar results. This could imply that on average response addition was slightly more than additive.

   Marking and Mauck (1975) measured the toxicity to rainbow trout of 20 out of 21 possible paired mixtures of 7 insecticides in the ratio of 1:1 of their respective p LC50 (of unspecified time). For 9 pairs, joint toxicity was between 0.5 and 0.7 times less than additive, for nine others it was not significantly different from additive, and for the remaining two it was 1.4 and 1.7 times more than additive.

   Statham and Lech (1975a and b) measured the percentage survival of rainbow trout exposed for 4 h to either 2,4-D butyl ester, dieldrin, rotenone or penta-chlorophenol, each in the presence of carbaryl, a choline esterase inhibitor, at a concentration of 0.11 of the 96-h LC50, to which the fish had been exposed for 2 h immediately beforehand. More than additive interaction was found in all cases, and in the case of 2,4-D, toxicity (expressed as 4.5 h LC50) was increased 2.7-fold. The more than additive effect of carbaryl on dieldrin and 2,4-D was shown to be reduced considerably in the presence of 10 mg/ℓ atropine, and the additive effect of arecoline on the toxicity of 2,4-D and PCB was also reduced by atropine. The authors (Statham and Lech, 1975a and b) suggested that the effect of carbaryl was related to its muscarine action, and later (Statham and Lech, 1976) showed that carbaryl at a concentration which increased the acutely lethal toxicity of 2,4-D and also of Bayer 73 (2.3-fold in terms of 4.5-h LC50), also significantly increased the concentration of these substances in the blood and whole body of the fish, possibly by affecting the permeability of the gill rather than blood flow, but did not decrease their rates of elimination. Atropine, alone of several blocking agents, also inhibited the carbaryl-induced increase in concentration of 2,4-D and Bayer 73 in the blood.

Anderson and Weber (1975a) found that the effects of PCB and HEOD were response additive, while Marking and Dawson (1975) measured the 96-h LC50 to bluegill of malathion and delnav and found that joint action was markedly (8.2-fold) more than additive.

The 24-h LC50 of 2,4-D (tributyl ester) and trifluralin for insecticide-resistant strains of mosquitofish were about twice as high as the corresponding values for insecticide-susceptible fish (Fabacher and Chambers, 1974) suggesting possible pesticide-induced physiological changes in these organisms.

Fabacher *et al.* (1976) showed that the mortality of mosquitofish in a mixture of methyl parathion and the defoliant tributyl phosphorotrithioate in the ratio of 1:2 of fractions of their respective 48- and 24-h LC50 values was several-fold more than additive.

Dethlefsen (1977) concluded, from extensive studies of the development of eggs and the mortality of larvae of cod (*Gadus morhua*) made in the presence of DDT and DDE, that the adverse effects of the two together was generally slightly more than additive, depending on the parameter measured.

Koenig (1977) fed adults of the saltmarsh fish (*Adinia xenica*) with a diet containing either pp DDT or mirex, or both, and observed the mortality among the progeny embryos and larvae (expressed as LD50 of the dose administered to the parental females). Interaction between the toxicants was about 1.6 times more than additive. This is consistent with the independent action of these two toxicants in that mortality attributable to DDT occurred sooner after fertiliza-tion than that attributable to mirex, and that the symptoms of poisoning for the two toxicants (reviewed by the author) are quite different.

The mortality of rainbow trout dosed via their food with DDT, or methoxy-chlor, in the presence of dieldrin, was less than that resulting from dosing with DDT alone (Mayer *et al.*, 1972).

Krieger and Lee (1973) showed that simultaneous treatment of mosquitofish with diquat and an insecticide did not affect the toxicity of DDT, aldrin or para-thion, but markedly enhanced that of carbaryl and inhibited aldrin epoxidation.

Ludke *et al.* (1972) found, with several species of fish, a less than additive toxic effect with mixtures of parathion and aldrin, and similar results were obtained by Ferguson and Bringham (1966) with mosquitofish exposed to all possible paired combinations of endrin, DDT, toxaphene and methyl parathion.

Bender (1969) reported tests with fathead minnow which showed more than additive interaction between malathion and each of its two main products of hydrolysis.

Pesticides and surfactants Solon *et al.* (1969) measured the 96-h LC50 to fathead minnow of parathion, DDT and endrin alone, and each in the presence of 1 mg/ℓ (0.003 96-h LC50) LAS. The joint action between LAS and the insecticides was about 1.9, 1.2 and 0.9 times that expected of simple addition.

Solon and Nair (1970) carried out further tests on phosphate pesticides and confirmed the result obtained by Solon *et al.* (1969) for parathion, and also found that joint action of LAS and the pesticide was more than additive for methyl parathion (2.1 times), ronnel (1.2 times), trithion (1.7 times) and trichloronat (1.7 times), additive for guthion, and less than additive for EPN (0.85 times) and dicapton (0.85 times), all based upon p 48-h LC50. They commented that there was no correlation between the type of interaction found and chemical structure, and speculated that, because of the low aqueous solubility of all the toxicants tested, the additive joint action of LAS might be attributable to its increasing their solubility at the gill or skin membrane, although an effect of LAS on enzymes involved in oxidizing and detoxifying them was also seen as a possibility.

Dugan (1967) showed that there was a tendency for goldfish that had been exposed to 4 μg/ℓ of alkylbenzene sulphonate for several months to be more susceptible to subsequent exposure to 50 μg/ℓ dieldrin in the presence of 4 μg/ℓ ABS than fish not so exposed.

Pesticides and miscellaneous substances Howland (1969) reported additive joint action between p 96-h LC50 values for rotenone and antimycin but his results actually suggest that interaction is, if anything, (0.72 times) less than additive.

Marking (1977) reported that there was greater than additive joint action between rotenone and piperonyl butoxide (2.4 times) and rotenone and sulphoxide (between 1.4 and 3.1 times depending upon the ratio of the two used) when the toxicity (unspecified) was tested using rainbow trout.

A number of other examples, in which the lethal toxicity of mixtures of pesticides and other miscellaneous substances is greater than that predicted from the p LC50 of the constituents, are also cited by Alabaster (1969) for formulated products.

Summary While many data on the acute lethal toxicity of mixtures of pesticides and other substances to fish show that joint action is close to additive, a relatively high proportion, compared with toxicants commonly found in sewage and industrial wastes, show that it is several-fold more than additive.

11.3.4 FISH: THE TOXICITY OF OTHER SUBSTANCES

Chlorine and other substances Schaut (1939) found that, following chlorination of solutions containing potassium thiocyanide at a concentration of 6 mg/ℓ, 'minnows' were affected the same as by 3.6 mg/ℓ of sodium cyanide; he considered this to be a consequence of hydrogen cyanide production, although Allen, Blezard and Wheatland (1948) studied the same phenomenon and concluded that the poison was more likely to be cyanogen chloride. Chlorine can combine with a wide variety of organic substances to form stable organo-chlorine compounds (Jolley, 1973) some of which have been shown to be harmful to fish at concentrations as low as 0.001 mg/ℓ (e.g. Gehrs *et al.*, 1974). There is no information on the effect of chlorine in the presence of other poisons with which it does not react chemically.

Trifluoromethyl nitrophenol and Bayer 73   Bills and Marking (1976) measured the toxicity of a mixture of 3-trifluoromethyl-4-nitrophenol (TFM) and 2,5-dichloro-4-nitrosalicylanilide (Bayer 73) in the ratio 49:1, using fingerling brown trout (*Salmo trutta*), rainbow trout, lake trout (*Salvelinus namaycush*), brook trout (*Salvelinus fontinalis*), channel catfish (*Ictalurus punctatus*), bluegill and yellow perch (*Perca flavescens*) in soft water at 12 °C, and also rainbow trout in hard water, and eggs and fry of coho salmon (*Oncorhynchus kisutch*); in all cases joint action between the components was additive, except for rainbow trout tested at pH 6.5 and 8.5, when it was (0.7 and 0.6 times, respectively) less than additive. Although Howell *et al.* (1964) reported a mixture of these substances killing ammocoetes of sea lamprey (*Lampetra marinus*) at concentrations which were not toxic when applied singly, Dawson *et al.* (1977) found their effect additive or less than additive to this organism.

Antimycin and other substances   Berger (1971), quoted in Marking and Dawson (1975), reported that mixtures of antimycin and TFM were 'synergistically toxic' to black bullhead (*Ictalurus melas*), largemouth bass (*Micropterus salmoides*), and yellow perch, but Marking and Dawson (1975) found that the p 96-h LC50 values of antimycin and TFM were additive when tested with bluegill, suggesting that there may be differences between species.

Marking and Dawson (1975) also found additive joint action between antimycin and dibrom, when tested with rainbow trout, but a marked antagonistic reaction between antimycin and potassium permanganate (0.01 times as toxic as expected from additive joint action).

Marking (1969) showed that the interaction between the p 96-h LC50 values of antimycin and rhodamine B was additive.

Quinaldine sulphate and MS-222   Dawson and Marking (1973) measured the 24-h and 96-h of LC50 mixtures of quinaldine sulphate and MS-222, in the ratio of 1:2 and 1:4 p 96-h LC50 using rainbow trout, brown trout, brook trout and bluegill, and in the ratio 1:4 only using lake trout, and found that the joint action between the two, based upon their earlier work with the substances tested separately, was on average 1.3-fold more than additive (range 1.11 to 1.41), with no marked or significant differences between different ratios or species used. Berger (1969), quoted in Gilderhus *et al.* (1973) tested the toxic effect of MS-222 and quinaldine sulphate and a mixture of the two, and apparently found it slightly (1.3 times) more than additive in the mixture.

Others Leteux and Mayer (1972) reported that the efficacy of malachite green and formaldehyde as therapeutic agents was increased (about 1.8 times) when present together in a mixture. Devlaminck (1960) showed that it was possible to sum the toxic fractions of individual poisons in mixtures of 2,3 and 4 dissimilar substances over a 6 h exposure period.

Abram and Wilson (1979) studied the acute toxicity of o-chlorobenzaldehyde and malononitrile; their data show more than additive joint action between the two (1.4 to 2.7 times) in mixtures for median lethal concentrations between 12 and 96 hours and ratios of the LC50 values of the two substances from 1.3:1 to 8.7:1 (time was confounded with ratios).

Tsai and McKee (1980) measured the 96-h LC50 of LAS and chloramines and their mixtures in the ratio of 1:0.5 to 1:2 p 96-h LC50, using goldfish, and found that toxicity was slightly (1.2 to 1.4 times) more than additive.

The bulk of the results referred to so far relate to mixtures of no more than two or three toxicants. Könemann (1979) however, using the guppy, has worked with mixtures of three or more toxicants; with five mixtures containing respectively 3, 10, 10, 11 and 50 chemicals, mainly organic in nature, which were expected to exert 'simple similar action', the toxicity was, on average, 0.9 of that predicted assuming additive toxicity (range 0.7–1.1). With another mixture of 9, however, which contained organo-metal and inorganic chemicals, the figure was 0.4 of the predicted value.

Summary The data on the toxicity of mixtures of substances, other than pesticides and toxicants commonly found in sewage and industrial wastes, show that joint action is often close to additive.

11.3.5 FISH: CONCLUSIONS ON THE ADDITIVE EFFECT OF TOXICANTS

The extent to which the joint effect of toxicants on freshwater fish deviates from additive, may depend upon several factors, including the type of response (for example, whether long term or short term and whether lethal or non-lethal), the magnitude (percentage) of response, the type of toxicant and the proportion in which it is present in a mixture, water quality characteristics (such as hardness), species, stage in the life cycle of the fish and prior acclimation to toxicant, and size of the ration.

Additivity of acute lethal toxicity Examination of acutely lethal concentrations to freshwater fish of mixtures of toxicants from 76 sets of data, of which 62 relate to pairs of toxicants, and the remainder to mixtures of three, all referring to commonly occurring constituents of sewage and industrial wastes (namely, ammonia, phenol, cyanide, copper, zinc, cadmium, nickel, chromium, mercury and other metals and other substances), has shown that these are between 0.4 and 2.6 times those predicted from the sum of the proportions of the respective toxic units of the constituents, with a median value of 0.95; 87 per cent of the results were within 0.5 and 1.5 of the predicted values. Somewhat similar results have been found for 18 sewage effluents based upon the toxicity of toxicants known to be present and for 8 samples of river water, the toxicity of which has been increased experimentally by the addition of known amounts of ammonia, phenol, cyanide, copper and zinc, and also for several drilling fluids and a gas liquor; the median value for all of these is 0.85 of the predicted value. With pesticides and other substances, however, the mixtures tend to be somewhat more toxic than predicted, with a median value of 1.3. These results are summarized in *Table 11.2* and illustrated in *Figure 11.3*.

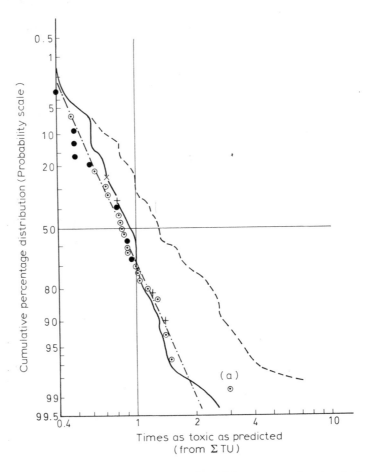

Figure 11.3 Summary of laboratory data on predicted/observed sum of toxic units for freshwater fish. Number of sets of data shown in parentheses. Results relate largely to short-term LC50 values to rainbow trout but include data on other species and effects on growth (see text) and also exclude those from sources referred to in the foreword
'(a)' represents effluent having a high content of industrial wastes including pesticides

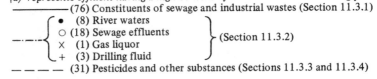

———— (76) Constituents of sewage and industrial wastes (Section 11.3.1)

—··—·· { • (8) River waters
         ○ (18) Sewage effluents
         × (1) Gas liquor   } (Section 11.3.2)
         + (3) Drilling fluid

— — — — (31) Pesticides and other substances (Sections 11.3.3 and 11.3.4)

Magnitude of response Most of the data reported on lethal concentrations relate to median values, but in one study with ammonia and copper (Herbert and Vandyke, 1964) the joint action, while additive in terms of the median, was 1.2 and 1.4 more than additive for the LC25 and LC10 values respectively. Also, in the case of the effect of mixtures of copper, zinc and cadmium on the production of eggs by fathead minnow, interaction was approximately additive for a reduction of 90 per cent but less than additive for a reduction of 50 per cent. However, it is possible that such a result is an artifact resulting from progressive differences in proportional bio-availability of the three chemicals with increase in total concentration.

Time of response Few data are available on the relation between short- and long-term joint toxic action of constituents in mixtures. However, it has been shown for mixtures of cadmium and mercury (L. A. Hewitt and P. D. Anderson, personal communication) and for mixtures of chromium and nickel (F. S. H. Abram, personal communication) that, while joint action may be additive in the short term (4-d LC50) it may be more than additive in the longer term (2-fold at 10 days for cadmium and mercury and up to 21-fold at 10 weeks for chromium and nickel).

Type of response Broderius and Smith (1979), examining mixtures of ammonia and cyanide, cyanide and zinc, and cyanide and chromium, found that the type of joint toxicity observed for fish exposed to lethal concentrations of these mixtures was not found when they were subject to sub-lethal levels of the same toxicants. For example, whereas the joint acutely lethal action of ammonia and cyanide on rainbow trout was 1.16 times more than additive, the joint effect on growth over 30 d was 0.6 times as additive. The corresponding figures for fathead minnow exposed to zinc and cyanide were 1.4 and 0.4 respectively although for this species exposed to chromium and cyanide the figures were 0.8 and between 0.6 and 0.8 respectively. There are few other data on the effect of mixtures on growth; the range of factors by which the observed effect differs from that predicted is 0.4 to 1.0, and for one set of data on fish production (without comparable data on acutely lethal effects) the figure is 0.6 (Neglinski, 1974) and for another on growth in the presence of HCN and arsenic (G. Leduc, personal communication) it is 0.6 to 0.8.

It is possible, therefore, that as concentrations of toxicants are reduced towards the level of no effect (NOEC), their potential for addition is also reduced.

However, this may not apply to sub-lethal physiological effects on the whole organism. Whereas zinc and copper were additive in terms of the threshold LC50 for Atlantic salmon (Sprague and Ramsay, 1965), their joint effect on avoidance behaviour was slightly (about 1.3 times) more than additive (Sprague, Elson and Saunders, 1965).

Relative proportion of toxicant Comparatively little attention has been given to the effect on joint toxicity of the relative proportions of the toxicants present, although it has been amply demonstrated that these can be profound in some cases (Sprague and Logan, 1979). It has been shown that one constituent at concentrations below a certain p LC50 may not contribute any toxic effect, for example with mixtures of ammonia and nitrate (Rubin and Elmaraghy, 1977), and with mixtures of copper and surfactant (Calamari and Marchetti, 1972). This reinforces the proposition made in the previous section.

Sprague (1970) pointed out that the toxicity of mixtures of ammonia, phenol and zinc was over estimated by Brown *et al.* (1969) in three of four cases when two of the toxicants were present at 0.1 to 0.14 TU, whereas when they were present at 0.2 TU or more, interaction was additive, and that their data suggest that the level of no effect for acute toxicity is about 0.2 TU for metals. If this were a general phenomenon, one would expect the results when plotted, as in *Figure 11.2*, to lie to the right and parallel to the line marked 'additive', but within the triangle marked 'less than additive'. Examination of all the data summarized in *Table 11.2*, however, shows only a slight tendency in this direction.

The most clear-cut picture relates to mixtures of phenol and other substances as plotted in *Figure 11.4*. In this case a relatively large number of tests have been carried out at low TUs of phenol, and while the figure can be interpreted as indicating less than additive joint action when the TU of phenol is less than about 0.3, it also shows that at a TU of phenol of about 0.1, there is an apparent marked antagonism between phenol and other toxicants. However, there are too few data from these experiments to be able to draw any general conclusions about the contribution of low TU values for the other toxicants present in the mixtures.

Species of fish   There are few data available to compare the additive effect of a given mixture on toxicity to two or more species of fish, and none are available to make this comparison for identical experimental conditions. Yet, from *Table 11.2* it can be seen that for mixtures of ammonia and phenol with rainbow trout and fathead minnow, and for mixtures of copper and zinc with rainbow trout, Atlantic salmon and longfin dace, similar results are obtained. However, for mixtures of cyanide and zinc, the joint action is apparently 0.4 times as additive for bluegill and 1.4 times as additive for fathead minnow, while the results for copper, zinc and cadmium are equivocal. In any event, there is no strong evidence for marked consistent differences between species in their response to the joint effect of mixtures of toxicants.

11.3.6 INVERTEBRATES

Fewer data are available on the effect of mixtures of substances on aquatic invertebrates than on fish.

Phenols   Herbes and Beauchamp (1977), in tests with *Daphnia magna*, demonstrated less than additive, and also antagonistic, joint action between methylquinoline and resorcinol, depending upon the relative p 48-h LC50 of each present in the mixture, the lowest LC50 of the mixture being about 0.6 of that predicted from additive joint action.

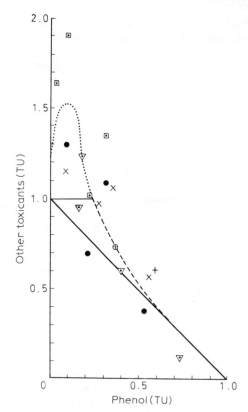

Figure 11.4 Toxic units of phenol and other toxicants in mixtures producing a given lethal response in fish (data calculated from those in Table 11.2)

●	Ammonia
▽	Ammonia + zinc
▣	Ammonia + sulphide
+	Copper
×	Sulphide
○	Copper + zinc
——	Additive
– – –	Less than additive } Joint
⋯⋯	Antagonistic } action

Copper and zinc Buikema *et al.* (1977), measuring the percentage response (immobility) of the rotifer *Philodina acuticornis* to mixtures of copper and zinc, obtained rather variable results, but found no evidence that joint action was not additive. Biesinger *et al.* (1974) give an example of chemical reduction in toxicity of copper and zinc by chelation with NTA using *Daphnia* as the test organism.

Zinc, and other substances Gray and Ventilla (1973) measured the depression in growth rates of a sediment-living marine protozoan, *Cristigera* sp., in the presence of zinc, lead and mercury singly, and in all their combinations, and found both more and less than additive interaction depending on the concentrations tested.

Maksimov (1979) measured the numbers of rotifers present in a natural plankton community at the end of a 17 d test period in the presence of mixtures of zinc and chromium. An examination of his data suggests that the joint effect of the toxicants in reducing numbers by one order of magnitude is about 2.4-fold more than additive.

Cadmium, malathion, methoxychlor and Arochlor 1245 Bahner and Nimmo (1975) using the estuarine shrimp *Penaeus duorarum*, concluded that in mixtures combining cadmium with malathion, or methoxychlor, or both methoxychlor and Arochlor 1254 (PCB), as well as in a complex industrial waste in which cadmium was present, interaction between the toxicants was additive. They (Nimmo and Bahner, 1976) also measured the survival of the shrimp for at least 25 days in the presence of cadmium and methoxychlor at several concentrations and in a mixture of the two. Examination of the results on the basis of the estimated 26-d LC50 values suggests that interaction between these two toxicants was more than additive. Further 10 d tests with different proportions of the two did not show more than additive interaction.

Chromium and other substances Buikema *et al.* (1977), measuring the percentage response (immobility) of the rotifer *Philodina acuticornis* to mixtures of two toxicants, obtained rather variable results, but found more than additive interaction with chromium and chlorine and no marked departure from additive interaction with mixtures of chromium and fluoride and of chromium and copper.

Other substances Nitrosalicylanilide and 4-nitro-3-trifluoromethyl phenol were tested individually and in mixtures of the two for toxicity to the ostracod (*Cypretta kawatai*) (Kawatski, 1973), and examination of the 96-h LC50 values shows that joint action is about 1.4 times more than additive for mixtures in which the toxicants are in the ratio of 1:1 and 49:1 of their respective p 96-h LC50 values.

Additive, less than additive, and non-interactive toxicity to *Daphnia magna* of mixtures of two and three chemicals was observed by Freeman and Fowler (1953) using inorganic substances or very similar organic compounds.

Pesticides Lichtenstein *et al.* (1973) measured the percentage mortality of third instar larvae of the mosquito (*Aedes aegypti*) held for 24 h in static solutions containing initial concentrations of either 0.016 mg/ℓ parathion or 0.18 mg/ℓ DDT alone (in which the percentage mortality was 15 and 10 respectively), and also in the presence of 10 mg/ℓ of one of four herbicides. The interaction between parathion and the herbicides was more than additive ($\times$ 5.3 for atrazine, $\times$ 4.5 for simazine, $\times$ 3.5 for monuron and $\times$ 3.2 for 2,4-D), while that between DDT and the herbicides was approximately additive, although the nominal concentration of DDT used was probably not maintained because it was higher than the solubility value.

Lichtenstein *et al.* (1974) showed that an aqueous extract of the plant, dill (*Anethum graveolus*), and a constituent of the plant, d-carvone, increased the percentage mortality of third instar larvae of the mosquito (*Aedes aegypti*) over 24 h in the presence of carbaryl, carbofuran, parathion and DDT.

Summary In general, the few data available for the joint effect of toxicants on aquatic invertebrates show, as in the case of fish, that for constituents commonly present in sewage and industrial wastes, where the concentration-addition model can be tested, it is approximately additive. Also, in the case of pesticides, the joint effects are generally markedly more than additive.

11.3.7 AQUATIC PLANTS

Fewer data are available on the combined effects of toxicants on aquatic plants than on other organisms.

Zinc and cadmium Hutchinson and Czyrska (1973) showed that, at a concentration of 10 μg Cd/ℓ, the growth of *Salvinia natans* under a variety of conditions (except when tested alone) and of *Lemna valdiviana* was generally slightly inhibited, an effect that was increased in the presence of either 50 or 80 μg Zn/ℓ (except when *Lemna* was tested when in competition with *Salvinia*), even though those concentrations of zinc alone were stimulatory. Similar results were obtained, however, with *Salvinia* (when tested alone) in the presence of 30 μg Cd/ℓ, both alone and with either 30 or 80 μg Zn/ℓ, and with *Lemna* (when in competition with *Salvinia*) when tested in the presence of 30 μg Cd/ℓ and 80 μg Zn/ℓ.

On the other hand, the data of Say (1977) showed that there was between 1.4 and 1.7 times more than additive interaction between cadmium and zinc in their combined effect on the inhibition of growth of the alga *Homidium rivalare*, a threshold response being obtained, for example at pt EC values of cadmium and zinc in the ratios 1:0.4 and 1:5.

Laborey and Lavollay (1967) measured the percentage reduction in the growth of *Aspergillus niger* in the presence of cadmium and zinc separately, and together in a number of mixtures, and examination of their data shows that the joint action was 0.4 and 0.5 times less than additive in the presence of 70 and 25 mg Mg/ℓ respectively.

Thus contradictory results have been obtained with mixtures of zinc and cadmium, depending upon species, but they are within the range 0.4 to 1.7 times as toxic as predicted.

Hutchinson and Czyrska (1973) found that the presence of zinc appeared to result in a higher cadmium uptake by *Lemna*.

Zinc and sulphide An example of a less than additive effect, attributable to chemical interaction in the water, is given by Hendricks (1978) for the effect of zinc and sulphide on oxygen production by the alga *Selenastrum capricornutum*.

Copper and nickel Hutchinson and Czyrska (1973) found that when nickel and copper were present at the same time the uptake rates of both metals by *Lemna* were increased.

Cadmium and nickel Stratton and Corke (1979) measured the percentage response of the alga *Anabaena inaequalis* to mixtures of cadmium and nickel, and an examination of their data, including those for the toxicants tested singly (from their other cited papers) to calculate concentrations corresponding to 50 per cent reduction in response compared with controls, suggests that joint action is less than additive both for growth at 10 days (0.5–0.74 times) and for acetylene reduction (up to 0.63 times), but inconsistent for the uptake of carbon dioxide.

Cadmium, nickel and mercury Stratton and Corke (1979) measured the percentage response of *Anabaena inaequalis* to mixtures of cadmium, nickel and mercury, and an examination of their data, including those for the toxicants tested singly (from their other cited papers) to calculate concentrations corresponding to 50 per cent reduction in response compared with controls, suggests that joint action is (0.4 times) less than additive (with the three toxicants in the ratio 1:0.9:1.1 of their respective p EC50 values). Joint action is, however, inconsistent for reduction of acetylene, being more than additive (1.2-fold) with the three toxicants in the ratio 1:3.6:0.4 of their respective p EC50 values and less than additive (0.6 times) with a corresponding ratio of 1:3.5:2; it is also inconsistent for uptake of carbon dioxide, being additive with a ratio of EC50 values of 1:1.2 and less than additive (0.5 times) with a corresponding ratio of 1:1:1.

Cadmium and mercury Stratton and Corke (1979) measured the percentage response of *Anabaena inaequalis* to mixtures of cadmium and mercury, and an examination of their data, including those for the toxicants tested singly (from their other cited papers) to calculate concentrations corresponding to 50 per cent reduction in response compared with controls, suggests that joint action is less than additive for growth at 10 days (0.46 times) and for uptake of carbon dioxide (up to 0.7 times), and more than additive for acetylene reduction (1.1 to 2.3 times). The results were, however, different when exposure to the two metals was in sequence rather than simultaneous, and depended also upon the concentrations of each used.

Cadmium and lead Pietiläinen (1975) using natural phytoplankton communities tested in the laboratory, measured the reduction in primary production within a 24 h period in the presence of cadmium, lead, and mixtures of the two. EC50 values calculated from these data showed that joint action was 0.7 times less than additive with cadmium and lead present in the ratio 1:0.1 of their respective EC50 values and about 0.2 times with a corresponding ratio of 1:11.

Nickel and mercury Stratton and Corke (1979) measured the percentage response of *Anabaena inaequalis* to mixtures of cadmium and nickel, and an examination of their data, including those for the toxicants tested singly (from their other cited papers) to calculate concentrations corresponding to 50 per cent reduction in response compared with controls, suggests that joint action is more than additive for growth at 10 days (1.2 times), unless exposure is not simultaneous, when it can be additive if exposure is to mercury followed by nickel and less than additive if exposure is first to nickel. Joint action appears to be less than additive for acetylene reduction (up to 0.8-fold) and inconsistent for carbon dioxide production.

Pesticides and other substances Mosser *et al.* (1974) observed substantial growth inhibition when a strain of the marine diatom *Thalassiosira pseudonana* was treated simultaneously with 10 μg/ℓ PCB and 100 μg/ℓ DDE, while growth of the diatom was only slightly reduced when treated with just one of these substances at the same concentrations, suggesting a more than additive joint action. In contrast, the joint action of PCB and DDT was less than additive; when the diatom was treated with 50 μg/ℓ PCB, growth was almost stopped, but the simultaneous addition of 500 μg/ℓ DDT restored growth to about two-thirds of that in control cultures. The addition of DDT 12 to 24 h after inoculation with PCB also reversed the inhibition caused by the latter. The mechanism appeared to be an intracellular interaction rather than a physical process, such as co-precipitation, because it was reversible on removal of the pesticide. Additive joint action was also demonstrated between DDT and DDE.

Recent data for the green alga (*Chlamydomonas*) tested in mixtures of arsenic and PCB (Christensen and Zielski, 1980) show that toxicity (concentrations producing 50 per cent reduction in growth) is about 0.8 times as great as expected from purely additive effects of the components.

Walsh *et al.* (unpublished, but quoted in Walsh, 1978) found that the herbicide 2,4-D inhibited the toxicity to algae of nickel and aluminium.

Tsay *et al.* (1976) demonstrated that copper ions inhibited toxicity of 2 mg/ℓ paraquat (1,1-dimethyl-4,4'-bipyridinium ion) to *Chlorella pyrenoidosa*, whereas cyanide ion enhanced it.

Summary Very few data are available on the joint effect of toxicants on plants compared with those for fish and other aquatic organisms. For heavy metals, results vary according to the species tested, for example, with zinc and cadmium, but even within a species such as *Anabaena* for which a considerable amount of data are available, results vary inconsistently according to the toxicant and proportion of toxicant used, and the response measured. Nevertheless all the data fall in the range 0.2 to 2.3 times as toxic as predicted for the concentration-addition model, with a median value of about 0.7.

For pesticides and other substances there are too few data on which to draw general quantitative conclusions but joint action is more than additive in some cases and less than additive in others.

11.4 Field studies

This section describes the evolution of field studies to confirm conclusions on the additivity of toxicants derived from laboratory experiments on the toxicity of mixtures of poisons to fish.

11.4.1 STREAM RECEIVING GAS LIQUOR

The recognition that the toxicity to fish of gas liquors from coke oven plants could be predicted in the laboratory by summing the proportions of the 24-h LC50s (Σ p 24-h LC50) for ammonia and gas liquor phenols (Herbert, 1962) was followed by investigations in a stream polluted by gas liquors. Batches of rainbow trout were held in cages in the stream below the discharge and water samples were taken every two hours for subsequent analysis. Values for Σ p 24-h LC50 for gas liquor phenols and un-ionized ammonia were compared with the observed fish mortality; a correct prediction was assumed if half a batch of fish died when the sum exceeded 1.0 for any period during the 24 h exposure period or when less than half the batch died and the sum did not exceed 1.0. Although the results of 40 individual days' observations gave an 80 per cent correct prediction on this basis, the predictive model had considerable deficiencies. The concentration of pollutants showed rapid fluctuations and on several days were very low. Inspection of the data shows that the 24-h LC50s for both ammonia and gas liquor phenols could be reduced by up to five-fold without affecting the accuracy of the predictions. These field experiments failed to confirm the laboratory findings.

11.4.2 RIVERS RECEIVING SEWAGE EFFLUENTS CONTAINING INDUSTRIAL WASTES

Following laboratory experiments on the predicted and observed toxicity to fish of sewage effluents containing industrial wastes (Lloyd and Jordan, 1963, 1964) a series of field experiments was carried out in which rainbow trout were exposed to polluted river waters either in cages, or, if the dissolved oxygen content of the water was too low, in aerated aquaria on the river bank. Again, water samples were taken every two hours and analyses of labile water quality characteristics were made immediately. Predictions of toxicity were made by summing the proportions of the threshold LC50 (Σ pt LC50) for ammonia, phenol, copper and zinc in the early studies (Herbert *et al.*, 1965) and cyanide was included later (Brown *et al.*, 1970). Other metals were analysed for, but the concentrations found were thought to be of insignificant importance for acute toxicity. The time series of Σ pt LC50 was compared with the observed mortalities. Mortalities usually occurred within the 3 days' observation period and since, in the hard river waters investigated, the threshold LC50s were close to the 48 h values, it was assumed that 50 per cent of the fish should die within 48 hours if the Σ pt LC50 exceeded unity during that period. Generally, it was found that the calculated toxicity tended to under-predict the observed mortalities, and, for some heavily polluted rivers, only 60 per cent of the observed toxicity was accounted for by the predictive method (Brown *et al.*, 1970). Where a river contained elevated levels of copper, which might have been complexed with soluble organic matter, a 48-h LC50 higher than the laboratory-derived value for copper in clean water was used by Herbert *et al.* (1965) to avoid over-prediction of toxicity.

These experiments showed that for those river waters which were acutely toxic to rainbow trout, the predicted toxicity was close to that observed, even though the concentrations of any one poison would have been insufficient alone to kill fish. Under-predictions could be explained by the probable presence of unmeasured pollutants. To this extent, the field investigations generally corroborated the laboratory experiments.

However, parallel attempts were made to extrapolate from the laboratory and field data on acute toxicity a prediction of the maximum values of Σ pt LC50 or 48-h LC50 which would allow natural fish populations to survive, as opposed to causing mortality among captive rainbow trout. For example, Herbert *et al.* (1965) thought that a fishery of some kind could be maintained in waters where the toxicity was kept below 0.2 of the threshold LC50, provided that the dissolved oxygen was maintained at a satisfactory level. A new approach to this aspect of the problem was begun by Edwards and Brown (1966) who attempted to find the limiting Σ pt LC50 above which a fishery would not exist. Pollutant concentrations in single water samples taken from 100 stations in the R. Trent, UK, were measured and the values of Σ pt LC50 for the individual poisons present were correlated with the status of the fish populations there. They concluded that non-salmonid fish populations could generally exist where the Σ pt LC50 for rainbow trout did not exceed 0.3 to 0.4, provided that the dissolved oxygen concentration was greater than 50 per cent of the air saturation value and the suspended solids no greater than 60 to 100 mg/ℓ. This value of 0.3 to 0.4 was similar to that obtained from a recalculation of data given by Allan *et al.* (1958) for the survival of a mixed non-salmonid fishery in a sewage effluent channel (Herbert *et al.*, 1965).

Later, Brown *et al.* (1970) criticized the adoption of these values on several grounds, referring to the tendency of predictions based on a limited number of pollutants to under-estimate the toxicity of river waters, and to the results of long-term experiments which showed that substantial mortalities occurred among rainbow trout exposed to concentrations as low as 0.2 of the 48-h LC50, particularly with chromium and cadmium. Also, the fish populations observed at field sampling stations may have been able to move in and out of the polluted stretch and were not necessarily continuously exposed to the toxic conditions.

To this list of potential sources of error at this stage can be added several others. The initial summation of proportions of toxic concentrations were based on threshold LC50s (Herbert, 1965) which, for the significant poisons and environmental conditions encountered in the field experiments, were close to the 48-h LC50s (Herbert *et al.*, 1965). Subsequently, 48-h LC50s were quoted in the basic method for calculating the toxicity of mixtures of toxicants (Brown, 1968) even though some of the values given (for example, copper and zinc in soft water) were for longer exposure periods. These data were still based on laboratory experiments with rainbow trout, and the relevance of the predictive model to field situations where a number of other, less sensitive, species of fish existed was not seriously questioned, mainly because of the lack of basic data for these species (Brown, 1968). Finally, in proposing limiting values for Σ p 48-h LC50 of up to a maximum of 0.4, it was not made clear that the mean values in rivers would be considerably less, and probably lower than 0.2.

It was this latter aspect that was developed by Alabaster *et al.* (1972), who studied the annual frequency distribution of Σ p 48-h LC50 at each of a number of sampling sites in the R. Trent catchment area; these distributions tended to be log normal. Data on the status of the fisheries at these sampling points indicated that some sort of non-salmonid fish population was present when the median Σ p 48-h LC50 (rainbow trout) was below 0.28, with a corresponding 95 percentile value of about 0.60. This upper limit was higher than those previously proposed; one possible cause was that, at the sites where the fish population was marginal, a significant proportion of the toxicity was caused by copper and although it was recognized from earlier work that the presence of organo-copper complexes would reduce the toxicity, an adjustment similar to that used by Herbert *et al.* (1965) was not made. However, it was recognized that the use of 48-h LC50s underestimated the toxic contribution made by cadmium and nickel in the long term and that values for Σ pt LC50 (rainbow trout) would be considerably higher for those sites where marginal fisheries existed. The scientific validity of using rainbow trout data in a model to predict the status of non-salmonid fisheries was questioned, but the general usefulness of the approach was defended on pragmatic grounds.

The same approach was also applied to data made available by the Yorkshire Water Authority, UK, on the quality of river water at 14 points in its area over a 6 year period, and results were similar to those found for the R. Trent catchment. There were too few data to define the exact boundary distribution of calculated toxicity between fishless and fish supporting waters, but the limiting Σ p 48-h LC50 (rainbow trout) found for the Trent discriminated clearly between 12 stations, there being one supporting only minnows and stickleback, on the fishless side of the boundary, and another marginal case where the river had for unknown periods been both fish-supporting and fishless (J. S. Alabaster and I. C. Hart, personal communication).

Solbé (1973) analysed chemical and fisheries data from the Willow Brook, UK, a stream polluted mainly by ammonia and zinc, and found that it was fishless where, over a 3 year period, the median and 95 percentile values of Σ p 48-h LC50 (rainbow trout) were 0.45 and 1.45 respectively. Good non-salmonid fish populations existed where the corresponding values were less than 0.25 and less than 0.9, and introduced brown and rainbow trout survived where values of 0.17 and 0.62 were found.

11.4.3 LAKE AND RIVER SYSTEMS RECEIVING HEAVY METALS

A similar exercise, but with monthly sampling, was reported by EIFAC (1977) in which the status of salmonid fish populations in a Norwegian lake and river system was correlated with the concentrations of copper and zinc present. In this study, the heavy metal concentrations (as 95 percentiles) were expressed as proportions of the corresponding EIFAC proposed water quality standards (synonymous with the no observed effect concentration, NOEC) for brown trout. A number of factors prevented this study from showing whether a satisfactory water quality for fisheries exists where the NOECs for individual pollutants are not exceeded, or whether the summed p NOECs should not exceed unity. Making allowances for the possible complexing of copper ions with soluble organic substances, salmonid populations were unaffected where the Σ p NOEC 95 percentile) was 2.0 but were absent at 5.0. In terms of Σ p 48-h LC50 (from EIFAC 1976, 1977), the corresponding 95 percentile values are 0.28 and 0.79.

Copper and zinc were also found to be the principal toxicants present in trout streams (hardness about $20\,mg/\ell$ as $CaCO_3$) in the catchment of the R. Mawddach in Wales, UK; where the annual median and 95 percentile Σ p 48-h LC50 (rainbow trout) of these two toxicants were about 0.3 and 0.8 respectively, the biomass of the fish was reduced, and where the corresponding values were about 0.5 and 1.0 respectively, fish were absent (Cremer and Warner, personal communication). The ratio of p 48-h LC50 of copper to that of zinc varied spatially and temporally, but annual median values ranged from 1:3 to 1:2 for different stations.

In a similar study of Canadian lakes in the Flin Flon area, Van Loon and Beamish (1977) found a slightly reduced population of fish in Hamell Lake (total hardness based on Ca of $40\,mg/\ell$ as $CaCO_3$) where the average concentrations in 3-monthly samples were up to $300\,\mu g$ Zn/ℓ and up to $15\,\mu g$ Cu/ℓ. There were only small seasonal differences in heavy metals content of the water. Based on EIFAC data, the zinc and copper present represented 0.22 and 0.17 of the t LC50 for salmonids respectively, giving a Σ pt LC50 of 0.39 and a corresponding Σ p NOEC (95 percentile) of 3.1. Cliff Lake, with a similar hardness, contained zinc concentrations of up to $120\,\mu g/\ell$ and copper up to $11\,\mu g/\ell$, representing a Σ pt LC50 of 0.21 and a Σ p NOEC (95 percentile) of 1.4; this lake contained an abundance of fish, including coregonids. These values are in agreement with those obtained in the Norwegian study.

It is possible, therefore, that concentrations of poisons of less than the individual NOECs do not have an additive action in mixtures; alternatively, since the pollution in these three study areas had been present for a considerable number of years, some acclimation by the fish populations, or genetic selection, may have occurred. There was certainly no evidence of more than additive joint action for these two metals.

11.4.4 CURRENT STUDIES

The approach outlined above is being extended in the UK; predictive models incorporating Σ p 48-h LC50s and Σ p NOEC for different fish species groups are being used to correlate water quality at contaminated river sites with the status of fisheries there (J. S. Alabaster, R. Lloyd and J. F. de L. G. Solbé, personal communication). One factor which has emerged is the importance of dissolved oxygen, which has had to be incorporated separately into the model.

11.4.5 SUMMARY

In summary, it has been shown that toxicity predictions based on chemical analysis can be made if the waters which are polluted are acutely lethal to fish, and that a fish population of some kind can exist where the median Σ pt LC50s (rainbow trout) is < 0.2. It is not known whether this condition is equivalent to a Σ p NOEC of < 1.0 (i.e. the sum of the individual fractions of the NOEC for the species present) or to a NOEC of < 1.0 for each individual toxicant (that is, where the fractions of the NOEC are not summed).

11.5 Uptake of toxicants

11.5.1 HEAVY METALS AND OTHER SUBSTANCES

Copper and zinc Wedmeyer (1968) was able to show that zinc[65] uptake by embryos of coho salmon was inhibited by dissolved copper in the range of 0 to 2.0 mg Cu/ℓ, but facilitated at 2.0 mg/ℓ. Although giving no further information on the interactions of these toxicants, he mentions that the differences could be related to their 'synergistic toxicity'. He also showed that Malachite green, commonly used to control fungus infections, also increased zinc permeability, presumably by reducing zinc binding on the chorion, especially when used at concentrations greater than about 1.0 mg/ℓ.

Copper, cadmium and lead Westernhagen *et al.* (1979) investigated the uptake of copper, cadmium and lead by embryo herring (*Clupea harengus*). Both copper and cadmium promoted the uptake of lead, but when concentrations of copper in the water were low, the presence of lead inhibited the uptake of cadmium while the presence of cadmium enhanced the uptake of copper. At relatively high concentrations of copper (0.075 to 0.133 mg Cu/ℓ), the uptake of copper was promoted by the presence of lead, but inhibited by the presence of cadmium at a given concentration of cadmium; increasing concentrations of copper also tended to impede the uptake of cadmium. Lead at 0.56 and 4.44 mg/ℓ promoted the accumulation of cadmium, but at 2.5 mg/ℓ, inhibited it.

Hewitt and Anderson (1978) showed that a reciprocal interaction occurs whereby copper and cadmium accumulated in gills at a higher rate when each agent was present in the ambient environment concurrently, rather than singly.

Zinc and cadmium Comparatively low levels of cadmium inhibited the uptake rate of zinc from water by mummichog, but inhibition of cadmium uptake by low levels of zinc was not observed (Eisler and Gardner, 1973).

Tests lasting 100 days, carried out by Spehar *et al.* (1978) with flagfish (*Jordanella floridae*) exposed to sub-lethal concentrations of mixtures of zinc and cadmium, showed that the uptake of one metal was not influenced by the presence of the other. This is consistent with their findings on the acute toxicity of the mixture, which was attributable mainly to zinc.

Zinc and DDT Accumulation of Zn^{65} from sea water by the alga (*Ulva rigida*) was investigated by Andryushchenko and Polikarpov (1974); they found that it was 12 to 36 per cent higher in the absence of DDT than in the presence of a concentration of 1 mg DDT/ℓ.

Cadmium and methoxychlor Nimmo and Bahner (1977) exposed shrimp (*Penaeus duorarum*) to cadmium and methoxychlor, to cadmium and methoxychlor separately and in combination, and showed that cadmium, but not methoxychlor, was accumulated by this organism, and that methoxychlor appeared to influence the processes of accumulation and loss of cadmium from the tissues.

Cadmium and PCB When PCB was present in the water together with cadmium, the accumulation of cadmium by the shrimp *(Penaeus duorarum)* was similar to that found when cadmium was applied alone (Nimmo and Bahner, 1977).

Mercury and magnesium (and azide and cyanide) Fujita *et al*. (1976) studied the accumulation of mercury by the freshwater diatom *Synedra ulna* and found that the rate of uptake was increased by the presence of magnesium at an optimal concentration of 0.1 mM Mg^{2+} in the standard buffer solution used to grow the organism. They suggested that this was attributable to an effect of magnesium on energy-linked metabolism and showed that azide and also cyanide (both inhibitors of respiratory enzymes) at a concentration of 0.01 mM CN markedly reduced the uptake of mercury.

Lead and xanthate Borg *et al*. (1976) found that the uptake of lead by trout-fry from soft water at $10\,^{\circ}C$ was increased by increased concentrations of xanthate, and they suggested that this might account for the increased toxicity of lead, it being assumed that lead xanthate was formed as an intermediary compound in the water close to the gill, and might also increase the solubility of lead in fat. They reviewed similar effects that occur with other types of organic sulphur compounds such as dimercaptopropanol, certain dithiocarbamates, and methyl mercaptan, in combination with metals such as copper and mercury.

11.5.2 PESTICIDES

DDT, dieldrin and methoxychlor Macek *et al*. (1970) found significant interaction between DDT and dieldrin in their uptake into the pyloric caecae of rainbow trout fed with these chemicals in their food. The presence of dieldrin increased the rate of accumulation of DDT and conversely the presence of DDT decreased the rate of accumulation of dieldrin. Dieldrin also reduced the elimination of DDT, although the converse was not true.

Mayer *et al*. (1970) measured the accumulation of DDT, methoxychlor and dieldrin in the fat of rainbow trout fed with these chemicals in their diet. The results were complicated. Dieldrin increased DDT storage whereas methoxychlor alone, and also interactively with dieldrin, reduced it. DDT and methoxychlor reduced dieldrin storage, depending upon the dose of dieldrin, and also reduced methoxychlor storage. Dieldrin and DDT interacted to reduce methoxychlor storage, depending on the dosage of the latter. To account for some of these results the authors suggested that DDT and possibly methoxychlor could cause selective induction of drug-metabolizing enzymes in the liver and cited and discussed supporting evidence for this.

DDE and heptachlor epoxide Veith *et al.* (1979) exposed fathead minnow to sub-lethal aqueous concentrations of DDE, heptachlor and a mixture of the two and found that concentration factors for each of the substances were similar whether or not they were present alone or together in the water.

Carbaryl and butylester and dichloro-nitrosalicylanilide Statham and Lech (1976) found a more than additive lethal effect of carbaryl on 2,4-D butylester and 2',5-dichloro-4'-nitrosalicylanilide in rainbow trout. They concluded that the increased toxicity could be caused by increasing the uptake of the toxic compounds from the water, but did not carry out residue analyses to confirm this.

Piperonyl butoxide, aldrin, methoxychlor, and trifluralin Reinbold and Metcalf (1976) found that piperonyl butoxide greatly increased the accumulation in green sunfish (*Lepomis cyanellus*) of methoxychlor (15 times), aldrin (21 times) and trifluralin (45 times). The effect was interpreted as a possible inhibition of mixed-function oxidases by piperonyl butoxide in preventing detoxication.

11.5.3 SUMMARY

The few data available on the joint effect of toxicants on their uptake by aquatic organisms allow only tentative conclusions to be drawn.

For heavy metals, there is evidence that the uptake of zinc, lead and cadmium by fish embryos is inhibited by low concentrations of copper and enhanced by high concentrations. The uptake of cadmium is similarly affected by lead but, in one study, inhibition by low concentrations of zinc was not found. There are also observations on fish showing that the uptake of either copper or cadmium can be enhanced by the presence of the other. The failure to find any reciprocal effect on uptake between zinc and cadmium in one study involving the use of flagfish may be attributable to the particular concentrations chosen.

Substances such as DDT, methoxychlor and xanthate have been shown to increase the uptake of heavy metals in aquatic organisms but some, such as PCB, have had no apparent effect, while others, such as magnesium, azide and cyanide, have reduced uptake.

With pesticides the effect of either dieldrin, DDT or methoxychlor or combinations of any two of these compounds, on the accumulation in fish through their food of any of the others, was generally inhibitory, except for the effect of DDT on the accumulation of dieldrin.

Accumulation of combinations of toxicants can be influenced by:

(a) inhibition of detoxifying enzymes which can influence the uptake or loss of xenobiotics;
(b) action upon biological surfaces, thereby affecting the permeability of membranes to other toxicants present;
(c) physiological effects, such as increasing the flow of blood through the gill, thereby increasing the uptake of toxicants; and
(d) external factors, such as forming of complexes (see also Introduction).

From the information available, no general rules for the uptake of toxicants in the presence of other toxicants can be deduced. There is no clear evidence of a correlation being found between the toxicity and the accumulation of combined toxicants, although several papers speculate on this subject.

This aspect of mixture toxicity would require much detailed research to achieve even a superficial understanding of the interaction involved. However, this should not detract from the need to carry out empirical studies on those factors (including toxicants) which affect the accumulation of substances in fish which may reach concentrations harmful to the health of consumers, including man.

11.6 Summary and conclusions

The choice of the most suitable model to study the joint effects of mixtures of poisons on fish and other organisms depends on the type of information required. For the production of mixtures with maximum lethality, for example in the development of pesticides, response addition has been widely used, whereas for the protection of freshwater organisms by the application of water quality standards, the concentration-addition model is more relevant. For this reason the experimental data reviewed in this report have been derived mainly from experiments based on the latter model and particular attention has been given to identifying the extent of the deviations from a strictly additive relationship. Where possible, raw data presented within a response-addition model have been re-examined on the basis of the concentration-addition model.

The conclusions drawn from the data are discussed in relation to the formulation of water quality criteria for freshwater fish regarding mixtures of toxicants. Attention is drawn to research needs.

11.6.1 SUMMARY OF DATA

Most of the laboratory data reviewed relate to freshwater fish. For these species, the extent to which the joint effects of toxicants deviate from additive may depend upon several factors, including the measured response (for example, whether long term or short term and whether lethal or non-lethal), the magnitude (percentage) of response, the type of toxicant and its proportional contribution to the toxicity of the mixture, water quality characteristics (such as hardness), species, stage in the life cycle of the fish and prior acclimation to toxicant, and size of the ration. Some research has been conducted which indicates the relative importance of these variables in the joint action of mixtures of toxicants but more is required.

For mixtures of commonly occurring constituents of sewage and industrial wastes (namely, ammonia, phenol, cyanide, copper, zinc, cadmium, nickel, chromium, mercury, other metals and other substances), it has been shown that the acute lethal toxicity is between 0.4 and 2.6 times that predicted from the sum of the proportions of the respective toxic units of the constituents, with a median value of 0.95; 87 per cent of the results lie within the range 0.5 to 1.5 of the predicted values. Somewhat similar results have been found for:

(a)   sewage effluents, based upon the predicted contribution of toxicants known to be present;
(b)   samples of river water, the toxicity of which has been increased experimentally by the addition of known amounts of ammonia, phenol, cyanide, copper and zinc; and
(c)   several drilling fluids and a gas liquor.

The median value for all of these is 0.85 of the predicted value.

For mixtures of pesticides and other substances, however, the acute lethal toxicity tends to be somewhat greater than predicted, with a median value of about 1.3.

Most of the data reported derived from a lethal response related to median lethal values (LC50s), but one study with rainbow trout using ammonia and copper showed that the joint action, while additive in terms of the LC50, was 1.4 times more than additive for the LC10 value. Whether this effect is of practical significance is a matter for conjecture and possibly further research.

Comparatively little attention has been given to the effect on joint toxicity of the relative toxic proportions of the chemicals present, although it has been amply demonstrated that these can be profound. In particular, it has been shown that one constituent at concentrations below a certain pt LC50 may not contribute any toxic effect, for example with mixtures of ammonia and nitrate, and of ammonia, phenol and zinc. Some data suggest that the critical pt LC50 is between 0.1 and 0.2 but the bulk of the data reviewed in this report have not been derived from experiments designed specifically to examine this question. In the case of phenol, however, there is fairly consistent evidence that, at p LC50 values above about 0.3, its joint effect with other toxicants is additive, while at p LC50 values lower than this, it is less than additive, and lower than 0.1, antagonistic.

Few data are available on the relation between the short- and long-term joint toxic action of constituents in mixtures. However, unpublished work has shown that, for mixtures of cadmium and mercury and of chromium and nickel the lethal toxicity may be additive in the short term, but markedly more than additive in the longer term. These investigations need to be extended to other mixtures, particularly to those comprising commonly occurring toxicants.

In contrast the few studies with mixtures of toxicants on sub-lethal responses of fish indicate that the effect on growth was consistently less additive than the corresponding effect on survival; furthermore, one study showed that the joint effect of toxicants both on fish growth and production was less than additive. It is possible, therefore, that as concentrations of toxicants are reduced towards the level of no effect (NOEC), their potential for addition is also reduced. A single exception is in the case of avoidance behaviour of salmonids where the joint effect of zinc and copper appeared to be slightly more than additive.

There are few data available to compare the joint effect of a given mixture of toxicants to two or more species of fish, and none are available to make this comparison for identical experimental conditions. Nevertheless, there is no strong evidence for inter-specific differences in response to the joint effect of mixtures of toxicants, and the greatest difference found relates to mixtures of cyanide and zinc, for which the joint action was apparently 0.4 times as additive for bluegill and 1.4 times as additive for fathead minnow.

The data available for aquatic invertebrates, like those for fish, show a generally additive joint action for constituents commonly present in sewage and industrial wastes and a generally more than additive joint action for pesticides. There are data for aquatic plants which also show generally slightly less than additive joint action of metals, but only inconsistent and unquantitative data are available for the joint effect of pesticides.

Field studies have shown that predictions of acute toxicity can be based on chemical analysis for those waters which contain sufficient common toxicants to be acutely lethal to fish; also that a fish population of some kind can exist in less polluted waters where the median Σ pt LC50s (rainbow trout) is < 0.2. It is not known whether this condition is equivalent to a Σ p NOEC of < 1.0 (that is, the sum of the individual fractions of the NOEC for the species present), or to a NOEC of < 1.0 for each individual toxicant (that is, fractions of the NOEC are not summed).

There are comparatively few data available on the joint effect of toxicants on their uptake in aquatic organisms. However, it is clear that, in the case of metals, the uptake of one may be increased or decreased according to the concentration of the other metal present; in the presence of other substances it may be either increased or decreased or not affected at all, depending on the substances present. With pesticides, feeding trials have shown the interaction between dieldrin, DDT and methoxychlor to be complicated but generally mutually inhibitory. In general, the joint effect of toxicants on the lethal and sub-lethal responses of fish are not explained by changes in the uptake of the substances concerned.

11.6.2 SCOPE FOR FURTHER RESEARCH

The research carried out so far has been directed mainly towards combinations of those toxicants commonly present in water, and for which valid water quality standards are required for the protection of aquatic life. Evaluation of the data suggests that, with a very few possible exceptions, markedly more than additive effects do not occur even when lethal responses are tested, and that normally joint effects are within the range of 0.5 to 2-fold times as additive. Furthermore, the general inference of the data reviewed here is that toxicant concentrations lower than the NOEC do not contribute to the toxicity of a mixture; in other words, they are 'levels of no effect' both singly and in mixtures. A more conservative approach is given in Water Quality Criteria (US Environmental Protection Agency 1972) suggesting that concentrations lower than 0.2 NOEC do not add to the toxicity of a mixture; this fraction was derived from a general feeling of what might be the case, rather than from the existence of explicit experimental evidence.

In the context of regulatory activities, the evidence reviewed in this report may form a sufficient basis for a working hypothesis; if not, then further research will be required in the following areas:

(a) effects of toxicants singly and in mixtures on biochemical and physiological processes and their interaction, including interaction at receptor sites,

(b) field studies on fish populations at sites where mixtures of toxicants occur at concentrations close to the NOEC.

Both these areas of research pose considerable problems. One of the main difficulties of extending the existing concentration-additive experimental techniques to mixtures containing toxicants at less than the NOEC is that there is no response common to all toxicants which can be measured with sufficient precision for additive effects to be detected at the low concentrations that have to be used.

In the absence of such a methodology, information has to be derived from other sources. At present, the knowledge of fish physiology and biochemistry has not reached the point where a quantitative prediction of individual toxicant effects is possible. Even with the knowledge of how a substance, by itself, affects each of a variety of biochemical and physiological processes, it may not be possible to predict the total effect on a particular function. With mixtures of toxicants the problem is even greater, even when the relationship between dose and response for the individual components is well described (Veldstra, 1956). For example, Lloyd and Swift (1976) in discussing various physiological and bio-chemical responses of rainbow trout to ammonia and phenol, singly and together, considered that knowledge was not yet sufficient to explain their joint effect on survival, or on the accumulation of phenol.

Studies of mechanisms of physiological interactions are expensive and time-consuming and represent an area where inspired research is required if new insights are to emerge.

The evaluation of the effect of toxicant mixtures on natural or captive fish populations in field situations poses a different set of problems. One of the major difficulties is the large number of chemical analyses required to quantify all the variables which might affect fish health. A detailed examination of contaminated lakes might be rewarding since the concentrations of toxicants there are less likely to fluctuate rapidly and thus sampling frequency can be reduced. When relating water quality to the presence or absence of fish, there is a need to measure toxicity directly, rather than rely on predictions alone. Even when un-diluted river water is not demonstrably toxic, it may be possible to make some estimate of the fractional LC50 of the water by making several separate labora-tory estimations based on the addition of different toxicants in sufficient quantity to make the water demonstrably toxic. Also, Esvelt *et al.* (1973) have demonstrated how, for individual samples (of effluent) in which there is less than 50 per cent kill, the toxicity expressed as a fraction of the LC50 can be estimated by extrapolation, provided a sufficient number of samples from the same source, but having a higher toxicity, have been tested, although it must be assumed that there are no marked differences in percentage composition between samples.

11.7 Tentative water quality criteria

The question arises as to whether the tentative water quality criteria for individual toxicants proposed by EIFAC (see Chapters 1–10) are appropriate or not to mix-tures of the toxicants concerned. Taking data for rainbow trout, for example, the recommended criteria for ammonia is 0.125 of the lethal threshold concen-tration; for monohydric phenols it is 0.25 of the 18-week LC50, and between 0.1 and 0.2 of the 24-h LC50; for zinc the 95 percentile and 50 percentile values are 0.1 and 0.03 respectively of the 7-d LC50; for 'soluble' copper, the corresponding figures are 0.2 and 0.05 of the 50-d LC50 value. In all cases, therefore, the recommended criteria are only small fractions of the lethal threshold concentrations. This conclusion would also be valid for non-salmonid species.

The information reviewed in this report on the effect of mixtures of toxicants on fish would support the conclusions that the tentative water quality criteria promulgated by EIFAC would be applicable to situations where more than one of the toxicants considered were present. Therefore, there would appear to be little justification to set more stringent standards in such situations.

11.8 Definitions

Σ pt LC50:   the sum of concentrations of toxicants expressed as a proportion (p) of their respective threshold (t) concentrations, lethal within an extended exposure period to 50 per cent of the fish (used particularly alongside data for short exposure periods).

Σ TU: as above (used particularly in discussing models of joint action).

Σ p 48-h LC50:   as above but for an exposure period of 48 h.

NOEC: the concentration having no observed effect.

11.9 References

ABRAM, F. S. H. and WILSON, P. (1979). The acute toxicity of CS to rainbow trout. *Water Res.* 13, 631–635

ABT, K., GRAUWILER, J. and SCHÖN, H. (1972). Acute toxicity of drug combinations. A method for evaluating the interaction of the active components. *Proc. Eur. Soc. Stud. Drug Toxicity* 13, 192–195

ADELMAN, I. R. and SMITH, L. L. Jr. (1976). Fathead minnows (*Pimephales promelas*) and goldfish (*Carassius auratus*) as standard fish in bioassays and their reaction to potential reference toxicants. *J. Fish. Res. Board Can.* 33(2), 209–214

ALABASTER, J. S. (1969). Survival of fish in 164 herbicides, insecticides, fungicides, wetting agents and miscellaneous substances. *Int. Pest Control.* 12 (March/April issue), 29–35

ALABASTER, J. S. (1981). Joint action of mixtures of toxicants on aquatic organisms. Soc. Chem. Ind. Symposium on joint action of mixtures of drugs or pesticides. *Chem. Ind.* 1 Aug, 529–534

ALABASTER, J. S., LLOYD, R. and CALAMARI, D. (1981). The joint effect of toxicants on aquatic life. Proc. Int. Symp. on principles for the interpretation of the results of testing procedures in ecotoxicology

ALABASTER, J. S., GARLAND, J. H. N., HART, I. C. and SOLBÉ, J. F. de L. G. (1972). An approach to the problem of pollution and fisheries. *Symp. Zool. Soc. Lond.*, 87–114

ALDERDICE, D. F. and FORRESTER, C. R. (1968). Some effects of salinity and temperature on early development and survival of the English sole (*Parophys vetulus*). *J. Fish. Res. Board Can.* 25(3), 495–521

ALLAN, I. R. H., HERBERT, D. W. M. and ALABASTER, J. S. (1958). A field and laboratory study of fish in a sewage effluent. *Fish. Invest. Min. Agric. Fish. Food G.B.* 6(2), 76. London, HMSO

ALLEN, L. A., BLEZARD, N. and WHEATLAND, A. B. (1948). Formation of cyanogen chloride during chlorination of certain liquids; toxicity of such liquids to fish. *J. Hyg.* **46**, 18–93

ANDERSON, P. D. and d'APOLLONIA, S. (1978). Aquatic animals. In *Principles of ecotoxicology*, ed. G. C. BUTLER, Section 3, Chapter 9 Wiley, London (SCOPE Report, **12**)

ANDERSON, P. D. and WEBER, L. J. (1975a). The toxicity to aquatic populations of mixtures containing certain heavy metals. In *Proceedings of the International Conference on heavy metals in the environment*, Canada, October 27–31. University of Toronto, Toronto Institute of Environmental Studies, 933–953

ANDERSON, P. D. and WEBER, L. J. (1975b). Toxic responses as a quantitative function of body size. *Toxicol. Appl. Pharmacol.* **33**, 471–483

ANDERSON, P. D. (1976). The multiple toxicity of certain heavy metals: additive actions and interactions. In *Proceedings of the Workshop on toxicity to biota of metal forms in natural waters*, ed. R. W. Andrew, P. V. Hodson and D. E. Konasewich. Windsor, Canada, International Joint Commission Research Advisory Board, 263–282

ANDERSON, P. D., HOROVITCH, H. and WEINSTEIN, N. L. (1979a). Pollutant mixtures in the aquatic environment: A complex problem in toxic hazard assessment. *Tech. Rep. Fish. Mar. Serv. Can.* **862**, 100–114

ANDERSON, P. E., HOROVITCH, H. and WEINSTEIN, N. L. (1979b). The multiple toxicity of vanadium, nickel and phenol to fish. Prepared for the *Alberta Oil Sands Environmental Research Program by Department of Biology*, Concordia University, AOSERP Report **79**, 109

ANDRYUSHCHENKO, V. V. and POLIKARPOV, G. G. (1974). Experimental study of uptake of Zn^{65} and DDT by *Ulva rigida* from seawater polluted with both agents. *Hydrobiol. J.* **10(4)**, 41–46

ARIENS, E. J. (1972). Adverse drug interactions. Interactions of drugs on the pharmaco-dynamic level. *Proc. Bur. Soc. Stud. Drug Toxicity* **13**, 137–163

ASHFORD, J. R. and COBBY, J. M. (1974). A system of models for the action of drugs applied singly or jointly to biological organisms. *Biometrics* **30**, 11–31

ASHFORD, J. R. and SMITH, C. S. (1964). General models for quantal response to the joint action of a mixture of drugs. *Biometrika* **51**, 413–428

ASHFORD, J. R. (1965). An alternative system for the classification of mathematical models for quantal responses to mixtures of drugs in biological assay. *Biometrics* **21**, 181–188

BAHNER, L. H. and NIMMO, D. R. (1975). Methods to assess effects of combinations of toxicants, salinity and temperatures on estuarine animals. In *Trace substances in environmental health*, ed. D. D. Hemphill, University of Missouri, Columbia, Missouri, 169–177

BANDT, H. J., (1946). Über Versteärkte Schadwirkungen auf Fische, insbesondere uber erhönte Giftwirkung durch Kombination von Abwassergiften. *Beitr. Wasser Chem.*, **1**, 15

BENDER, M. B. (1969). The toxicity of the hydrolysis and breakdown products of malathion to the fathead minnow (*Pimephales promelas*, Rafinesque). *Water Res.* **3**, 571–582

BENIJTS-CLAUS, C. and BENIJTS, F. (1976). The effect of low lead and zinc concentrations on the larval development of the mud-crab (*Rhithropanopeus harrisii* Gould). In *Sub-lethal effects of toxic chemicals on aquatic animals*, ed. J. H. Koeman, Elsevier, New York, 43–52

BIANUCCI, F. and LEGNAGNI, P. (1973). Toxicity to *Alburnus alburnus* var. *alborella* of mixtures of hexavalent chromium and anionic detergent. *Ig. Mod.* **60**, 531-537

BIESINGER, K. E., ANDREW, R. W. and ARTHUR, J. W. (1974). Chronic toxicity of NTA (nitrilotri-acetate) and metal-NTA complexes to *Daphnia magna*. *J. Fish. Res. Board Can.* **31**(4), 486-490

BILLS, T. D. and MARKING, L. L. (1976). Toxicity of 3-trifluoromethyl-4-nitrophenol (TFM), 2', 5-dichloro-4'-nitrosalicylanilide (Bayer 73), and a 98:2 mixture to fingerlings of seven fish species and to eggs and fry of coho salmon. *Invest. Fish Control USFWS*, **69**, 9

BLISS, C. I. (1939). The toxicity of poisons applied jointly. *Ann. Appl. Biol.* **26**, 585-615

BORG, H., KARLSSON, A.-M. and LITHNER, G. (1976). Inverkan av flotations-reagenset isopropylxantat på blyupptaget hos öring — resultat av laboratorieförsök (Effects of the flotation agent isopropylxanthate on lead uptake in trout (*Salmo trutta*); results of experimental studies). *Statens Naturvardsverk Undersoknings-laboratoriet*, SNV PM **754**, May, 41

BRODERIUS, S. J. and SMITH, L. L. (1979). Lethal and sub-lethal effects of binary mixtures of cyanide and hexavalent chromium, zinc or ammonia to the fathead minnow (*Pimephales promelas*) and rainbow trout (*Salmo gairdneri*). *J. Fish. Res. Board Can.* **36**(2), 164-172

BROWN, C. C. (1978). The statistical analysis of dose-effect relationships. In *Principles of ecotoxicology*, ed. G. C. Butler, Wiley, London, Chapter 6, SCOPE Report **12**

BROWN, V. M. (1968). The calculation of the acute toxicity of mixtures of poisons to rainbow trout. *Water Res.* **2**, 723-733

BROWN, V. M. and DALTON, R. A. (1970). The acute lethal toxicity to rainbow trout of mixtures of copper, phenol, zinc and nickel. *J. Fish. Biol.* **2**, 211-216

BROWN, V. M., JORDAN, D. H. M. and TILLER, B. A. (1969). The acute toxicity to rainbow trout of fluctuating concentrations and mixtures of ammonia, phenol and zinc. *J. Fish Biol.* **1**, 1-9

BROWN, V. M., MITROVIC, V. V. and STARK, G. T. C. (1968). Effects of chronic exposure to zinc on toxicity of a mixture of detergent and zinc. *Water Res.* **21**, 255-263

BROWN, V. M., SHURBEN, D. G. and SHAW, D. (1970). Studies on water quality and the absence of fish from some polluted English streams. *Water Res.* **4**, 363-382

BUCKSTEEG, W., THIELE, H. and STOLTZEL, K. (1955). Die Beeinflussund von Fischen durch Giftstoffe aus Abwassern. *Vom Wasser* **22**, 194-211

BUIKEMA, A. L., Jr., SEE, C. L. and CAIRNS, J. Jr. (1977). Rotifer sensitivity to combinations of inorganic water pollutants. *OWRT Project A-071-VA VPI-VWRRC-BULL 92*, December

CAIRNS, J. and SCHEIER, A. (1968). A comparison of the toxicity of some common industrial waste components tested individually and combined. *Prog. Fish-Cult.* **30**, 3-8

CALAMARI, D. and ALABASTER, J. S. (1980). An approach to theoretical models in evaluating the effects of mixtures of toxicants in the aquatic environment. *Chemosphere* **2**, 533-538

CALAMARI, D. and MARCHETTI, R. (1970). L'analisi tossicologica nel controllo delle acque: interazioni fra inquinanti. *Ig. Mod.* **63**, 455-471

CALAMARI, D. (1972). Applicazione di un modello per lo studio delle interazioni tra due sostanze in tossicologia ittica. *N. Ann. Ig. Microbiol.* **23**, 419–425

CALAMARI, D. (1973). The toxicity of mixtures of metals and surfactants to rainbow trout (*Salmo gairdneri* Rich.). *Water Res.* **7**, 1453–1464

CHERKINSKY, S. N. (1957). The theoretical basis for hygienic standardization of simultaneous pollution of watercourses with several harmful substances. *Gig. Sanit.* **22**(8), 3–9 (in Russian, English summary)

CHRISTENSEN, E. R. and ZIELSKI, A. A. (1980). Toxicity of arsenic and PCB to a green alga (*Chlamydomonas*). *Bull. Environ. Contam. Toxicol.* **25**, 43–48

COCHRAN, W. G. and COX, G. M. (1957). *Experimental designs.* Wiley, New York, 2nd edn

COOPER, V. A. and SOLBE, J. F. de L. G. (1978). Reducing the toxicity of cadmium sulphate to rainbow trout (*Salmo gairdneri*) by preliminary exposure of fish to zinc sulphate, with and without intermittent exposure to cadmium. A progress report. *Water Res. Cent. ILR*, **750**, 8

DAS, M. N. and KULKARNI, G. A. (1966). Incomplete block designs for bioassays. *Biometrics* **22**, 706–729

DAWSON, V. K. and MARKING, L. L. (1973). Toxicity of mixtures of quinaldine sulfate and MS-222 to fish. *Invest. Fish Control USFWS* **53**, 11

DAWSON, V. K., CUMMING, K. B. and GILDERHUS, P. A. (1977). Efficacy of 3-trifluoromethyl-4-nitrophenol (TFM), 2',5-dichloro-4'-nitrosalicylanilide (Bayer 73), and a 98:2 mixture as lampricides in laboratory studies. *Invest. Fish Control USFWS*, **77**, 11

DETHLEFSEN, V. (1977). The influence of DDT and DDE on the embryogenesis and the mortality of larvae of cod (*Gadus morhua* L.). *Meeresforschung* **25**, 115–148

DEVLAMINCK, F. (1960). Etude de mélanges de toxiques, appliquée a l'évaluation de la nocivité, a l'egard du poisson, des effluents de cokeries. *Liège, Centre Belge pour l'Etude et Documentation des Eaux*

DOUDOROFF, P. (1952). Some recent developments in the study of toxic industrial wastes. *Proc. Pac. N.W. Ind. Waste Conf.* **4**, 21–25

DOUDOROFF, P., LEDUC, G. and SCHNEIDER, C. R. (1966). Acute toxicity to fish of solutions containing complex metal cyanides, in relation to concentrations of molecular hydrocyanic acid. *Trans. Am. Fish. Soc.* **95**, 6–22

DUGAN, P. R. (1967). Influence of chronic exposure to anionic detergents on toxicity of pesticides to goldfish. *J. Water Pollut. Control Fed.* **39**, 63–71

EATON, J. G. (1973). Chronic toxicity of a copper, cadmium and zinc mixture to the fathead minnow (*Pimephales promelas* Rafinesque). *Water Res.* **7**, 1723–1736

EDWARDS, R. W. and BROWN, V. M. (1967). Pollution and fisheries:a progress report. *Water Pollut. Control* **66**, 63–78

EIFAC (1975). Working Party on Toxicity Testing Procedures. Report on fish toxicity testing procedures. *EIFAC Tech. Pap.* **24**, 25

EIFAC (1976). Working Party on Water Quality Criteria for European Freshwater Fish with the Cooperation of the United Nations Environment Programme (UNEP). Report on copper and freshwater fish. *EIFAC Tech. Pap.* **27**, 21

EIFAC Working Party on Biological Monitoring. (1977). Report on the effect of zinc and copper pollution on the salmonid fisheries in a river and lake system in central Norway. *EIFAC Tech. Pap.* **29**, 34

EISLER, R. and GARDNER, G. R. (1973). Acute toxicology to an estuarine teleost of mixtures of cadmium, copper and zinc salts. *J. Fish Biol.* **5**, 131–142

ESVELT, L. A., KAUFMAN, W. J. and SELLECK, R. E. (1973). Toxicity assessment of treated municipal waste-waters. *J. Water Pollut. Control Fed.* **45**, 1558-1572

FABACHER, D. L. and CHAMBERS, H. (1974). Resistance to herbicides in insecticide-resistant mosquito-fish (*Gambusia affinis*). *Environ. Lett.* **7**, 15-20

FABACHER, D. L., DAVIS, J. D. and FABACHER, D. A. (1976). Apparent potentiation of cotton defoliant DEF by methyl parathion in mosquitofish. *Bull. Environ. Contam. Toxicol.* **16**, 716-718

FEDELI, L., MENEGHINI, L., SANGIOVANNI, M., SCROLLINI, F. and GORI, E. (1972). Quantitative evaluation of joint drug action. *Proc. Eur. Soc. Stud. Drug Toxicity* **13**, 231-245

FERGUSON, D. E. and BRINGHAM, C. R. (1966). The effects of combinations of insecticides on susceptible and resistant mosquitofish. *Bull. Environ. Contam. Toxicol.* **1**, 97-103

FINNEY, D. J. (1964). *Statistical methods in biological assays*. Griffin, London, 2nd edn.

FINNEY, D. J. (1971). *Probit analysis*. CUP, 3rd edn, 318

FITZGERALD, G. P. (1963). Factors affecting the toxicity of copper to algae and fish. Paper presented to the *Division of Water and Waste Chemistry, American Chemical Society*, ACS National Meeting, September 8-13

FREEMAN, L. and FOWLER, I. (1953). Toxicity of combinations of certain inorganic compounds to *Daphnia magna* Straus. *Ind. Wastes* **25**, 1191-1195

FRIEDLAND, S. A. and RUBLEVA, M. N. (1958). The problem of hygienic standards for waters simultaneously polluted with several harmful substances. *Gig. Sanit.* **23**, 12-6 (in Russian, English summary)

FUJITA, M., TAKABATAKE, E. and IWASAKI, K. (1976). Effects of light, magnesium, and cyanide on accumulation of mercury by a freshwater diatom, *Synedra*. *Bull. Environ. Contam. Toxicol.* **16**, 164-172

GADDUM, J. M. (1953). Bioassays and mathematics. *Pharmacol. Rev.* **5**, 87-134

GALLIMORE, B. and ANDERSON, P. D. (1979). Life cycle patterns in lethal tolerance of fish exposed to cadmium, zinc and their mixtures. *Pharmacology* **21**(3), 250 (abstr.)

GEHRS, C. W., EYMAN, L. D., JOLLEY, R. L. and THOMPSON, J. E. (1974). Effects of stable chlorine-containing organics on aquatic environments. *Nature, Lond.* **249**, 675-676

GRAY, J. S. and VENTILLA, R. J. (1973). Growth rates of sediment-living marine protozoan as a toxicity indicator for heavy metals. *Ambio* **2**, 118-121

HEISINGER, J. F., HANSEN, C. D. and KIM, J. H. (1979). Effect of selenium dioxide on the accumulation and acute toxicity of mercuric chloride in goldfish. *Arch. Environ. Contam. Toxicol.* **8**, 279-283

HENDRICKS, A. C. (1978). Response of *Selenastrum capricornutum* to zinc sulfides. *J. Water Pollut. Control Fed.* **50**, 163-168

HERBERT, D. W. M. (1962). The toxicity to rainbow trout of spent still liquors from the distillation of coal. *Ann. Appl. Biol.* **50**, 755-777

HERBERT, D. W. M. and SHURBEN, D. G. (1964). The toxicity to fish of mixtures of poisons. 1. Salts of ammonia and zinc. *Ann. Appl. Biol.* **53**, 33-41

HERBERT, D. W. M. and VANDYKE, J. M. (1964). The toxicity to fish of mixtures of poisons. 2. Copper-ammonia and zinc-phenol mixtures. *Ann. Appl. Biol.* **53**, 415-421

HERBERT, D. W. M., JORDAN, D. H. M. and LLOYD, R. (1965). A study of some fishless rivers in the industrial Midlands. *J. Inst. Sewage Purif.* **1965**, 569-582

HERBES, S. E. and BEAUCHAMP, J. J. (1977). Toxic interaction of mixtures of two coal conversion effluent components (resorcinol and 6-methyl-quinoline) to *Daphnia magna. Bull. Environ. Contam. Toxicol.* **17**, 25–32

HEWITT, L. A. and ANDERSON, P. D. (1979). Aspects of supra-additive interactions between cadmium and copper in fish exposed to lethal mixtures. *Pharmacology* **21**(3), 210 (abstr.)

HEWLETT, P. S. and PLACKETT, R. L.(1959). A unified theory for quantal responses to mixtures of drugs: non-interactive action. *Biometrics* **15**, 591–610

HEWLETT, P. S. and PLACKETT, R. L. (1979). *An introduction to the interpretation of quantal responses in biology.* Edward Arnold, London. 82

HODSON, P. V., ROSS, C. W., NIIMI, A. J. and SPRY, D. J. (1977). Statistical considerations in planning aquatic bioassays. *Environ. Prot. Serv. Tech. Rep. Can.* **(EPS-5-AR-77-1)**, 15–31

HOWELL, J. H., KING, E. L., SMITH, A. J. and HANSON, L. H. (1964). Synergism of 5,2′-dichloro-4′-nitrosalicylanilide and 3-trifluormethyl-4-nitrophenol in a selective lampricide. *Tech. Rep. Great Lakes Fish. Comm.* **8**, 21

HOWLAND, R. M. (1969). Interaction of antimycin A and rotenone in fish bioassays. *Prog. Fish-Cult.* **31**(1), 33

HUCKABEE, J. W. and GRIFFITH, N. A. (1974). Toxicity of mercury and selenium to the eggs of carp (*Cyprinus carpio*). *Trans. Am. Fish. Soc.* **103**(4), 822–825

HUTCHINSON, T. C. (1973). Comparative studies of the toxicity of heavy metals to phytoplankton and their synergistic interactions. *Water Pollut. Res. Can.* **8**, 68–90

HUTCHINSON, T. C. and CZYRSKA, H. (1973). Cadmium and zinc toxicity and synergism to aquatic plants. *Water Pollut. Res. Can.* **7**, 59–65

Istituto di Ricerca sulle Acque (Italian Institute for Water Research). (1975). Rapporto sulla attività dell 'Istituto nel biennio, 1973–1974. *Quad. Ist. Ric. Acque Roma*, **26**

JENKINS, C. R. (1964). A study of some toxic components in oil refinery effluents. Ph.D. Thesis submitted to *Oklahoma State University*. Stillwater, Oklahoma, USA, 73

JELLEY, R. L. (1973). Chlorination effects on organic constituents in effluents from domestic sanitary sewage treatment plants. *Publ. Oak Ridge Natl. Lab.* **(ORNL-RM-4290)**

KATZ, B. M. and COHEN, G. M. (1976). Toxicities of 'excessively' chlorinated organic compounds. *Bull. Environ. Contam. Toxicol.* **15**(6), 611–617

KAWATSKI, J. A. (1973). Acute toxicities of antimycin A, Bayer 73, and TFM to the ostracod *Cyptetta kawatai. Trans. Am. Fish. Soc.* **102**, 829–831

KEMPTHORNE, O. (1952). *The design and analysis of experiments.* Wiley, New York

KIM, J. H., BIRKS, B. and HEISINGER, J. F. (1977). Protective action of selenium against mercury in northern creek chubs. *Bull. Environ. Contam. Toxicol.* **17**, 132–136

KOENIG, C. C. (1977). The effects of DDT and Mirex alone and in combinations on the reproduction of a salt marsh cyprinodont fish (*Adinia xenica*). In *Physiological responses of marine biota to pollutants*, ed. F. J. Vernberg et al., Academic Press, New York, 357–376

KÖNEMANN, W. H. (1979). Fish toxicity tests with mixtures of more than two chemicals: a proposal for a quantitative approach and experimental results. In *Quantitative structure-activity relationships for kinetics and toxicity of aquatic pollutants and their mixtures in fish*, Thesis for doctorate by W. H. Könemann, University of Utrecht, 55–67

KRIEGER, R. I. and LEE, P. W. (1973). Inhibition of *in vivo* and *in vitro* epoxidation of aldrin and potentiation of toxicity of various insecticide chemicals by diquat in two species of fish. *Arch. Environ. Contam. Toxicol.* 1, 112

LABOREY, F. and LAVOLLAY, J. (1967). Sur la toxicité exercée par Zn^{++} et Cd^{++} dans la croissance d'*Aspergillus niger*, l'antagonisme de ces ions et l'interaction Mg^{++} Zn^{++} Cd^{++}. *C. R. Hébd. Séances Acad. Sci. Paris (Ser. D. Sci. Nat.)* 24, 2937-2940

LaROCHE, G., GARDNER, G. R., EISLER, R., JACKIM, E. H., YEVISH, P. P. and ZAROOGIAN, G. E. (1973). Analysis of toxic response in marine poikilotherms. In *Bioassay techniques and environmental chemistry*, ed. G. E. Glass. Ann Arbor Science Publishers Inc. 199-216

LEACH, J. M. and THAKORE, A. N. (1975). Isolation and identification of constituents toxic to juvenile rainbow trout (*Salmo gairdneri*) in caustic extraction effluents from kraft pulp mill bleach plants. *J. Fish. Res. Board Can.* 32(8), 1249-1257

LEACH, J. M. and THAKORE, A. N. (1977). Compounds toxic to fish in pulp mill waste streams. *Prog. Wat. Tech.* 2, 787-798

LETEUX, F. and MAYER, F. P. (1972). Mixtures of malachite green and formalin for controlling *Ichthyophthirius* and other protozoan parasites of fish. *Prog. Fish-Cult.* 34(1), 21-26

LEWIS, M. (1978). Acute toxicity of copper, zinc and manganese in single and mixed salt solutions to juvenile longfin dace, *Agosia chrysogaster. J. Fish Biol.* 13, 695-700

LICHTENSTEIN, E. P., LIANG, T. T., SCHULTZ, K. R., SCHNOES, H. K. and CARTER, G. T. (1974). Insecticidal and synergistic components isolated from dill plants. *J. Agric. Food Chem.* 22, 658-664

LICHTENSTEIN, E. P., LIANG, T. T. and ANDEREGG, B. N. (1973). Synergism of insecticides by herbicides. *Science, Wash.* 181, 847-849

LLOYD, R. (1960). Toxicity of zinc sulphate to rainbow trout. *Ann. Appl. Biol.* 48(1), 84-94

LLOYD, R. (1961). The toxicity of mixtures of zinc and copper sulphates to rainbow trout (*Salmo gairdneri* Richardson). *Ann. App. Biol.* 49, 535-538

LLOYD, R. and JORDAN, D. H. M. (1963). Predicted and observed toxicities of several sewage effluents to rainbow trout. *J. Proc. Inst. Sewage Purif.* 1963, 167-173

LLOYD, R. and JORDAN, D. H. M. (1964). Predicted and observed toxicities of several sewage effluents to rainbow trout: a further study. *J. Proc. Inst. Sewage Purif.* 1964, 163-186

LLOYD, R. and SWIFT, D. J. (1976). Some physiological responses by freshwater fish to low dissolved oxygen, high carbon dioxide, ammonia and phenol with special reference to water balance. In *Effects of pollutants on aquatic organisms*, ed. A. P. M. Lockwood. CUP, Cambridge, 46-69

LOEWE, S. (1953). The problem of synergism and antagonism of combined drugs. *Arzneimitt.-Forsch.* 3, 285-290

LUDKE, J. L., GIBSON, J. R. and LUSK, G. (1972). Mixed-function oxidase activity in freshwater fishes. Aldrin epoxidation and parathion activation. *Toxicol. Appl. Pharmacol.* 21

MACEK, K. J. (1975). Acute toxicity of pesticide mixtures to bluegills. *Bull. Environ. Contam. Toxicol.* 14, 648-652

MACEK, K. J., RODGERS, C. R., STALLING, D. L. and KORN, S. (1970). The uptake, distribution and elimination of dietary ^{14}C-DDT and ^{14}C-dieldrin in rainbow trout. *Trans. Am. Fish. Soc.* **99(4)**, 689-695

MARKING, L. L. (1969). Toxicity of rhodamine B and fluorescein sodium to fish and their compatibility with antimycin A. *Prog. Fish-Cul.* **31(3)**, 139-142

MARKING, L. L.(1971). Method for assessing additive toxicity of chemical mixtures. In *Aquatic toxicology and hazard evaluation*, ed. F. W. Mayer and Hamelink. American Society for Testing and Materials, Philadelphia, **STP634**

MARKING, L. L. and DAWSON, V. K. (1975). Method for assessment of toxicity or efficacy of mixtures of chemicals. *Invest. Fish Control, USFWS* **67**, 1-8

MARKING, L. L. and MAUCK, W. L. (1975). Toxicity of paired mixtures of candidate forest insecticides to rainbow trout. *Bull. Environ. Contam. Toxicol.* **13**, 518-523

MARUBINI, E. and BONANOMI, L. (1970). Quantitative evaluation of toxicity tests carried out on mixtures of drugs. *Proc. Eur. Soc. Stud. Drug Toxicity* **11**, 113-121

MAYER, F. L., Jr., STREET, J. C. and NEUHOLD, J. M. (1970). Organo-chlorine insecticide interactions affecting residue storage in rainbow trout. *Bull. Environ. Contam. Toxicol.* **5**, 300-310

MAYER, F. L., Jr., STREET, J. C. and NEUHOLD, J. M. (1972). DDT intoxication in rainbow trout as affected by dieldrin. *Toxicol. Appl. Pharmacol.* **22**, 347-354

MORSE, P. M. (1978). Some comments on the assessment of joint action in herbicide mixtures. *Weed Sci.* **26**, 58-71

MOSSER, J. L., TENG, T.-C., WALTHER, W. G. and WURSTER, C. P. (1974). Interaction of PCBs, DDT and DDE in a marine diatom. *Bull. Environ. Contam. Toxicol.* **12**, 665-668

MUSKA, C. C. and WEBER, L. J. (1977). An approach for studying the effects of mixtures of toxicants. *Proc. West. Pharmacol. Soc.* **20**, 427-430

NEGILSKI, D. S. and DAVIS, G. E. (1974). Individual and combined effects of cyanide, pentachlorophenol and zinc on juvenile chinook salmon (*Oncorhynchus tshawytscha*) (Walbaum) and invertebrates in model stream communities. *Tech. Pap. Ore. Agric. Exp. Stn.* **4238**, 21

NIMMO, W. R. and HAHNER, L. W. (1977). Metals, pesticides and PCBs: Toxicities to shrimp singly and in combination. In *Estuarine proceedings Vol. 1. Uses, stresses and adaptation to the estuary*, ed. M. Wiley. Academic Press, New York. 523-532

PIETILÄINEN, K. (1975). Synergistic and antagonistic effects of lead and cadmium on aquatic primary production. In *Proceedings of the International Conference on heavy metals in the environment*, Canada, October 27-31. University of Toronto, Institute of Environmental Studies, 861-874

PLACKETT, R. and HEWLETT, P. S. (1948). Statistical aspects of the independent joint action of poisons, particularly insecticides. 1. The toxicity of a mixture of poisons. *Ann. Appl. Biol.* **35**, 347-58

PLACKETT, R. and HEWLETT, P. S. (1952). Quantal responses to mixtures of poisons. *J. R. Statist. Soc.* **14**, 141-163

PURI, P. S. and SENTURIA, J. (1972). On the mathematical theory of quantal response assays. *Proc. Berkeley Symp. Math. Stat. Probab.* **6(4)**, 231-247

REINBOLD, K. A. and METCALF, R. L. (1976). Effects of the synergist piperonyl butoxide on metabolism of pesticides in green sunfish. *Pest. Biochem. Phys.* **5**, 401-412

ROALES, R. R. and PERLMUTTER, A. (1974a). Toxicity of zinc and cygon, applied singly and jointly to zebrafish embryos. *Bull. Environ. Contam. Toxicol.* **12**, 475–480

ROALES, R. R. and PERLMUTTER, A. (1974b). Toxicity of methylmercury and copper, applied singly and jointly to the blue gourami (*Trichogaster trichopterus*). *Bull. Environ. Contam. Toxicol.* **12**, 633–639

ROALES, R. R. and PERLMUTTER, A. (1977). Effects of sub-lethal doses of methyl-mercury and copper, applied singly and jointly, on immune response of blue gourami (*Trichogaster trichopterus*) to viral and bacterial antigens. *Arch. Environ. Contam. Toxicol.* **5**, 325–331

RUBIN, A. J. and ELMARAGHY, G. A. (1977). Studies on the toxicity of ammonia, nitrate and their mixtures to guppy fry. *Water Res.* **11**, 927–935

SAY, P. J. (1977). Microbial ecology of high zinc level streams. Ph.D. Thesis, *University of Durham*, 295

SCHAUT, G. G. (1939). Fish catastrophes during droughts. *J. Am. Water Works Assoc.* **31**, 771–822

SERVIZI, J. A., MARTENS, D. W. and GORDON, R. W. (1978). Acute toxicity at Annacis Island Primary sewage treatment plant. *Prog. Rep. Int. Pac. Salmon Fish. Comm.* **38**, 12

SJÖQUIST, F. and ALEXANDERSON, B. (1972). Drug interaction. A critical look at their documentation and clinical importance. *Proc. Eur. Soc. Stud. Drug Toxicity* **13**, 167–179

SMITH, L. L., BRODERIUS, S. J., OSEID, D. M., KIMBALL, G. L., KOENST, W. M. and LIND, D. T. (1979). Acute and chronic toxicity of HCN to fish and inverte-brates. *US Environmental Protection Agency*, Washington. **EPA-600/3-79-009**, 115

SOLBÉ, J. F. de L. G. (1973). The relation between water quality and the status of fish populations in Willow Brook. *Water Treat. Exam.* **22**, 41–61

SOLON, J. M. and NAIR, J. M. (1970). The effect of a sub-lethal concentration of LAS on the acute toxicity of various phosphate pesticides to fathead minnow (*Pimephales promelas* Rafinesque). *Bull. Environ. Contam. Toxicol.* **5**, 408–413

SOLON, J. M., LINCER, J. L. and NAIR, J. M. (1969). The effect of sub-lethal con-centration of LAS on the acute toxicity of various insecticides to fathead minnow. *Water Res.* **3**, 767–775

SOUTHGATE, B. A. (1932). The toxicity of mixtures of poisons. *Q. J. Pharmacol.* **5**, 639–648

SPEHAR, R. L., LEONARD, E. N. and DeFOE, D. L. (1975). Chronic effects of cadmium and zinc mixtures on flagfish (*Jordanella floridae*). *Trans. Am. Fish. Soc.* **107**(2), 354–360

SPRAGUE, J. B. (1964). Lethal concentrations of copper and zinc for young Atlantic salmon. *J. Fish. Res. Board Can.* **21**(1), 17–26

SPRAGUE, J. B. (1970). Measurement of pollutant toxicity to fish. 2. Utilizing and applying bioassay results. *Water Res.* **4**, 3–22

SPRAGUE, J. B. and LOGAN, W. J. (1979). Separate and joint toxicity to rainbow trout of substances used in drilling fluids for oil exploration. *Environ. Pollut.* **19**(4), 269–282

SPRAGUE, J. B. and RAMSAY, B. A. (1965). Lethal levels of mixed copper-zinc solutions for juvenile salmon. *J. Fish. Res. Board Can.* **22**(2), 425–432

SPRAGUE, J. B., ELSON, P. F. and SAUNDERS, R. L. (1965). Sub-lethal copper-zinc pollution in a salmon river – a field and laboratory study. *Int. J. Air Water Pollut.* **9**, 531–543

STATHAM, C. N. (1975a). Synergism of the acute toxic effects of 3,4-D butyl ester, dieldrin, rotenone and pentachlorophenol in rainbow trout by carbaryl. *Toxicol. Appl. Pharmacol.* 33, 188

STATHAM, C. N. (1975b). Potentiation of the acute toxicity of several pesticides and herbicides in trout by carbaryl. *Toxicol. Appl. Pharmacol.* 34, 83–87

STATHAM, C. N. and LECH, J. J. (1976). Studies on the mechanism of potentiation of the acute toxicity of 2,4-D N-butyl ester and 2',5-dichloro-4'-nitrosalicylanicide in rainbow trout by carbaryl. *Toxicol. Appl. Pharmacol.* 36, 281–296

STRATTON, G. W. and CORKE, C. T. (1979). The effect of mercuric, cadmium and nickel ion combinations on a blue-green alga. *Chemosphere* 8(10), 731–740

STREET, J. C., MAYER, F. L. and WATSTAFF, D. J. (1970). Ecological significance of pesticide interactions. In *Pesticides Symposia*, ed. Deichman. Halos, Miami

SUN, L. T. and GORMAN, M. L. (1973). The toxicity to fish of herbicides recommended for weed control in the Rewa. *Fiji Agric. J.* 35, 31–33

THOMPSON, K. W., HENDRICKS, A. C. and CAIRNS, J. (1980). Acute toxicity of zinc and copper singly and in combination to the bluegill (*Lepomis macrochirus*). *Bull. Environ. Contam. Toxicol.* 25, 122–129

TSAI, C. and McKEE, J. A. (1980). Acute toxicity to goldfish of mixtures of chloramine, copper and linear alkylate sulfonate. *Trans. Am. Fish. Soc.* 109, 132–141

TSAY, S.-F., LEE, J.-M. and LYND, J. Q. (1976). The interactions of Cu^{++} and Cn^- with paraquat phytotoxicity to a *Chlorella*. *Weed Sci.* 18, 596–598

US Environmental Protection Agency (1973). Water quality criteria, 1972. Washington, D.C., *Environmental Protection Agency*, EPA.R3.73.003, 594

VAMOS, R. and TASNADI, R. (1967). Ammonia poisoning in carp. 3. The oxygen content as a factor in influencing the toxic limit of ammonia. *Acta Biol. Szeged* 13, 99–105

VAN LOON, J. C. and BEAMISH, R. J. (1977). Heavy-metal contamination by atmospheric fallout of several Flin Flon area lakes and the relation to fish populations. *J. Fish. Res. Board Can.* 34(7), 899–906

VERMA, S. R., RANI, S. and DALELA, R. C. (1981). Synergism, antagonism and additivity of phenol, pentachlorophenol and dinitrophenol to a fish (*Notropterus notropterus*). *Arch. Environ. Contam. Toxicol.* 10, 365–370

VEITH, G. D., DeFOE, D. L. and BERGSTEDT, B. V. (1979). Measuring and estimating the bioconcentration factor of chemicals in fish. *J. Fish. Res. Board Can.* 36(9), 1040–1048

WALSH, G. E. (1978). Toxic effects of pollutants on plankton. In *Principles of ecotoxicology*, ed. Butler. Wiley, London. Chapter 12 SCOPE Report 12

WARREN, C. E. (1971). *Biology and water pollution control.* W. B. Saunders Company, Philadelphia. 434

WEDEMEYER, G. (1968). Uptake and distribution of Zn^{65} on the coho salmon egg (*Oncorhynchus kisutch*). *Comp. Biochem. Physiol.* 26, 271–279

WEINSTEIN, N. L. and ANDERSON, P. D. (1978). Lethal and sub-lethal toxicities of copper-nickel mixtures to the zebrafish (*Brachydanio rerio*). *Tech. Rep. Fish. Mar. Serv. Can.* 818

WESTERNHAGEN, H. von, DETHLEFSEN, V. and ROSENTHAL, H. (1979). Combined effects of cadmium, copper and lead on developing herring eggs and larvae. *Helgoländer Wiss. Meeresunters.* 32(3), 257–278

12

FISH TOXICITY TESTING PROCEDURES

Foreword

The preparation of the original report on Fish Toxicity Testing Procedures was accomplished largely by Mr. R. Lloyd who prepared the basic manuscript to be reviewed by other members of the Working Party on Toxicity Testing Procedures.

The chapter has two appendices. Appendix 1 describes various standard test techniques which measure the short-term acute lethal effects of poisons. Appendix 2 contains a list of terms relating to fish toxicity testing, which was prepared with the help of Mr V. M. Brown, who produced an initial list of definitions for review by members of the Working Party.

12.1 Introduction

Within the last 25 years there have been considerable advances in the techniques of measuring the effect of pollution on fish in the understanding of the effect of chemical and physical variables both on the toxicity of poisons and on the susceptibility of fish to them, and also in the statistical treatment of the results. Concomitant with this has been the development of various standard test techniques, some of which, such as the U.S. and U.K. methods, became nationally adopted. Example of such tests, which measure the short-term acute lethal effects of poisons, are given in Appendix 1. However, although these tests were satisfactory for a limited purpose, they tended to become used for providing information beyond their original purpose and capability; for example, 'safe concentrations' were assumed to be 10 per cent of a 1- or 2-day LC50, and although this may be valid for some poisons it cannot be taken as a general rule. It is not intended to review these tests in detail, nor indeed to set out fully the requirements for fish bioassays since this had already been carried out by Sprague in some detail (1969, 1970, 1971) as well as in a simplified version (Sprague, 1973). Instead, the types of pollutional situations which may cause hazards to fish and fisheries will be considered so as to indicate the type or types of bioassay procedure which would give the type of data appropriate for the control of pollution in each case.

Pollutional situations may be separated into five main groups:

(a)   Theoretically, most chemicals could find their way into aquatic environment as a result of accidental discharges, either from storage depots or while being transported by air, land, or water or from irresponsible or ill-informed disposal of unwanted surplus material. Such discharges are likely to be isolated occurrences, in which the initial concentration of chemicals will decrease due to their subsequent dispersal, dilution and degradation. Information is required on the degree of risk attending such accidents so that the necessary steps can be taken to minimize their possible occurrence.

Some chemicals may find their way into lakes or rivers as a result of normal usage or misusage and again, assessment is required of the degree of risk involved for fisheries. If the likely maximum concentration of a particular chemical in the environment is very much smaller (say by a factor of 10^{-4})* than the acutely lethal level for a particular species of fish, then it might be safe to assume that such a chemical poses no pollutional problems for fisheries. The type of test procedure required to give a measure of the acute lethal concentration for fish can be termed a preliminary *screening test*. Such a screening test could also be used to determine the potentially least toxic of a group of chemicals or products which may find their way into rivers and lakes from normal usage, so that the use of the least hazardous substance can be investigated further.

(b)   However, there are many poisons which appear in the environment at levels greater than 10^{-4} times the acute lethal level, as a result of industrial, agricultural, and domestic effluent discharges, or from direct application to water (as with aquatic herbicides). Such chemicals may remain in the aquatic ecosystem for long periods of time, perhaps permanently, and for these substances much more information is required to assess the hazard, formulate water quality criteria and impose water quality standards. The nature and extent of the additional tests depend upon the nature of the substance and the degree of risk which its use entails. The test procedures necessary to provide such information can be described as tests to *establish water quality criteria*.

(c)   Normally, the quality standards set for an effluent are described in chemical terms and the subsequent monitoring of the effluent is carried out by chemical analysis. However, where effluents contain substances or complex mixtures which are hazardous to fisheries and which are difficult to analyse, fish toxicity tests have to be carried out to estimate the extent of the risk and a simple test used for subsequent monitoring of the effluent. Such a test can be called an *effluent monitoring test*.

---

*The value of 10^{-4} is only an approximate guide. The safety factor for persistent or accumulating toxic substances may be less than this value.

(d)   Where the quality standards set for those effluents described above need to be legally binding, a closely defined, reproducible test procedure is necessary to establish evidence in a court of law of a failure to comply with a fish toxicity standard. Such a test can be described as a *legal test*.

(e)   As mentioned above, rivers can be suddenly polluted from a variety of sources, giving rise to hazards for water-users downstream. In such cases, a monitoring system can be of some value whereby a continuous surveillance of a few test fish for signs of stress can provide an early warning of unfavourable conditions, and allow the water supply to, say, water treatment works or fish farms to be temporarily shut off. Such tests can be described as *river monitoring tests,* although they could also be used for monitoring lakes, if necessary.

In the following sections, appropriate test procedures will describe for each of the five categories.

12.2 Screening test

12.2.1 INTRODUCTION

The object of this test is to obtain an approximate indication of the concentration of a substance likely to be hazardous to fish and fisheries in the natural environment. Results obtained from such tests are only a rough guide to the ecological implications of the appearance of this substance in the environment and cannot be used for an accurate prediction of the risk involved. Since the number of substances to be tested is large and likely to increase rapidly, there is a need for an international standard screening test procedure so that data obtained in many countries are readily comparable. Such a test needs to be reproducible and therefore closely defined; it follows that such a test should be carried out only in a properly equipped laboratory by competent technical personnel.

  In the present state of knowledge, there is no commonly accepted alternative to the use of the response of the whole living fish to a toxicant and to choosing death as the response, although it may be possible in the future to use a sublethal response or a cultured tissue.

12.2.2 TEST PROCEDURE

Apparatus

It is well known that, for many poisons, continuous-flow type tests (where the solution to which the fish are exposed is constantly renewed) give similar results to those from static tests, in which the fish are exposed to fixed volumes of solutions which are not renewed. However, similar results from these two types of test may not be obtained if the pollutant is either volatile, chemically unstable, biodegradable, or rapidly absorbed by the fish. For a standard international screening test, the need for reproducible results for the whole spectrum of substances likely to be tested makes a continuous-flow procedure an ideal choice, although for some substances or effluents, particularly those containing insoluble matter, a static test procedure is unavoidable.

Basically, the apparatus should be capable of mixing accurately a solution of the test substance with dilution water and delivering a series of dilutions to test vessels which contain the fish. The preparation and dosing of the test dilutions can be either continuous (for example, by using metering or peristaltic pumps) or made at frequent intervals. There is considerable scope in the variety of apparatus which will fulfil this requirement. The test apparatus should be capable of supplying at least six test vessels at such a rate that:

(a)   any subsequent absorption or degradation of the test substance is kept to a minimum, and

(b)   the dissolved oxygen of the incoming water is sufficient to meet the needs of the test fish without further aeration of the test vessel; the dissolved-oxygen content of the outflowing water should be greater than 70 per cent of the air saturation value.

Obviously, the rate of replacement is dependent on the size of test fish used, their activity and oxygen demand, and the type of substance to be tested. Guidelines for the calculation of replacement rates are given by Sprague (1973). In general, a replacement rate of 2–3 litres water/gram fish-day have been found to be sufficient. If, after requirement (b) is satisfied, the volume of test water is made equal to the total flow in 8 h, then there will be about 95 per cent replacement of molecules in 24 h, assuming good mixing.

Dilution water

Since the calcium content and pH values of natural waters can have a marked effect on the toxicity of some poisons to fish, a standard screening test should use an artificial dilution water, prepared by adding minerals to distilled or de-ionized water. This water should be of a medium hardness value within the range 75–125 mg/ℓ as $CaCO_3$, with a pH value in the range 7.0–7.5, although for any adopted standard test the hardness and pH values would need to be more closely defined. A dilution of a hard natural water with de-ionized water to achieve the required hardness would be acceptable if parallel tests showed that it gave the same results, for a range of test substances, as a synthetic dilution water; the chemical composition of such waters should be stated. A simple, non-standard test could be carried out at the same time as the standard screening test to determine whether differences in water hardness and pH value affected the toxicity of the substance under test. The temperature of the test vessels should be the optimum for the species of fish used; a warm-water species would be useful in this respect since a higher-than-ambient temperature is more readily maintained in a test apparatus than a lower temperature. Temperature control should be within ± 1°C.

The test substance

Where the chemical to be tested is readily soluble in water and does not subsequently degrade or slowly hydrolyse, sufficient stock solution can be made up, in standard dilution water, to last for the duration of the test. Unstable solutions would have to be freshly prepared more frequently to enable the concentrations in the test vessels to be kept constant. Substances of low aqueous solubility need to be dissolved first in a solvent of low fish toxicity before preparing the final stock solution; acetone has been used successfully for this purpose. Difficulties can arise in the testing of finely divided solids, which may be incorporated into some products; careful design of the test apparatus can usually overcome the problems caused by the settling out of the particles. No single standard procedure can be laid down for the preparation of stock solutions; in any report it is necessary to state the method used.

If the substance to be tested is marketed as a formulation (for example, some pesticides have wetting agents and fillers added), both the designated active ingredients and the formulations should be tested and any report should clearly state whether the results refer to the pure substance or to the marketed product. For those substances which can become degraded in water, either chemically or biologically, both the original chemical and the individual degradation products (especially any stable compounds) should be tested for their toxicity to fish.

Chemical analysis of the dilutions in the test vessels is desirable to ensure that the required concentrations are in fact present, but it is recognized that this is not always possible, and reliance then has to be placed on the accuracy of the test dosing apparatus.

Species of fish

The species of fish used should be easy to rear and/or widely available throughout the year; it should be capable of being bred and cultivated either at fish farms or in the laboratory, under disease- and parasite-free conditions, so that the test animals will be healthy and of known parentage. It would be an advantage if the species used was generally sensitive to a wide range of possible pollutants. No single species is outstanding in all respects; the use of a tropical species is not ruled out, providing it is suitably sensitive. The fish should be available in a range of small, uniform sizes throughout the year.

Stocks of fish should be maintained in water of a similar quality and temperature to that used in the screening test for at least seven days before use in the test; unless reared there, they should not be held for a lengthy period (more than two months) in the laboratory. Normal prophylactic treatments for the prevention of outbreaks of disease can be used, including the use of medicated food pellets, but no attempt should be made to cure and then use diseased fish; such fish should be removed and destroyed. If more than 10 per cent of a batch of fish become diseased, or die (after any immediate mortality on delivery), then the whole batch should be discarded. The fish can be fed on natural or proprietary food, but should be starved for 24 h before being used for a test.

The numbers of fish and dilutions to be tested

The accuracy of the test results depends not only on the constant composition of the dilutions of stock solution added to the test vessels but also on the number of fish used, and the number and numerical spacing of the dilutions tested.

Sufficiently accurate results can be obtained if between seven and ten fish are used for each dilution tested. Fewer fish would give less accurate results and the extra accuracy derived from the use of more than ten fish is unnecessary for this type of test.

At least five dilutions should be tested; the concentrations should be spaced at approximately logarithmic intervals (for example, 0.5, 1.0, 2.0, 4.0, 8.0 mg/ℓ). The concentrations should be arranged so that a complete mortality occurs within a day in the highest concentration used and no mortalities occur in the lowest concentration in the period of the test. A partial mortality in at least two intermediate concentrations should be obtained within the test period. For some poisons a wider range of concentrations may be required to fulfil this demand, and for others a closer spacing of the concentrations to be tested. A control test vessel, supplied with dilution water only, should be included in the test series; if more than one fish dies in this vessel, the test should be discarded and re-run. These tests should continue for at least 48 h and preferably for 96 h, and the fish should not be fed during this period.

Collection and processing of results

Observations of the state of the fish in the test vessels should be made at fixed intervals from the start of the test, for example, at 3, 6, 12, 24, 48 and 96 hours; a record should be made of the number of fish alive, overturned and dead in each concentration. From these data, the LC50 values for these time intervals can be calculated by probit analysis as shown by Sprague (1973). The 95 per cent confidence limits of the LC50 values should be calculated, and all the data should be given in any publication to show the relation between survival time and concentration of poison; graphical representation of the results can be of considerable value in the interpretation of the data. Overturning times are useful if the test substance has a pronounced anaesthetic effect. Any unusual reactions by the fish under test, and any visible external effect of the poison, should be noted. Additionally, chemical analyses may be carried out on dead fish and fish surviving the test (including the controls) to provide preliminary information on the net uptake of the test chemical in fish tissues.

12.2.3 SUMMARY

The specifications outlined above represent the minimum requirements for a test procedure which will give accurate, reproducible results for the wide range of substances likely to be screened for their toxicity to fish. It should be stressed again, however, that the data obtained can only be used as a very approximate estimate of the minimum concentration of a substance which is likely to be lethal to fish, and to give a ranking of groups of substances in the approximate order of their toxicity; they cannot be used alone for the preparation of water quality criteria.

12.3 Tests to establish water quality criteria

12.3.1 INTRODUCTION

Where the predicted or measured concentration of a potential pollutant in the aquatic environment is greater than 10^{-4} times the 2- or 4-day LC50, as determined by a screening test, it is clear that further tests have to be made to determine more accurately the degree of risk entailed so that suitable control measures can, if necessary, be applied to the use and disposal of the substance. The extent to which other tests have to be used, and their type, is a function of the degree of risk subsequently found and the nature of the pollutant. The experience of the Working Party on Water Quality Criteria for European Freshwater Fish is that, for common pollutants, an extensive knowledge is required of their chemistry and toxicity to fish under a wide range of conditions, both lethal and sublethal, before even tentative quality criteria can be established. On the other hand, a less comprehensive programme of testing would be required to assess the hazard arising from the discharge of a specific effluent at a single location. Tests to provide such information cannot be standardized since much depends on the nature of the substance and its harmful effect. For example, a constant flow type of apparatus is unnecessary if the required concentration of poison can be maintained in fixed volume test vessels with infrequent replacement of solutions. However, certain basic guidelines can be laid down which will enable the test results to be fully used in the preparation of water quality criteria.

12.3.2 LETHAL TOXICITY TESTS

Effect of chemical and physical variables

For most poisons, the relation between the logarithm of concentration and the logarithm of median period of survival of the test fish is curvilinear and a concentration exists where the curve becomes asymptotic to the time axis. This is known as the threshold LC50 value. The effect on the threshold LC50 value of water hardness, pH value, temperature, salinity, and dissolved-oxygen concentration, over the whole range likely to be encountered by the fish, should be measured and these factors controlled to within close limits during the experiments (for example, pH value ± 0.1 unit, temperature ± 1°C). It should be remembered that variables such as pH value and temperature are important for those poisons which dissociate in solution to form ionized and un-ionized molecules, of which only one type may be predominantly toxic. A review of the factors that can affect the chemical nature of pollutants and their subsequent harmful effects has been published by Lee (1973). Other factors, including temperature and dissolved-oxygen concentrations, can affect the susceptibility of fish to poisons; bicarbonate and free carbon dioxide concentrations can affect the toxicity of dissociating molecules, such as ammonia (Chapter 4).

Fish

Tests should be made to compare the sensitivity of the major fish species of commercial or sport value, at different stages in their life cycle from egg to adult. Again, results should be obtained in terms of the threshold LC50 value. The care of the fish should be similar to that outlined on p. 319, paras 4 and 5 except that, as wild fish may have to be used, great care has to be taken to avoid injury by the method of capture, precautions against disease in the laboratory stock are even more important and the degree of parasitism should be investigated and recorded in the published results, as also should be the size, weight and age of the fish used. During lengthy tests the fish should be fed (although this may not be necessary at very low temperatures) and the test vessels should be kept as free as possible from unconsumed food and faeces.

Analysis of results

The tests should be continued until a definite threshold LC50 is obtained; construction of log concentration–log survival time curves can be obtained in one of two ways. If individual survival times of fish are recorded, the median survival time at each concentration can be derived graphically using log probit paper and a line drawn through the resultant values. This method is capable of providing more information than the fixed-time inspection procedure outlined on p. 320, para. 4 for reasons given by Sprague (1973) although it is also somewhat time-consuming since the fish may have to be inspected at more frequent intervals. The effect of different environmental variables on the toxicity of a poison to fish can be more readily perceived if the data are expressed graphically than if they are presented in tabular form only; published results should include both forms of data presentation.

Special case of accumulative poisons

For those poisons which are persistent in the environment and which accumulate in the fish, it is necessary to know the rate of uptake, the level in the tissues which are associated with mortality, and the rate of loss when fish given a non-lethal exposure to the poison are placed in clean water. Such data on the level of residues at death are much more relevant to environmental monitoring programmes than are LC50 values for aqueous solutions.

12.3.3 SUBLETHAL TESTS

So far, the measured response to a pollutant has been death, whereas in setting a standard for a pollutant it is necessary to know the concentration which will not adversely affect fish. Considerable attention has been given in recent years to non-lethal responses of fish to low levels of pollutants. Such tests have measured changes at the cellular level, tissue and organ level, and in the whole animal, involving a wide range of experimental techniques and apparatus. No one test published so far has been shown to be capable alone of providing data on which criteria or standards can be set; information has to be gathered from experiments covering a wide range of responses by fish to the pollutant under review. It is not the intention here to describe the tests used in detail, but only to give a brief indication of the general principles to be followed when such tests are designed. The following examples have been selected to provide illustrations rather than a comprehensive review; the general rules laid down on p. 319 for the care of fish and for the preparation of dilutions of pollutant apply also to all these tests.

The chemical and physical factors known to affect the toxicity of the pollutant should be closely controlled and the values for the mean, standard deviation and range should be reported.

Biochemical studies

Most common of biochemical studies are those on enzyme induction and inhibition; such experiments are useful if they shed light on the nature of the toxic action which may then provide a wider understanding of the effect of the poison on the animal and lead to the prediction of important side-effects. But too often the significance of the results in terms of the effect on the viability of the species is not given, nor can it be readily obtained.

Histological studies

Prepared sections of tissues and organs from animals exposed to lethal and sublethal levels of toxic substances can give an indication of the site of toxic action, particularly where the tissue damage is severe, for example, the destruction of the gill epithelial tissue of fish exposed to acutely lethal levels of heavy metal salts. It becomes more difficult to assess the significance of slight tissue aberrations in that these may be the result of adaptation by the fish to the stress imposed by the pollutant. Any such tests should show both the existence of a graded response and the concentration of poison which represents a level of no effect. Techniques are now available for measuring such histological effects and these should become more widely used.

Histochemical studies as used, for example, for heavy metals, can be of value if the target organ for the poison is either small or cannot readily be excised for chemical analysis, since in those cases, coupled with other sublethal tests, they could be used in monitoring programmes. Haematological parameters have been measured to assess a sublethal response and such studies may increase in value with more experience in the interpretation of the results; at present, the range of normal variations is not fully understood.

Physiological effects

These include tests on the effect of poisons on the ability of fish to osmoregulate, to adapt to temperature changes, and on changes in heart and respiration rates. Again, it is important to demonstrate that the reaction being studied is of vital importance, that a graded response exists, and that a level of no effect is obtained.

However, such tests are normally of short duration and the possibility remains that a longer exposure to sublethal levels may adversely affect a system not studied.

Growth rate

Measurements of changes in growth rate have much to commend them, since an organism growing at a normal rate can be presumed to be healthy and it is an important factor for species of commercial importance.

For tests with persistent poisons, the fish should first be allowed to accumulate them to a predetermined level, otherwise the growth rate is measured during a period when the toxic substance rises from zero to a low level in the tissues and the toxic effect may not be immediately apparent. Both the food supply and its presentation should be as natural as possible.

Life cycle tests

Tests in which fish are exposed to a pollutant for a year or longer are probably more illuminating than any other type, and quite unsuspected effects of poisons can be discovered. Not only can fecundity and viability of progeny be measured but also growth rate and resistance to disease. Their drawback is that the number of species that can be investigated in this way is limited and, because of the length of time taken, only a few poisons under a limited range of environmental conditions can be investigated unless considerable experimental facilities are available. Also, as in most other tests, the test species are normally exposed to a constant level of poison, whereas this is unlikely to occur in the natural ecosystem except, perhaps, in lakes. Too little is known at present about the effect of fluctuating levels of poison around the 'no effect' concentration. Standard procedures for chronic bioassays have been published by the Environmental Protection Agency (1973).

Behaviour

Because fish may actively avoid polluted areas, laboratory tests have been made to measure their reaction to a choice of clean or contaminated water. Such tests are normally made in a small apparatus with a clear interface between the two conditions; the results indicate the ability of fish to discriminate between the two by its reaction toward them in the absence of other environmental stimuli. It is often difficult to extrapolate from such data to field conditions where a sharp interface between clean and polluted water is lacking, and where other stimuli, such as territorial, migratory or feeding behaviour patterns may have an overriding effect. Other aspects of behaviour, such as learning or physical reaction to stimuli, have also been tested in the presence of poisons. Those in which the species are exposed to a poison for a short period of time and their behaviour pattern then tested, may be of doubtful value if the ecological significance of the altered behaviour pattern is difficult to ascertain. However, poisons which act on the sensory mechanisms may effect fish-feeding behaviour or migration, and may also influence their response to other poisons.

Activity

It has been shown that an increase in activity in freshwater fish makes them more susceptible to poisons, but the increase in sensitivity in terms of threshold LC50 values is small. Also, swimming speeds are affected by concentrations lower than the lethal levels.

Hazards to fish predators, including man

Although not strictly relevant to the subject of this report, some toxic substances can exist in fish at low, non-lethal concentrations which may affect their quality or wholesomeness. For example, phenolic substances produce undesirable taint-ing in fish flesh at concentrations well below the lethal level and this aspect of pollution should be investigated where commercially important species are at risk (Chapter 5). The problems associated with organo-chlorine and mercury compounds are well documented.

Summary

Of the tests described above, it is clear that none can be used alone for the formu-lation of reliable, safe concentration criteria; the life cycle test is basically superior, but is limited by the species which can be used, and the time and space require-ments. The remaining tests, and others not described here, contribute only partially to the knowledge required on the effects of pollution on the ability of fish and fisheries to survive. It cannot be stressed too strongly that the results of the experiments should be obtained in such a way that they should be capable of interpretation in terms of the survival of the species in the ecosystem and, especi-ally where persistent poisons are used, the observed effect related to the concen-tration of toxic substance in the tissues.

12.3.4 FIELD OBSERVATIONS

So far, only the interaction between a fish and a pollutant under laboratory conditions has been considered; it is necessary to relate such findings to the effect of pollutants on fisheries in natural ecosystems.

For a pollutant already present in significant amounts in the aquatic environ-ment, surveys can be made of the status of fisheries at various pollution levels and results compared with data obtained from laboratory tests. However, diffi-culties occur if the fisheries are exposed to more than one pollutant; also, an extensive chemical sampling programme is required. Useful data can be obtained from experiments with caged fish in rivers and lakes, in which observed mortali-ties are correlated with predictions based on the concentration of the pollutants as determined by chemical analysis and their known lethal effects from laboratory experiments. Again, it is important that such experiments are accompanied by an extensive monitoring programme for the pollutant, since the concentrations in the water can fluctuate widely over short periods of time. However, it may be much more convenient (and essential for those substances which are present in the environment at levels too low to cause mortality or for those whose use is under consideration) to obtain pertinent data from artificial ecosystems, such as small streams supplied with controlled dilutions of effluents, or ponds to which the pollutant has been added. Such tests can provide useful information on the effect of a pollutant on fisheries within the natural ecosystem. Again, it is of the greatest importance that those chemical and physical variables which have been shown to affect the toxicity of the pollutant in laboratory tests are also monitored in field surveys and experiments.

12.4 Effluent monitoring tests

12.4.1 INTRODUCTION

The practice of keeping fish in aquaria or ponds supplied with effluent from industries or sewage disposal works to demonstrate that their wastes are not harmful to fish, is increasing and such practices.should be encouraged. However, there are many situations where effluents, mainly from industries, are lethal to fish and where this practice cannot be used. In such cases, the effluent can often be monitored for its toxic constituents by chemical analysis but there are other instances where the toxic substance or substances are difficult to detect or measure by such means, and only a fish toxicity test can provide a quantitative measure of the harmfulness of the effluent. Each such pollutional situation is usually unique in that the individual characteristics of both the effluent and the water in the receiving river or lake are unlikely to be found elsewhere. What is required, therefore, is a simple toxicity test to enable the harmfulness of the effluent to be monitored by unskilled personnel.

12.4.2 TEST PROCEDURES

There are two ways in which this can be done:

(a) The effluent can be passed to an aquarium containing fish, after dilution with the receiving water, to give final concentrations equal to or greater than the concentration obtained in the river or lake. Alternatively, a series of dilutions can be prepared to give a range of concentrations to which fish are exposed. Such a test will show whether the effluent is causing harm and is useful if the discharge varies considerably in quality over a period of time, or contains volatile or degradable pollutants, and when a single sample would not be representative of the daily or weekly discharge. Section 12.6 gives details of elaboration of this type of test.

(b) Samples of effluent can be taken at regular intervals, serial dilutions with receiving water prepared in simple aquaria and fish exposed to them without replacement of the test solutions. Such a test has value if the effluent quality is fairly constant and the pollutants are stable, and it has the advantage of providing a quantitative measure of the toxicity of the discharge. This, together with information on the dilution of the effluent after discharge, indicates whether the effluent is likely to be harmful.

These tests can be made under static conditions; if necessary the solutions can be gently aerated. The temperature need not be held constant but could be that of the receiving water at the time of the test. Fish mortalities can be recorded after either 24 or 48 h and the LC50 calculated as described on p. 320, para. 4. Because such tests are likely to be carried out by unskilled personnel, the procedures adopted by any one effluent discharger need to be explicit to give maximum guidance, as, for example, in the proposals made by the Biological Water Quality Committee, ORSANCO, for the effluent monitoring test to be used by dischargers to the R. Ohio, U.S.A.

12.4.3 FISH SPECIES

Since these are non-standard tests, a particular fish species need not be specified; it would be desirable but not essential to use the most sensitive of the common species which are commercially or recreationally important and locally available in the receiving water. Conditions for the care of such wild species of fish before they are used for testing need to be similar to those outlined on p. 322, para. 1.

12.4.4 EFFLUENT INVESTIGATIONAL TEST

With effluent discharges that are demonstrably toxic to fish, there is a need to determine the extent to which the toxicity can be explained in terms of its constituent effluent streams and known toxic components. For this purpose, tests similar to those described above are required to identify streams whose treatment would most effectively improve overall effluent quality because their constituent poisons were most amenable to reduction in concentrations. Where the effluent streams include commonly occurring poisons, the species of fish used in the test should be those whose responses to these substances are well documented, so that the effect of the less well known poisons can be assessed. In this case also, the test solutions should be analysed for those factors which influence the toxicity of the common poisons present.

12.5 Legal tests

12.5.1 INTRODUCTION

All effluents discharged to fresh water should be subject to quality and quantity standards set by a regulating authority for pollution prevention. Wherever possible, as in Section 12.4.1, the levels of toxic constituents should be controlled by chemical analysis but there may be cases where a fish toxicity standard is essential because the toxic constituents are not readily determined by chemical analysis. Such a standard requires a test procedure which is simple yet reproducible, and which is described in sufficient detail to enable the results to be defended in a court of law.

12.5.2 TEST PROCEDURE

The type of test required will, of course, depend on the way in which the standard is set. For the purpose of providing an example, the following standard will be considered:

> 'When the effluent is diluted X times with the specified dilution water and tested by the required procedure, no more than Y fish shall die within the prescribed period of the test.'

It will be seen that, with such a standard, only one dilution needs to be tested and the effluent either passes or fails the test; it is not essential to know to what degree the effluent passes or fails, although in some cases this might be advantageous. There has been little experience of this type of test and the procedure put forward is based on one used to a very limited extent in the U.K.; a similar test is used in the province of Milan, Italy.

Essentially, the tests should be simple and therefore static tests with fixed volumes of solutions are required. The dilutions of effluent should be prepared with a standard water as described on p. 318, para. 6; the solution should be gently aerated, if necessary, to maintain the dissolved-oxygen concentration at near saturation levels. Commercially available cultivated fish should be used and the size specified within close limits; they should be kept in the artificial dilution water for at least seven days before use, and cared for as on p. 319, paras 1 and 2. The temperature should be conveniently above normal ambient room temperature and controlled to within $\pm 1°C$; the species of fish used should have this temperature within its optimum range and be sensitive to toxic substances. Ten fish should be used in the test dilution, and a further ten as a control in standard dilution water only. Mortalities in the control aquaria invalidate the test. The test should continue for at least 24 h and preferably for 48 h; shorter-term tests are less likely to give reproducible results. The effluent fails the test if more than five of the ten fish die in the test concentration.

A basically similar test procedure has been proposed by the Working Group on Effluent Toxicity Requirements, Canada Department of the Environment, for the setting of effluent standards for the pulp and paper industry. The effluents from these plants, when treated by biological methods, should not on average be acutely toxic to fish. A common standard is being proposed, therefore, whereby 50 rainbow trout (2–10 g) are exposed in batches of ten to a 65 per cent dilution of the effluent at $15°C$, and a similar number are held in clean water as controls; the apparatus should be of a continuous flow type and the test continued for 96 h. The sample fails the test if the number of fish mortalities in the effluent dilutions are statistically significantly greater than those in the controls (J. S. Loch, personal communication).

12.5.3 USE OF TEST

It is first necessary to determine the minimum dilution which the effluent must receive if it is not to harm fisheries in the river or lake into which it is discharged. This can only be achieved by a series of lethal and sublethal tests as described in Section 12.3, although because pollution at a single site only is being considered the extent of the testing may be considerably less than that required for common and widespread pollutants. Then, if an effluent has to be diluted, say, Y times by the receiving water before it becomes harmless to fish, and, with the maximum rate of discharge, the minimum dilution of the effluent in the receiving water is $2Y$ times, then the toxicity of the effluent could increase twofold before it becomes harmful. A series of dilutions of the effluent is then prepared to find the level at which five out of ten fish only are killed using this legal test procedure; if this dilution was, say, $0.1Y$ times, then the standard may be set at a dilution of $0.2Y$ times. Obviously, the actual standard set would depend upon other considerations, including local circumstances; the above procedure only indicates the general principle involved. It is clear, however, that the test conditions should be made as sensitive as possible, otherwise undiluted or very low dilutions of effluent may have to be tested.

It must be emphasized that the dilution of effluent specified for the fish toxicity test is not the same as the actual dilution of the effluent which is safe for the population of fish in a river. Furthermore, the legal test is an empirical procedure and is suitable for no other purpose than that given above.

12.6 River monitoring tests

12.6.1 INTRODUCTION

Because considerable advances have been made in this field within the past few years, these tests will be described in more detail than those in previous sections. The objective of these tests is to provide continuous monitoring of a river (or perhaps effluent) in such a way that action can be taken if the water quality becomes harmful to fish. Such action may include the diversion of an effluent to holding tanks, the taking of water samples for analysis or the closing down of intakes to downstream potable water supply undertakings or fish farms. The basic apparatus consists of an aquarium through which the water to be monitored is pumped; fish are placed in this chamber and their reactions are recorded.

The detailed construction of the apparatus depends on the response chosen for measurement. Clearly, it is desirable to choose a response which gives the maximum early warning of a serious deterioration of water quality, but yet does not give rise to an excessive number of false alarms (the proportion of false alarms which can be tolerated depends upon the degree of risk presented by a deterioration in water quality). The retention time of water in the apparatus should be as short as possible to reduce the time delay of the measured response.

12.6.2 THE MEASURED RESPONSE

Death

Although death of the fish has been used as a measured response, it is of limited value in this context, and the least sensitive of the possible responses which can be measured.

Inability to swim

The most commonly monitored response is the inability of fish to maintain swimming activity in a water current. In such tests, the aquarium consists of a tube through which water is pumped; the fish is confined to the anterior part of the chamber by a screen, which may be either physical or electrical, or by shining a strong light into the posterior part of the chamber, or the chamber can be narrowed toward the screen to provide an increased water velocity there. Loss of swimming ability by the fish brings it into contact with the physical screen or causes its passage through the electrical screen into the posterior chamber. The recording devices can monitor the frequency with which a fish touches a mechanical screen or its passive passage through a combined mechanical–electrical screen (composed of vertical wires attached to micro-switches) or its presence in the posterior chamber. Both optical and sonar detecting devices have been used; the latter has the advantage of being unaffected by changes in water turbidity (the use of a mechanical triggering screen requires a filtered water supply to avoid clogging with debris). It is usual to have several such units operating in parallel, or a single unit with several fish, and the alarm is only triggered if a significant number of fish demonstrate a sudden inability to swim.

Such a monitoring system would respond only to sudden changes in water quality, and a long-term deterioration, which may cause widely-spaced responses in the fish, would not be so readily detected.

Alteration in behaviour pattern

A more sensitive response is the changing activity patterns of fish in a large aquarium to which water is pumped either horizontally or vertically or perhaps alternatively horizontally or vertically. Normal activity patterns are monitored by an array of photoreceptors and a change can be detected either as a direct abnormality (all fish at the surface) or a change in pattern from that obtained at the same time during previous days where there may have been a diel activity pattern. In such tests the normal pattern has to be established before any change can be monitored.

Alteration in respiratory frequency

Probably the most sensitive response measured so far may be the change in respiratory frequency, in which the signals recorded are the nerve impulses to the opercular muscles. Again, the rates which are monitored on the first day (and which are slightly higher than normal) are taken as the control value and any subsequent rise above these values is taken as an indication of stress.

Evaluation of methods

None of these systems has been tested with a wide range of fish species and pollutants, so no detailed evaluation can be made. However, it is likely that the most common usage of these tests will require a simple, sensitive and reliable procedure and, at the present time, the methods based on the loss of swimming ability seem to be superior to the remainder. The inability of a fish to avoid an electrical barrier, and subsequent interruption of a sonar beam, is likely to provide a very positive response. Maximum sensitivity can be achieved by an appropriate choice of fish species and water current (which may have to be varied in summer and winter), the latter providing a stress onto which the pollutional stress would be added. More refined techniques of monitoring behaviour and respiratory patterns require more sophisticated apparatus, screened from all external stimuli except that of water quality, and are more liable to produce false alarms. There is a clear case here for a programme of rigorous comparative testing of techniques to evaluate their respective merits for a range of pollutional situations and needs.

12.6.3 CARE OF FISH

As with previous tests, it is essential that the fish used should be healthy and free from disease, otherwise false alarms will occur. They should be kept in clean water near to the monitoring site, so that pre-test handling is kept to a minimum. Normal feeding regimes can be followed for the stock fish, and fish used in those tests described in p. 329, para. 5 and p. 330, para. 1 may be fed during the test, if necessary with medicated food. Feeding of fish in those tests which monitor behaviour patterns can only be carried out if it does not cause anomalous results. The length of time a fish is kept in the apparatus will vary with the species and techniques used, but 3-4 weeks would appear to be a satisfactory period if the fish are fed, and 3-5 days if they are starved.

12.6.4 SUMMARY

It is clear that river monitoring tests have a considerable potential value, but they are still in the development stage. Comparative tests should be carried out to find a simple, reliable, sensitive test for different pollutional situations; increases in complexity to obtain a slight increase in sensitivity may not be warranted if, as a result, the technique becomes less reliable.

12.7 References

ALABASTER, J. S. (1970). Testing the toxicity of effluents to fish. *Chem. Ind.* 759-764

BESCH, W. K. and JUHNKE, I. (1971). Un nouvel appareil d'étude toxicologique utilisant des carpillons. *Ann. Limnol.* 7, 1-6

BESCH, W. K. *et al.* (1974). Warntest zum Nachweis akut toxischer Konzentrationen von Wasserinhaltsstoffen. *Arch. Hydrobiol.* 74, 551-565

BIOLOGICAL WATER QUALITY COMMITTEE. (1973). ORSANCO 24 hour bioassay. Ohio River Valley Water Sanitation Commission, (Ms)

BROWN, V. M. (1968). The calculation of the acute toxicity of mixtures of poisons to rainbow trout. *Wat. Res.* 2, 723-733

CAIRNS, J. Jr. and WALLER, W. T. (1971). The use of fish movement patterns to monitor zinc. *Wat. Pollut. Control Res. Ser.* 18050 DP 12

332 *Fish toxicity testing procedures*

CAIRNS, J. Jr. SPARKS, R. E. and WALLER, W. T. (1973). The use of fish as
sensors in industrial waste lines to prevent fish kills. *Hydrobiologia* **41** (2),
151–167

ENVIRONMENTAL PROTECTION AGENCY, U.S. (1973). Biological field and
laboratory methods for measuring the quality of surface waters and effluents.
Envir. Monitor. Ger. EPA (EPA-670/4-73001)

ERMISCH, R. and JUHNKE, I. (1973). Automatische Nachweisvorrichtung für
akut toxische Einwirkungen auf Fische in Strömungstest. *Gewässer und
Abwässer* **52**, 16–23

HEATH, A. G. (1972). A critical comparison of methods for measuring fish
respiratory movements. *Water. Res.* **6**, 1–7

HERBERT, D. W. M. and SHURBEN, D. G. (1963). A preliminary study of the effect
of physical activity on the resistance of rainbow trout (*Salmo gairdneri*
Richardson) to two poisons. *Ann. appl. Biol.* **52**, 321–326

IRSA (Instituto di Recerca sulla Acque). (1977). Metodi analitici per le acque.
Quad. IRSA, Roma **11**(3)

JUHNKE, I. (1973). Neukonstruktion des Strömungsbeckens für die automatische
Nachweisvorrichtung von akuten Intoxikationen. *Gewäss. Abwäss.* **52**, 24–27

JUNG, K. D. (1973). Extrem fischtoxische Substanzen und ihre Bedeutung für ein
Fischtest-Warnsystem-gwf. *Wäss. Abwäss.* **114**, 232–234

LEE, G. F. (1973). Chemical aspects of bioassay techniques for establishing water
quality criteria. *Wat. Res.* **7**, 1525–1546

LLOYD, R. (1970). Problems in determining water quality criteria for freshwater
fisheries. *Proc. R. Soc. (B)* **180**, 439–449

MINISTRY OF HOUSING AND LOCAL GOVERNMENT, U.K. (1969). *Fish toxicity tests.*
London, H.M.S.O.

SPARKS, R. E., CAIRNS, J. and HEATH, A. G. (1972). The use of bluegill breathing
rates to detect zinc. *Wat. Res.* **6**, 895–911

SPRAGUE, J. B. (1969). Measurement of pollutant toxicity to fish. 1. Bioassay
methods for acute toxicity. *Wat. Res.* **3**, 793–821

SPRAGUE, J. B. (1970). Measurement of pollutant toxicity to fish. 2. Utilizing
and applying bioassay results. *Wat. Res.* **4**, 3–32

SPRAGUE, J. B. (1971). Measurement of pollutant toxicity to fish. 3. Sub-lethal
effects and 'safe' concentrations. *Wat. Res.* **5**, 245–266

SPRAGUE, J. B. (1973). The ABC's of pollutant bioassay using fish. *Spec. Tech.
Publ. Am. Soc. Test. Mater.* **528**, 6–30

12.8 Appendix 1 Standard test techniques

During the past 25 years, a variety of tests has been used to assess the acute
toxicity of substances to fish. Several of these have become widely used, either
in their original form or adopted with modifications to suit individual preferences
or requirements. The following descriptions are of a selection of such tests which
serve to illustrate some different types which have been developed; it is not
possible to assess the relative merits of these tests since much depends on the
substances to be tested and, to some extent, on the laboratory facilities available.

1. APHA/AWWA/WPCF. (1971). STANDARD METHODS FOR THE EXAMINATION OF WATER AND WASTE WATER. 13TH EDITION. WASHINGTON, D. C. 20036, U.S.A.

Test fish. The species selected should be the most sensitive of the important species which live in the water to which the substance or effluent is to be discharged. They should be acclimated to the test dilution water and temperature for 10-30 days.

Dilution water. When testing an effluent, the water used should be taken from upstream of the point of discharge. For other substances, either an unpolluted natural water of known quality or a synthetic dilution water should be used.

Test temperature. This should be appropriate to the species, usually $15 \pm 2\,^{\circ}C$ for cold water species and $25 \pm 2\,^{\circ}C$ for warm water species.

Dissolved oxygen. This should be greater than 4 mg/ℓ for warm water species and greater than 5 mg/ℓ for cold water species. Aeration of the test solutions is not permitted when volatile substances are being tested.

Number of fish. There should be ten in each concentration.

Controls. If more than 10 per cent mortality occurs in the control batch, the test is invalidated.

Duration. This should be 48 or 96 h with the fish being observed every 24 h and their condition noted.

Analysis. This should be frequent for dissolved oxygen and pH, and also for the toxicant where possible.

Apparatus. A choice is given of static or constant flow tests.

Static tests. The size of the test vessels is not specified, but it is recommended that they should be of 20 ℓ capacity and have a depth of greater than 150 mm for species of fish 50-75 mm long. The containers should be made of glass or other non-toxic or non-reactive material. The total weight of the fish should not exceed 1 g/ℓ of test solution. If necessary, fish can be transferred to fresh solutions at intervals of 24 h or less.

Constant flow tests. A variety of apparatus can be used. Test vessels should be sufficiently large not to overcrowd the fish, and the water depth should be greater than 15 mm. The test volume of solution in each container should be replaced at least every 6 h, or more frequently if the dissolved oxygen falls to an unacceptable level, or if toxic substances are rapidly lost from solution.

Similar static tests are used in Italy (Metodi Analitici per le Acque Vol. 3; *Quaderni dell'Istituto di Recerca sulle Acque,* 1973) in which for a general test (method A) the test species recommended are rainbow trout (*Salmo gairdneri*), brown trout (*Salmo trutta*), minnow (*Phoxinus phoxinus*), bleak (*Alburnus alburnus*) and chub (*Leuciscus cephalus*). For a more precise test (method B), goldfish (*Carassius auratus*) only are tested, using a standard synthetic dilution water at $19-21\,^{\circ}C$.

2. U.K. MINISTRY OF AGRICULTURE, FISHERIES AND FOOD: ALABASTER, J. S. AND ABRAM, F. S. H. (1965). ESTIMATING THE TOXICITY OF PESTICIDES TO FISH. PANS (C), **11 (2),** 91-97

Test fish. Harlequin fish (*Rasbora heteromorpha*), 13-30 mm long, were chosen because their sensitivity to common pollutants was similar to that of rainbow trout, and enabled the size of the apparatus, and therefore the volume of toxicant and dilution water, to be kept to a minimum. Test fish are acclimated to the dilution water at 20 °C for a few days before use in a test.

Dilution water. A synthetic soft dilution water is used, prepared by the addition of salts to de-ionized water to give a total hardness of 20 mg/ℓ as $CaCO_3$.

Test temperature. 20 ± 0.5 °C.

Dissolved oxygen. No requirements are stated, but the constant flow through the specified apparatus maintains an adequate level.

Number of fish. There should be ten in each concentration of toxicant.

Controls. The test is invalidated if a fish dies in the control vessel containing dilution water only.

Duration. The test continues for up to a week, with calculation of the 1- and 2-day LC50 values and estimation of the threshold LC50.

Apparatus. This is a precisely defined constant-flow type, using 500 mℓ flasks as the test containers and provision for 100 mℓ of fresh solution to be added to them every 10 min.

3. STANDARD JAPANESE METHOD FOR AGRICULTURAL CHEMICALS: NISHIUCHI, Y. (1974). TESTING METHODS FOR THE TOXICITY OF AGRICULTURAL CHEMICALS TO AQUATIC ORGANISMS. JAPANESE PESTICIDE INFORMATION No. 19, 15–19

Test fish. The principle species used is the carp (*Cyprinus carpio*) with an average length of 50 mm. For chemicals not applied to paddies, *Pseudorasbora parva* or *Oryzias latipes* can be used, using sodium pentachlorophenate as a reference substance. They should be acclimated for at least one week to the test conditions.

Dilution water. This should be well-water or dechlorinated public supply water.

Temperature. This should be within the range 20–28 °C, with variations of ± 2 °C from the chosen temperature.

Dissolved oxygen. No requirements are stated but the ratio of fish/test volume is sufficient to maintain a satisfactory dissolved-oxygen concentration.

Number of fish. Between five and ten are used in each concentration to be tested.

Controls. Not more than 10 per cent mortality should occur in the control vessel containing dilution water only.

Duration. This should be 72 h with calculations of the 1- and 2-day LC50.

Apparatus. Cylindrical or rectangular glass test vessels of at least 10 ℓ capacity are used to hold at least 1 ℓ/gram fish or 1 ℓ/fish where the fish are less than 1 g weight. The surface area of the test vessel should neither be unduly large nor too small.

4. AMERICAN SOCIETY FOR TESTING MATERIALS. STANDARD METHOD OF TEST FOR EVALUATING ACUTE TOXICITY OF INDUSTRIAL WATER TO FRESHWATER FISHES. ASTM B 1345-59 (APPROVED 1970)

Test fish. This can be any species common to the water receiving the waste discharge and which can be maintained in the laboratory. The following families are recommended: Centrarchidae, Salmonidae, Cyprinidae and Catostomidae. The fish should be acclimated for at least ten days to the experimental conditions;

the size of the largest fish should not be more than 1.5 times that of the smallest. No more than 10 per cent of the fish should die or become diseased within the four days preceding the test.

Dilution water. For effluent tests, the dilution water should be taken either upstream of the discharge or elsewhere, i.e., of a similar quality, whether natural or semi-artificial. For comparative purposes, a standard water is used and prepared by adding salts to pure water.

Temperature. This should be between 20 and 25 °C for warm water species, and 12–18 °C for cold water species. Temperature should be controlled to ± 1 °C.

Dissolved oxygen. This should be maintained at greater than 4 mg/ℓ for warm water fish and greater than 5 mg/ℓ for cold water species. Controlled aeration with air or oxygen can be used if the concentration of pollutants is not thereby affected.

Number of fish. This is not specifically stated; the weight of fish used should not exceed 2 g/ℓ of the test solution, and preferably should be about 1 g/ℓ.

Controls. No reference is made to control tests.

Duration. This should be 48 or 96 h.

Apparatus. This is a static test utilizing 5 (U.S.) gal capacity wide-mouthed glass jars, closed with rubber stoppers through which tubes are passed to provide aeration facilities.

5. POLISH INSTITUTE OF WATER ECONOMY, WARSAW. (1972). ANALYTICAL PROCEDURES FOR THE DETERMINATION OF POLLUTION IN SURFACE WATER AND EFFLUENTS: BIOLOGICAL TEST WITH FISH

Test fish. The species chosen should represent the natural population in the river under consideration, and should be resistant to handling and transportation. Natural waters are divided into three classes, and the following test species are representative of each class.

Class 1: Brown trout (*Salmo trutta*), rainbow trout (*Salmo gairdneri*) and bullhead (*Cottus gobio*).

Class 2: Roach (*Rutilus rutilus*), rudd (*Scardinius erythrophthalmus*), perch (*Perca fluviatilis*), bream (*Abramis brama*) and silver bream (*Blicca bjoerkna*).

Class 3: Goldfish (*Carassius auratus*), carp (*Cyprinus carpio*), tench (*Tinca tinca*) and *Carassius auratus gibelio*.

Sighting tests can be carried out with the guppy (*Lebistes reticulatus*). Fish should either be obtained from fish farms or upstream of the source of pollution in the receiving river. The largest fish should not be more than 1.5 times the length of the smallest, and the most convenient size is about 70 mm. The fish should be acclimated to the test conditions for at least seven days. Mortalities should not exceed 10 per-cent in four days.

Dilution water. This should be taken either from the body of water being investigated, or from the public water supply (dechlorinated and stored for ten days).

Temperature. For salmonid fish the temperature should be 15 ± 1 °C and for other species of fish, 20 ± 1°C.

Dissolved oxygen. Levels should be maintained at greater than 6 mg/ℓ for salmonid species and greater than 4 mg/ℓ for other types of fish.

Number of fish. Between six and ten fish should be used for each final test concentration.

Duration. The test should continue for 24 h.

Apparatus. This is a static test utilizing 15-20 ℓ test vessels. No provision is made for replacement or renewal of solutions.

6. OFFICIAL SWISS TEST: EIDGENÖSSISCHES DEPARTMENT DES INNERN: RICHT-LINIEN FÜR DIE PROBENAHME UND NORMUNG VON WASSERUNTERSUCHUNGS-METHODEN II TEIL, 1-76 BERN, 1971

Test fish. The recommended species are rainbow trout (*Salmo gairdneri*), brown trout (*Salmo trutta*) and chub (*Leuciscus cephalus*); the minnow (*Phoxinus phoxinus*) is also a possible species for use. The fish should be acclimated to the test conditions of temperature, lighting and dissolved-oxygen concentrations for 1-2 weeks. During this period, mortality should not exceed 10 per cent in eight days. For routine tests, fish should measure 60-150 mm long, but for any one batch the size range should be ± 20 mm of the average length.

Dilution water. This should be either water specific to the region of effluent discharge, or elsewhere if of a similar quality, either natural or semi-artificial. For comparative test purposes a potable water supply of average hardness and pH value (7.5) should be used.

Test temperature. This should be $16 \pm 0.2\,^\circ\text{C}$ for comparative tests.

Dissolved oxygen. This should be maintained at greater than 90 per cent of the air saturation value.

Number of fish. This should be two to five fish per concentration in preliminary tests, with ten fish in each concentration for longer term tests.

Controls. These are not specified.

Duration. This is not specified, but can usually be taken as 24 h for preliminary tests and a longer period of time for those tests to determine threshold LC50s and long-term investigations.

Analyses. pH values should be measured at intervals.

Apparatus. For static screening tests, glass aquaria of 5-10 ℓ capacity can be used, although larger tanks are required if the test fish are greater than 100 mm long. These vessels can be aerated with air.

To determine the threshold LC50, an annular aquarium is used of 30 and 50 ℓ capacity in which the fish are required to swim against a current (about 50 mm /s) during the test period. Fish which can no longer swim and are held by the current against a barrier screen for 1 min are removed to clean water to test their potential for recovery. Survival times (lethal times) are recorded as the time when no subsequent recovery takes place.

12.9 Appendix 2 Terminology used in fish toxicity testing procedures

Acclimation: A physiological adaptation of fish to some selected experimental conditions, including any adverse stimulus which is involved (used by Sprague as equivalent to 'tolerance' as defined here).

Acclimatization: The genetic adaptation of a fish species to some change of natural or applied environmental condition.

Acute toxicity: The harmful properties of a substance which are demonstrated within a short period (hours to days) of exposure. Typically associated with breakdown of tissues and physiological systems at rates which exceed rates of repair or adaptation. Commonly applied to rapidly lethal effects.

Acute toxicity test: A test to determine the acute toxicity of a substance or waste.

Additive toxicity: The toxicity of a mixture of poisons which is equal to that expected from a simple summation of the known toxicities of the individual poisons involved (i.e., algebraic summation of effects).

Air saturation value of dissolved oxygen: The concentration of oxygen dissolved in water in equilibrium with atmospheric air at normal barometric pressure. The value varies with temperature and is, for example, 14.6 mg/ℓ at 0 °C and 8.3 mg/ℓ at 25 °C.

Alkalinity: The acid-neutralizing (i.e., proton-accepting) capacity of a water; the abundance of compounds in a water which shift the pH to the alkaline side of neutrality. In natural wastes the usual cause of alkalinity is the presence of carbonates and bicarbonates.

Antagonism: Commonly used to define a mixture of poisons whose toxicity is less than that which would be expected from a knowledge of the toxicities of the individual poisons involved (i.e., algebraic subtraction of effects). The term 'less-than-additive' has been substituted for this response by Sprague, to the limit where one poison fails to exert any effect at all within the mixture. The term 'antagonism' is restricted to any effect which it would have alone at a much lower level in the absence of the second substance.

Application factor: The factor by which a concentration observed as causing some harmful effect in a short-term experiment is converted to give what is frequently arbitrarily considered as an acceptable level in the environment. Thus, for example, the 4-day LC50 is frequently multiplied by 0.1 or 0.01 to give this level; data obtained from chronic tests are, however, also used to derive such a factor.

Asymptotic threshold concentration: The concentration of poison at which some specified proportion of a test population shows itself to be in a state of approximate homeostasis for some prolonged period of time (but not necessarily absolutely); demonstrated as the concentration at which the toxicity curve is approximately or effectively asymptotic to the time axis.

Avoidance reaction: A response in which a fish actively moves away from an unfavourable stimulus.

Bioassay: The use of living material to measure the concentration of a substance in water, by determining its potency in producing some specific effect. Frequently involves the use of standard reference compounds. Strictly speaking a fish toxicity test is not a bioassay.

Bioevaluation: The use of living organisms to evaluate some effect of a specific concentration of a poison. May apply to the use of tissues, or of one or more animals, or to a community. Includes toxicity tests.

Biotest: (a) bioassay, (b) a test for the presence or absence of life, (c) bioevaluation.

Chronic: Of long duration; for example, chronic toxicity test = long-term toxicity test.

Concentration–response curve: The curve obtained when, after a given period of exposure, the different percentage responses of batches of fish exposed to different concentrations of poison are plotted against those concentrations.

95 per cent confidence limits: The upper and lower limits of the 95 per cent confidence interval; effectively the limits within which, at a probability level of 0.95, the true EC50 for the population of fish under test lies. Thus, if tests were made on a large number of separate samples of fish taken from a single large population, and the EC50 and its 95 per cent confidence interval for each test sample were determined, then in about 95 tests in 100, the true value of the population EC50 would come within the sample confidence limits.

Constant-flow test: A toxicity test in which constant partial replacement of a test solution takes place at frequent fixed intervals, so that the flow of liquid is effectively continuous.

Continuous flow test: A toxicity test in which the flow of the test solution continues without interruption.

Criteria (water quality): The relation between the concentration of a pollutant and its measured effect on a target organism.

Cumulative: Increasing by successive additions.

Death time: Survival time.

Delayed: Put off in time; delayed effects of a poison are those not exerted until some considerable time after first exposure to a poison or, when the period of exposure to poisoning is brief, not until after exposure has ceased.

Dose–response curve: Similar to concentration–response curve except that the dose (i.e., the quantity) of poison received by the fish is known and takes the place of concentration in plotting the data.

Dynamic test: A test with constant flow or continuous flow.

EC50: Median effective concentration; the concentration of poison (or intensity of other stimulus) which produces some selected response in one half of a test population of fish.

Effective concentration: That concentration of poisoning producing some selected/defined effect.

Effluent monitoring test: A monitoring test applied to an effluent.

ET50: Median effective time; the interval of time between initial exposure of a test population of fish to a single intensity of stimulus and the response of one half of that population.

Exposure period: The interval of time during which a fish is exposed to a stimulus.

Fiducial limits: In practical terms effectively the same as confidence limits, but distinction has been made between the two by some statisticians because orthodox statistical philosophy denies the possibility of assigning a true frequency or probability distribution to an unknown population parameter. However, other statisticians question the reality of the distinction.

Flight reaction: Reaction in which fish swim rapidly away from an adverse stimulus.

Flow-through test: A test with constant flow or continuous flow.

Hardness: Theoretically, the concentration of all the metallic cations, except those of the alkali metals, present in a water; in general, for all practical purposes, hardness is a measure of the concentration of calcium and magnesium ions in a water. Frequently expressed as mg/ℓ calcium carbonate equivalent. (Also expressed as degree of hardness:

$^\circ$Clark = $^\circ$English   = 1 grain $CaCO_3$/imperial gallon
$^\circ$German (Deutsch) = 1 part CaO_3 in 10^5 parts water
$^\circ$French   = 1 part $CaCO_3$ in 10^5 parts water.)

ILL: *Incipient lethal level*: (a) point in the zone of respiratory dependence where the maximum rate of oxygen uptake is reduced to a point where it is no longer sufficient to meet the minimum oxygen requirements of the animal [i.e., and the fish die] ; (b) the oxygen concentration at which 50 per cent mortality occurs within the experimental period; (c) upper and lower [temperature] level where temperature is beginning to have a lethal effect.
Incipient: Beginning, for example, an incipient effect is an effect beginning to occur.
Incipient LC50: That level of toxicant which is lethal for 50 per cent of individuals exposed for periods sufficiently long that acute lethal action has ceased.
Independent action: Action of a mixture of poisons whose constituents act independently; in this type of action the mortalities and not the concentrations are additive.
Irritation: Morbid stimulation of a fish, or of some vital function (e.g., mucus secretion), without necessarily producing an inflammatory tissue response.

Joint action: The effects of two or more poisons exerting their effects simultaneously.

LC50: Median lethal concentration; the concentration of a poison lethal to one half of a test population of fish.
LD50: Median lethal dose; the dose (i.e., the quantity received by the body) which is lethal to one half of a test population of fish. A quantity not normally known for fish from toxicity tests, where LC50 is the correct term to use.
Legal test: A toxicity test designed to satisfy a legal requirement and whose results are formally accepted in law.
Less-than-additive: *see* Antagonism.
Lethal: Mortal; causing death.
Lethal phase: The stage reached by a fish in a toxicity test when the progression toward death cannot be reversed.
Lethal threshold concentration: (a) the threshold concentration producing death, for example, the median lethal threshold concentration or threshold LC50 is the concentration of poison lethal to half of a test population; (b) the concentration at which a poison is first lethal to fish.
Lethal time: Survival time.
Level of no-effect: That upper concentration of a poison at which some selected effect fails to be produced, usually within some specified period of exposure. Should not be taken as indicating that the effect would not be produced with increase in the period of exposure, or that other, unsought for, harmful effects are not occurring.
Limit of toxicity: *see* Asymptotic threshold concentrations.
Long-term toxicity test: A toxicity test of prolonged duration (months to years)

which may include more than one generation of the test organism; effects less severe than those observed under conditions of acute poisoning, or the absence of adverse effects, are sought; chronic toxicity test.

LT50: Median lethal time; the survival time of one half of a population of fish in a given concentration of poison.

Manifestation time (= disturbance time): The time interval between initial exposure of fish to a poison (or other stimulus) and appearance of the first reaction to it.

Maximum safe concentration: The maximum concentration of poison to which fish can be continuously exposed without harm (often interpreted as 'without causing death').

Median period of survival: LT50; median survival time.

Monitoring test: A toxicity test designed to be applied on a routine basis, with some implication of control, to ensure that the quality of, for example, a river water or effluent does not exceed some prescribed standard.

More-than-additive: *see* Synergism.

Mortality: Death.

Overturning time: The time interval between initial exposure of a fish to a poison (or other harmful stimulus) and its loss of equilibrium.

Parameter: A quantity which serves to define some item; the item itself, a numerical characteristic of a population of items. For physical and chemical properties of water, the term 'water quality characteristic' should be used.

Percentage saturation dissolved oxygen: The concentration (mg/ℓ of dissolved oxygen in water at any given conditions expressed as a percentage of the air saturation value under that same condition.

Percentile: The value below which the stated percentage of a series of measurements falls (e.g., the 95 percentile indicates the value for some parameter below which 95 per cent of the results of a statistical population falls).

Poison: In the present context, any chemical in an aquatic ecosystem at such a concentration that it can, when taken into the body of a fish, impair health or cause death by its specific chemical properties. Includes all toxins.

Pollution: A change in the quality of a water which makes that water unfavourable to fish. Such impairment may occur as a result of natural phenomena, but is more usually associated with the addition, either accidental or deliberate, of wastes typically originating in the activities of man.

Potentiation: More-than-additive. However, frequently used elsewhere to describe a mixture of substances, one of which is without toxic effect at the concentration used, but whose presence greatly enhances the toxicity of a second substance.

Preference: A response in which a fish actively moves toward, and remains within the influence of, a stimulus.

Probit: Unit of probability or standard deviation.

Reaction period: Manifestation time, response time.

Resistance: Ability of an animal to survive for a limited period in an environment that will eventually exert a lethal effect.

Resistance time: The finite period of time for which a fish can live beyond the incipient lethal level.

Response: The reaction of a fish (or some system thereof) to a stimulus. Both nature and time of onset of the response should be defined.

Response time: Manifestation time; reaction period, for example, of individual fish in a test batch or of a given proportion.

Ring-test: A conjoint test made under strictly standardized and uniformly applied conditions to assess the precision and accuracy with which different laboratories and operatives determine, for example, the toxicity of a chemical or waste. A test designed to measure statistically the reproducibility of a test method, or to compare the results obtained from the use of different test methods.

River monitoring test: A monitoring test applied to a river water.

Safe concentration: A concentration of a chemical harmless to the greater part of a fish population even with prolonged exposure.

Safe-to-lethal ratio: The ratio between the concentration at which a poison is observed to exert no specified effect on an experimental batch of fish and the LC50 for that species for any given period.

Safety factor: Application factor; can also describe some unmeasured effect in a water which reduces the toxicity expected from a given concentration of poison (e.g., complexing of metals).

Screening test: A test used to detect the ability of a chemical or waste to produce some selected effect.

Short-term toxicity test: A toxicity test of short duration, usually an acute toxicity test.

Standard deviation: Root-mean-square deviation; a measure of the dispersion about the mean value of those describing some characteristic (e.g., length, weight) of the fish within a sample. The standard deviation of a sample (denoted as s) of n observations $x_1, x_2, \ldots, x_n$ is:

$$s = \sqrt{\frac{1}{n-1} \sum_{i=1}^{n} (x_i - \bar{x})^2}$$

or, for large samples (>30 fish)

$$s = \sqrt{\frac{1}{n} \sum_{i=1}^{n} (x_i - \bar{x})^2}$$

Standard error: The standard deviation of a sampling distribution; for example, the standard error of the mean of a sample. This is used to define at some selected level of probability (usually 0.95) the limits within which the population mean lies.

Standard test: A test in which all conditions, for example, water quality, fish species and numbers, duration, methodology, conform rigidly to specified requirements.

Standard (water quality): The limiting concentration of a pollutant (or degree of intensity of some other adverse condition) which is permitted in a water. Standards are determined from a considered judgement of the criteria involved.

Static test: A toxicity test in which either no replacement of test solution takes place, or in which all, or the greater part (>95 per cent) of the test solution is replaced batchwise only after relatively prolonged intervals (e.g., 12 or 24 h).

Stimulus: The factor producing some response.

Subacute: Having effects less severe than those observed under conditions of acute poisoning and usually not demonstrated until after perhaps some weeks of exposure.

Sublethal: Not killing; usually applied to toxicity tests with poison concentrations which are not lethal within the period of the experiment. Both period of exposure and observation, as well as the percentage of fish referred to, should be defined.

Survival time: The time interval between initial exposure of fish to a harmful stimulus and death.

Synergism: Any joint action of poisons, but commonly used in fish studies to describe toxicity of a mixture of poisons which is greater than that which is to be expected from a knowledge of the toxicities of the individual poisons involved (i.e., greater than the algebraic summation of effects). The term 'more-than-additive' has been substituted for this type of response.

Threshold concentration: (a) The minimum concentration of poison required to produce a selected response in a single test animal under controlled conditions. Can be used, if desired, to describe the threshold concentration for any particular percentage response in a test population, of fish (b) that concentration allowing survival time equal to that of the control.

Time-response curve: The curve obtained when the cumulative percentage response of a test batch of fish to a single concentration of poison is plotted against time.

TL50: TL_m; LC50

TL_m: The median tolerance limit; the concentration of poison, or intensity of some harmful stimulus, lethal to one half of a test population of fish. ('Tolerance' here has the meaning 'the intensity of stimulus required'.)

Tolerance: Acquired resistance of fish to a poison or other stimulus (e.g., high temperature, low-dissolved oxygen) following continuous or repeated exposure. Other definitions: (a) the ability to survive indefinitely under a given set of circumstances; (b) the oxygen pressure which just fails to bring about 50 per cent mortality in a sample of fish.

Tolerance limit: The lowest oxygen level permitting indefinite survival of fish; the highest poison concentration permitting the indefinite survival of fish.

Toxic: Poisonous; having the properties of a poison.

Toxicant: Poison.

Toxicity: The harmful qualities of a substance.

Toxicity curve: The curve produced when, for example, the median period of survival of test batches of fish exposed to different concentrations are expressed in a graphical form. The curve obtained when, for example, the LC50 values of a test population of fish after different periods of exposure are plotted. Resistance curve.

Toxicity test: The use of living material to define the nature and degree of harmful effects produced by a single poison or by a mixture of poisons.

Toxic substance: Poison.

Toxic units: The concentration of a poison expressed as a proportion of its asymptotic median threshold concentration; commonly or conveniently expressed as a proportion of some approximation (e.g., 2-day LC50, 4-day LC50) of this concentration.

Toxin: Usually albuminous substance of high molecular weight produced by an animal or plant and which is capable of impairing health or causing death of other animals. Does not include all poisons.

Ultimate incipient lethal level: The lowest level of dissolved oxygen to which fish can be acclimated without suffering more than 50 per cent mortality.

Ultimate median tolerance limit: The concentration of poison at which half of the test animals are killed eventually after periods of exposure greater than, for example, 4 days, while the rest survive indefinitely.

Ultimate upper incipient level: The highest level [temperature] to which fish can be acclimated.

Zone of tolerance: Thermal zone in which fish can live free from the lethal effects of temperature.

INDEX

Abramis balleus, phenolic wastes
affecting, 108
Abramis brama,
acidity affecting, 27
ammonia affecting, 92
cadmium toxicity, 235
lethal temperature, 59
phenolic wastes affecting, 106, 108,
109
sensitivity to dissolved oxygen, 131
tainted by phenol, 116
temperature of spawning, 53
water temperature affecting embryos,
50
zinc toxicity, 170
zinc uptake in, 172
Abramis spp., temperature of spawning,
53
ABS, toxicity of, 34
Acclimation, definition of, 336
Acerina cernus,
lethal temperature, 60
sensitivity to dissolved oxygen, 136
temperature of spawning, 55
Acidity,
avoidance reactions, 31
fish kills with, 28
food supply affected by, 33
growth affected by, 33
mode of toxic action, 29
size and age of fish and, 24
Acid pollution *see also* pH values;
Acidity
effects of, 21, 23
lethal effect of, 23
Acipenser guldenstaedti,
phenolic wastes affecting, 108
sensitivity to dissolved oxygen, 131
temperature of spawning, 55
Acipenser rhutenus, preferred
temperature, 62
Acipenser stellatus,
phenolic wastes affecting, 108
temperature of spawning, 55

Acipenser stellatus (cont.)
water temperature tolerated by, 52
Acroneuria lycorias, 209
Adinia zenica, 282
Agosia chrysogaster, toxicant mixtures
affecting, 267
Alborella, effect of toxicant mixtures
on, 273
Alburnus alburnus,
effect of temperature on gonads, 62
lethal temperature, 59
Alburnus punctatus, phenol uptake in,
115
Alburnus spp., temperature of spawning,
54
Aldrin, 300
Algae,
cadmium affecting, 241
copper affecting, 207
DDT uptake in, 298
effect of pesticides, 293
effect of phenolic wastes, 116
toxicant mixtures affecting, 291, 292
Alkalinity,
acclimation, 36
ammonia and, 89
avoidance reactions to, 38
definition, 337
direct lethal action, 35
effect of size, 35
food supply affected by, 39
growth affected by, 39
mode of toxic action, 38
Alkalis, affects of, 23
Alosa falax, sensitivity to dissolved
oxygen, 136, 137
American shad,
sensitivity to dissolved oxygen, 135
Ammonia, 85–102, 288
acclimation to, 90
alkalinity and, 89
avoidance reactions, 95
combined with zinc and phenol, 168,
264

Walleye,
  sensitivity to dissolved oxygen, 135
  solids affecting, 5, 7
  turbidity affecting, 12
Water quality criteria, 304, 321
Water velocity, phenol toxicity and, 109
White bream, water temperature affecting,
    61
Whitefish,
  acclimation to water temperature, 52
  turbidity affecting, 12
  water temperature affecting, 61
White sucker,
  cadmium toxicity, 228
  chlorine toxicity, 147
  copper activity in, 193
Winter, water temperature during, 48, 67
Winter flounder, 193
Wood pulp, 5

Xanthate, 299
Xiphophorus maculatus, zinc toxicity, 167
Xylenols *see also under* Phenol, toxicity of,
  acclimation to, 109
  effect on invertebrates, 117
  symptoms of poisoning, 106
  toxicity of, 103, 104, 111

Yellow perch, reproduction in, solids
    affecting, 7

Zebra fish,
  cadmium uptake, 226
  toxicant mixtures affecting, 268, 269,
    272
  zinc affecting, 174
Zinc, 159–188
  acclimation to, 166

Zinc (*cont.*)
  ammonia and, 264
  background value of, 161
  behavioural effects of, 173
  combined with ammonia, 93
  cyanide and, 266
  direct lethal action, 161
  effect on aquatic vegetation, 177, 291
  effect on growth, 172
  effect on reproduction, 172
  fish population surveys and, 175
  in toxicant mixtures, 264, 265, 266,
    267, 268, 269, 271, 286
    effect on invertebrates, 289
    uptake of, 298
  mixed with copper and phenol, 113
  resistance to disease and, 174
  sublethal effects of, 171
  symptoms of poisoning, 161
  toxic properties of, 3
  toxicity of, 34, 39, 159, 197, 198,
    204
    action with heavy metals, 167
    action with other poisons, 168
    acutely lethal values, 169
    age and size of fish and, 166
    dissolved oxygen and, 163
    factors influencing lethal levels, 162
    field experiments, 174
    mode of action, 161
    organic matter and, 165
    pH and, 163
    salinity and, 165
    suspended solids and, 165
    temperature and, 162
    water hardness and, 164
  uptake and loss of, 171
  wastes, 161
  water criteria, 181
Zinc chloride, interaction with oxygen, 134
Zooplankton, water temperature affecting,
    64